PARTIAL DIFFERENTIAL EQUATIONS OF MATHEMATICAL PHYSICS

Volume I

HOLDEN-DAY SERIES IN MATHEMATICAL PHYSICS

Julius J. Brandstatter, Editor

S. G. Lekhnitskii, *Theory of Elasticity of an Anisotropic Elastic Body*

D. A. Pogorelov, *Fundamentals of Orbital Mechanics*

A. N. Tychonov and A. A. Samarski, *Partial Differential Equations of Mathematical Physics*

M. M. Vainberg, *Variational Methods for the Study of Nonlinear Operators*

A. N. Tikhonov

A. N. Tychonov and A. A. Samarski

PARTIAL DIFFERENTIAL EQUATIONS OF MATHEMATICAL PHYSICS

Volume I

Translated by S. Radding

HOLDEN-DAY, INC.
San Francisco, London, Amsterdam
1964

6-4-64
P file 7-6-64
recd 9-28-64

Library of Congress Catalog Card Number: 64-15462
Printed in the United States of America

EDITOR'S PREFACE

This text reflects the authors' unique approach to the study of the basic types of partial differential equations of mathematical physics. The systematic presentation of the material offers the reader a natural entrée to the subject. Each of the basic types of equations which are to be studied is motivated by its physical origins. The derivation of an equation from the physics to its final mathematical structure is very instructive to the student.

The authors have gone to great length to make clear the meaning of a solution to an initial value or boundary-value problem. Various methods of solving such problems are treated in great detail, as are the questions of existence and uniqueness of solutions. Thus, the student gains an appreciation of the theoretical foundations of the subject and simultaneously acquires the manipulative skills for solving such problems.

The exercises which accompany each chapter have been selected to test the student's ability both to formulate the correct mathematical statement of the problem and to apply the appropriate method for its solution. The applications treated by the authors are non-trivial and are completely worked out in detail.

The present volume covers the two dimensional class of partial differential equations of mathematical physics and is well suited as a basic text for both the undergraduate and graduate level at the university. The second volume will cover the three dimensional counterparts of the present volume and contain an additional chapter on the special functions which arise in mathematical physics.

In view of the dearth of texts having the scope and depth of the present one, Holden-Day felt the need for a careful and articulate translation of Tychonov and Samarski's valuable contribution to the literature in the field. The translator and editor exercised great care in making the English edition read smoothly and correctly. Several misprints and other flaws have been corrected, and we are pleased to make this excellent text available to the English-reading scientific community.

Julius J. Brandstatter
Stanford Research Institute

FROM THE PREFACE TO THE RUSSIAN EDITION

The class of problems of mathematical physics are closely bound to different physical processes. To these belong the phenomena which are treated in hydrodynamics, in the theory of elasticity, in electrodynamics, etc. The mathematical problems which are associated with these phenomena contain many common features and form the subject matter of mathematical physics.

For this purpose, a knowledge of the characteristic methods of investigation is in its nature mathematical; however, the representation of the problems of mathematical physics proceeds in certain directions. Thus, for example, the initial and final states of a qualitative process are of different character and therefore require different mathematical methods for their description.

We have attempted to choose the subject matter following conventional physical viewpoints; these also correspond to the arrangement of the basic types of differential equations.

Each chapter begins with the simplest physical problems which lead to equations of the type considered therein, and each chapter contains exercises of which several are also of physical interest.

Since the simplest problems treated in the text do not accurately represent the multiplicity of the problems and their role in mathematical physics, each chapter concludes with physical applications in which the methods first presented in the main body of the chapter are used for the solution. We have also included examples which go beyond the scope of the problems treated in the text.

The text contains only a part of the material which comprises the methods of mathematical physics; thus we have not treated integral equations in detail nor have we discussed variational methods. Approximate methods of solution are only briefly mentioned.

The present text is an outgrowth of lectures given by A. Tychonov before the Physics Faculty of the Moscow Lomonossov University. We wish to thank our students and our colleagues, V.B. Glasko, V.A. Iljin, A.V. Lukianov,O.I. Panuch,B.L. Roshdestvenski, A.B. Vassiliewa, A.G. Svechnikov, and D.N. Chetaev, without whose help we could not have compiled this book in a reasonable time, and to J.L. Rabinovich who read the manuscript and gave us valuable suggestions. We wish to thank both V.I. Smirnov for many valuable comments and A.G. Svechnikov for his aid in the preparation of the second edition.

A. Tychonov
A. Samarski

PREFACE TO THE GERMAN EDITION

Just as geometric representation is necessary for the study of differential and integral calculus, so physical representation is required in the study of partial differential equations. In this book, we have placed most emphasis on the formulation of the basic problems of mathematical physics and on the physical interpretation of the solutions of boundary value problems of partial differential equations. We hope that our book will prove useful as an introduction to mathematical physics.

We wish to take this opportunity to give thanks to Dipl. Math. Gerhard Tesch for his careful translation, to Dr. Herbert Goering and Dr. Wolfgang Schmidt for the scientific editing and to VEB Deutscher Verlag der Wissenschaften for the publication of this book.

Moscow, January 1959

A. Tychonov
A. Samarski

TABLE OF CONTENTS

1

CLASSIFICATION OF PARTIAL DIFFERENTIAL EQUATIONS OF THE SECOND ORDER

Many problems of mathematical physics lead to partial differential equations. Differential equations of the second order occur most frequently; in this chapter we shall consider their classification.

1-1. DIFFERENTIAL EQUATIONS OF THE SECOND ORDER WITH TWO INDEPENDENT VARIABLES

A relation between an unknown function $u(x, y)$ and its partial derivatives[1] up to and including the second order derivatives is designated as a partial differential equation of the second order in the two independent variables x and y:

$$\varphi(x, y, u, u_x, u_y, u_{xx}, u_{xy}, u_{yy}) = 0 .$$

The equation has an analogous form for more than two independent variables.

A partial differential equation of the second order is called linear with respect to the highest derivative, if it has the form

$$a_{11}u_{xx} + 2a_{12}u_{xy} + a_{22}u_{yy} + F(x, y, u, u_x, u_y) = 0 , \qquad (1\text{-}1.1)$$

where the coefficients a_{11}, a_{12}, and a_{22} are functions of x and y.

If the coefficients are not only functions of x and y, but also F is a function of x, y, u, u_x, and u_y, then it is called a quasilinear differential equation.

The equation is called linear if it is linear in the higher derivatives u_{xx}, u_{xy}, u_{yy}, also in the function $u(x, y)$, and in the first derivatives u_x, u_y:

$$a_{11}u_{xx} + 2a_{12}u_{xy} + a_{22}u_{yy} + b_1u_x + b_2u_y + cu + f = 0 , \qquad (1\text{-}1.2)$$

where a_{11}, a_{12}, a_{22}, b_1, b_2, c, and f are functions which depend only on x and y. If the coefficients are independent of x and y, then Eq. (1-1.2) is a linear differential equation with constant coefficients. Equation (1-1.2) is called homogeneous if $f(x, y) \equiv 0$.

With the aid of a unique inverse transformation

[1] For the derivatives we use the symbols

$$u_x = \frac{\partial u}{\partial x}, \quad u_y = \frac{\partial u}{\partial y}, \quad u_{xx} = \frac{\partial^2 u}{\partial x^2}, \quad u_{xy} = \frac{\partial^2 u}{\partial x \partial y}, \quad u_{yy} = \frac{\partial^2 u}{\partial y^2}.$$

$$\xi = \varphi(x, y)\,, \qquad \eta = \psi(x, y)$$

we obtain, under certain assumptions on φ and ψ, a new differential equation which is equivalent to the original equation. There now arises the question of how the variables ξ and η are to be selected so that the transformed differential equation assumes as simple a form as possible. This question will be answered now for a linear equation of the form (1-1.1) with two independent variables x and y.

If we transform the derivatives to the new variables, we obtain

$$\begin{aligned} u_x &= u_\xi \xi_x + u_\eta \eta_x \\ u_y &= u_\xi \xi_y + u_\eta \eta_y \\ u_{xx} &= u_{\xi\xi}\xi_x^2 + 2u_{\xi\eta}\xi_x\eta_x + u_{\eta\eta}\eta_x^2 + u_\xi \xi_{xx} + u_\eta \eta_{xx} \\ u_{xy} &= u_{\xi\xi}\xi_x\xi_y + u_{\xi\eta}(\xi_x\eta_y + \xi_y\eta_x) + u_{\eta\eta}\eta_x\eta_y + u_\xi\xi_{xy} + u_\eta\eta_{xy} \\ u_{yy} &= u_{\xi\xi}\xi_y^2 + 2u_{\xi\eta}\xi_y\eta_y + u_{\eta\eta}\eta_y^2 + u_\xi\xi_{yy} + u_\eta\eta_{yy}\,. \end{aligned} \tag{1-1.3}$$

If these expressions are inserted into (1-1.1) an equation results of the form

$$\bar{a}_{11}u_{\xi\xi} + 2\bar{a}_{12}u_{\xi\eta} + \bar{a}_{22}u_{\eta\eta} + \bar{F} = 0\,, \tag{1-1.4}$$

where

$$\begin{aligned} \bar{a}_{11} &= a_{11}\xi_x^2 + 2a_{12}\xi_x\xi_y + a_{22}\xi_y^2 \\ \bar{a}_{12} &= a_{11}\xi_x\eta_x + a_{12}(\xi_x\eta_y + \eta_x\xi_y) + a_{22}\xi_y\eta_y \\ \bar{a}_{22} &= a_{11}\eta_x^2 + 2a_{12}\eta_x\eta_y + a_{22}\eta_y^2 \end{aligned}$$

and $\bar{F}$ is independent of the partial derivatives of the second order of $u(\xi, \eta)$ with respect to ξ and η. If the initial equation is linear, that is,

$$F(x, y, u, u_x, u_y) = b_1u_x + b_2u_y + cu + f(x, y)\,,$$

then $\bar{F}$ has the form

$$\bar{F}(\xi, \eta, u, u_\xi, u_\eta) = \beta_1 u_\xi + \beta_2 u_\eta + \gamma u + \delta(\xi, \eta)\,;$$

that is, the transformed differential equation is likewise linear.[2]

We now want to choose the transformation such that the coefficient $\bar{a}_{11}$ vanishes. To this end, we examine a partial differential equation of the first order of the form

$$a_{11}z_x^2 + 2a_{12}z_xz_y + a_{22}z_y^2 = 0\,. \tag{1-1.5}$$

Let $z = \varphi(x, y)$ be an arbitrary particular solution of this equation. If we set $\xi = \varphi(x, y)$, then the coefficient $\bar{a}_{11}$ is obviously equal to zero. In this manner the above-mentioned problem of the selection of the new independent variables ξ and η is linked with the solution of Eq. (1-1.5).

First we shall prove the following lemmas.

Lemma 1. If $z = \varphi(x, y)$ is a particular solution of the equation

[2] If the transformation of the variables is linear, then $\bar{F} = F$, since the second derivatives of ξ and η vanish in formula (1-1.3), and in the expression for $\bar{F}$ none of the transformations of the second derivatives appears in the preceding sums.

$$a_{11}z_x^2 + 2a_{12}z_xz_y + a_{22}z_y^2 = 0 ,$$

then $\varphi(x, y) = C$ is a general integral of the ordinary differential equation

$$a_{11}dy^2 - 2a_{12}dx\,dy + a_{22}\,dx^2 = 0 . \qquad (1\text{-}1.6)$$

Lemma 2. Conversely, if $\varphi(x, y) = C$ is a general integral of the ordinary differential equation

$$a_{11}\,dy^2 - 2a_{12}\,dx\,dy + a_{22}\,dx^2 = 0 , \qquad (1\text{-}1.6)$$

then $z = \varphi(x, y)$ satisfies Eq. (1-1.5).

Proof of the first lemma. Since the function $z = \varphi(x, y)$ satisfies Eq. (1-1.5), the equation

$$a_{11}\left(\frac{\varphi_x}{\varphi_y}\right)^2 - 2a_{12}\left(-\frac{\varphi_x}{\varphi_y}\right) + a_{22} = 0 \qquad (1\text{-}1.7)$$

is valid for all x, y of the region in which $z = \varphi(x, y)$ is defined and $\varphi_y(x, y) \neq 0$. The relation $\varphi(x, y) = C$ is a general integral of Eq. (1-1.6) if the function y defined implicitly by $\varphi(x, y) = C$ satisfies Eq. (1-1.6). If, namely, $y = f(x, C)$ is this function, then it satisfies

$$\frac{dy}{dx} = -\left[\frac{\varphi_x(x, y)}{\varphi_y(x, y)}\right]_{y=f(x,C)} \qquad (1\text{-}1.8)$$

and hence

$$a_{11}\left(\frac{dy}{dx}\right)^2 - 2a_{12}\frac{dy}{dx} + a_{22} = \left[a_{11}\left(-\frac{\varphi_x}{\varphi_y}\right)^2 - 2a_{12}\left(-\frac{\varphi_x}{\varphi_y}\right) + a_{22}\right]_{y=f(x,C)} = 0 ,$$

so that $y = f(x, C)$ satisfies Eq. (1-1.6). The expression in the brackets vanishes, not only for $y = f(x, C)$, but for all values of x, y.

Proof of the second lemma. Let $\varphi(x, y) = C$ be a general integral of Eq. (1-1.6). We can show that for each point (x, y)

$$a_{11}\varphi_x^2 + 2a_{12}\varphi_x\varphi_y + a_{22}\varphi_y^2 = 0 \qquad (1\text{-}1.7)$$

is valid. Let (x_0, y_0) be any given point. If it can be shown that Eq. (1-1.7) is satisfied at this point, it follows that Eq. (1-1.7) is valid at all points, since (x_0, y_0) is arbitrarily chosen. The function $\varphi(x, y)$ then represents a solution of Eq. (1-1.7). We now construct through (x_0, y_0) an integral curve of Eq. (1-1.6) in which we set $\varphi(x_0, y_0) = C_0$ and consider the curve $y = f(x, C_0)$. Obviously, $y_0 = f(x_0, C_0)$. For all points of this curve the following equation is valid,

$$a_{11}\left(\frac{dy}{dx}\right)^2 - 2a_{12}\frac{dy}{dx} + a_{22} = \left[a_{11}\left(-\frac{\varphi_x}{\varphi_y}\right)^2 - 2a_{12}\left(-\frac{\varphi_x}{\varphi_y}\right) + a_{22}\right]_{y=f(x,C_0)} = 0 .$$

If we set $x = x_0$ in this equation, we obtain

$$a_{11}\varphi_x^2(x_0, y_0) + 2a_{12}\varphi_x(x_0, y_0)\varphi_y(x_0, y_0) + a_{22}\varphi_y^2(x_0, y_0) = 0 ,$$

which was to be proved.[3]

Equation (1-1.6) is called the characteristic equation of the differential Eq. (1-1.1); its integrals are called characteristics.

If we set $\xi = \varphi(x, y)$, where $\varphi(x, y) = \text{const.}$ is a general integral of Eq. (1-1.6), then we find that the coefficient of $u_{\xi\xi}$ vanishes. Likewise the coefficient of $u_{\eta\eta}$ equals zero if $\psi(x, y) = \text{const.}$ is an additional general integral of (1-1.6) independent of $\varphi(x, y)$ [see footnote 5] and if we set $\eta = \psi(x, y)$.

Equation (1-1.6) yields two equations

$$\frac{dy}{dx} = \frac{a_{12} + \sqrt{a_{12}^2 - a_{11}a_{22}}}{a_{11}} \tag{1-1.9}$$

$$\frac{dy}{dx} = \frac{a_{12} - \sqrt{a_{12}^2 - a_{11}a_{22}}}{a_{11}} , \tag{1-1.10}$$

The sign of the expression under the root determines the type of the differential equation

$$a_{11}u_{xx} + 2a_{12}u_{xy} + a_{22}u_{yy} + F = 0 . \tag{1-1.1}$$

At the point M we shall say that it is[4]

of the hyperbolic type if at this point $a_{12}^2 - a_{11}a_{22} > 0$,
of the elliptic type, if at this point $a_{12}^2 - a_{11}a_{22} < 0$,
of the parabolic type, if at this point $a_{12}^2 - a_{11}a_{22} = 0$.

We can easily show the validity of the expression

$$\bar{a}_{12}^2 - \bar{a}_{11}\bar{a}_{22} = (a_{12}^2 - a_{11}a_{22})\,(\xi_x\eta_y - \xi_y\eta_x)^2 ,$$

from which the invariance of the type of equation follows under a transformation of the variables. At different points of the region of definition, the equation can be of changing type.

For the following considerations we take as basic a region G, at each point of which Eq. (1-1.1) is of one and the same type. Through each point of the region G two characteristics arise which are real and distinct for a differential equation of the hyperbolic type, complex and distinct for a differential equation of the elliptic type, and real and equal for a differential equation of the parabolic type. We shall investigate each of these cases separately.

1. For an equation of the hyperbolic type $a_{12}^2 - a_{11}a_{22} > 0$, the right sides of the differential Eqs. (9) and (10) are real and distinct. The general

[3] This relationship between Eqs. (1-1.5) and (1-1.6) is the equivalent of the well-known relation between a linear partial differential equation of the first order and a system of ordinary differential equations. This can be shown if the left side of Eq. (1-1.5) is represented as the product of two linear differential expressions.

[See V. I. Smirnov: Course in Higher Mathematics, Part II, 2d ed., Berlin, 1958, p. 62, and V. V. Stepanov: Textbook of Differential Equations, Berlin, 1956, p. 328 (Translated from Russian).

[4] This terminology is taken from the theory of curves of the second order.

we obtain a new expression for the quadratic form

$$\sum_{k=1}^{n} \sum_{l=1}^{n} \bar{a}_{kl}^{0} \eta_k \eta_l$$

where

$$\bar{a}_{kl}^{0} = \sum_{i=1}^{n} \sum_{j=1}^{n} a_{ij}^{0} \alpha_{ik} \alpha_{jl}$$

The coefficients of the principal parts of the equation transform like the coefficients of a quadratic form under a linear transformation. As is well known, with the help of a suitable linear transformation the coefficient matrix (a_{ij}^{0}) of a quadratic form can be transformed into a diagonal matrix in which

$$|\overline{a_{ii}^{0}}| = 1 \text{ or } 0 \qquad \text{and} \qquad \overline{a_{ij}^{0}} = 0 \qquad i \neq j; i = 1, 2, \cdots, n .$$

This is called the transformation of the quadratic form to the normal form. According to a theorem of Sylvester, the so-called inertia rule for quadratic forms, the number of coefficients of $\overline{a_{ii}^{0}}$ distinct from zero is equal to the rank of the coefficient matrix, and the number of negative coefficients is invariant.

We call Eq. (1-2.1) at the point M_0 of the elliptic type if all n coefficients of $\bar{a}_{ii}^{0}$ are different from zero and have equal signs; of the hyperbolic (or of normal-hyperbolic) type, if, likewise, all $\bar{a}_{ii}^{0} \neq 0$, $n-1$ coefficients of $\bar{a}_{ii}^{0}$ have the same sign, and one coefficient is different from the other in the signs; of the ultrahyperbolic type if m coefficients of $\bar{a}_{ii}^{0}$ are equal and $n-m$ have opposite signs ($m > 1$, $n-m > 1$); and of the parabolic type if at least one of the coefficients $\bar{a}_{ii}^{0}$ vanishes.

We choose the new independent variables ξ_i so that at the point M_0

$$\alpha_{ik} = \frac{\partial \xi_k}{\partial t_i} = \alpha_{ik}^{0} ,$$

where α_{ik}^{0} is the coefficient of the transformation which converts the quadratic form (1-2.2) to the canonical form, in which we can set $\xi_k = \sum \alpha_{ik}^{(0)} x_i$. Then Eq. (1-2.1) at the point M_0 can be transformed to one of the following canonical forms:

elliptic type: $\quad u_{x_1x_1} + u_{x_2x_2} + \cdots + u_{x_nx_n} + \Phi = 0$

hyperbolic type: $\quad u_{x_1x_1} = \sum_{i=2}^{n} u_{x_ix_i} + \Phi$

ultrahyperbolic type: $\quad \sum_{i=1}^{m} u_{x_ix_i} = \sum_{i=m+1}^{n} u_{x_ix_i} + \Phi$

parabolic type: $\quad \sum_{i=1}^{n-m} (\pm u_{x_ix_i}) + \Phi = 0 \qquad m > 0$

The further classification of equations of the parabolic type into equations of the elliptical-parabolic type, hyperbolic-parabolic type, etc., will not be discussed here.

integrals $\varphi(x, y) = C$ and $\psi(x, y) = C$ of these equations determine a real set of characteristics. We shall set

$$\xi = \varphi(x, y) \qquad \eta = \psi(x, y) \tag{1-1.11}$$

and reduce Eq. (1-1.4) after division by the coefficient of $u_{\xi\eta}$ to the form

$$u_{\xi\eta} = \Phi(\xi, \eta, u, u_\xi, u_\eta) \qquad \text{with} \qquad \Phi = -\frac{\bar{F}}{2\bar{a}_{12}} \qquad \bar{a}_{12} \neq 0 .$$

This is the so-called canonical form for an equation of the hyperbolic type.[5]

Frequently, a second canonical form is used. If we set

$$\xi = \alpha + \beta \qquad \eta = \alpha - \beta$$

i.e.,

$$\alpha = \frac{\xi + \eta}{2} \qquad \beta = \frac{\xi - \eta}{2}$$

where α and β are the new variables, then

$$u_\xi = \frac{1}{2}(u_\alpha + u_\beta) \qquad u_\eta = \frac{1}{2}(u_\alpha - u_\beta) \qquad u_{\xi\eta} = \frac{1}{4}(u_{\alpha\alpha} - u_{\beta\beta}) ,$$

whereby Eq. (1-1.4) finally assumes the form

$$u_{\alpha\alpha} - u_{\beta\beta} = \Phi_1 \qquad \Phi_1 = 4\Phi$$

2. For an equation of the parabolic type, $a_{12}^2 - a_{11}a_{22} = 0$. Consequently Eqs. (1-1.9) and (1-1.10) coincide, and we obtain only a single general integral of Eq. (1-1.6): $\varphi(x, y) = \text{const.}$ In this case, we set

$$\xi = \varphi(x, y) \qquad \text{and} \qquad \eta = \eta(x, y) ,$$

where $\eta(x, y)$ is an arbitrary function independent of φ. By this choice of the variables we find

$$\bar{a}_{11} = a_{11}\xi_x^2 + 2a_{12}\xi_x\xi_y + a_{22}\xi_y^2 = (\sqrt{a_{11}}\,\xi_x + \sqrt{a_{22}}\,\xi_y)^2 = 0 ,$$

[5] The introduction of the new variables ξ and η through the functions φ and ψ is only possible when these functions are independent of each other. Thus it is sufficient that the corresponding functional determinant obtained from these functions be distinct from zero. This is the case here, since if

$$\begin{vmatrix} \varphi_x & \psi_x \\ \varphi_y & \psi_y \end{vmatrix}$$

at any point M were zero, then for this point the columns of the determinant would be proportional to each other; hence

$$\frac{\varphi_x}{\varphi_y} = \frac{\psi_x}{\psi_y} ,$$

but since

$$\frac{\varphi_x}{\varphi_y} = -\frac{a_{12} + \sqrt{a_{12}^2 - a_{11}a_{22}}}{a_{11}} \qquad \text{and} \qquad \frac{\psi_x}{\psi_y} = -\frac{a_{12} - \sqrt{a_{12}^2 - a_{11}a_{22}}}{a_{11}} \qquad a_{12}^2 - a_{11}a_{22} > 0 ,$$

this is impossible (without loss of generality we assume $a_{11} \neq 0$). Thus, the independence of functions φ and ψ is demonstrated.

since $a_{12} = (a_{11})^{1/2}(a_{22})^{1/2}$; from this it follows that

$$\bar{a}_{12} = a_{11}\xi_x\eta_x + a_{12}(\xi_x\eta_y + \xi_y\eta_x) + a_{22}\xi_y\eta_y$$
$$= (\sqrt{a_{11}}\,\xi_x + \sqrt{a_{22}}\,\xi_y)\,(\sqrt{a_{11}}\,\eta_x + \sqrt{a_{22}}\,\eta_y) = 0 \,.$$

After dividing Eq. (1-1.4) by the coefficient of $u_{\eta\eta}$, the canonical form

$$u_{\eta\eta} = \Phi(\xi, \eta, u, \eta_\xi, u_\eta) \qquad \text{with} \qquad \Phi = -\frac{\bar{F}}{\bar{a}_{22}} \qquad \bar{a}_{22} \neq 0$$

results for an equation of the parabolic type. If, in particular, u_ξ does not appear in this equation, then it is an ordinary differential equation with ξ as a parameter.

3. For an equation of the elliptic type, $a_{12}^2 - a_{11}a_{22} < 0$, and the right sides of Eqs. (1-1.9) and (1-1.10) are complex conjugates of each other. Thus, if

$$\varphi(x, y) = C$$

is a complex integral of the differential Eq. (1-1.9), then

$$\varphi^*(x, y) = C \,,$$

where φ^* is a complex function conjugate to φ, a general integral of Eq. (1-1.10), and a complex conjugate to (1-1.9). We introduce now complex variables by setting

$$\xi = \varphi(x, y) \qquad \eta = \varphi^*(x, y) \,.$$

In this way an equation of the elliptic type, as in the case of the hyperbolic type, is converted to another form.

In order to avoid calculations with complex variables we introduce new real variables α and β, through

$$\alpha = \frac{\varphi + \varphi^*}{2} \qquad \beta = \frac{\varphi - \varphi^*}{2i} \,,$$

such that

$$\xi = \alpha + i\beta \qquad \eta = \alpha - i\beta \,.$$

Thus we obtain

$$a_{11}\xi_x^2 + 2a_{12}\xi_x\xi_y + a_{22}\xi_y^2$$
$$= (a_{11}\alpha_x^2 + 2a_{12}\alpha_x\alpha_y + a_{22}\alpha_y^2) - (a_{11}\beta_x^2 + 2a_{12}\beta_x\beta_y + a_{22}\beta_y^2)$$
$$+ 2i(a_{11}\alpha_x\beta_x + a_{12}(\alpha_x\beta_y + \alpha_y\beta_x) + a_{22}\alpha_y\beta_y) = 0 \,,$$

from which it follows that

$$\bar{a}_{11} = \bar{a}_{22} \qquad \text{and} \qquad \bar{a}_{12} = 0 \,.$$

After dividing by the coefficient of $u_{\alpha\alpha}$, Eq. (1-1.4) takes the form[6]

[6] Such a transformation is valid only if the coefficients of Eq. (1-1.1) are analytic functions. Namely, if $a_{12}^2 - a_{11}a_{22} < 0$, then Eqs. (1-1.9) and (1-1.10) are complex; consequently, the function y takes on complex values. We can only speak of the solutions of such equations when the coefficients of $a_{ik}(x, y)$ are defined for complex values of y. For the conversion of the differential equation of the elliptic type to canonical form we shall limit ourselves to equations with analytic coefficients.

$$u_{\alpha\alpha} + u_{\beta\beta} = \Phi(\alpha, \beta, u, u_\alpha, u_\beta) \qquad \text{with} \qquad \Phi = -\frac{\bar{F}}{\bar{a}_{22}} \qquad \bar{a}_{22} \neq 0 \,.$$

Depending on the sign of the discriminant $a_{12}^2 - a_{11}a_{22}$, the following canonical forms of Eq. (1-1.1) result:

hyperbolic type:	$u_{xx} - u_{yy} = \Phi$	or	$u_{xy} = \Phi$
elliptic type:	$u_{xx} + u_{yy} = \Phi$		
parabolic type:	$u_{xx} = \Phi$		

1-2. DIFFERENTIAL EQUATIONS OF THE SECOND ORDER WITH SEVERAL INDEPENDENT VARIABLES

We shall consider now the linear differential equation with real coefficients.

$$\sum_{j=1}^{n}\sum_{i=1}^{n} a_{ij}u_{x_ix_j} + \sum_{i=1}^{n} b_iu_{x_i} + cu + f = 0 \qquad a_{ij} = a_{ji} \,, \tag{1-2.1}$$

where a, b, c, and f are functions of $x_1, x_2, \cdots, x_n$. We introduce a new variable ξ_k by

$$\xi_k = \xi_k(x_1, x_2, \cdots, x_n) \qquad k = 1, \cdots, n \,.$$

Then

$$u_{x_i} = \sum_{k=1}^{n} u_{\xi_k}\alpha_{ik}$$

$$u_{x_ix_j} = \sum_{k=1}^{n}\sum_{l=1}^{n} u_{\xi_k\xi_l}\alpha_{ik}\alpha_{jl} + \sum_{k=1}^{n} u_{\xi_k}(\xi_k)_{x_ix_j} \,,$$

where for brevity $\alpha_{ik} = \partial\xi_k/\partial x_i$ is introduced.

If now we substitute the expressions for the partial derivatives into the initial equation, we obtain

$$\sum_{k=1}^{n}\sum_{l=1}^{n} \bar{a}_{kl}u_{\xi_k\xi_l} + \sum_{k=1}^{n} \bar{b}_ku_{\xi_k} + cu + f = 0$$

with

$$\bar{a}_{kl} = \sum_{i=1}^{n}\sum_{j=1}^{n} a_{ij}\alpha_{ik}\alpha_{jl}$$

$$\bar{b}_k = \sum_{i=1}^{n} b_i\alpha_{jk} + \sum_{i=1}^{n}\sum_{j=1}^{n} a_{ij}(\xi_k)_{x_ix_j} \,.$$

We now consider the quadratic form

$$\sum_{i=1}^{n}\sum_{j=1}^{n} a_{ij}^0 y_iy_j \,, \tag{1-2.2}$$

whose coefficients coincide with the coefficient of a_{ij} of the initial equation at a point $M_0(x_1^0, \cdots, x_n^0)$. Under a linear transformation

$$y_i = \sum_{k=1}^{n} \alpha_{ik}\eta_k$$

If Eq. (1-2.1) at a given point M belongs to a definite type, it can be transformed to the corresponding canonical form.

We now investigate further whether an equation in a definite neighborhood of a point M can be transformed into the corresponding canonical form, if at all points of this neighborhood it belongs to one and the same type. If Eq. (1-2.1) can be transformed to the simplest form in a region in which the elements of the coefficient matrix off the principal diagonal vanish, then the functions

$$\xi_i(x_1, x_2, \cdots, x_n) \qquad i = 1, 2, \cdots, n$$

must satisfy the relation $\bar{a}_{kl} = 0$ for $k \neq 1$. The number of these relations is equal to $n(n-1)/2$, and hence for $n > 3$ it is larger than the number n of the functions ξ_i to be determined. For $n = 3$ the nondiagonal elements of the coefficient matrix $(\bar{a}_{ik})$ usually can be made to vanish; then, however, the elements of the principal diagonal can be distinct from each other.

Consequently, for $n \geqq 3$ it is impossible in a neighborhood of the point M to transform the differential Eq. (1-2.1) to canonical form. For $n = 2$, it can happen that the single nondiagonal coefficient of the second-order matrix vanishes, and the two coefficients on the principal diagonal are equal to each other as outlined earlier in this section.

If the coefficients of Eq. (1-2.1) are constant, then after a transformation of (1-2.1) to canonical form at a point M we obtain an equation which has the same canonical form in the entire region of definition.

1-3. THE CANONICAL FORMS OF LINEAR EQUATIONS WITH CONSTANT COEFFICIENTS

In the case of two independent variables, a linear equation of the second order with constant coefficients has the form

$$a_{11}u_{xx} + 2a_{12}u_{xy} + a_{22}u_{yy} + b_1u_x + b_2u_y + cu + f(x, y) = 0\,. \tag{1-3.1}$$

A characteristic equation with constant coefficients corresponds to it. Consequently, the characteristics in this case are the straight lines

$$y = \frac{a_{12} + \sqrt{a_{12}^2 - a_{11}a_{22}}}{a_{11}}\,x + C_1 \qquad y = \frac{a_{12} + \sqrt{a_{12}^2 - a_{11}a_{22}}}{a_{11}}\,x + C_2\,.$$

After a corresponding transformation of the variables, (1-3.1) assumes one of the following simple forms:

elliptic type: $$u_{\xi\xi} + u_{\eta\eta} + b_1u_\xi + b_2u_\eta + cu + f = 0 \tag{1-3.2}$$

hyperbolic type: $$\begin{cases} u_{\xi\eta} - b_1u_\xi + b_2u_\eta + cu + f = 0 \quad \text{or} \\ u_{\xi\xi} - u_{\eta\eta} + b_1u_\xi + b_2u_\eta + cu + f = 0 \end{cases} \tag{1-3.3}$$

parabolic type: $$u_{\xi\xi} + b_1u_\xi + b_2u_\eta + cu + f = 0 \tag{1-3.4}$$

For further simplification we introduce

$$u = e^{\lambda\xi + \mu\eta}\,v\,,$$

which yields a new function of v where λ and μ are still undetermined constants. Then

$$\begin{aligned} u_\xi &= e^{\lambda\xi+\mu\eta}(v_\xi + \lambda v) \\ u_\eta &= e^{\lambda\xi+\mu\eta}(v_\eta + \mu v) \\ u_{\xi\xi} &= e^{\lambda\xi+\mu\eta}(v_{\xi\xi} + 2\lambda v_\xi + \lambda^2 v) \\ u_{\xi\eta} &= e^{\lambda\xi+\mu\eta}(v_{\xi\eta} + \lambda v_\eta + \mu v_\xi + \lambda\mu v) \\ u_{\eta\eta} &= e^{\lambda\xi+\mu\eta}(v_{\eta\eta} + 2\mu v_\eta + \mu^2 v) \end{aligned}$$

If we substitute these expressions for the derivatives in Eq. (1-3.2), after division by $e^{\lambda\xi+\mu\eta}$ we obtain

$$v_{\xi\xi} + v_{\eta\eta} + (b_1 + 2\lambda)\, v_\xi + (b_2 + 2\mu)\, v_\eta + (\lambda^2 + \mu^2 + b_1\lambda + b_2\mu + c)\, v + f_1 = 0\,.$$

If in this equation the parameters λ and μ are so chosen that there are two coefficients, say in which both of the first derivatives are made to vanish, that is, $\lambda = -(b_1/2)$ and $\mu = -(b_2/2)$, then we obtain

$$v_{\xi\xi} + v_{\eta\eta} + \gamma v + f_1 = 0\,,$$

where γ is a constant defined by c, b_1, and b_2, and $f_1 = f\cdot e^{-(\lambda\xi+\mu\eta)}$. In the same manner we can derive the equations corresponding to (1-3.3) and (1-3.4). Thus, we are led to the following canonical forms for differential equations with constant coefficients:

elliptic type: $\quad v_{\xi\xi} + v_{\eta\eta} + \gamma v + f_1 = 0$

hyperbolic type: $\quad \begin{cases} v_{\xi\eta} + \gamma v + f_1 = 0 & \text{or} \\ v_{\xi\xi} - v_{\eta\eta} + \gamma v + f_1 = 0 \end{cases}$

parabolic type: $\quad v_{\xi\xi} + b_2 v_\eta + f_1 = 0$

We have already noted (1–2) that a differential equation with constant coefficients in the case of several independent variables,

$$\sum_{i=1}^{n}\sum_{j=1}^{n} a_{ij} u_{x_i x_j} + \sum_{i=1}^{n} b_i u_{x_i} + cu + f = 0\,,$$

under a suitable linear transformation of the variables, can be transformed to a canonical form which is the same for all points in the region of definition. If now we set

$$u = e^{\sum_{i=1}^{n}\lambda_i x_i}\, v\,,$$

a new function of v is introduced, and if λ_i is selected appropriately, the transformed equation can be further simplified so that in the case $n = 2$, a corresponding canonical form obtains.

Problems

1. Determine the region in which

$$u_{xx} + y u_{yy} = 0$$

is hyperbolic, elliptic, or parabolic, and transform the differential equation, in the region in which it is hyperbolic, to canonical form.

2. Transform the following differential equations to canonical form:

a) $u_{xx} + xyu_{yy} = 0$.

b) $yu_{xx} - xu_{yy} + u_x + yu_y = 0$.

c) $e^{2x}u_{xx} + 2e^{x+y}u_{xy} + e^{2y}u_{yy} = 0$.

d) $u_{xx} + (1+y)^2 u_{yy} = 0$.

e) $xu_{xx} + 2\sqrt{xy}\, u_{xy} + yu_{yy} - u_x = 0$.

f) $(x-y)u_{xx} + (xy - y^2 - x + y)u_{xy} = 0$.

g) $y^2 u_{xx} - e^{2x}u_{yy} + u_x = 0$.

h) $\sin^2 y u_{xx} - e^{2x}u_{yy} + 3u_x - 5u = 0$.

i) $u_{xx} + 2u_{xy} + 4u_{yy} + 2u_x + 3u_y = 0$.

3. Transform the following differential equation to canonical form and simplify it as much as possible:

$$au_{xx} + 2au_{xy} + au_{yy} + bu_x + cu_y + u = 0\,.$$

4. Simplify the following equations with constant coefficients by introducing the function $v = ue^{\lambda x + \mu y}$ and by a suitable selection of the parameters λ and μ:

a) $u_{xx} + u_{yy} + \alpha u_x + \beta u_y + \gamma u = 0$.

b) $u_{xx} = \dfrac{1}{a^2} u_y + \alpha u + \beta u_x$.

c) $u_{xx} - \dfrac{1}{a^2} u_{yy} = \alpha u_x + \beta u_y + \gamma u$.

d) $u_{xy} = \alpha u_x + \beta u_y$.

2

HYPERBOLIC DIFFERENTIAL EQUATIONS

Partial differential equations of the second order of the hyperbolic type occur principally in physical problems connected with vibration processes. The simplest hyperbolic differential equation

$$u_{xx} - u_{yy} = 0$$

is usually called the differential equation of the vibrating string. In this and the following chapters we shall restrict ourselves to the treatment of linear differential equations.

2-1. SIMPLE PROBLEMS WHICH LEAD TO HYPERBOLIC DIFFERENTIAL EQUATIONS AND BOUNDARY-VALUE PROBLEMS

1. The differential equation of small transverse vibrations of a string

Each point of a string of length l can be characterized by the value of its abscissa x. The vibration of a string can be described by the position of the points of the string at different times. In order to characterize the position of the string at time t, it is sufficient to know the components $u_1(x, t)$, $u_2(x, t)$, $u_3(x, t)$ of the displacement vector $\boldsymbol{u}$ at time t at the point x.

We shall consider now the simplest problem related to the vibrating string; we shall assume the displacement of the string takes place in a plane, for example, the x, u plane, and the displacement vector $\boldsymbol{u}$ always lies perpendicular to the x axis. Then the vibration process can be described by a single function $u(x, t)$ which characterizes the vertical displacement of the string. We consider the string to be a flexible-elastic filament. The flexibility is expressed mathematically by the assumption that the tension in the string is always in the direction of the tangent to the existing profile of the string (Figure 1). This requirement states that the string offers no resistance to bending.

The magnitude of the tension, which arises in the string because of the elasticity, can be calculated using Hooke's law. We shall consider only small vibrations and can therefore neglect the square of u_x, since this quantity is small compared with unity. In accordance with these requirements, we can calculate the elongation which a segment (x_1, x_2) of the string undergoes.

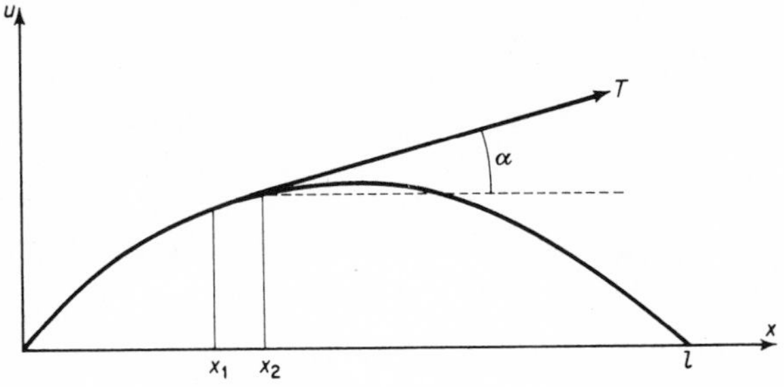

FIG. 1.

The length of arc belonging to this segment is equal to

$$S' = \int_{x_1}^{x_2} \sqrt{1 + (u_x)^2}\, dx \approx x_2 - x_1 = S .$$

Thus no elongation of a single segment of the string occurs within the scope of our required limits of accuracy, whereas according to Hooke's law it follows that at each point, the tension T is independent of x, i.e.,

$$T = T_0 = \text{const.}$$

For the projection of the tension on the x and u axes, indicated by T_x and T_u, we find

$$T_x(x) = T(x) \cos \alpha = \frac{T}{\sqrt{1 + (u_x)^2}} \approx T(x)$$

$$T_u(x) = T(x) \sin \alpha \approx T(x) \operatorname{tg} \alpha = T(x) u_x$$

where α is the angle between the tangent to the curve $u(x, t)$ and the x axis.

A tensile force, an external force, and an inertial force act on the segment (x_1, x_2). The sum of the projections of all these factors on the x axis must be equal to zero (since we consider only transverse vibrations). Since the inertial force and the external force act along the u axis according to hypothesis, there results

$$T_x(x_2) - T_x(x_1) = 0 \qquad \text{or} \qquad T(x_1) = T(x_2) . \tag{2-1.1}$$

But since x_1 and x_2 were selected arbitrarily, it follows that the tension is not dependent on x; i.e., for all x and t values,

$$T \equiv T_0 . \tag{2-1.2}$$

To derive the equation of a transverse vibrating string, we use Newton's second law. The total momentum of an element (x_1, x_2) in the direction of the u axis is, first of all, equal to

$$\int_{x_1}^{x_2} u_t(\xi, t) \rho(\xi) d\xi ,$$

where ρ denotes the linear density of the string. We now set the change of momentum during the time $\Delta t = t_2 - t_1$,

$$\int_{x_1}^{x_2} \rho(\xi)[u_t(\xi, t_2) - u_t(\xi, t_1)]d\xi ,$$

equal to the impulse of the acting force which arises from the tension $T_0 u_x$ at the points x_1 and x_2, as well as from the external force. The latter we assume as continuously distributed with the density ρ (the load) and denote it (per unit of length) by $f(x, t)$. Thus we obtain the equation of a transverse vibrating string in integral form

$$\int_{x_1}^{x_2} [u_t(\xi, t_2) - u_t(\xi, t_1)]\rho(\xi)d\xi = \int_{t_1}^{t_2} T_0[u_x(x_2, \tau) - u_x(x_1, \tau)]d\tau + \int_{x_1}^{x_2}\int_{t_1}^{t_2} f(\xi, \tau)d\xi d\tau . \tag{2-1.3}$$

In order to go from this integral equation to a differential equation, we assume the existence and continuity of the second derivative of $u(x, t)$.[1] Equation (2-1.3) is then transformed, after a twice-repeated application of the mean-value theorem, to

$$u_{tt}(\xi^*, t^*)\rho(\xi^*)\Delta t\Delta x = \{T_0[u_{xx}(\xi^{**}, t^{**})] + f(\xi^{***}, t^{***})\}\Delta t\Delta x ,$$

where

$$\xi^*, \xi^{**}, \xi^{***} \in (x_1, x_2) , \qquad t^*, t^{**}, t^{***} \in (t_1, t_2) .$$

If we now divide by $\Delta x \Delta t$ and carry out the limit as $x_2 \to x_1$, $t_2 \to t_1$, then we obtain the differential equation of a transverse vibrating string:

$$T_0 u_{xx} = \rho u_{tt} - f(x, t) . \tag{2-1.4}$$

In the case of a constant density ρ, this equation is usually written in the form

$$u_{tt} = a^2 u_{xx} + F(x, t) \qquad \left(a = \sqrt{\frac{T_0}{\rho}}\right) , \tag{2-1.5}$$

where

$$F(x, t) = \frac{1}{\rho} f(x, t) \tag{2-1.6}$$

is the force density per unit of mass. If no external force acts, we obtain the homogeneous equation

$$u_{tt} = a^2 u_{xx} \quad \text{or} \quad u_{xx} - u_{yy} = 0 , \qquad y = at ,$$

which describes the free vibrations of a string. This equation represents the simplest example of a hyperbolic differential equation.

If a concentrated force $f_0(t)$ acts at the point x_0 where $x_1 < x_0 < x_2$ (Figure 2), then Eq. (2-1.3) takes the form

[1] By the assumption that the function $u(x, t)$ is twice continuously differentiable, we have practically asserted that we shall consider only those functions that possess this property. This does not mean, however, that no functions exist which satisfy the vibration equation in integral form and have no second derivatives. Such functions exist and are, in practice, of extraordinary interest. More details will be discussed later (2-7).

$$\int_{x_1}^{x_2} \rho(\xi)[u_t(\xi, t_2) - u_t(\xi, t_1)]d\xi - \int_{x_1}^{x_2}\int_{t_1}^{t_2} f(\xi, \tau)d\xi d\tau$$
$$= \int_{t_1}^{t_2} T_0[u_x(x_2, \tau) - u_x(x_1, \tau)]d\tau + \int_{t_1}^{t_2} f_0(\tau)d\tau .$$

Since the velocity of a point of a string is bounded, the integral on the left side of this equation tends towards zero as $x_1 \to x_0$ and $x_2 \to x_0$ and (2-1.3) assumes the form

$$\int_{t_1}^{t_2} T_0[u_x(x_0 + 0, \tau) - u_x(x_0 - 0, \tau)]d\tau = -\int_{t_1}^{t_2} f_0(\tau)d\tau . \tag{2-1.7}$$

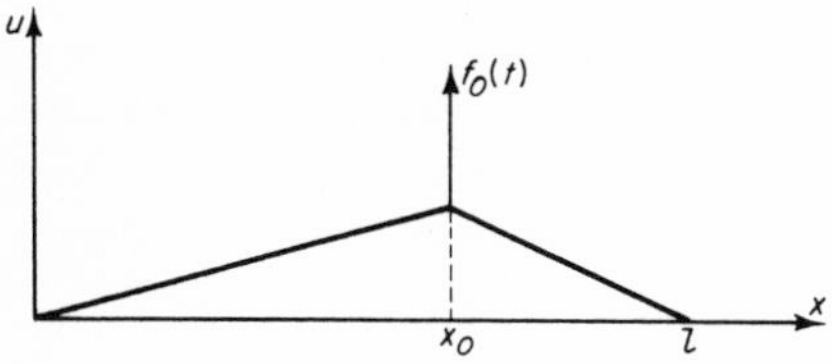

FIG. 2.

By using the mean-value theorem after dividing both sides of the equation by Δt and taking the limit as $t_2 \to t_1$ we obtain

$$u_x(x, t)\Big|_{x_0-0}^{x_0+0} = -\frac{1}{T_0} f_0(t) .$$

Hence, we see that the first derivative has a discontinuity at the point at which a concentrated force acts. The differential equation loses its meaning for $x = x_0$. At this point, both conditions

$$\begin{aligned} u(x_0 + 0, t) &= u(x_0 - 0, t) \\ u_x(x_0 + 0, t) - u_x(x_0 - 0, t) &= -\frac{1}{T_0} f_0(t) \end{aligned} \tag{2-1.8}$$

must be fulfilled. The first expresses the continuity of the string, while the second determines the magnitude of the jump of the derivative at x_0 in terms of $f_0(t)$ and the tension T_0.

2. Differential equations of longitudinally vibrating rods and strings

Longitudinal vibrations of rods, strings, and springs lead to equations of the same type. We shall consider a rod which lies in the interval $(0, l)$ of the x axis. Then the longitudinal vibration can be described by a single function $u(x, t)$ which represents at time t the displacement of those points which had abscissa x in the equilibrium state.[2] In longitudinal vibrations

[2] The geometric variable x chosen here is called the Lagrange coordinate. In the Lagrange coordinates, each physical point of a rod in the course of an entire process is characterized by one and the same geometric coordinate x. A physical point, which at the initial time (in the equilibrium state) is at the point x, is found after an arbitrary time t at the point with the coordinate $X = x + u(x, t)$. If we choose any geometric point A with the coordinate X, then at different times different physical points (with different Lagrange coordinates x) would be found at this point. Frequently we also use the Eulerian variables X, t, where X is the geometric coordinate. If $U(X, t)$ denotes the displacement of the point with the Eulerian coordinate X, then the Lagrange coordinate is $x = X - U(X, t)$. An example of the use of Eulerian coordinates is found in § 2-6.

the displacement is along the rod. To derive the vibration equation, we shall assume that the tension which causes the vibration is given by Hooke's law.

First we shall calculate the relative elongation of the elements $(x, x + \Delta x)$ at time t. The end points of these elements at time t have the coordinate values

$$x + u(x, t)\,, \qquad x + \Delta x + u(x + \Delta x, t)\,,$$

so that the relative elongation is equal to

$$\frac{[\Delta x + u(x + \Delta x, t) - u(x, t)] - \Delta x}{\Delta x} = u_x(x + \theta\Delta x, t)\,, \qquad 0 \leqq \theta \leqq 1\,.$$

Taking the limit as $\Delta x \to 0$, it follows that the relative elongation at the point x is defined by $u_x(x, t)$. According to Hooke's law, the tension $T(x, t)$ satisfies the equation

$$T(x, t) = k(x)u_x(x, t)\,, \tag{2-1.9}$$

where $k(x)$ denotes Young's modulus at the point x.

By applying the law for the change of momentum we then arrive at the vibration equation in integral form:

$$\int_{x_1}^{x_2} [u_t(\xi, t_2) - u_t(\xi, t_1)]\rho(\xi)d\xi$$
$$= \int_{t_1}^{t_2} [k(x_2)u_x(x_2, \tau) - k(x_1)u_x(x_1, \tau)]d\tau + \int_{x_1}^{x_2}\int_{t_1}^{t_2} f(\xi, \tau)d\xi d\tau \tag{2-1.10}$$

where $f(x, t)$ is the density of the external force per unit of length.

If now the second derivative of the function $u(x, t)$ exists and is continuous, then by use of the mean-value theorem and after taking the limits[3] as $\Delta x = x_2 - x_1 \to 0$ and $\Delta t = t_2 - t_1 \to 0$ we obtain

$$[k(x)u_x]_x = \rho u_{tt} - f(x, t) \tag{2-1.11}$$

as the equation of a longitudinal vibrating rod.[4]

If the rod is homogeneous, then this equation becomes

$$u_{tt} = a^2 u_{xx} + F(x, t)\,, \qquad a = \sqrt{\frac{k}{\rho}}\,, \tag{2-1.12}$$

where

$$F(x, t) = \frac{f(x, t)}{\rho} \tag{2-1.13}$$

represents the density of force per unit of mass.

[3] In the following we shall waive the discussion of such details for a transverse vibrating string.

[4] The requirement that the vibrations be sufficiently small depends in the present case only on the limits of applicability of Hooke's law. Generally, $T = k(x, u_x)u_x$; we then arrive at the quasilinear equation $[k(x, u_x)u_x]_x = \rho u_{tt} - f(x, t)$.

3. Energy of vibration of a string

We now seek an expression for the energy $E = K + U$ of a transverse vibrating string where K is the kinetic and U is the potential energy. An element dx of the string moving with velocity u_t possesses the amount of kinetic energy given by

$$\frac{1}{2}mv^2 = \frac{1}{2}\rho(x)dx(u_t)^2 ,$$

so that the kinetic energy K of the entire string is given by

$$K = \frac{1}{2}\int_0^l \rho(x)[u_t(x, t)]^2 dx . \tag{2-1.14}$$

The potential energy of a transverse vibrating string which has the form $u(x, t_0) = u_0(x)$ at time $t = t_0$ is equal to the work done in transforming the string from the equilibrium state to the state $u_0(x)$. The profile of the string at time t is given by the function $u(x, t)$. Thus

$$u(x, 0) = 0 , \qquad u(x, t_0) = u_0(x) .$$

The element dx under the influence of the resultant tension force is related to the displacement by

$$T\frac{\partial u}{\partial x}\bigg|_{x+dx} - T\frac{\partial u}{\partial x}\bigg|_x = Tu_{xx}dx ,$$

whereas the time dt is related by means of $u_t(x, t)dt$. The work done is equal to

$$\left\{\int_0^l T_0 u_{xx}u_t dx\right\}dt = \left\{T_0 u_x u_t \,|_0^l - \int_0^l T_0 u_x u_{xt} dx\right\}dt$$

$$= \left\{-\frac{1}{2}\frac{d}{dt}\int_0^l T_0(u_x)^2 dx + T_0 u_x u_t \,|_0^l\right\}dt .$$

By integration over t from 0 to t we obtain

$$-\frac{1}{2}\int_0^l T_0(u_x)^2 dx \,|_0^{t_0} + \int_0^{t_0} T_0 u_x u_t \,|_0^l dt = -\frac{1}{2}\int_0^l T_0[u_x(x, t_0)]^2 dx + \int_0^{t_0} T_0 u_x u_t \,|_0^l dt .$$

The meaning of the latter terms of this equation is easy to see; indeed, $T_0 u_x |_{x=0}$ is the magnitude of the tension at the end point $x = 0$; $u_t(0, t)$ is the displacement of the end point while the integral

$$\int_0^{t_0} T_0 u_x u_t \,|_{x=0}\, dt \tag{2-1.15}$$

represents the work which must be expended by the displacement of the end point $x = 0$. The meaning of the terms corresponding to the case $x = l$ is analogous. If the end points of the string are fixed, then the work done at these points is zero; here $u(0, t) = 0$ and $u_t(0, t) = 0$. Consequently, by a displacement of a string with fixed end points from the equilibrium state $u = 0$ to a state $u_0(x)$ the work done does not depend on the manner in which the string is brought into this new state; indeed the work equals

$$-\frac{1}{2}\int_0^l T_0[u_0'(x)]^2 dx\,, \tag{2-1.16}$$

i.e., it equals the potential energy of the string at time $t = t_0$ but with opposite sign. Therefore we have

$$E = \frac{1}{2}\int_0^l [T_0(u_x)^2 + \rho(x)(u_t)^2]dx \tag{2-1.17}$$

as the total energy of the string. We similarly obtain the potential energy of a longitudinal vibrating rod. Moreover, we arrive at the potential energy of the rod starting from the formula

$$U = \frac{1}{2}k\left(\frac{l - l_0}{l_0}\right)^2 l_0\,.$$

From this it follows directly that

$$U = \frac{1}{2}\int_0^l k(u_x)^2 dx\,.$$

4. Derivation of the equation of electrical vibrations in conductors

The passage of an electric current through a conductor with distributed parameters can be characterized by the current strength i and the voltage v, which are functions of the position x and the time t. From Ohm's law for an element of the conductor of length Δx it follows that the decrease in voltage in the element of the conductor Δx is equal to the sum of the electromotive forces:

$$-v_x\Delta x = iR\Delta x + i_t L\Delta x\,, \tag{2-1.18}$$

where R is the resistance and L is the coefficient of self-induction (both are expressed per unit of length).

The amount of electricity flowing through the conducting element Δx during the time Δt is given by

$$[i(x, t) - i(x + \Delta x, t)]\Delta t = -\, i_x\Delta x\Delta t \tag{2-1.19}$$

and is equal to the sum

$$C[v(x, t + \Delta t) - v(x, t)]\Delta x + G\Delta x \cdot v\Delta t = (Cv_t + Gv)\Delta x\Delta t\,, \tag{2-1.20}$$

which is the amount of electricity necessary for the charging of the element Δx plus the amount which is lost due to insufficient insulation, where C is the capacity and G is the loss coefficient (both are expressed per unit of length). We assume that the magnitude of the loss is proportional to the voltage at those points of the conductor under consideration.

From (2-1.18), (2-1.19), and (2-1.20) we then obtain the so-called system of telegraphic equations[5]

[5] These equations within the structure of the theory of electromagnetic fields have only approximate validity, since the electromagnetic vibrations in the material-filled space are neglected.

$$\begin{aligned} i_x + Cv_t + Gv &= 0 \\ v_x + Li_t + Ri &= 0 \,. \end{aligned} \tag{2-1.21}$$

In order to obtain only a single equation defining the function i, we differentiate the first of the two equations (2-1.21) with respect to x and the second with respect to t after we have multiplied these by C. By subtraction of the equations thus obtained we then find, under the assumption that the coefficients are constant,

$$i_{xx} + Gv_x - CLi_{tt} - CRi_t = 0 \,.$$

If we insert for v_x the value given by the second equation of (2-1.21), we obtain the differential equation for the current strength in the conductor

$$i_{xx} = CLi_{tt} + (CR + GL)i_t + GRi \,. \tag{2-1.22}$$

Analogously, the equation for the voltage reads

$$v_{xx} = CLv_{tt} + (CR + GL)v_t + GRv \,. \tag{2-1.23}$$

The differential Eq. (2-1.22) or (2-1.23) is called the telegraphic equation. If the insulation loss can be neglected and the resistance is very small ($G \approx R \approx 0$), we obtain from (2-1.23), the well-known vibration equation

$$v_{tt} = a^2 v_{xx} \,, \qquad a = \sqrt{\frac{1}{LC}} \,. \tag{2-1.24}$$

5. Transverse vibrations of a membrane

By a membrane we mean a sufficiently thin elastic film whose boundary is stretched firmly into a closed-plane curve C and offers no resistance to stretching and distortion. Of interest are the transverse vibrations of the membrane by which the stretching occurs perpendicular to the plane of the membrane.

Let ds be the element of arc length of an arbitrary closed curve lying on the membrane surface through the point $M(x, y)$. A tension of magnitude $\boldsymbol{T}ds$ acts on this element. Based on the above hypothesis about the membrane, the vector $\boldsymbol{T}$ lies in the tangent plane of the instantaneous membrane surface and is perpendicular to the element of arc ds. On the same basis the magnitude of the tension is also independent of the direction of the element ds. The stress vector $\boldsymbol{T} = \boldsymbol{T}(x, y, t)$ is therefore a function of x, y, and t alone. Obviously this is the mathematical expression for the absence of resistance to stretching or distortion.

In the following, we will investigate the small vibrations of a membrane in which the square of the first derivatives u_x and u_y can be neglected. From this assumption it then follows directly that the projection $T_h(x, y, t)$ of the tension on the x, y plane is equal to the absolute magnitude of the tension. For arbitrary orientation of the arc element ds, namely, the angle γ' between the vector $\boldsymbol{T}$ and the x, t plane is not larger than the angle γ which is formed by the normal to the membrane surface at the point (x, y) and the z axis. Thus,

$$\cos \gamma' \geqq \cos \gamma = \frac{1}{\sqrt{1 + u_x^2 + u_y^2}} \approx 1 , \qquad \text{i.e., } \cos \gamma' \approx 1 ,$$

and

$$T_h(x, y, z, t) = T \cos \gamma' \approx T(x, y, z, t) . \tag{2-1.25}$$

The vertically acting tension is obviously equal to $T_u = T(\partial u/\partial n)$. Now we choose an element on the membrane surface whose projection on the x, y plane forms a rectangle $ABCD$, whose sides are parallel to the coordinate axes (Figure 3). On this element acts a tension force of magnitude defined by

$$\boldsymbol{T}^* = \oint_{ABCD} \boldsymbol{T} ds . \tag{2-1.26}$$

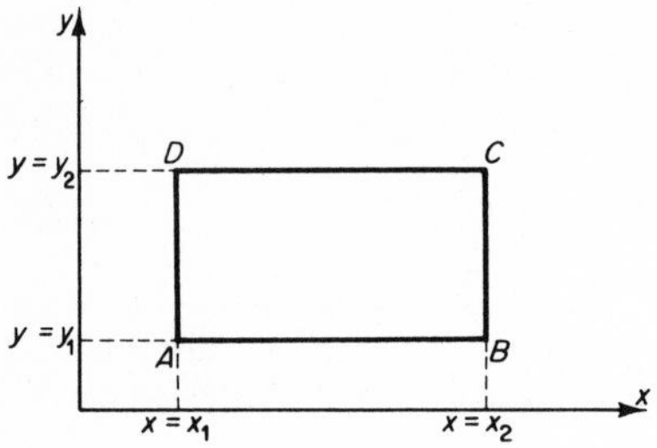

FIG. 3.

Since along the x and y axes no displacement occurs, the projections of $\boldsymbol{T}^*$ on these axes equal zero; thus

$$T_x^* = \int_B^C T(x_2, y, t)dy - \int_A^D T(x_1, y, t)dy$$

$$= \int_{y1}^{y2} \{T(x_2, y, t) - T(x_1, y, t)\}dy = 0$$

or

$$T_y^* = \int_{x_1}^{x2} \{T(x, y_2, t) - T(x, y_1, t)\}dx = 0 .$$

Hence according to the mean-value theorem, since the surface $ABCD$ is arbitrarily chosen, it follows that

$$\begin{aligned} T(x, y_1, t) &= T(x, y_2, t) \\ T(x_1, y, t) &= T(x_2, y, t) , \end{aligned} \tag{2-1.27}$$

i.e., the tension T does not vary with x and y and therefore can only be a function of t alone.

The surface area of a membrane element at time t in the sense of our approximation is equal to

$$\iint \frac{dxdy}{\cos \gamma} = \iint \sqrt{1 + u_x^2 + u_y^2}\, dxdy = \iint dxdy . \tag{2-1.28}$$

Consequently, no extension occurs during the vibration process, whereby according to Hooke's law the independence of the tension on time follows. Therefore, the independence of the tension on all three variables x, y, and t is proved; i.e.,

$$T(x, y, t) = \text{const.} = T_0 . \tag{2-1.29}$$

We shall now derive the equation of a vibrating membrane. For this purpose we proceed from the law for the change of momentum. Let S_1 be the projection of any one membrane element on the x, y plane, and let

C_1 be the boundary of S_1. We set the change of momentum equal to the impulse of the vertical components of the tension and the externally acting force whose density is $f(x, y, t)$. Then we obtain the equation of the vibrating membrane in the integral form

$$\int_S\int [u_t(x, y, t_2) - u_t(x, y, t_1)]\rho(x, y)dxdy$$

$$= \int_{t_1}^{t_2}\int_{C_1} T_0\frac{\partial u}{\partial n}dsdt + \int_{t_1}^{t_2}\int_{S_1}\int fdxdydt\,, \qquad (2\text{-}1.30)$$

where $\rho(x, y)$ is the surface density of the membrane and $f(x, y, t)$ is the density of the external force.

In order to go from this equation to a differential equation we shall assume the function $u(x, y, t)$ to be twice continuously differentiable. First we transform the line integral by means of Green's theorem[6] into a surface integral

$$\int_{C_1}\frac{\partial u}{\partial n}ds = \int_{S_1}\int (u_{xx} + u_{yy})dxdy\,.$$

Then the above vibration equation is transformed from the integral form into

$$\int_{t_1}^{t_2}\int_{S_1}\int \{\rho u_{tt} - T_0(u_{xx} + u_{yy}) - f(x, y, t)\}dxdydt = 0\,.$$

If we now apply the mean-value theorem and take into consideration that both S_1 and the time interval (t_1, t_2) are arbitrary, then we see that the expression in the brackets must vanish identically. In this manner we arrive at the differential equation of a vibrating membrane:

$$\rho u_{tt} = T_0(u_{xx} + u_{yy}) + f(x, y, t)\,. \qquad (2\text{-}1.31)$$

For a homogeneous membrane the vibration equation can also be written in the form

$$u_{tt} = a^2(u_{xx} + u_{yy}) + F(x, y, t)\,, \qquad a^2 = \frac{T_0}{\rho} \qquad (2\text{-}1.32)$$

where $F(x, y, t)$ is the force density per unit of mass of the membrane.

6. Basic equations of hydrodynamics and acoustics

In order to describe the motion of a fluid one uses three functions $v_1(x, y, z, t)$, $v_2(x, y, z, t)$, and $v_3(x, y, z, t)$, which are the components of the velocity vector $\boldsymbol{v}$ at the point (x, y, z) at time t. Further quantities for the characterization of a fluid motion are the density $\rho(x, y, z, t)$, the pressure $p(x, y, z, t)$, and the density of the external force given in units of mass $\boldsymbol{F}(x, y, z, t)$, in case such forces are present.

We consider a fixed portion of a fluid occupying a region of space T, and calculate the force acting on it. Moreover we shall neglect the friction forces

6 See V. I. Smirnov, Textbook of Higher Mathematics, 2d ed., Part II, Berlin, 1958, p. 175; in the literature it is also called Gauss' integral theorem.

caused by the viscosity, i.e., we consider an ideal fluid. For the resultant of the pressure forces we obtain the following expression in the form of a surface integral

$$-\int_S\int p\boldsymbol{n}dS\,, \tag{2-1.33}$$

where S is the surface of the region T and $\boldsymbol{n}$ is the unit vector in the direction of the outward directed normal. The formula of Green then yields

$$-\int_S\int p\boldsymbol{n}dS = -\iint_T\int \operatorname{grad} p\,d\tau\,. \tag{2-1.34}$$

For the calculation of the acceleration of any fluid element, naturally the displacement of the points themselves are to be considered. If $x = x(t)$, $y = y(t)$, and $z = z(t)$ are the paths of the points of this element, then the derivative of the velocity with respect to time is

$$\frac{d\boldsymbol{v}}{dt} = \frac{\partial \boldsymbol{v}}{\partial t} + \frac{\partial \boldsymbol{v}}{\partial x}\dot{x} + \frac{\partial \boldsymbol{v}}{\partial y}\dot{y} + \frac{\partial \boldsymbol{v}}{\partial z}\dot{z} = \frac{\partial \boldsymbol{v}}{\partial t} + \frac{\partial \boldsymbol{v}}{\partial x}v_1 + \frac{\partial \boldsymbol{v}}{\partial y}v_2 + \frac{\partial \boldsymbol{v}}{\partial z}v_3 = \frac{\partial \boldsymbol{v}}{\partial t} + (\boldsymbol{v}\nabla)\boldsymbol{v}\,,$$

where

$$\nabla = \boldsymbol{i}\frac{\partial}{\partial x} + \boldsymbol{j}\frac{\partial}{\partial y} + \boldsymbol{k}\frac{\partial}{\partial z}\,.$$

This derivative with respect to time, which takes into account the motion of a single element of the medium (the substance), is called the substantive derivative. The equation of motion of a fluid which describes the connection between the acceleration of the element and the forces acting upon it is given by

$$\iint_T\int \rho\frac{d\boldsymbol{v}}{dt}d\tau = -\iint_T\int \operatorname{grad} p\,d\tau + \iint_T\int \rho\boldsymbol{F}d\tau\,. \tag{2-1.35}$$

The last integral represents the resultant of the external forces which act on the region of space T. But since T was chosen arbitrarily we obtain the equation of motion of an ideal fluid in Eulerian form:

$$\boldsymbol{v}_t + (\boldsymbol{v}\nabla)\boldsymbol{v} = -\frac{1}{\rho}\operatorname{grad} p + \boldsymbol{F}\,. \tag{2-1.36}$$

To derive the needed continuity equation, we shall assume that at all points of the streaming fluid region T no additional fluid is introduced, i.e., we limit ourselves to the study of source-free streams, in which we regard a sink as a negative source. Then the change in the amount of fluid contained in T per unit of time is equal to the flux through the boundary S of the region

$$\frac{d}{dt}\iint_T\int \rho\,d\tau = -\int_S\int \rho\boldsymbol{v}\boldsymbol{n}dS\,. \tag{2-1.37}$$

The transformation of the surface integral to a volume integral yields

$$\iint_T\int\left(\frac{\partial\rho}{\partial t} + \operatorname{div}\rho\boldsymbol{v}\right)d\tau = 0\,.$$

Since this relation is valid for an arbitrarily small region, there follows the continuity equation

$$\frac{\partial \rho}{\partial t} + \operatorname{div}(\rho \boldsymbol{v}) = 0$$

or

$$\frac{\partial \rho}{\partial t} + \boldsymbol{v} \operatorname{grad} \rho + \rho \operatorname{div} \boldsymbol{v} = 0\,. \tag{2-1.38}$$

To Eqs. (2-1.36) and (2-1.38) there is still to be added the thermodynamic equation of state which we shall write here in the form

$$p = f(\rho)\,.$$

Thus we obtain a system of five equations for the five unknown functions v_x, v_y, v_z, p, and ρ. If the equation of state also includes the temperature, then a heat-conduction equation must be added. The system of equations

$$\begin{gathered}\frac{\partial \boldsymbol{v}}{\partial t} + (\boldsymbol{v}\nabla)\boldsymbol{v} = \boldsymbol{F} - \frac{1}{\rho}\operatorname{grad} p \\ \frac{\partial \rho}{\partial t} + \operatorname{div}(\rho \boldsymbol{v}) = 0 \\ p = f(\rho)\end{gathered} \tag{2-1.39}$$

thus represents the complete system of equations for the motion of an ideal fluid.

To use the hydrodynamic equations for the propagation of sound in a gas, we make the following assumptions: (1) no external forces are present; (2) the process of sound propagation in a gas proceeds adiabatically, so that Poisson's adiabatic equation

$$\frac{p}{p_0} = \left(\frac{\rho}{\rho_0}\right)^{\gamma}, \qquad \gamma = \frac{c_p}{c_v}$$

can be taken as the equation of state (ρ_0 designates the initial density and p_0 is the initial pressure, c_p and c_v are the specific heats at a fixed pressure and a fixed volume); and (3) the vibrations of the gas are sufficiently small so that the higher powers of the velocity, the gradients of the velocity, and the gradients of the density can be neglected.

For the condensation of the gas we designate the relative change in density by the quantity

$$s(x, y, z, t) = \frac{\rho - \rho_0}{\rho_0}\,. \tag{2-1.40}$$

Then the condensation is defined by

$$\rho = \rho_0(1 + s)\,. \tag{2-1.41}$$

With the above assumptions the hydrodynamic equations take the form

$$v_t = -\frac{1}{\rho_0} \operatorname{grad} p$$

$$\rho_t + \rho_0 \operatorname{div} \boldsymbol{v} = 0 \tag{2-1.42}$$

$$p = p_0(1+s)^\gamma \approx p_0(1+\gamma s)$$

since

$$\frac{1}{\rho}\operatorname{grad} p = \frac{1}{\rho_0}(1 - s + \cdots)\operatorname{grad} p = \frac{1}{\rho_0}\operatorname{grad} p + \cdots$$

$$\operatorname{div} \rho\boldsymbol{v} = \boldsymbol{v}\operatorname{grad}\rho + \rho\operatorname{div}\boldsymbol{v} = \rho_0 \operatorname{div}\boldsymbol{v} + \cdots$$

where the dots denote the terms which are of second and higher order of smallness. With the notation $a^2 = \gamma p_0/\rho_0$ we rewrite the system (2-1.42) in the form

$$\begin{aligned} \boldsymbol{v}_t &= - a^2 \operatorname{grad} s \\ s_t + \operatorname{div}\boldsymbol{v} &= 0\,. \end{aligned} \tag{2-1.42$'$}$$

If we now apply the divergence operator to the first equation of (2-1.42′) and interchange the order of differentiation, we obtain

$$\frac{d}{dt}\operatorname{div}\boldsymbol{v} = - a^2 \operatorname{div}(\operatorname{grad} s) = - a^2\nabla^2 s = - a^2\Delta s\,,$$

where

$$\nabla^2 = \Delta = \frac{\partial^2}{\partial x^2} + \frac{\partial^2}{\partial y^2} + \frac{\partial^2}{\partial z^2}$$

is the Laplace operator. Then the second expression of (2-1.42′) can be used to yield the vibration equation

$$\Delta s = \frac{1}{a^2} s_{tt} \tag{2-1.43}$$

or

$$a^2(s_{xx} + s_{yy} + s_{zz}) = s_{tt}\,.$$

From this and from (2-1.40) we obtain the density equation

$$a^2(\rho_{xx} + \rho_{yy} + \rho_{zz}) = \rho_{tt}\,.$$

We now introduce the velocity potential and show that it satisfies the same vibration Eq. (2-1.43), as does the condensation. From the expression

$$\boldsymbol{v}_t = - a^2 \operatorname{grad} s$$

follows

$$\boldsymbol{v}(x, y, z, t) = \boldsymbol{v}(x, y, z, 0) - a^2 \operatorname{grad}\left(\int_0^t s\,dt\right), \tag{2-1.44}$$

where $\boldsymbol{v}(x, y, z, 0)$ is the initial velocity distribution. If the velocity field at the initial time possesses the potential

$$\boldsymbol{v}\,|_{t=0} = - \operatorname{grad} f(x, y, z)\,, \tag{2-1.45}$$

we can obtain the expression

$$v = -\operatorname{grad}\left[f(x, y, z) + a^2\int_0^t s\,dt\right] = -\operatorname{grad} U. \qquad (2\text{-}1.46)$$

This means that a velocity potential $U(x, y, z, t)$ exists. The knowledge of the velocity potential yields for the determination of the complete process of motion the following:

$$\begin{aligned} v &= -\operatorname{grad} U \\ s &= \frac{1}{a^2} U_t\,. \end{aligned} \qquad (2\text{-}1.47)$$

By inserting these quantities into the continuity equation

$$s_t + \operatorname{div} v = 0\,,$$

we obtain the vibration equation for the potential:

$$a^2(U_{xx} + U_{yy} + U_{zz}) = U_{tt}$$

or

$$U_{tt} = a^2 \Delta U\,. \qquad (2\text{-}1.48)$$

Equations for the pressure p and the velocity v similar to Eq. (2-1.48) can be derived. These are usually called the equations of acoustics.

For the solution of two- and one-dimensional problems the Laplace operator is replaced in Eq. (2-1.48) by $\partial^2/\partial x^2 + \partial^2/\partial y^2$ or $\partial^2/\partial x^2$.

For the vibrations of a gas in a bounded region of space, specific boundary conditions must be fulfilled; that is, certain restrictions are imposed which are to be applied directly on the sought functions at the boundary of the gas-filled region of space. The simplest example is for the case of a gas moving in a vessel whose walls are fixed. Since the stream velocity must always be directed tangentially on these walls, the normal component of the velocity must be equal to zero. This leads to the condition

$$\left.\frac{\partial U}{\partial n}\right|_{\Sigma} = 0 \quad \text{or} \quad \left.\frac{\partial s}{\partial n}\right|_{\Sigma} = 0\,. \qquad (2\text{-}1.49)$$

The constant

$$a = \sqrt{\frac{\gamma p_0}{\rho_0}}$$

possesses the dimension of velocity and, as will be shown later, represents the velocity of propagation of sound.

We shall now calculate the velocity of sound in air at normal atmospheric pressure. In this case, we have $\gamma = 7/5$, $\rho_0 = 1.293 \cdot 10^{-3}\,\mathrm{g\,cm^{-3}}$, and $p_0 = 1.033\,\mathrm{kg\,cm^{-2}}$; consequently,

$$a = \sqrt{\frac{\gamma p_0}{\rho_0}} = 336\ \mathrm{m\,sec^{-1}}\,.$$

7. Boundary and initial conditions

For the mathematical description of a physical process, a problem must first of all be defined; that is, the conditions must be formulated which are sufficient for the unique determination of the process.

Both ordinary and naturally partial differential equations possess, in general, infinitely many solutions. Therefore, in those cases in which the physical problem to be considered leads to a partial differential equation, for a unique characterization of the process it is necessary to add further conditions on the differential equation.

For an ordinary differential equation of the second order the solution can be determined from the initial conditions, i.e., from the initial value of the function itself and its first derivative at the initial value of the argument. Also possible are other forms of the conditions of state; for example, the function can be prescribed at two distinct points (problem of the catenary). For partial differential equations there are, likewise, different forms of the conditions of state.

We shall consider, first, the simple problem of a transverse vibrating string fixed at the ends. Here $u(x, t)$ denotes the displacement of the string from its equilibrium position (x axis). If the ends of the string $0 \leqq x \leqq l$ are held fixed, the boundary conditions which must be satisfied are

$$u(0, t) = 0 , \qquad u(l, t) = 0 . \tag{2-1.50}$$

On the other hand, there are initial conditions to be satisfied, i.e. the displacement and velocity of the string at the initial time t_0, say

$$\begin{aligned} u(x, t_0) &= \varphi(x) \\ u_t(x, t_0) &= \psi(x) . \end{aligned} \tag{2-1.51}$$

The conditions of state therefore consist of boundary and initial conditions. Later we shall show that these conditions completely determine the solution of the vibration equation

$$u_{tt} = a^2 u_{xx} . \tag{2-1.52}$$

If the end points of the string move in a prescribed way, then the boundary conditions assume another form:

$$\begin{aligned} u(0, t) &= \mu_1(t) , \\ u(l, t) &= \mu_2(t) , \end{aligned} \tag{2-1.50$'$}$$

where $\mu_1(t)$ and $\mu_2(t)$ are prescribed functions of the time t. The statement of problems for longitudinal vibrating rods or springs reads analogously.

Boundary conditions occur also in other forms. We shall consider, for example, a longitudinal vibrating spring which is fastened at one end (suspended point) while the other is free to move. The motion of the free end is not known and is thus the function to be determined. At the point of suspension $x = 0$ there can be no displacement,

$$u(0, t) = 0 ;$$

while at the free-end point $x = l$ the spring tension is given by

$$T(l, t) = k\frac{\partial u}{\partial x}\bigg|_{x=l} \tag{2-1.53}$$

and equals zero (no external force), so that the mathematical formulation of the conditions for the free end takes the form

$$u_x(l, t) = 0 .$$

If the fixed end $x = 0$ moves according to a definite law $\mu(t)$, whereas at $x = l$ the prescribed force $\bar{\nu}(t)$ acts, then we write

$$u(0, t) = \mu(t) , \qquad u_x(l, t) = \nu(t) \qquad \text{with} \qquad \nu(t) = \frac{1}{k}\bar{\nu}(t) .$$

Typical also is a condition of an elastic constraint, say at $x = l$:

$$ku_x(l, t) = -\alpha u(l, t)$$

or

$$u_x(l, t) = - hu(l, t) , \qquad h = \frac{\alpha}{k} , \tag{2-1.54}$$

about which the end point $x = l$ can be displaced, while the elastic force of the constraint at this point gives rise to a tension which causes the displaced point to return to its earlier position. The rigidity of the constraint is characterized by the coefficient α.

If at a point of a system at which an elastic constraint acts, the displacement and its deviation from the initial position is given by the function $\theta(t)$, then the boundary conditions read

$$u_x(l, t) = - h[u(l, t) - \theta(t)] \qquad \text{with} \qquad h = \frac{\alpha}{k} . \tag{2-1.55}$$

Note that in the case of a rigid constraint (large α), even when small displacements cause large tensions, the last boundary condition is transformed into the first for $\mu(t) = \theta(t)$. For a weak constraint (small α), in which large displacements produce only small tensions, the condition for a free-end point occurs in place of the last noted boundary condition.

In the following, we shall speak of three principal types of boundary conditions:

1. The first type $u(0, t) = \mu(t)$, a prescribed motion of the end point $x = 0$;
2. The second type $u_x(0, t) = \nu(t)$, a prescribed force;
3. The third type $u_x(0, t) = h[u(0, t) - \theta(t)]$, an elastic constraint.

In an analogous way we formulate the boundary conditions for the second end point $x = l$. If the functions on the right sides—$\mu(t)$, $\nu(t)$, or $\theta(t)$—equal zero, then one speaks of homogeneous boundary conditions.

Combinations of these different types of boundary conditions result in six types of simple boundary-value problems. Complicated boundary conditions occur, for example, for an elastic constraint which does not satisfy Hooke's law—that is, if the tension at the end point is a non-linear function of the displacement $u(l, t)$, namely,

$$u_x(l, t) = \frac{1}{k} F[u(l, t)] . \tag{2-1.56}$$

This boundary condition is, in contrast with the law stated above, non-linear. In addition, the relations between the displacements and the tensions are possible at different points of the system; e.g., the boundary conditions for problems of the vibrations of a ring, where $x = 0$ and $x = l$ designate one and the same point, read:

$$u(l, t) = u(0, t) , \qquad u_x(0, t) = u_x(l, t) \tag{2-1.57}$$

and amount to the requirement that u and u_x are continuous. In the boundary conditions the derivative with respect to t can also occur. If the end of a spring undergoes a resistance from the outside, which is proportional to its velocity (perhaps by a disc fastened to the end of the spring, and for which the plane of the disc is perpendicular to the spring axis), the boundary conditions read:

$$ku_x(l, t) = - \alpha u_t(l, t) . \tag{2-1.58}$$

If a mass m is suspended at the end of the spring $x = l$, then the condition

$$mu_{tt}(l, t) = -ku_x(l, t) + mg \tag{2-1.59}$$

must be fulfilled at $x = l$.

In the following discussion we shall limit ourselves to the consideration of the three simplest types of boundary conditions, directing attention to an example of boundary conditions of the first type, and indicate only incidentally the peculiarities which occur in connection with the second and third types.

To formulate the first boundary-value problem for Eq. (2-1.52), let us seek a function $u(x, t)$ which satisfies the equation

$$u_{tt} = a^2 u_{xx} \qquad \text{for} \qquad 0 < x < 1 , \qquad t > 0$$

as well as the boundary and initial conditions

$$\begin{aligned} u(0, t) &= \mu_1(t) \\ u(l, t) &= \mu_2(t) \\ u(x, 0) &= \varphi(x) \\ u_t(x, 0) &= \psi(x) . \end{aligned} \tag{2-1.60}$$

We speak of the second or third boundary-value problem if boundary conditions of the second or third type are imposed at both ends. If the boundary conditions for $x = 0$ and $x = l$ are of different types, then we mean mixed boundary-value problems without classifying them more precisely.

We now turn to the limiting cases of these problems. The influence of the boundary conditions at a point M_0 which is sufficiently far from the boundary, first enters the expression at a sufficiently large interval of time.

Of interest to us is the behavior during a small time interval in which the influence of the boundary conditions is still negligible; then instead of treating the complete problem, we can consider the problem with initial conditions for an unbounded region. Thus we seek a solution of the equation

$$u_{tt} = a^2 u_{xx} + f(x, t) \quad \text{for} \quad -\infty < x < \infty , \quad t > 0 ,$$

with the initial displacement

$$[u(x, t)]_{t=0} = \varphi(x) \quad \text{for} \quad -\infty < x < \infty , \tag{2-1.61}$$

and the initial velocity distribution

$$[u_t(x, t)]_{t=0} = \psi(x) \quad \text{for} \quad -\infty < x < \infty .$$

This problem of the infinite string is ordinarily known as Cauchy's problem.

If, however, we wish to study the behavior in the neighborhood of the boundary, and if the influence of the boundary condition of one boundary on the other in the course of a prescribed time interval remains insignificant, we are led to a problem for a semi-infinite line $0 \leqq x < \infty$, where apart from the differential equation itself we also have the conditions

$$\begin{aligned} u(0, t) &= \mu(t) , \quad && t \geqq 0 \\ u(x, 0) &= \varphi(x) , \quad && \\ u_t(x, 0) &= \psi(x) . && 0 \leqq x < \infty \end{aligned} \tag{2-1.62}$$

The character of the process for a time interval which is sufficiently long from the initial time $t = 0$, is completely defined by the boundary values since the influence of the initial conditions, because of the friction which occurs in every real system, vanishes with increasing t.[7] Such cases occur mostly when the system under consideration is acted on by a periodic boundary influence which persists for an indefinitely long time. The formulation of such problems without initial conditions is as follows:

Find a solution of the considered equation for $0 \leqq x \leqq l$ and $t > -\infty$ with the boundary conditions

$$\begin{aligned} u(0, t) &= \mu_1(t) \\ u(l, t) &= \mu_2(t) . \end{aligned} \tag{2-1.63}$$

This is analogous to the problem without initial conditions for the semi-infinite line.

Besides the fundamental boundary-value problems, we shall also consider in what follows the limiting cases:

1. Problems for an infinite region when one or both boundaries lie at infinity.
2. Problems without initial conditions when the solutions considered are defined in the course of an infinitely large time interval.

8. Reduction of the general problem

For the solution of complicated problems one endeavors to trace them back to the solution of simpler problems. To this end we shall represent

[7] The vibration equation, taking into consideration the influence of friction which is proportional to the velocity, has the form $u_{tt} = a^2 u_{xx} - \alpha u_t$, where $\alpha > 0$. For details of the above problem without initial conditions for $\alpha = 0$, see § 3-7.

the solution of the general boundary-value problem as a superposition of the solution of specific boundary-value problems.

The functions $u_i(x, t)$, where $i = 1, 2, \cdots, n$, are required to satisfy the equations

$$\frac{\partial^2 u_i}{\partial t^2} = a^2 \frac{\partial^2 u_i}{\partial x^2} + f^i(x, t) \qquad \text{for} \qquad 0 < x < l,\ t > 0 \tag{2-1.64}$$

and the conditions

$$\begin{aligned} u_i(0, t) &= \mu_1^i(t) \\ u_i(l, t) &= \mu_2^i(t) \\ u_i(x, 0) &= \varphi^i(x) \\ \frac{\partial u_i}{\partial t}(x, 0) &= \psi^i(x) . \end{aligned} \tag{2-1.65}$$

Obviously, the solutions can be superposed in such a way that the function

$$u^{(0)}(x, t) = \sum_{i=1}^{n} u_i(x, t) \tag{2-1.66}$$

satisfies the analogous equation with

$$f^{(0)}(x, t) = \sum_{i=1}^{n} f^i(x, t) \tag{2-1.67}$$

and the conditions with right sides given by

$$\begin{aligned} &\mu_k^{(0)}(t) \sum_{i=1}^{n} \mu_k^i(t) , \qquad k = 1, 2 \\ &\varphi^{(0)}(x) = \sum_{i=1}^{n} \varphi^i(x) \\ &\psi^{(0)}(x) = \sum_{i=1}^{n} \psi^i(x) . \end{aligned} \tag{2-1.68}$$

We see that this superposition principle is valid not only for the aforementioned problem, but also for every linear equation with linear auxiliary conditions. We shall use this property repeatedly in the following.

The solution of the general boundary-value problem

$$\begin{aligned} u_{tt} = a^2 u_{xx} + f(x, t) , \qquad (0 < x < l ,\ t > 0) \\ u(0, t) = \mu_1(t) \\ u(l, t) = \mu_2(t) \\ u(x, 0) = \varphi(x) \\ u_t(x, 0) = \psi(x) \end{aligned} \tag{2-1.69}$$

can be represented as a sum

$$u(x, t) = u_1(x, t) + u_2(x, t) + u_3(x, t) + u_4(x, t) , \tag{2-1.70}$$

where u_1, u_2, u_3, u_4 are solutions of the particular boundary-value problems

$$\frac{\partial^2 u_i}{\partial t^2} = a^2 \frac{\partial^2 u_i}{\partial x^2}, \qquad i = 1, 2, 3\,,$$
$$\frac{\partial^2 u_4}{\partial t^2} = a^2 \frac{\partial^2 u_4}{\partial x^2} + f(x, t)\,, \qquad 0 < x < l\,,\ t > 0\,, \tag{2-1.71}$$

$$\begin{array}{llll} u_1(0, t) = 0 & u_1(l, t) = 0 & u_1(x, 0) = \varphi(x) & u_{1_t}(x, 0) = \psi(x) \\ u_2(0, t) = \mu_1(t) & u_2(l, t) = 0 & u_2(x, 0) = 0 & u_{2_t}(x, 0) = 0 \\ u_3(0, t) = 0 & u_3(l, t) = \mu_2(t) & u_3(x, 0) = 0 & u_{3_t}(x, 0) = 0 \\ u_4(0, t) = 0 & u_4(l, t) = 0 & u_4(x, 0) = 0 & u_{4_t}(x, 0) = 0\,. \end{array}$$

We shall limit ourselves for this formal reduction to the characterization of those special boundary-value problems which are important intermediate ones for the solution of the general problem. An analogous reduction can also be obtained for the limiting cases of the general problem.

9. Formulation of boundary-value problems for several variables

We have considered above only the formulation of boundary-value problems for the case of one independent geometric variable x and the time t. If the number n of the geometric variables is larger than one (for example, $n = 3$), then the first boundary-value problem reads:

We seek a function $u(M, t) = u(x, y, z, t)$ which is defined in the interior of a prescribed region T with boundary Σ; in the interior of T the function must satisfy the equation

$$u_{tt} = a^2 \Delta u + f(x, y, z, t)\,, \qquad M(x, y, z) \in T, \qquad t > 0 \tag{2-1.72}$$

and on the boundary Σ must satisfy the boundary condition

$$u\,|_\Sigma = \mu(x, y, z, t)\,, \qquad M(x, y, z) \in \Sigma, \qquad t > 0\,; \tag{2-1.73}$$

it also must satisfy the initial conditions

$$\begin{aligned} u\,(x, y, z, 0) &= \varphi(x, y, z)\,, \\ u_t(x, y, z, 0) &= \psi(x, y, z) \end{aligned} \qquad M(x, y, z) \in T\,, \tag{2-1.74}$$

where $u(x, y, z, t)$ is a function defined on Σ.

The reduction of the general boundary-value problem to a series of simpler problems is analogous to that in §2-8. It is to be noted that here also the limiting case for an unbounded region, semi-infinite space, etc., can be considered.

10. Uniqueness theorem

In the solution of boundary-value problems both of the following questions arise.

1. Are auxiliary conditions sufficient for the determination of a unique solution?
2. Will the problem be overdetermined by the auxiliary conditions, i.e., are these conditions incompatible?

The first question is answered by the uniqueness theorem, the second by the existence theorem. The proof for the existence of solutions depends strictly on the method that one uses for its determination. In the following we shall prove the uniqueness theorem.

The differential equation

$$\rho\frac{\partial^2 u}{\partial t^2} = \frac{\partial}{\partial x}\left(k\frac{\partial u}{\partial x}\right) + F(x, t)\,, \qquad 0 < x < l, t > 0 \tag{2-1.75}$$

possesses only one solution which satisfies the initial and boundary conditions

$$\begin{aligned} u\,(x, 0) &= \varphi\,(x) \\ u_t(x, 0) &= \psi\,(x) \\ u\,(0, t) &= \mu_1(t) \\ u\,(l, t) &= \mu_2(t)\,. \end{aligned} \tag{2-1.76}$$

Here it is assumed that the function $u(x, t)$ and its first and second derivatives are continuous in the interval $0 \leqq x \leqq l$ for $t \geqq 0$, and $\rho(x) > 0$, $k(x) > 0$ are continuous functions.

Suppose there are two solutions

$$u_1(x, t) \qquad \text{and} \qquad u_2(x, t)$$

of the problem under consideration. Their difference

$$v(x, t) = u_1(x, t) - u_2(x, t)$$

obviously then satisfies the homogeneous equation

$$\rho\frac{\partial^2 v}{\partial t^2} = \frac{\partial}{\partial x}\left(k\frac{\partial v}{\partial x}\right) \tag{2-1.77}$$

and the homogeneous auxiliary conditions

$$\begin{aligned} v\,(x, 0) &= 0 \\ v_t(x, 0) &= 0 \\ v\,(0, t) &= 0 \\ v\,(l, t) &= 0\,. \end{aligned} \tag{2-1.78}$$

Then we shall prove that the function $v(x, t)$ defined by the conditions (2-1.78) is identically zero.

To this end, we consider the function

$$E(t) = \frac{1}{2}\int_0^l \{k(v_x)^2 + \rho(v_t)^2\}dx \tag{2-1.79}$$

and prove that it is independent of t. Physically the function $E(t)$ represents the total energy of the string at time t. We differentiate $E(t)$ with respect to t; since the second derivatives are continuous we can differentiate under the integral sign. This gives

$$\frac{dE(t)}{dt} = \int_0^l (kv_x v_{xt} + \rho v_t v_{tt}) dx .$$

An integration by parts of the first term of the sum on the right side gives

$$\int_0^l kv_x v_{xt} dx = [kv_x v_t]_0^l - \int_0^l v_t (kv_x)_x dx . \qquad (2\text{-}1.80)$$

On the basis of the boundary conditions the expression in brackets vanishes; $v_t(0, t) = 0$ follows from $v(0, t) = 0$, and similarly for $x = l$. Thus

$$\frac{dE(t)}{dt} = \int_0^l [\rho v_t v_{tt} - v_t (kv_x)_x] dx = \int_0^l v_t [\rho v_{tt} - (kv_x)_x] dx = 0 ;$$

this means $E(t) = \text{const.}$ By taking into consideration the initial conditions we find further that

$$E(t) = \text{const.} = E(0) = \frac{1}{2}\int_0^l [k(v_x)^2 + \rho(v_t)^2]_{t=0}\, dx = 0 \qquad (2\text{-}1.81)$$

because

$$v(x, 0) = 0 \qquad \text{and} \qquad v_t(x, 0) = 0 .$$

Since by hypothesis $\rho(x)$ and $k(x)$ are always positive, it follows from (2-1.79) and (2-1.81) that

$$v_x(x, t) \equiv 0 \qquad \text{and} \qquad v_t(x, t) \equiv 0$$

and hence the identity

$$v(x, t) = \text{const.} = C_0 . \qquad (2\text{-}1.82)$$

From the corresponding initial conditions we then find

$$v(x, 0) = C_0 = 0 ,$$

and therefore we prove that

$$v(x, t) \equiv 0 . \qquad (2\text{-}1.83)$$

If, therefore, $u_1(x, t)$ and $u_2(x, t)$ are two functions which satisfy all the conditions of our theorem, then $u_1(x, t) \equiv u_2(x, t)$.

For the second boundary-value problem the function $v = u_1 - u_2$ satisfies the boundary conditions

$$v_x(0, t) = 0 , \qquad v_x(l, t) = 0 , \qquad (2\text{-}1.84)$$

so that the brackets in (2-1.80) vanish again. The rest of the proof remains unchanged.

With regard to the third boundary-value problem, the proof of the uniqueness theorem requires several changes. If we again consider two solutions u_1 and u_2, then for their difference, $v(x, t) = u_1 - u_2$, the differential Eq. (2-1.77) results, while the boundary conditions read:

$$\begin{aligned} v_x(0, t) - h_1 v(0, t) = 0 , \qquad h_1 \geqq 0 \\ v_x(l, t) + h_2 v(l, t) = 0 , \qquad h_2 \geqq 0 . \end{aligned} \qquad (2\text{-}1.85)$$

Next we shall write the expression in the brackets in (2-1.80)

$$[kv_xv_t]_0^l = -\frac{k}{2}\frac{\partial}{\partial t}[h_2v^2(l, t) + h_1v^2(0, t)].$$

If we integrate dE/dt from 0 to t, we find

$$E(t) - E(0) = \int_0^t\int_0^l v_t[\rho v_{tt} - (kv_x)_x]dxdt$$

$$- \frac{k}{2}\{h_2[v^2(l, t) - v^2(l, 0)] + h_1[v^2(0, t) - v^2(0, 0)]\}$$

from which, with respect to the equation and the initial conditions, it follows that

$$E(t) = -\frac{k}{2}[h_2v^2(l, t) + h_1v^2(0, t)] \leqq 0. \tag{2-1.86}$$

However, since the integrand is non-negative, then $E(t) \geqq 0$, from which necessarily follow

$$E(t) \equiv 0 \tag{2-1.87}$$

and

$$v(x, t) \equiv 0. \tag{2-1.88}$$

Thus the uniqueness theorem is proved also for the third boundary-value problem.

The method of proof used here, which was based on the use of the expression for the total energy, is often used for the proof of uniqueness theorems in different branches of mathematical physics (for example, in electrodynamics, elasticity theory, and hydrodynamics).

The proof of existence for these and other boundary-value problems will be discussed later when we consider the corresponding questions.

Problems

1. Prove that the differential equation for small torsional vibrations of a rod has the form

$$\Theta_{tt} = a^2\Theta_{xx}, \quad a = \sqrt{\frac{GJ}{k}},$$

where Θ is the angle of torsion of the cross section of the rod at the abscissa x, G is the modulus of torsion, J is the polar moment of inertia of the cross section, and k is the moment of inertia per unit of length of the rod. Give a physical interpretation of the first, second, and third boundary conditions for this problem.

2. Let an absolutely flexible homogeneous cable be fastened at one end. Under the influence of its weight, it is aligned then with the vertical axis. Find the differential equation for small vibrations of the cable.

Solution:

$$\frac{\partial^2 u}{\partial t^2} = a^2\frac{\partial}{\partial x}\left[(l - x)\frac{\partial u}{\partial x}\right] \quad \text{with } a^2 = g,$$

where $u(x, t)$ is the displacement of the points, l is the length of the cable, and g is the acceleration due to gravity.

3. A heavy homogeneous cable of length l, which is fastened at its upper end ($x = 0$) of a vertical axis, rotates about this axis with a uniform angular velocity ω. Derive the differential equation for small vibrations in the neighborhood of the vertical state of equilibrium.

Solution:

$$\frac{\partial^2 u}{\partial t^2} = a^2 \frac{\partial}{\partial x}\left[(l - x)\frac{\partial u}{\partial x}\right] + \omega^2 u \qquad \text{with} \qquad a^2 = g .$$

4. Find the equation of a transverse vibrating string which exists in a medium whose resistence is proportional to the velocity.

Solution:

$$v_{tt} = a^2 v_{xx} - h^2 v_t .$$

5. Formulate the boundary conditions for the differential equation of a longitudinal vibrating elastic spring where the upper end of the spring is rigidly fixed and, in contrast, a weight P hangs at the lower end when

(a) The rod in the equilibrium state under the action of an immovable weight P, which is fixed at its lower end, exists in a state of elongation (static deformation).

(b) The rod in the state of equilibrium is unstretched. This arises, for example, when at the initial time under the weight, the support on which the weight was previously resting, has moved; at first, the weight begins to stretch the rod.

6. Determine the differential equation and the auxiliary conditions for the torsional vibrations of a rod, at both ends of which discs are fastened.

Solution: For $x = 0$ and $x = l$ the boundary conditions

$$\Theta_{tt}(0, t) = \alpha_1^2 \Theta_x(0, t) , \qquad \Theta_{tt}(l, t) = -\alpha_2^2 \Theta_x(l, t)$$

must be satisfied.

7. At an arbitrary point $x = x_0$ of a string ($0 \leqq x \leqq l$) let there be placed a weight of mass M. Find the conditions determining the state of the vibration.

8. A weight of mass M is at the end $x = l$ of an elastic rod which is elastically fixed at the point $x = 0$. Determine the differential equaticn and the conditions for the longitudinal vibrations of the rod under the assumption that it is acted on by an external force. Hence there are two cases to be considered:

(a) The force is distributed along the rod with the density $f(x, t)$.

(b) The force is concentrated at a point $x = x_0$ and equals $F_0(t)$.

9. Consider small vibrations of an ideal gas in a cylindrical tube. Derive first the fundamental differential equations of hydrodynamics and, next, under the assumption that the process proceeds adiabatically, [equations] for (a) the density ρ, (b) the pressure p, (c) the velocity potential φ of the gas particles, (d) the velocity v, and (e) the displacement of particles u. In addition, construct an example which realizes the boundary conditions of the first, second, and third types for these differential equations.

10. What similarities exist between the phenomena of mechanical, accoustical, and electrical vibrations?
11. Construct an example of the boundary conditions of the first, second, and third types for telegraphic equations.
12. Consider the longitudinal vibrations in an inhomogeneous rod ($k = k_1$ for $x < x_0$, $k = k_2$ for $x > x_0$), and derive the conditions which must be satisfied at the boundary between segments of inhomogeneous rod (for $x = x_0$).
13. Give a physical interpretation of the boundary conditions

$$\alpha u_x(0, t) + \beta u_t(0, t) = 0 .$$

14. Give an example of a mechanical model which can be described by the equation

$$u_{tt} = a^2 u_{xx} + bu_t + cu .$$

2-2. WAVE-PROPAGATION METHOD

1. The D'Alembert method

The subject of the following investigations is methods for the construction of boundary-value problems for hyperbolic differential equations. We begin by considering the problem of an infinite string with the initial conditions

$$u_{tt} - a^2 u_{xx} = 0 , \tag{2-2.1}$$

$$\begin{aligned} u(x, 0) &= \varphi(x) , \\ u_t(x, 0) &= \psi(x) . \end{aligned} \tag{2-2.2}$$

First we transform this equation to the canonical form in which the mixed derivative is obtained. The characteristic equation

$$dx^2 - a^2 dt^2 = 0$$

reduces to two equations

$$dx - adt = 0 , \qquad dx + adt = 0 .$$

Their integrals are the straight lines

$$x - at = C_1 , \qquad x + at = C_2 .$$

As in the previous chapter, we introduce the new variables

$$\xi = x + at , \qquad \eta = x - at .$$

If we then calculate the derivatives

$$\begin{aligned} u_x &= u_\xi + u_\eta , & u_{xx} &= u_{\xi\xi} + 2u_{\xi\eta} + u_{\eta\eta} , \\ u_t &= a(u_\xi - u_\eta) , & u_{tt} &= (u_{\xi\xi} - 2u_{\xi\eta} + u_{\eta\eta})a^2 , \end{aligned}$$

we see that the equation of a vibrating string can be transformed to the form

$$u_{\xi\eta} = 0 . \tag{2-2.3}$$

Obviously for each solution of Eq. (2-2.3)

$$u_\eta(\xi, \eta) = f^*(\eta)$$

is valid, where $f^*(\eta)$ is a function of η alone. By integration of this equation with respect to η for fixed ξ we get

$$u(\xi, \eta) = \int f^*(\eta)d\eta + f_1(\xi) = f_1(\xi) + f_2(\eta)\,, \tag{2-2.4}$$

where f_1 depends only on ξ and f_2 only on η. Conversely, any arbitrary differentiable functions f_1 and f_2 which define the function $u(\xi, \eta)$ through (2-2.4) represent solutions of Eq. (2-2.3). Since every solution of Eq. (2-2.3) for a suitable choice of f_1 and f_2 can be represented in the form (2-2.4), then (2-2.4) yields the general solution of this equation. Consequently,

$$u(x, t) = f_1(x + at) + f_2(x - at) \tag{2-2.5}$$

is the general solution of the differential equation (2-2.1).

Now we assume that a solution of the problem under consideration exists. This is then given by (2-2.5). The functions f_1 and f_2 are determined so that the initial conditions

$$u(x, 0) = f_1(x) + f_2(x) = \varphi(x) \tag{2-2.6}$$

$$u_t(x, 0) = af_1'(x) - af_2'(x) = \psi(x) \tag{2-2.7}$$

are fulfilled. By integration of the second equation we obtain

$$f_1(x) - f_2(x) = \frac{1}{a}\int_{x_0}^{x} \psi(\alpha)d\alpha + C\,,$$

where x_0 and C are constants. From the equations

$$f_1(x) + f_2(x) = \varphi(x)$$

$$f_1(x) - f_2(x) = \frac{1}{a}\int_{x_0}^{x} \psi(\alpha)d\alpha + C$$

we then find

$$\begin{aligned} f_1(x) &= \frac{1}{2}\varphi(x) + \frac{1}{2a}\int_{x_0}^{x} \psi(\alpha)d\alpha + \frac{C}{2} \\ f_2(x) &= \frac{1}{2}\varphi(x) - \frac{1}{2a}\int_{x_0}^{x} \psi(\alpha)d\alpha - \frac{C}{2}\,. \end{aligned} \tag{2-2.8}$$

In this manner, f_1 and f_2 are defined by the given functions φ and ψ, where Eq. (2-2.8) must be satisfied for arbitrary values of the argument.[8] By substitution of the arguments of f_1 and f_2 as in (2-2.5) we obtain

$$u(x, t) = \frac{\varphi(x + at) + \varphi(x - at)}{2} + \frac{1}{2a}\left\{\int_{x_0}^{x+at} \psi(\alpha)d\alpha - \int_{x_0}^{x-at} \psi(\alpha)d\alpha\right\}$$

[8] In formula (2-2.5), f_1 and f_2 are not uniquely defined. That is, if we subtract from f_1 any fixed number c_1 and add this to f_2, u remains unchanged. In 2-2.8, however, the constant C is not determined by φ and ψ. It can be omitted or replaced by another without changing the value of u. When f_1 and f_2 are added, the sum differs by $\pm\, C/2$.

or

$$u(x, t) = \frac{\varphi(x + at) + \varphi(x - at)}{2} + \frac{1}{2a}\int_{x-at}^{x+at} \psi(\alpha)d\alpha\,. \tag{2-2.9}$$

Formula (2-2.9), the so-called D'Alembert formula, was derived under the assumption that a solution of the given problem exists. This formula proves the uniqueness of the solution. If there were to exist another solution of the differential Eq. (2-2.1) with initial conditions (2-2.2) then it would have to be a solution of the form (2-2.9) and hence would coincide with the first solution. It can be shown that the function $u(x, t)$, defined by (2-2.9) under the assumption that φ be twice differentiable and that ψ is only once differentiable, satisfies both Eq. (2-2.1) and also the initial conditions (2-2.2), so that the D'Alembert method besides proving uniqueness also proves the existence of the solution of the given problem.

2. Physical interpretation

The function $u(x, t)$ which appears as a solution of the wave equation with initial conditions, is the sum of two functions

$$u_1(x, t) = \frac{\varphi(x + at) + \varphi(x - at)}{2}$$
$$u_2(x, t) = \frac{1}{2a}\int_{x-at}^{x+at} \psi(\alpha)d\alpha\,. \tag{2-2.10}$$

The first sum $u_1(x, t)$ represents the path of propagation of the initial displacement without the initial velocity, $\psi(x) = 0$; the second sum $u_2(x, t)$ contains the initial velocity (the initial impulse) for vanishing initial displacement. The function $u(x, t)$ can be interpreted geometrically as a surface in u, x, t space (Fig. 4a). The intersection of this surface with the plane

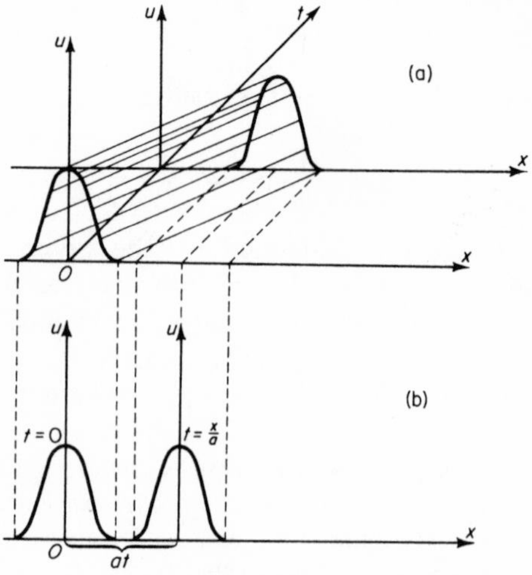

FIG. 4.

$t = t_0$ is analytically given by $u = u(x, t_0)$ and yields the profile of the string at time t_0. On the other hand, the intersection of the surface $u(x, t)$ with the plane $x = x_0$ gives $u = u(x_0, t)$, which is the path of motion of the points x_0.

The function $u(x, t)$ given by $u = f(x - at)$ is described in physics as a propagating wave.[9] The displaced profile defined by this function at different times t can be easily illustrated in the following manner: We shall assume that an observer moves parallel to the x axis with the velocity a (Figure 4b). If the observer then is found at the initial time $t = 0$ at a position $x = 0$, then up to time t he has moved along the path toward the right. If we now introduce a new coordinate system through

$$x' = x - at \qquad \text{and} \qquad t' = t$$

which moves with the observer, then $u = f(x - at)$ is defined in the new coordinate system by

$$u(x', t') = f(x');$$

i.e., the observer during the entire time t sees one and the same profile $f(x')$, which coincides with the profile $f(x)$ at the initial time $t = 0$.

Therefore $f(x - at)$ represents a fixed profile $f(x')$ moving toward the right with the velocity a (propagating wave).

If we consider the x, t phase plane, then the function $u = f(x - at)$ remains constant on the straight line

$$x - at = \text{const.}$$

The surface $u = f(x - at)$ is also a cylindrical surface whose generators are parallel to the straight lines $x = at$. Thus the form of the cylindrical surface is determined by the profile of the initial displacement.

In the interval (x_1, x_2) let the function $f(x)$ now be different from zero and outside of this interval equal to zero. The straight lines $x - at = x_2$ and $x - at = x_1$ represent the forward surface and the rear surface of the propagating wave $f(x - at)$. These lines divide the x, t plane into three regions I, II, and III.

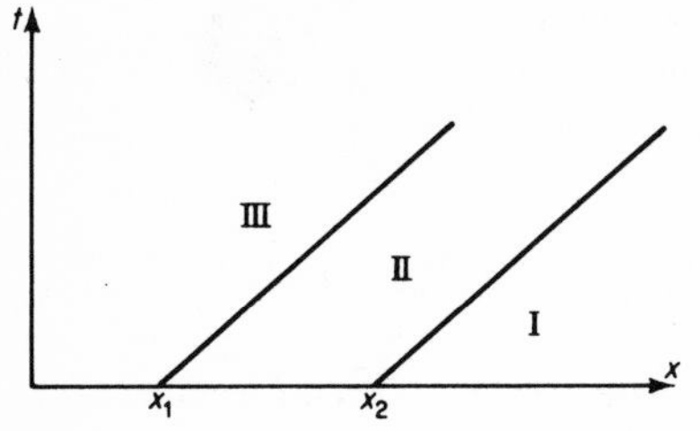

FIG. 5.

The regions I and III consist of the points (x, t) which correspond at the time t considered to the point x of the string that lies behind the forward propagating wave. On the other hand, the points (x, t) of region II correspond to those points x through which, at time t, the forward propagating wave travels (Figure 5).

It is obvious that $f(x + at)$ represents a wave propagating toward the left at a velocity a. For this wave a similar inter-

[9] In physics one uses the form $u = f\left(t - \frac{x}{a}\right)$.

pretation can be given. The function $u_1(x, t)$ which describes the propagation of the initial displacement $\varphi(x)$ with vanishing initial velocity, $\psi(x) = 0$, is given by formula (2-2.10) as the sum of two waves propagating to the right and left at a velocity a. Thus the initial form of both waves is characterized by the function $\varphi(x)/2$, which is equal to one half of the original displacement.

As a first simple example we shall consider the propagation of an original displacement which has the form of an equilateral triangle. The string preserves this form if it lengthens in the middle of the interval (x_1, x_2) while the points x_1 and x_2 remain fixed. Figure 6 shows the successive behavior of the string after a time interval of amount

$$\Delta t = \frac{x_2 - x_1}{8a} .$$

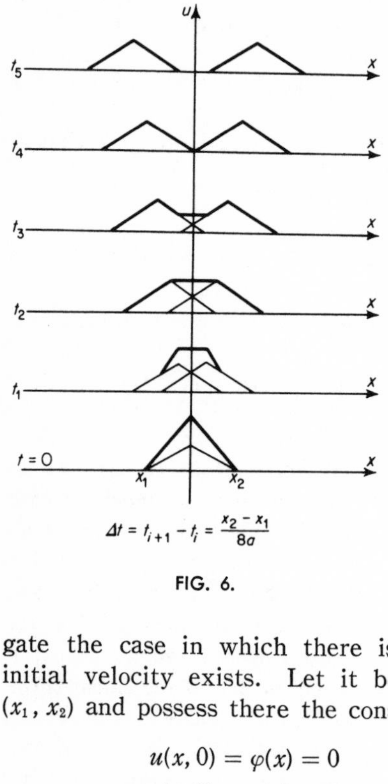

FIG. 6.

If one wishes to exhibit the behavior of the string in the course of a sufficiently small time interval, then one can, so to speak, group together snapshots of the propagation of the original length.

If we place the characteristics in the x, t phase plane through the end points of the intervals $P(x_1, 0)$, $Q(x_2, 0)$ (Fig. 7), the plane is divided into six regions—regions I and V at the time t considered in which lengthening has yet to occur, region III in which maximum lengthening has already occurred, and regions II, IV, and VI in which lengthening has just occurred.

As a second example we shall investigate the case in which there is no initial lengthening, but in which an initial velocity exists. Let it be different from zero only in the interval (x_1, x_2) and possess there the constant value ψ_0. Then we can write

$$u(x, 0) = \varphi(x) = 0$$

$$u_t(x, 0) = \varphi(x) = \psi_0 \qquad \text{for} \qquad x_1 \leqq x \leqq x_2 ,$$

$$= 0 \qquad \text{for} \qquad x > x_2 \qquad \text{or} \qquad x < x_1 .$$

Formula (2-2.9) then takes the form

$$u(x, t) = u_2(x, t) = \frac{1}{2a}\int_{x-at}^{x+at} \psi(\alpha)d\alpha = [\Psi(x + at) - \Psi(x - at)] .$$

The function $u(x, t)$ is given also in this case as the sum of two waves. Thus $\Psi(x)$ is the integral of $\psi(\alpha)$ and represents the profile of a wave propagating to the left:

$$\Psi(x) = \frac{1}{2a}\int_{x_0}^{x} \psi(\alpha)d\alpha .$$

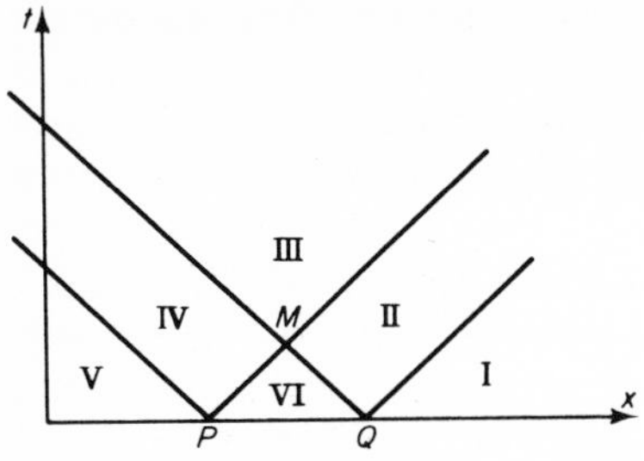

FIG. 7.

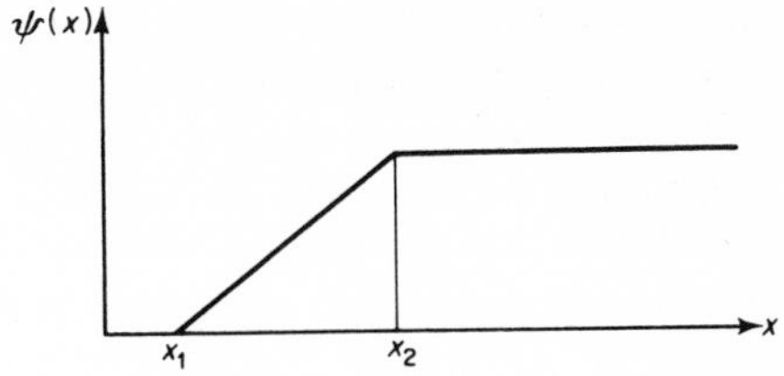

FIG. 8.

We choose $x_0 = x_1$ appropriately. The auxiliary function $\Psi(x)$ so obtained is represented in Figure 8. Hence,

$$\begin{aligned} \Psi(x) &= 0 && \text{for} \quad x \leqq x_1 , \\ &= \frac{1}{2a}(x - x_1)\psi_0 && \text{for} \quad x_1 \leqq x \leqq x_2 , \\ &= \frac{1}{2a}(x_2 - x_1)\psi_0 && \text{for} \quad x \geqq x_2 . \end{aligned}$$

In order to find $u(x, t)$ we must form the difference of the left and right waves defined by $\Psi(x)$. Figure 9 shows the position of these waves and their difference after a time interval $\Delta t = (x_2 - x_1)/8a$. For $t > (x_2 - x_1)/2a$ the profile of the displacement is given by a trapezoid which expands uniformly with the time. If $\psi(x)$ is not a constant, the problem under consideration remains essentially unchanged. By using the phase plane (Figure 7) we can easily show in which region the lengthening has not yet occurred (I and V), where the lengthening has already attained its maximum value (III), and where this is not yet the case (II, IV, and VI).

Consequently, the lengthening of the string occurs not only at one but at many places; thus we obtain the form of a propagating wave in which one adds the lengthenings corresponding to the influence of single moving points. The two examples consequently illustrate the propagation of waves also in the general case.

As a third example we shall consider the vibration of a string under the influence of a concentrated acting impulse. By striking the string at the point $(x, x + \Delta x)$ with any object (for example, with a hammer), we produce an impulse I at this position which is equal to the

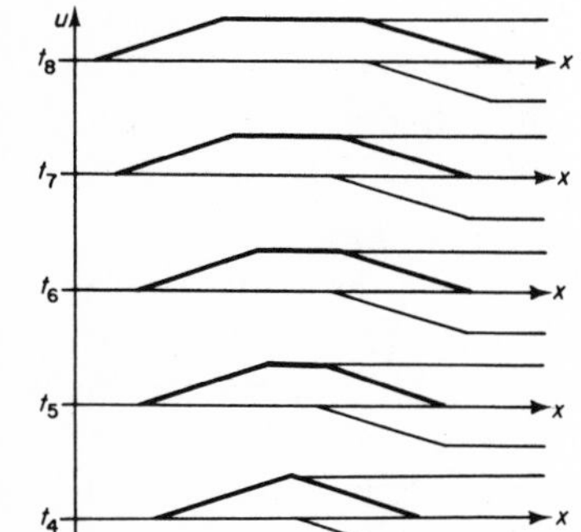

$\Delta t = t_{i+1} - t_i = \frac{x_2 - x_1}{8a}$

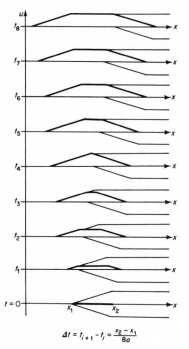

FIG. 9.

change of the momentum of the object struck during the time of the stroke. Let the change in velocity of the point in the interval Δx be equal to v, where v is the initial velocity. Under the assumption that the initial velocity v is constant in Δx, then we obtain the change of momentum,

$$\rho v \Delta x = I ,$$

where ρ is the linear density of the string. Consequently, we must solve the wave equation with the initial velocity,

$$\psi_{\text{int}} = v = \frac{I}{\rho \Delta x} \qquad x,\ x + \Delta x ,$$

$$\psi_{\text{ext}} = 0 \qquad x,\ x + \Delta x ,$$

for the initial displacement.

The lengthening obtained by the action of the impulse can be described by a trapezoid whose lower base equals $(2at) + \Delta x$ and whose upper base equals $(2at) - \Delta x$, for $t > \Delta x/2a$. Obviously, the quantity $I/\Delta x = I_0$ can be interpreted as the impulse density. As $\Delta x \to 0$ the following results for the form of the displacement: the lengthening is equal to zero everywhere outside the interval $(x - at,\ x + at)$, and inside it is equal to $1/2a \cdot 1/\rho$. Loosely speaking, one can say that the displacement is produced by the point impulse I.

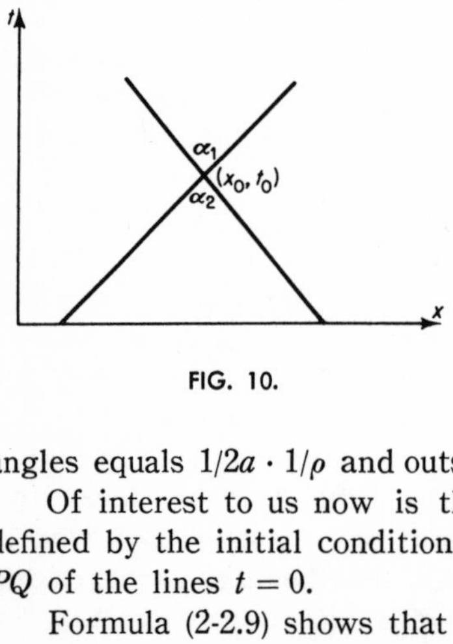

FIG. 10.

We consider now the x, t phase plane (Figure 10) and place the two characteristics through (x_0, t_0):

$$x - at = x_0 - at_0$$
$$x + at = x_0 + at_0 .$$

They determine two angles α_1 and α_2, the so-called upper and lower characteristic angles at the point (x_0, t_0).

The action of a point impulse at the point (x_0, t_0) produces a lengthening which in the interior of the above characteristic angles equals $1/2a \cdot 1/\rho$ and outside the interval equals zero.

Of interest to us now is the region in which the solution is uniquely defined by the initial conditions when these are prescribed in a given interval PQ of the lines $t = 0$.

Formula (2-2.9) shows that it suffices for the determination of the function u at any point $M(x, t)$ of the x, t phase plane (Figure 7) when the initial conditions in the interval PQ are known. Thus, P, Q are the points of the x axis with the coordinates $x - at$ and $x + at$. The segments MP and MQ of the characteristics passing through the point M and the segment PQ of the x axis form a triangle MPQ called the characteristic triangle of the point M.

If the initial conditions are not given on the entire line $-\infty < x < \infty$ but are given only in a fixed interval PQ, then these initial conditions define the solution uniquely within the characteristic triangle which has the interval PQ as a base.

3. Stability of the solution

The solution of Eq. (2-2.1) is uniquely determined by the initial conditions (2-2.2). We shall prove that between this solution and the initial conditions exists a continuous dependence and, in fact, we have the theorem:

For each time interval $0 \leqq t \leqq t_0$ and for arbitrary ε there exists a number $\delta(\varepsilon, t_0)$ such that two solutions $u_1(x, t)$ and $u_2(x, t)$ of Eq. (2-2.1) differ from each other by an amount less than ε:

$$|u_1(x, t) - u_2(x, t)| < \varepsilon, \qquad 0 \leqq t \leqq t_0,$$

provided that the initial values

$$u_1(x, 0) = \varphi_1(x) \qquad\qquad u_2(x, 0) = \varphi_2(x)$$
$$\text{and}$$
$$\frac{\partial u_1}{\partial t}(x, 0) = \psi_1(x) \qquad\qquad \frac{\partial u_2}{\partial t}(x, 0) = \psi_2(x)$$

differ from each other by an amount less than δ:

$$|\varphi_1(x) - \varphi_2(x)| < \delta, \qquad |\psi_1(x) - \psi_2(x)| < \delta. \tag{2-2.11}$$

The proof of this theorem is surprisingly simple. The functions $u_1(x, t)$ and $u_2(x, t)$ are linked to the initial values by formula (2-2.9), so that

$$|u_1(x, t) - u_2(x, t)| \leqq \frac{|\varphi_1(x + at) - \varphi_2(x + at)|}{2}$$
$$+ \frac{|\varphi_1(x - at) - \varphi_2(x - at)|}{2} + \frac{1}{2a}\int_{x-at}^{x+at} |\psi_1(\alpha) - \psi_2(\alpha)|\, d\alpha,$$

whereas on the basis of the inequality (2-2.11), there follows

$$|u_1(x, t) - u_2(x, t)| \leqq \frac{\delta}{2} + \frac{\delta}{2} + \frac{1}{2a}\delta \cdot 2at \leqq \delta(1 + t_0).$$

Hence our assertion is proved if we take

$$\delta = \frac{\varepsilon}{1 + t_0}.$$

Every physically defined process must be capable of description through functions which depend continuously on those initial conditions determining the process. If the solution of a boundary-value problem depends continuously on the initial conditions, then one also says that the boundary-value problem is well set or the solution is stable.

If this continuous dependence did not exist, there could be two essentially different processes corresponding to practically the same set of initial conditions (whose difference lies within the limits of the accuracy of measurement); that is, the solution would not be stable. It cannot be asserted that such processes are determined by the initial conditions (in a physical sense). From the above theorem, it follows that the vibrations of a string are determined not only mathematically but also physically by the initial conditions.

We shall now consider such a problem in which the solution is not stable. The functions resulting as solutions of the Laplace equation

$$u_{xx} + u_{yy} = 0$$

are defined uniquely by its initial conditions[10]

$$u(x, 0) = \varphi(x)\,, \qquad u_y(x, 0) = \psi(x)\,.$$

The functions

$$u^{(1)}(x, y) \equiv 0 \qquad \text{and} \qquad u^{(2)}(x, y) = \frac{1}{\lambda}\sin \lambda x \cdot \cosh \lambda y$$

satisfy the Laplace equation. In $u^{(2)}(x, y)$, λ plays the role of a parameter. The initial conditions

$$u^{(1)}(x, 0) = 0\,, \qquad u^{(2)}(x, 0) = \varphi(x) = \frac{1}{\lambda}\sin \lambda x$$

$$u_y^{(1)}(x, 0) = 0\,, \qquad u_y^{(2)}(x, 0) = \psi(x) = 0$$

differ arbitrarily little from each other for sufficiently large λ. On the other hand the solution $u^{(2)}(x, y)$ for a fixed value of y can become arbitrarily large. Therefore, the problem with initial conditions for the Laplace equation is not well set.

We note the following. Obviously, a function $u(x, t)$ defined by

$$u(x, t) = \frac{\varphi(x + at) + \varphi(x - at)}{2} + \frac{1}{2a}\int_{x-at}^{x+at} \psi(\alpha)d\alpha$$

can only be a solution of Eq. (2-2.1) provided $\psi(x)$ is once and $\varphi(x)$ is twice differentiable. Hence, it follows that the functions represented in Figures

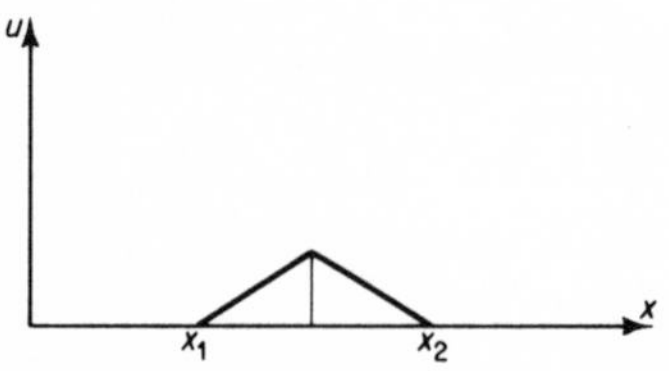

FIG. 11.

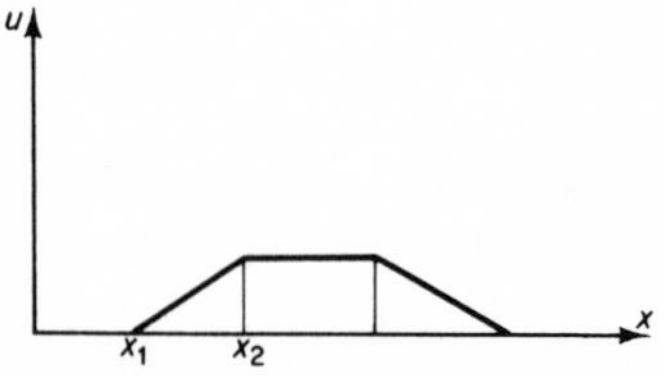

FIG. 12.

11 and 12 cannot be solutions of Eq. (2-2.1) because they are not twice differentiable throughout. Beyond this, the assertion holds in that a solution of the wave equation does not exist which satisfies the initial conditions (2-2.2) when $\varphi(x)$ and $\psi(x)$ do not possess the required derivatives. By repeating

[10] These conditions define uniquely the solution of the Laplace equation mathematically. The origin of the function $u_y(x, 0)$, is, of course, equivalent to the origin of the function $v_x(x, 0)$, where $v(x, y)$ is the harmonic function conjugate to $u(x, y)$. Hence that analytic function of which the function $u(x, y)$ is the real part is defined uniquely up to an arbitrary constant. (See § 4-1, 4-5.)

the reasonings which led us to formula (2-2.9) we can show that from the existence of a solution of the wave equation its representation follows according to (2-2.9). If, however, φ and ψ are not a sufficient number of times differentiable, then (2-2.9) defines a function which does not satisfy Eq. (2-2.1), i.e., no solution to the problem exists.

If, however, we change the initial conditions a little—replace them by differentiable functions $\varphi(x)$ and $\psi(x)$—then these new initial conditions correspond to a solution of Eq. (2-2.1). Moreover, it is still to be noted that according to the proof of the last theorem we have in fact proved the continuous dependence of the functions φ and ψ defined by formula (2-2.9)—independent of whether these are or are not differentiable. If, therefore, certain functions φ, ψ do not correspond to a solution of the wave equation which satisfies the conditions (2-2.2), then the functions defined by (2-2.9) are boundary values of the solutions of the wave equation with somewhat smoother initial conditions.

4. Semi-infinite line and the method of continuation

In the following we shall concern ourselves with the propagation of a wave along the semi-infinite line $x \geqq 0$. This problem plays an essential role in the investigation of the reflection of a wave at one end.

Statement of the Problem: Find a solution of the wave equation

$$a^2 u_{xx} = u_{tt} \qquad \text{for} \qquad 0 < x < \infty\,, \quad t > 0\,,$$

which satisfies the boundary conditions

$$u(0, t) = \mu(t) \qquad \text{or} \qquad u_x(0, t) = \nu(t)$$

and the initial conditions

$$u(x, 0) = \varphi(x)\,, \qquad u_t(x, 0) = \psi(x)\,.$$

Our first concern is the homogeneous boundary conditions

$$u(0, t) = 0 \qquad \text{or} \qquad u_x(0, t) = 0\,,$$

i.e., the propagation of the initial displacement of a string with a fixed end point $x = 0$ (or a free end point).

For the solutions of the wave equation which are defined for the infinite straight line, the following two lemmas are valid.

1. If the functions $\varphi(x)$ and $\psi(x)$ occurring in the initial conditions with respect to any point x_0 are odd, the corresponding solution at this point is equal to zero.
2. If the functions $\varphi(x)$ and $\psi(x)$ occurring in the initial conditions are even with respect to any point x_0, then the derivative of the corresponding solution with respect to x at this point equals zero.

Proof of the first lemma. We select x_0 as the origin of coordinates, i.e., $x_0 = 0$. The conditions on the function in question are odd; therefore we have

$$\varphi(x) = -\varphi(-x)\,; \quad \psi(x) = -\psi(-x)\,.$$

Consequently, for $x = 0$, the function $u(x, t)$ defined by (2-2.9) equals

$$u(0, t) = \frac{\varphi(at) + \varphi(-at)}{2} + \frac{1}{2a}\int_{-at}^{at} \psi(\alpha)d\alpha = 0\,;$$

then the first summand vanishes, since $\varphi(x)$ is odd, whereas the second, the integral of an odd function within the limits shown, is symmetrical with respect to the origin and likewise is equal to zero.

Proof of the second lemma. The conditions on the functions in question are even; therefore we have

$$\varphi(x) = \varphi(-x)\,; \quad \psi(x) = \psi(-x)\,.$$

Now the derivative of an even function is odd, i.e.,

$$\varphi'(x) = -\varphi'(-x)\,.$$

Therefore, it follows from (2-2.9) that

$$u_x(0, t) = \frac{\varphi'(at) + \varphi'(-at)}{2} + \frac{1}{2a}[\psi(at) - \psi(-at)] = 0\,;$$

then the first term of the sum vanishes since $\varphi'(x)$ is odd and the second vanishes, since $\psi(x)$ is even.[11]

With the help of these two lemmas the following problems can be solved: Find a solution of Eq. (2-2.1) which satisfies the initial conditions

$$\begin{aligned} u\,(x, 0) &= \varphi(x) \\ u_t(x, 0) &= \psi(x)\,, \end{aligned} \qquad 0 < x < \infty \qquad \text{(2-2.2)}$$

and the boundary condition

$$u(0, t) = 0$$

(first boundary-value problem).

The functions $\Phi(x)$ and $\Psi(x)$ defined by the relations

$$\Phi(x) = \begin{cases} \varphi(x) & \text{for} \quad x > 0 \\ -\varphi(-x) & \text{for} \quad x < 0 \end{cases}$$

$$\Psi(x) = \begin{cases} \psi(x) & \text{for} \quad x > 0 \\ -\psi(-x) & \text{for} \quad x < 0 \end{cases}$$

are the odd continuations of $\varphi(x)$ and $\psi(x)$.

The function

$$u(x, t) = \frac{\Phi(x + at) + \Phi(x - at)}{2} + \frac{1}{2a}\int_{x-at}^{x+at} \Psi(\alpha)d\alpha$$

defined with their help is defined for all x and $t > 0$. According to the first

[11] These two lemmas are consequences of the fact that for even (or odd) initial conditions the function $u(x, t)$, given by the formula of D'Alembert, for $t > 0$ is likewise even (or odd); we leave the proof of this to the reader. Geometrically, one sees immediately that an odd continuous function, as well as the derivative of an even differentiable function, vanishes at $x = 0$.

lemma, there results

$$u(0, t) = 0 .$$

Moreover, $u(x, t)$ for $t = 0$ satisfies the initial conditions

$$\left.\begin{aligned} u(x, 0) &= \Phi(x) = \varphi(x) \\ u_t(x, 0) &= \Psi(x) = \psi(x) , \end{aligned}\right. \quad x > 0 .$$

Consequently, the function $u(x, t)$, which we should consider only for $x > 0$, $t > 0$, satisfies all the requirements of the given problem.

With regard to our original functions, we have

$$\begin{aligned} u(x, t) &= \frac{\varphi(x + at) + \varphi(x - at)}{2} + \frac{1}{2a}\int_{x-at}^{x+at} \psi(\alpha)d\alpha \quad \text{for} \quad t < \frac{x}{a}, \; x > 0 \\ &= \frac{\varphi(x + at) - \varphi(at - x)}{2} + \frac{1}{2a}\int_{at-x}^{x+at} \psi(\alpha)d\alpha \quad \text{for} \quad t > \frac{x}{a}, \; x > 0 . \end{aligned} \tag{2-2.12}$$

In the region $t < x/a$ the influence of the boundary conditions does not enter into the expression. For these values of t, the expression $u(x, t)$ coincides with the solution of (2-2.9) for the infinite straight line.

We proceed in a corresponding way when a free end exists at the point $x = 0$,

$$u_x(0, t) = 0 ,$$

and, in fact, we take the even continuations of $\varphi(x)$, and $\psi(x)$

$$\Phi(x) = \begin{matrix} \varphi(x) & \text{for} & x > 0 \\ \varphi(-x) & \text{for} & x < 0 \end{matrix}$$

$$\Psi(x) = \begin{matrix} \psi(x) & \text{for} & x > 0 \\ \psi(-x) & \text{for} & x < 0 . \end{matrix}$$

As a solution of the wave equation we then obtain

$$u(x, t) = \frac{\Phi(x + at) + \Phi(x - at)}{2} + \frac{1}{2a}\int_{x-at}^{x+at} \Psi(\alpha)d\alpha$$

or

$$\begin{aligned} u(x, t) &= \frac{\varphi(x + at) + \varphi(x - at)}{2} + \frac{1}{2a}\int_{x-at}^{x+at} \psi(\alpha)d\alpha \quad \text{for} \quad t < \frac{x}{a} \\ &= \frac{\varphi(x + at) + \varphi(at - x)}{2} \\ &\quad + \frac{1}{2a}\left\{\int_0^{x+at} \psi(\alpha)d\alpha + \int_0^{at-x} \psi(\alpha)d\alpha\right\} \quad \text{for} \quad t > \frac{x}{a} . \end{aligned}$$

This solution in the region $x \geqq 0$ satisfies the initial conditions (2-2.2) and the boundary condition

$$u_x(0, t) = 0 .$$

In the following we shall frequently have occasion to use the above application of the method of continuation, even if the initial conditions are defined only for a finite subregion. We shall reiterate the results obtained in the two following rules:

1. For the solution of a problem of a semi-infinite line with the boundary conditions $u(0, t) = 0$, the initial conditions are continued oddly along the entire axis.
2. For the solution of a problem of a semi-infinite line with the boundary condition $u_x(0, t) = 0$, the initial conditions are continued evenly along the entire axis.

We shall consider two examples. Let the initial conditions be given on the semi-infinite line $x \geqq 0$ bounded by $x = 0$ and different from 0 only in the interval $0 < a < x < b$. In this interval an initial displacement given by the function $\varphi(x)$ occurs, which is represented by an isosceles triangle, whereas $\psi(x) = 0$. We arrive at the solution of this problem if we continue the initial conditions oddly along the entire straight line. Figure 13 shows the course of the wave propagation. First the propagation proceeds as though both sides of the straight line were unbounded. The initial displacement is distributed on two waves which progress at a constant velocity with respect to the

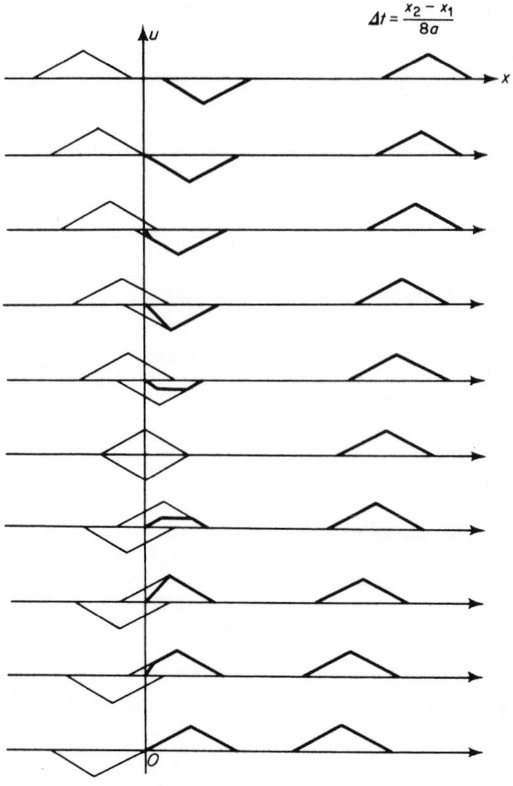

FIG. 13.

different sides. This continues as long as the half-wave propagating toward the left has not reached the point $x = 0$ (Figure 13). When the half-wave reaches the point $x = 0$, where the corresponding process is taking place, a wave with opposite phase arises. Accordingly a reflection of two half-waves occurs at the fixed ends. Figure 13 shows the reflection process in its individual stages. The resulting profile of the string is shortened, the displacement vanishes, after which a displacement (with a negative phase) begins again, and finally the reflected half-wave moves toward the right following the half-wave which likewise is propagating toward the right. Consequently, the phase of the wave due to reflection of the wave changes its sign at the boundary point.

For the investigation of the second example we shall assume that nowhere on the semi-infinite line $x \geqq 0$ bounded by $x = 0$ does an initial displacement occur, and further, that the initial velocity $\psi(x)$ is different from 0 only in an interval $0 < x_1 < x < x_2$. Hence $\psi(x) = \text{const.}$ For the solution of this problem the initial conditions are continued oddly. Then the displacement is split into each of the intervals (x_1, x_2) and $(-x_1, -x_2)$ which resemble the displacements represented in Figure 14. As seen from these figures, the

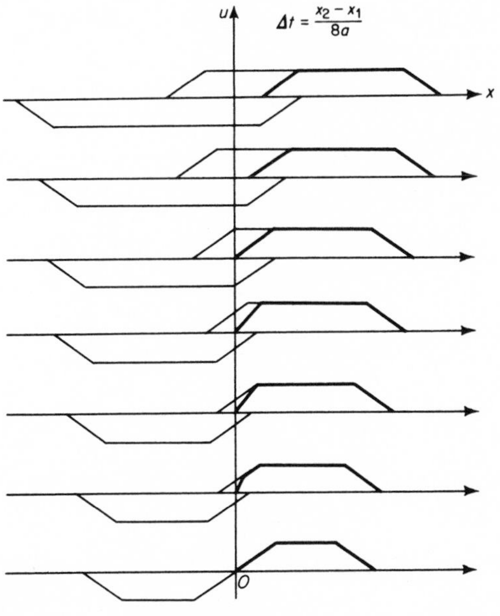

FIG. 14.

process proceeds for $x > 0$ as if it were initially on the infinite straight line. Accordingly, the reflection occurs at the fixed end, and finally a wave moves, whose profile in this case is an isosceles trapezoid with constant velocity toward the right.

The investigation of the reflection at a free end proceeds analogously only if the initial conditions are continued evenly, so that the reflection of the wave at the free end does not proceed with a changing phase but with the same phase.

Finally, we shall consider problems with homogeneous boundary conditions

$$u(0, t) = \mu(t) = 0$$

or

$$u_x(0, t) = \nu(t) = 0 .$$

In the general case of nonhomogeneous boundary conditions the solution can be written as a sum, each of whose terms satisfies only one of the stated conditions (either the boundary or the initial condition).

We turn now to the solutions of differential equations with homogeneous initial conditions and prescribed boundary conditions. Let

$$\bar{u}(x, 0) = 0 , \qquad \bar{u}_t(x, 0) = 0 , \qquad \bar{u}(0, t) = \mu(t) , \qquad t > 0 .$$

Obviously such a boundary condition produces a wave which moves away from the string toward the right with the velocity a. This wave has the analytical form

$$\bar{u}(x, t) = f(x - at) .$$

The function f is defined by the boundary condition

$$\bar{u}(0, t) = f(-at) = \mu(t) .$$

Then

$$f(z) = \mu\left(-\frac{z}{a}\right),$$

and therefore

$$\bar{u}(x, t) = \mu\left(-\frac{x - at}{a}\right) = \mu\left(t - \frac{x}{a}\right).$$

This function is defined, however, only for the region $x - at \leqq 0$ since $\mu(t)$ is defined only for $t \geqq 0$. In Figure 15 this region is shown as the shaded part of the phase plane. Now in order to determine $\bar{u}(x, t)$ for all the values

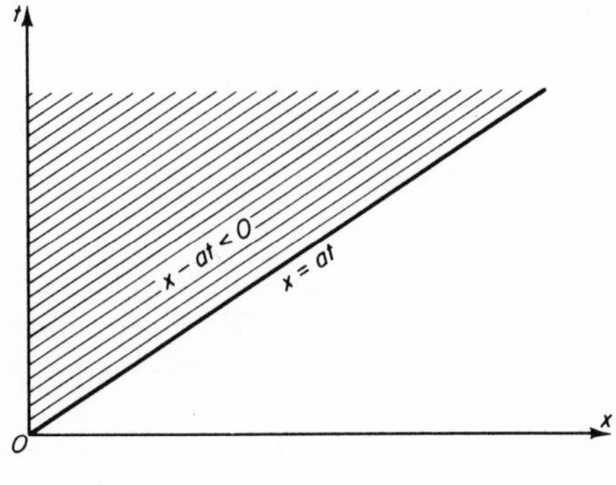

FIG. 15.

of the argument, we define $\mu(t)$ also for negative values of t setting $\mu(t) = 0$ for $t < 0$. Then

$$\bar{u}(x, t) = \mu\left(t - \frac{x}{a}\right)$$

is defined for all values of the argument and satisfies the homogeneous initial conditions.

The sum of these and function (2-2.12) defined earlier represent the solution of the first boundary-value problem for the homogeneous wave equation:

$$\begin{aligned} u(x, t) &= \frac{\varphi(x + at) + \varphi(x - at)}{2} + \frac{1}{2a}\int_{x-at}^{x+at} \psi(\alpha) d\alpha && \text{for} \quad t < \frac{x}{a} \\ &= \mu\left(t - \frac{x}{a}\right) + \frac{\varphi(x + at) - \varphi(at - x)}{2} + \frac{1}{2a}\int_{at-x}^{x+at} \psi(\alpha) d\alpha && \text{for} \quad t > \frac{x}{a} . \end{aligned} \tag{2-2.13}$$

Analogously one can construct the solution of the second boundary-value problem. For the third boundary-value problem see page 61. We shall limit ourselves here to the solution of the boundary-value problem for the homogeneous wave equation. For the solution of the nonhomogeneous wave equation see page 61.

5. Problems for a bounded interval

We shall take now a bounded interval $(0, l)$ as a basis and begin our investigation with the search for the solution of

$$u_{tt} = a^2 u_{xx} ,$$

which satisfies the boundary conditions

$$\left.\begin{aligned} u(0, t) &= \mu_1(t) \\ u(l, t) &= \mu_2(t) , \end{aligned}\right\} \quad t \geqq 0$$

and the initial conditions

$$\left.\begin{aligned} u(x, 0) &= \varphi(x) \\ u_t(x, 0) &= \psi(x) , \end{aligned}\right\} \quad 0 \leqq x \leqq l .$$

Moreover, we shall consider introducing the case of homogeneous boundary conditions

$$u(0, t) = u(l, t) = 0 .$$

For these we shall seek the solution by means of the method of continuation. Hence we construct the expression (Ansatz)

$$u(x, t) = \frac{\Phi(x + at) + \Phi(x - at)}{2} + \frac{1}{2a}\int_{x-at}^{x+at} \Psi(\alpha) d\alpha ,$$

where the functions Φ and Ψ are still to be defined appropriately. First Φ and Ψ are determined only for the interval $(0, l)$ by the boundary conditions

$$\left.\begin{aligned} u(x, 0) &= \Phi(x) = \varphi(x) \\ u_t(x, 0) &= \Psi(x) = \psi(x) , \end{aligned}\right\} \quad 0 \leqq x \leqq l .$$

In order that now $\Phi(x)$ and $\Psi(x)$ satisfy the homogeneous boundary conditions, we require that $\Phi(x)$ and $\Psi(x)$ be odd with respect to the point $x = 0$, $x = l$, i.e.,

$$\Phi(x) = -\Phi(-x)\,, \qquad \Phi(x) = -\Phi(2l - x)$$
$$\Psi(x) = -\Psi(-x)\,, \qquad \Psi(x) = -\Psi(2l - x)\,.$$

From these equations it follows that

$$\Phi(x') = \Phi(x' + 2l)\,, \qquad (x' = -x)\,.$$

A corresponding relation holds for $\Psi(x)$, i.e., Φ and Ψ are periodic functions with a period of $2l$.

Obviously the continuations of $\Phi(x)$ and $\Psi(x)$ are such that these functions will be odd and, moreover, periodic with respect to the origin of coordinates, and are defined on the entire straight line $-\infty < x < \infty$. By introducing these continuations into formula (2-2.9) we obtain the solution of the problem.

Figure 16 combines the x, t phase plane and the x, u plane, in which the initial displacement and its continuations are included. In the phase plane the shaded strips represent the regions in which the displacement is different from zero (see Figure 7). The plus or minus signs in the strips indicate the

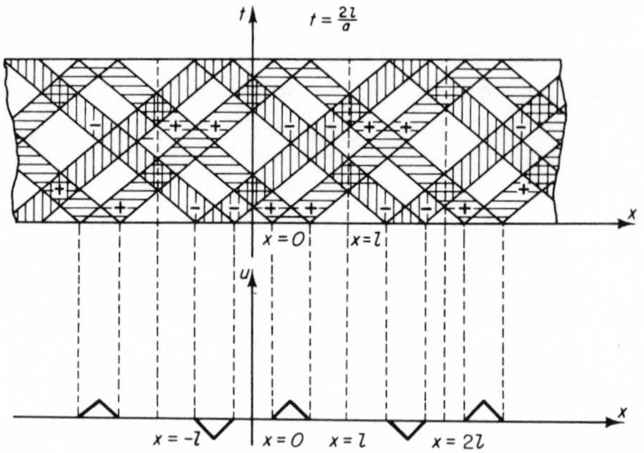

FIG. 16.

signs (the phase) of the displacement (in the form of an isosceles triangle). With the aid of this figure one can easily illustrate the profile of the string at any arbitrary time t. Thus one can recognize at time $t = 2l/a$ a displacement which coincides with the original displacement. The function $u(x, t)$ is therefore a periodic function of t with period $T = 2l/a$.

We shall now consider the propagation of the boundary effects. For this purpose we shall seek the solution of the equation

$$u_{tt} = a^2 u_{xx}$$

with the homogeneous initial conditions

$$u(x, 0) = \varphi(x) = 0\,, \qquad u_t(x, 0) = \psi(x) = 0$$

and the boundary conditions

$$\begin{aligned} u(0, t) &= \mu(t) \\ u(l, t) &= 0\,. \end{aligned} \qquad t > 0$$

From the results of Section 4 it was shown that for $t < l/a$ the function

$$u(x, t) = \bar{\mu}\left(t - \frac{x}{a}\right) \qquad \text{with} \qquad \bar{\mu}(t) = \begin{matrix} \mu(t), & t > 0 \\ 0, & t < 0 \end{matrix}$$

is a solution. This function, however, does not satisfy the boundary condition

$$u(l, t) = 0 \qquad \text{for} \qquad t > \frac{l}{a}\,.$$

The reflected wave which propagates to the left and at $x = l$ has a displacement of magnitude $\bar{\mu}(t - l/a)$ is represented analytically by the equation

$$\bar{\mu}\left(t - \frac{l}{a} - \frac{l - x}{a}\right) = \mu\left(t - \frac{2l}{a} + \frac{x}{a}\right).$$

The difference between the two waves, i.e.,

$$\bar{\mu}\left(t - \frac{x}{a}\right) - \bar{\mu}\left(t - \frac{2l}{a} + \frac{x}{a}\right),$$

is then obviously a solution of the equation for $t < 2l/a$.

By repeating this process one obtains a solution in the form of the series

$$u(x, t) = \sum_{n=0}^{\infty} \bar{\mu}\left(t - \frac{2nl}{a} - \frac{x}{a}\right) - \sum_{n=1}^{\infty} \bar{\mu}\left(\frac{2nl}{a} + \frac{x}{a}\right). \qquad (2\text{-}2.14)$$

This contains only a finite number of terms distinct from zero since the argument with each new reflection about $2l/a$ is decreased whereas $\bar{\mu}(t) = 0$ for $t < 0$. That the boundary conditions are satisfied we prove directly when we set $x = 0$ in (2-2.14). The summand for $n = 0$ of the first sum is then equal to $\mu(t)$, whereas the remaining terms of the first and second sums are cancelled pairwise for equal n values. Thus $u(0, t) = \mu(t)$.

If we now replace n by $n - 1$ and vary accordingly the summation limits, then the first sum reads

$$\sum_{n=1}^{\infty} \bar{\mu}\left(t - \frac{2nl}{a} + \frac{2l - x}{a}\right).$$

If we now set $x = l$, it can be seen directly that the summands of the first and second sums mutually cancel each other.[12]

Formula (2-2.14) has a simple physical significance. First

$$\bar{\mu}\left(t - \frac{x}{a}\right)$$

[12] The initial conditions can likewise be proven directly, since the arguments of all functions for $t = 0$ are negative.

represents a wave caused by the effect of the boundary at $x = 0$, independent of the effect at the point $x = l$, as though it were an infinitely long string $(0 < x < \infty)$. The remaining summands represent the successive reflections at the point $x = l$ (the second sum) and at the point $x = 0$ (the first sum).

Correspondingly,

$$u(x, t) = \sum_{n=0}^{\infty} \bar{\mu}\left(t - \frac{(2n+1)l}{a} + \frac{x}{a}\right) - \sum_{n=1}^{\infty} \bar{\mu}\left(t - \frac{(2n+1)l}{a} + \frac{x}{a}\right)$$

is the solution of the homogeneous equation with homogeneous initial conditions $u(x, 0) = 0$, $u_t(x, 0) = 0$ and the boundary conditions $u(0, t) = 0$, $u(l, t) = \mu(t)$. Here we shall not go further into the uniqueness proof and the proof of the continuous dependence of the solution on the initial and boundary conditions.

6. Wave dispersion

We have seen that the equation

$$u_{tt} = a^2 u_{xx}$$

of propagating waves has solutions of arbitrary form. On the basis of the class of partial differential equations, we ask which wave solutions are of arbitrary form. We shall limit ourselves, therefore, to the consideration of linear differential equations of the second order with constant coefficients,

$$a_{11}u_{xx} + 2a_{12}u_{xt} + a_{22}u_{tt} + b_1 u_x + b_2 u_t + cu = 0 . \tag{2-2.15}$$

Our problem thus consists of constructing relationships between the coefficients which guarantee that the differential equation will be solved by functions of the form

$$u(x, t) = f(x - at) , \tag{2-2.16}$$

where f represents an arbitrary function and a is a constant.

By inserting (2-2.16) into (2-2.15) we obtain the linear differential equation

$$f''(x - at)[a_{11} - 2a_{12}a + a_{22}a^2] + f'(x - at)[b_1 - b_2 a] + cf(x - at) = 0 ,$$

that the wave profile must satisfy. For arbitrary f it is obviously solvable when all the coefficients are equal to zero:

$$\begin{aligned} a_{11} - 2a_{12}a + a_{22}a^2 &= 0 \\ b_1 - b_2 a &= 0 \\ c &= 0 . \end{aligned} \tag{2-2.17}$$

If the differential equation for waves has solutions of arbitrary form then we speak of a lack of wave dispersion. For this, it is necessary and sufficient that the conditions (2-2.17) be satisfied.

From the first relationship follows the wave velocity:

$$a = \frac{a_{12} \pm \sqrt{a_{12}^2 - a_{11}a_{22}}}{a_{22}} .$$

Two velocities of wave propagation exist for hyperbolic differential equations ($a_{12}^2 - a_{11}a_{22} > 0$); the requirement for the fulfillment of all three relations for both values of a gives

$$b_1 = b_2 = c = 0.$$

Consequently, a solution in the form of a propagating wave with two possible velocities exists only for an equation of the form

$$a_{11}u_{xx} + 2a_{12}u_{xt} + u_{22}u_{tt} = 0\,. \tag{2-2.18}$$

If $a_{22} \neq 0$ then (2-2.18) represents a wave equation in a moving coordinate system; that is, if we set

$$\xi = x - \gamma t\,, \qquad \eta = t\,,$$

we obtain the equation

$$(a_{11} - 2a_{12}\gamma + a_{22}\gamma^2)u_{\xi\xi} + (2a_{12} - 2a_{22}\gamma)u_{\xi\eta} + a_{22}u_{\eta\eta} = 0\,,$$

which for $\gamma = a_{12}/a_{22}$ coincides with the equation of the vibrating string.

In this case we have

$$u_{\eta\eta} = a^2 u_{\xi\xi}$$

with

$$a^2 = \frac{a_{12}^2 - a_{11}a_{22}}{a_{22}^2} > 0\,.$$

For elliptic differential equations ($a_{12}^2 - a_{11}a_{22} < 0$), waves with real velocities as solutions are not possible. For parabolic differential equations ($a_{12}^2 - a_{11}a_{22} = 0$), solutions in the form of waves with real velocities likewise are rejected. There is an exception in the case of Eq. (2-2.15), which degenerates into an ordinary differential equation.

By taking into consideration that $a_{12} = \sqrt{a_{11}} \cdot \sqrt{a_{22}}$, $a = a_{12}/a_{22} = \sqrt{a_{11}/a_{22}}$, and $c = 0$, as well as the relation $a = b_1/b_2 = \sqrt{a_{11}/a_{22}}$, we obtain

$$b_1u_x + b_2u_t = \frac{b_2}{\sqrt{a_{22}}}(\sqrt{a_{11}}\,u_x + \sqrt{a_{22}}\,u_t)\,.$$

The resulting equation can be written in the form

$$\left(\sqrt{a_{11}}\frac{\partial}{\partial x} + \sqrt{a_{22}}\frac{\partial}{\partial t}\right)\left(\sqrt{a_{11}}\frac{\partial}{\partial x} + \sqrt{a_{22}}\frac{\partial}{\partial t}\right)u + \frac{b_2}{\sqrt{a_{22}}}\left(\sqrt{a_{11}}\frac{\partial}{\partial x} + \sqrt{a_{22}}\frac{\partial}{\partial t}\right)u = 0$$

and is reduced to the ordinary differential equation

$$\frac{d^2u}{d\xi^2} + b\frac{du}{d\xi} = 0\,, \qquad b = \frac{b_2}{\sqrt{a_{22}}}$$

when we introduce the new variables

$$x = \sqrt{a_{11}}\,\xi\,, \qquad t = \sqrt{a_{22}}\,\xi + \eta\,.$$

There also exists the relation

$$\frac{d}{d\xi} = \sqrt{a_{11}}\frac{\partial}{\partial x} + \sqrt{a_{22}}\frac{\partial}{\partial t} .$$

Consequently, in this case every arbitrary function of the variables

$$\eta = t - \frac{\sqrt{a_{22}}}{\sqrt{a_{11}}}x = t - \frac{x}{a}$$

is a solution of the equation. Solutions in the form of propagating waves are thus possible for the simplest wave equations in a moving or nonmoving coordinate system.

In physics the concept of wave dispersion is usually introduced somewhat differently.

Thus, consider a harmonic wave of the form

$$u(x, t) = e^{i(\omega t - kx)} , \tag{*}$$

where ω is the frequency, $k = 2\pi/\lambda$ is the wave number, and λ is the wave length.

The velocity with which the phase of the wave moves in space,

$$\alpha = \omega t - kx ,$$

is called the phase velocity and is obviously equal to

$$a = \frac{\omega}{k} .$$

One speaks of wave dispersion if the phase velocity of the harmonic wave is dependent on the frequency.

An impulse or a signal of an arbitrary form can be represented by a superposition of harmonic waves of the form (*), that is, by a Fourier integral. If the phase velocity depends on the frequency, the harmonic signals are displaced relative to each other so that a distorted signal appears. In this case the wave dispersion takes place in the sense of the definition on page 54.

If the solution of the equation under consideration, which yields a wave of arbitrary form, can be inverted, the phase velocity can be determined from the first equation of (2-2.17) and thus does not depend on the frequency. The concept of wave dispersion in the sense of our definition therefore coincides with the property that the phase velocity depends on the frequency.

We shall now determine the class of Eq. (2-2.15) which permit solutions in the form of damped waves

$$u(x, t) = \mu(t) f(x - at) ,$$

where $\mu(t)$ is a function of t.

We shall substitute this expression into Eq. (2.2.15) to obtain

$$f''\mu(t)(a_{11} - 2a_{12}a + a_{22}a^2) + f'[(b_1 - b_2 a)\mu + 2(a_{12} - a_{22}a)\mu'] + f(c\mu' + b_2\mu' + a_{22}\mu'') = 0 .$$

Since f is arbitrary, the coefficients of f'', f', and f must be equal to zero.

The function $\mu(t)$ thus satisfies an ordinary differential equation with constant coefficients and has the form

$$\mu = e^{-kt} .$$

If we set the coefficients of the last equation equal to zero, then we obtain for the determination of a and k the relations

$$\begin{aligned} a_{11} - 2a_{12}a + a_{22}a^2 &= 0 \\ (b_1 - b_2 a) - 2k(a_{12} - a_{22}a) &= 0 \\ a_{22}k^2 - b_2 k + c &= 0 . \end{aligned} \tag{2-2.19}$$

By elimination of a and k from (2-2.19) we obtain a condition for the compatibility of these three relations. The first equation shows that only the hyperbolic differential equation allows damped waves as solutions. The damping coefficient k is obtained from the second relation. Accordingly if we insert k into the third equation, we arrive at the following relation between the coefficients:

$$4(a_{12}^2 - a_{11}a_{22})c + (a_{11}b_2^2 - 2a_{12}b_1b_2 + a_{22}b_1^2) = 0 . \tag{2-2.20}$$

If these are satisfied, solutions of the equation exist in the form of damped waves.

Example: The "telegraphic" equation

$$u_{xx} = CLu_{tt} + (CR + LG)u_t + GRu \tag{2-2.21}$$

does not permit a propagating wave as a solution if G or R are different from zero. We shall investigate whether it has solutions in the form of damped waves. The velocity of the damped wave is given by the first equation of (2-2.19), namely,

$$1 - a^2CL = 0 .$$

From the second equation, we obtain the damping coefficient

$$k = \frac{CR + LG}{2CL} .$$

The condition for the validity of Eq. (2-2.19) reads:

$$4CLGR - (CR + LG)^2 = -(CR - LG)^2 = 0$$

or

$$CR = LG .$$

If these are satisfied, the damped wave

$$u(x, t) = e^{-kt}f(x - at) , \quad k = \frac{R}{L} = \frac{G}{C} , \quad a = \sqrt{\frac{1}{CL}} ,$$

where f is an arbitrary function, is a solution of Eq. (2-2.15).

That no damping of the wave occurs with propagation in a cable is of special importance in telephonic propagation over great distances. If the signal can be propagated undamped, then by a corresponding reinforcement an undistorted reproduction of the acoustical effect can be obtained. The wave dispersion which occurs encroaches on the purity of reception independent of the quality of the telephonic apparatus. The dispersion phenomenon has a corresponding significance for telegraphy over great distances.

7. The integral equation for waves

As the starting point for the derivation of the differential equation of waves, Eq. (2-1.3) was used as the basis for the conservation of momentum. In order to go from this integral equation to a differential equation we assume the function $u(x, t)$ to be twice differentiable. Every limitation on the class of functions under consideration naturally requires us to reject those functions which do not satisfy these requirements. Thus in going from the integral to the differential equation we exclude from consideration all of those functions which are not twice differentiable.

To prove that a theory in the class of piecewise continuous differentiable functions can be developed, we start with the integral form of the wave equation

$$\int_{x_1}^{x_2}\left[\left(\frac{\partial u}{\partial t}\right)_{t_2}-\left(\frac{\partial u}{\partial t}\right)_{t_1}\right]\rho d\xi=\int_{t_1}^{t_2}\left[\left(k\frac{\partial u}{\partial x}\right)_{x_2}-\left(k\frac{\partial u}{\partial x}\right)_{x_1}\right]d\tau+\int_{x_1}^{x_2}\int_{t_1}^{t_2}Fd\xi d\tau \qquad (2\text{-}2.22)$$

and cast it into the form

$$\int_C\left(\rho\frac{\partial u}{\partial t}dx+k\frac{\partial u}{\partial x}dt\right)+\int_G\int Fdxdt=0\,, \qquad (2\text{-}2.23)$$

where G is the region of the x, t plane bounded by the piecewise smooth curve C. For a homogeneous medium this relation assumes the form

$$\int_C\left(\frac{\partial u}{\partial t}dx+a^2\frac{\partial u}{\partial x}dt\right)+\iint_G fdxdt=0\,,\quad f=\frac{F}{\rho}\,. \qquad (2\text{-}2.23')$$

If C is the contour of a rectangle whose sides are parallel to the coordinate axes, then formulas (2-2.22) and (2-2.23) coincide. If C consists only of segments parallel to the coordinate axes, then G can be written as the sum of rectangles. If we sum the boundary integral which corresponds to individual summands, we see that the summands belonging to the interior boundaries mutually cancel each other, since the sense of integration in each case is taken in the opposite sense. The remaining summands yield formula (2-2.23) directly. Further, C now contains an arc $\bar{C}$ which is not parallel to the axes on which the integrand has no point of discontinuity. Then in the plane we construct a system of squares with parallel axes and consider the set G^* of squares of the net which have a point in common with G. Let C^* be the boundary of G^*. In G^*, formula (2-2.23) is applicable. Finally, if we make an unlimited refinement of the net, then formula (2-2.23) holds exactly for the boundary curve C.

If we apply formula (2-2.23) to G^* then the first summand consists of summands of the form

$$\int_{\bar{C}_n} \Phi(x, t)dx \qquad \text{or} \qquad \int_{\bar{C}_n} \Phi(x, t)dt ,$$

where $\Phi(x, t)$ is a continuous function and $\bar{C}_n$ is the arc of the boundary C^*, which approximates $\bar{C}$ (Figure 17).

Let $t = t_n(x)$ be the equation of $\bar{C}_n$ and $t = t(x)$ be the equation of $\bar{C}$. Obviously then $t_n(x)$ converges uniformly towards $t(x)$ and we can write

$$\lim_{n\to\infty} \int_a^b \Phi[x, t_n(x)]dx = \int_a^b \Phi[x, t(x)]dx ,$$

whereby passage to the limit is proven.[13]

If there exists an arc C on which functions to be integrated have discontinuities, then formula (2-2.23) remains valid when we take for the value of the integrand its limit value as we approach the curve C from the interior of the region G. With this observation, the representation of (2-2.22) in the form of (2-2.23) also has been completely proven for this case.

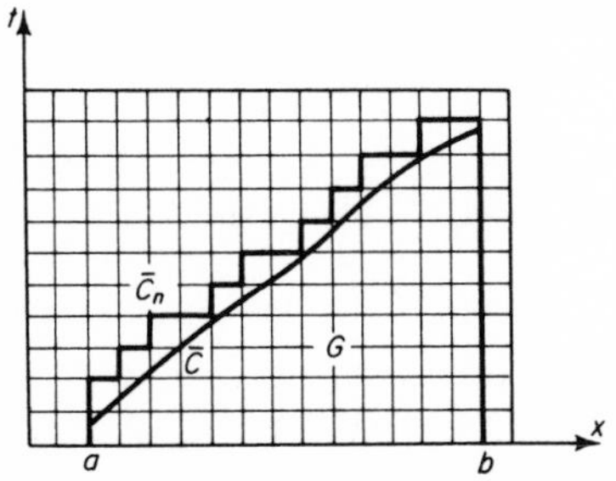

FIG. 17.

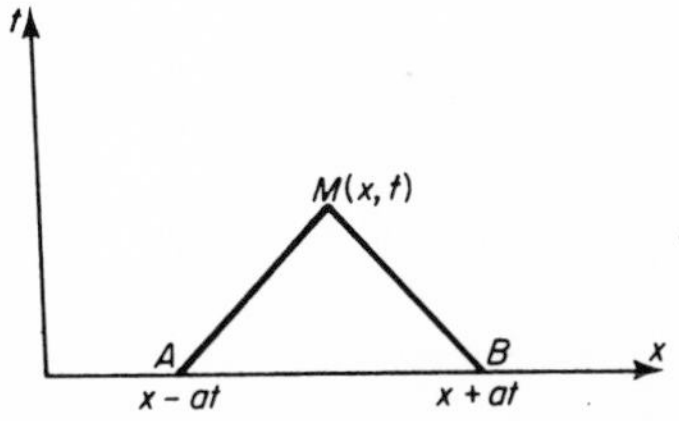

FIG. 18.

We shall consider now the following problems:

Find a piecewise smooth function $u(x, t)$ defined on $-\infty < x < \infty$ and which satisfies the equation

$$\int_C \left(\frac{\partial u}{\partial t}dx + a^2\frac{\partial u}{\partial x}dt\right) + \iint_G f(x, t)dxdt = 0 \qquad (2\text{-}2.23')$$

and the initial conditions

$$u(x, 0) = \varphi(x)$$
$$u_t(x, 0) = \psi(x) .$$

Solution: Let $\varphi(x)$ be piecewise smooth and $\psi(x)$ and $f(x, t)$ be piecewise continuous. C is an arbitrary piecewise smooth curve which lies in the region $t \geqq 0$. We shall prove that this problem has a single solution which can also be determined by the D'Alembert formula.

Let us assume that the function $u(x, t)$ is a solution of our problem. Then we shall consider the triangle ABM, whose base lies on the x axis,

[13] Since $dx = 0$ at the vertical parts of the polygonal arc $\bar{C}_n$, $t = t_n(x)$ represents in this formula the equation of a horizontal part of the polygonal arc $\bar{C}_n$.

whose upper vertex is the point $M(x, t)$, and whose remaining sides have been formed from the corresponding segments of the characteristics $x - at = \text{const.}$ and $x + at = \text{const.}$ (Figure 18). Within this triangle we apply formula (2-2.23′). Since along AM the relation $dx/dt = a$ is valid, it follows that

$$\frac{\partial u}{\partial t}dx + a^2\frac{\partial u}{\partial x}dt = a\left(\frac{\partial u}{\partial t}dt + \frac{\partial u}{\partial x}dx\right) = a\,du\,.$$

Along MB, by contrast, $dx/dt = -a$ is valid; we obtain, therefore,

$$\frac{\partial u}{\partial t}dx + a^2\frac{\partial u}{\partial x}dt = -a\left(\frac{\partial u}{\partial t}dt + \frac{\partial u}{\partial x}dx\right) = -a\,du\,.$$

Consequently, the integrand along the characteristics is a total differential, and by integration along BM and MA we immediately obtain

$$\int_B^M\left(\frac{\partial u}{\partial t}dx + a^2\frac{\partial u}{\partial x}dt\right) = -a[u(M) - u(B)]$$

$$\int_M^A\left(\frac{\partial u}{\partial t}dx + a^2\frac{\partial u}{\partial x}dt\right) = a[u(A) - u(M)]\,.$$

Formula (2-2.23′) thus reads

$$u(M) = \frac{u(B) + u(A)}{2} + \frac{1}{2a}\int_A^B\frac{\partial u}{\partial t}dx + \frac{1}{2a}\iint_{ABM} f\,dx\,dt$$

or

$$u(x, t) = \frac{\varphi(x + at) + \varphi(x - at)}{2} + \frac{1}{2a}\int_{x-at}^{x+at}\psi(\xi)d\xi + \frac{1}{2a}\int_0^t d\tau\int_{x-a(t-\tau)}^{x+a(t-\tau)} f(\xi, \tau)d\xi\,. \tag{2-2.24}$$

Consequently, the existence of a solution to our problem proves it is uniquely determined by the initial conditions. In the case of a homogeneous equation ($f = 0$), Eq. (2-2.24) coincides with the D'Alembert formula.

As one easily confirms, every function of the form

$$u(x, t) = f_1(x + at) + f_2(x - at) + \int_0^t d\tau\int_{x-a(t-\tau)}^{x+a(t-\tau)} f_3(\xi, \tau)d\xi\,,$$

where f_1, f_2 are piecewise smooth and f_3 is piecewise continuous, satisfies Eq. (2-2.22) and therefore also Eq. (2-2.23). The solutions of the problems considered as examples in § 2–4 are piecewise smooth functions and thus are accounted for by the above theory.

We shall now turn to the first boundary-value problem for the semi-infinite line and seek a solution of Eq. (2-2.23) at a point $M(x, t)$ for $t > x/a$, since in the region $t < x/a$ (outside the characteristic $x = at$) the influence of the boundary conditions still does not enter into the phenomenon and the solution

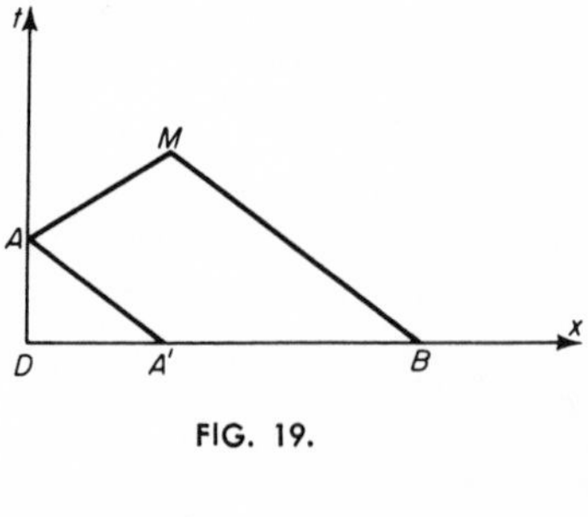

FIG. 19.

there is defined by formula (2-2.24). First we apply formula (2-2.23) to the quadrangle $MAA'B$. Here MA, MB, and AA' are segments of the characteristics (Figure 19). By integration along MA, MB, and AA' we obtain

$$2au(M) = 2au(A) + au(B) - au(A') + \int_{A'}^{B} \frac{\partial u}{\partial t} dx + \iint_{MAA'B} f\,dx\,dt\,.$$

If we insert the coordinates of M, A, B, and A' there finally results

$$u(x,t) = u\left(0, t - \frac{x}{a}\right) + \frac{u(x+at, 0) - u(at-x, 0)}{2} + \frac{1}{2a}\int_{at-x}^{x+at}\left(\frac{\partial u}{\partial t}\right)_{t=0} dx + \frac{1}{2a}\int_0^t d\tau \int_{|x-a(t-\tau)|}^{x+a(t-\tau)} f(\xi,\tau)d\xi$$

or

$$u(x,t) = \mu\left(t - \frac{x}{a}\right) + \frac{\varphi(x+at) - \varphi(at-x)}{2} + \frac{1}{2a}\int_{at-x}^{x+at} \psi(\xi)d\xi + \frac{1}{2a}\int_0^t d\tau \int_{|x-a(t-\tau)|}^{x+a(t-\tau)} f(\xi,\tau)d\xi\,, \quad t > \frac{x}{a}\,. \tag{2-2.25}$$

For $f = 0$, this formula, as is easily seen, coincides with formula (2-2.13). Similarly, one obtains the solution of the second boundary-value problem, as well as the solution of problems for a bounded interval.

For the investigation of the first boundary-value problem we saw prescribing both the initial conditions

$$u(x,0) = \varphi(x)\,, \qquad u_t(x,0) = \psi(x)$$

and the boundary condition

$$u(0,t) = \mu(t)$$

was sufficient for the complete determination of the solution. Hence it follows that a relation must exist which connects the functions φ, ψ, μ, ν with $\nu(t) = u_x(0,t)$. If we differentiate (2-2.25) with respect to x and set $x = 0$, we get

$$\nu(t) = \frac{1}{a}\{\psi(at) - [\mu'(t) - a\varphi'(at)]\}\,, \tag{2-2.26}$$

where for simplicity we have set $f = 0$. With the relation (2-2.26), for example, the third boundary-value problem can be reduced to the first.

8. Distribution of the points of discontinuity along the characteristics

In the following, we will be concerned with the points of discontinuity of the first kind in the derivatives of the solution of Eq. (2-2.23). We shall prove that the points of discontinuity of a function $u(x, t)$, which is a solution of (2-2.23), can only lie along the characteristics

$$x - at = \text{const.} \qquad x + at = \text{const.}$$

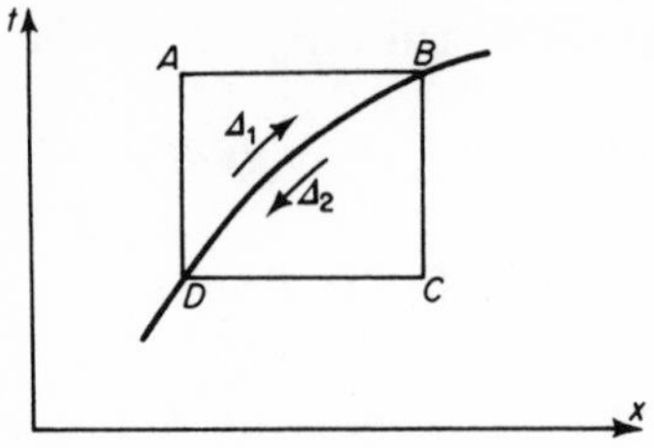

FIG. 20.

Let us assume that a differentiable curve

$$x = x(t)$$

exists, on which the derivative of the continuous piecewise smooth function $u(x, t)$ possesses a point of discontinuity. For convenience of calculation we shall assume $x(t)$ to be a monotone increasing function. Then we apply formula (2-2.23′) to the quadrangle $ABCD$ (Figure 20):

$$\int_{BA+AD}\left(\frac{\partial u}{\partial t}dx + a^2\frac{\partial u}{\partial x}dt\right) + \int_{DC+CB}\left(\frac{\partial u}{\partial t}dx + a^2\frac{\partial u}{\partial x}dt\right) = 0$$

and also along the curvilinear triangle $\Delta_1 = BAD$ and $\Delta_2 = BDC$:

$$\int_{BA+AD}\left(\frac{\partial u}{\partial t}dx + a^2\frac{\partial u}{\partial x}dt\right) + \int_{DB}\left(\frac{\partial u}{\partial t}x' + a^2\frac{\partial u}{\partial x}\right)_1 dt = 0\,,$$

$$\int_{DC+CB}\left(\frac{\partial u}{\partial t}dx + a^2\frac{\partial u}{\partial x}dt\right) - \int_{DB}\left(\frac{\partial u}{\partial t}x' + a^2\frac{\partial u}{\partial x}\right)_2 dt = 0\,,$$

where the parentheses $(\ )_1$ and $(\ )_2$ will indicate that the corresponding limit values are taken from the interior of Δ_1 or Δ_2 respectively. By subtraction of the first equation from the sum of the last two equations we obtain

$$\int_{DB}\left\{\left(\frac{\partial u}{\partial t}x' + a^2\frac{\partial u}{\partial t}\right)_1 - \left(\frac{\partial u}{\partial t}x' + a^2\frac{\partial u}{\partial x}\right)_2\right\}dt = 0$$

or, since DB was chosen arbitrarily,

$$\left[\frac{\partial u}{\partial t}\right]x' + a^2\left[\frac{\partial u}{\partial x}\right] = 0\,. \tag{2-2.27}$$

The square brackets indicate here, as is usual, the magnitude of the jump of the function, i.e.,

$$[f] = f_2 - f_1\,.$$

We now form the derivative of the function $u(x, t)$ with respect to t

$$\frac{d}{dt}u(x(t), t) = \left(\frac{\partial u}{\partial x}\right)_i x' + \left(\frac{\partial u}{\partial t}\right)_i, \qquad i = 1, 2\,.$$

Therefore, we can choose both the value of the derivatives and the limit values corresponding to Δ_1 and Δ_2 (taken from the interior). The difference of the right sides for $i = 1$ and $i = 2$ is

$$\left[\frac{\partial u}{\partial t}\right] + x'\left[\frac{\partial u}{\partial x}\right] = 0\,.$$

If we equate this equation with (2-2.27) and assume at least one of the jumps $[\partial u/\partial t]$, $[\partial u/\partial x]$ to be different from zero, we see that both equations are simultaneously satisfied if the determinant of the system vanishes:

$$\begin{vmatrix} x' & a^2 \\ 1 & x' \end{vmatrix} = (x')^2 - a^2 = 0$$

or

$$x = \pm at + \text{const.}$$

Consequently the points of discontinuity of the derivatives of a function $u(x, t)$ which is a solution of the wave equation lie along the characteristics.

Problems

1. Construct a profile of a string at different times for the following cases:

(a) The unbounded string

(1) The initial velocity is equal to zero $[\psi(x) = 0]$, while the initial profile of the string is given as in Figure 21.

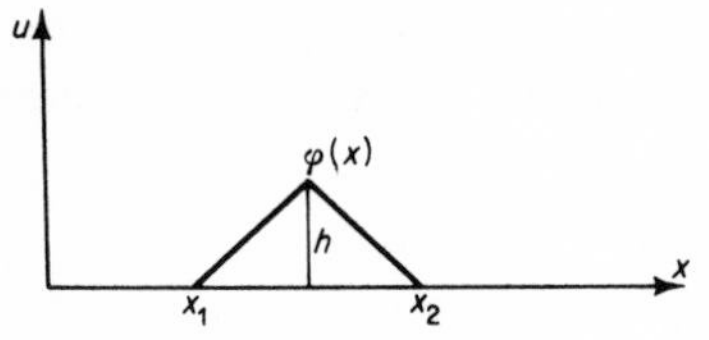

FIG. 21.

(2) The initial displacement is equal to zero while the initial velocity of an element (x_1, x_2) of the string possesses a constant value $u_t(x, 0)$ and outside of the latter is equal to zero.

(3) The initial conditions have the form

$$\varphi(x) = 0\,; \qquad \psi(x) = 0 \qquad \text{for } x < c$$
$$= \frac{h}{2c^2}x(2c - x) \qquad \text{for } c < x < 2c$$
$$= 0 \qquad \text{for } x > 2c\,.$$

(b) The one-sided bounded string

(4) The initial velocity is equal to zero $[\psi(x) = 0]$ while the initial displacement has the form of the triangle given in Figure 21. One end of the string is assumed to be fixed.

(5) As in (4), but for a free end $x = 0$.

(6) The initial conditions read

$$\varphi(x) = 0\,, \qquad \psi(x) = 0 \qquad \text{for } 0 < x < c$$
$$= \psi_0 = \text{const.} \qquad \text{for } c < x < 2c$$
$$= 0 \qquad \text{for } x > 2c$$

and the end $x = 0$ is assumed to be fixed.

(7) As in (6), but again for a free end $x = 0$. The string profile is indicated for all the problems (1) through (7) at the times

$$t_0 = 0\,, \qquad t_k = \frac{c}{8a}k\,, \qquad k = 1, 2, \cdots, 8\,.$$

They are in the x, t phase plane, which is interpreted for the zones corresponding to the different states.

2. Find the solution of **1**(1) for all values of x and t (thus the formula representing $u(x, t)$ which differs for the different zones of the phase plane).

3. Determine the displacement at a point (x_0, t_0) by using the x, t phase plane and the x, u plane in which (Figure 21) an initial displacement ($\psi = 0$) is given for an unbounded string and also for a semi-infinite string with a fixed (or a free) end.

4. At one end of a long cylindrical tube filled with gas there is a piston which moves according to an arbitrary law $x = f(t)$ with the velocity $v = f'(t) < a$. The initial displacement and the initial velocity of the gas particles are equal to zero. Find the displacement of the gas at the plane with coordinate x. In this case assume that the piston moves with a constant velocity $c < a$. What can be said about the solution of the problem if the piston at a certain time has a velocity $v > a$?

5. A wave $u(x, t) = f(x - at)$ propagates along an unbounded string. Choose the condition of the string at the time $t = 0$ as the initial condition and then solve the wave equation with the corresponding initial conditions; compare with problem **1**(1).

6. By joining two elastic rods with the characteristics

$$k_1, \quad \rho_1, \quad a_1 = \sqrt{\frac{k_1}{\rho_1}} \qquad \text{for } x < 0$$

$$k_2, \quad \rho_2, \quad a_2 = \sqrt{\frac{k_2}{\rho_2}} \qquad \text{for } x > 0$$

at point $x = 0$, an elastic infinitely long rod is obtained.

(a) In the region $x < 0$ a wave

$$u(x, t) = f\left(t - \frac{x}{a}\right)$$

is prescribed where f is the given function. Find the reflection and transmission coefficients that are due to the passage of the wave at the boundary ($x = 0$). Investigate the conditions under which no reflection of the wave occurs.

(b) Solve the corresponding problem when the local initial displacement

$$\begin{aligned} u(x, 0) &= 0 && \text{for } x < x_1 \\ &= \varphi(x) && \text{for } x_1 < x < x_2 < 0 \\ &= 0 && \text{for } x > x_2 \end{aligned}$$

is given and the initial velocity is equal to zero.

7. At any point $x = x_0$ of a string hangs a weight of mass M, and in the region $x < 0$ the wave

$$u(x, t) = f\left(t - \frac{x}{a}\right)$$

is prescribed. Determine the transmission and the reflection of the wave.

8. At one end ($x = 0$) of a semi-infinite tube ($x > 0$) filled with an ideal gas, there is a freely moving piston of mass M. At time $t = 0$ the piston acquires an initial velocity v_0 by an impulse. Find the path of the wave propagation in the gas when it is known that the initial displacement and the initial velocity of the gas particles are equal to zero. Consider the solution of the wave equation for $x > 0$. Also use the boundary condition

$$Mu_{tt}(0, t) = S\gamma p_0 u_x(0, t),$$

where p_0 is the initial gas pressure, S is the area of the cross section of the tube, $\gamma = c_p/c_v$, and the initial conditions at the boundary are $u(0, 0) = 0$, $u_t(0, 0) = 0$.
Solution:

$$u(x, t) = \frac{aMv_0}{\gamma p_0 S}[1 - e^{(\gamma p_0 S/Ma^2)(x-at)}] \qquad \text{for } x - at < 0$$

$$u(x, t) = 0 \qquad \text{for } x - at > 0\,.$$

9. An infinite string, which at point $x = 0$ has a concentrated mass M, is in a state of equilibrium. At the initial moment $t = 0$, the center of gravity of the mass M acquires by an impulse an initial velocity v_0. Prove that the string at time $t > 0$ has the form shown in Figure 22 where $u_1(x, t)$ and $u_2(x, t)$ are defined by

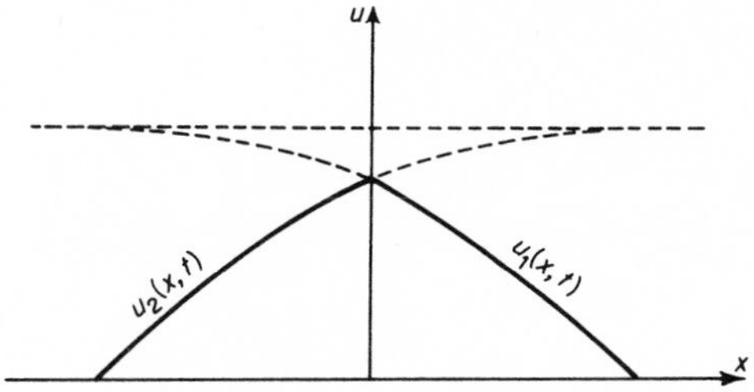

FIG. 22.

direct wave:

$$u_1(x, t) = \frac{Mav_0}{2T}[1 - e^{(2T/Ma^2)(x-at)}] \qquad \text{for } x - at < 0$$

$$= 0 \qquad \text{for } x - at > 0$$

reflected wave:

$$u_2(x, t) = \frac{Mav_0}{2T}[1 - e^{-(2T/Ma^2)(x+at)}] \qquad \text{for } x - at < 0$$

$$= 0 \qquad \text{for } x - at > 0\,.$$

Use the conditions

$$M\frac{\partial^2 u_1}{\partial t^2}(0, t) = M\frac{\partial^2 u_2}{\partial t^2}(0, t) = T\frac{\partial u_1}{\partial x}(0, t) = T\frac{\partial u_2}{\partial x}(0, t)\,.$$

10. Solve the problem of the propagation of electrical vibrations in an unbounded conductor with the condition

$$\frac{G}{C} = \frac{R}{L}\,.$$

and with arbitrary initial conditions.
Solution:

$$v(x, t) = e^{-(R/L)t}[\varphi(x - at) + \psi(x + at)]$$

$$i(x, t) = \sqrt{\frac{C}{L}} e^{-(R/L)t}[\varphi(x - at) - \psi(x + at)] .$$

If

$$v(x, 0) = f(x) \qquad i(x, 0) = \sqrt{\frac{C}{L}} F(x) ,$$

then the following holds:

$$\varphi(x) = \frac{f(x) + F(x)}{2} \qquad \psi(x) = \frac{f(x) - F(x)}{2} .$$

11. Find the solution of the integral wave equation for a semi-infinite string when the boundary conditions prescribed are of the third kind.
12. A membrane is fastened at the end $x = 0$ of a semi-infinite spring. It is undergoing resistance due to the longitudinal vibrations of the spring and is proportional to the velocity $u_t(0, t)$. Investigate the course of vibrations if the initial displacement is known and $u_t(x, 0) = \psi(x) = 0$.

2-3. SEPARATION OF VARIABLES

1. The free vibrations of a string

The method of separation of variables, also called the Fourier method, is one of the best-known methods for the solution of partial differential equations. We shall investigate this method using as an example the vibrations of a string fastened at both ends. We shall discuss the problem in detail and then refer to the investigations which follow without repeating the individual proofs.

First, we seek a solution of the equation

$$u_{tt} = a^2 u_{xx} , \tag{2-3.1}$$

which satisfies the homogeneous boundary conditions

$$u(0, t) = 0 , \qquad u(l, t) = 0 , \tag{2-3.2}$$

and the initial conditions

$$u(x, 0) = \varphi(x) , \qquad u_t(x, 0) = \psi(x) . \tag{2-3.3}$$

The differential Eq. (2-3.1) is linear and homogeneous. Hence the sum of individual solutions again is a solution of this equation. Accordingly, when we have a sufficient number of individual solutions, the desired solution is obtained by summing the individual solutions when each solution is multiplied by a suitable coefficient.

For this purpose we shall consider the following fundamental lemma:

Find a solution of (2-3.1), which does not vanish identically, which satisfies the homogeneous boundary conditions (2-3.2), and which is represented in the form of a product

$$u(x, t) = X(x)T(t)\,, \tag{2-3.4}$$

where $X(x)$ is a function of x alone and $T(t)$ is a function of t alone.

By inserting expression (2-3.4) into Eq. (2-3.1) we obtain

$$X''T = \frac{1}{a^2}T''X \tag{2-3.5}$$

or, after dividing by XT,

$$\frac{X''(x)}{X(x)} = \frac{1}{a^2}\frac{T''(t)}{T(t)}\,. \tag{2-3.6}$$

Thus, if the function defined by (2-3.4) is a solution of (2-3.1), Eqs. (2-3.5) and (2-3.6) must be identical, i.e., for all values of x, such that $0 < x < l$, $t > 0$. The right side of (2-3.6) is a function of t alone, while the left side is dependent only on x. If, for example, x is fixed and t changes (or conversely), we see that the right and the left sides of (2-3.6), for changes in their arguments, remain constant:

$$\frac{X''(x)}{X(x)} = \frac{1}{a^2}\frac{T''(t)}{T(t)} = -\lambda\,, \tag{2-3.7}$$

where λ is a constant which for the following investigations is appropriately marked with a minus sign. Nothing will be assumed about the sign of λ.

From the relation (2-3.7) we then obtain for the determination of $X(x)$ and $T(t)$ the ordinary differential equations

$$X''(x) + \lambda X(x) = 0 \tag{2-3.8}$$

$$T''(t) + a^2\lambda T(t) = 0\,. \tag{2-3.9}$$

The boundary conditions (2-3.2) yield

$$u(0, t) = X(0)T(t) = 0$$

$$u(l, t) = X(l)T(t) = 0\,.$$

Hence it follows that $X(x)$ must satisfy the auxiliary conditions

$$X(0) = X(l) = 0 \tag{2-3.10}$$

while in particular if

$$T(t) \equiv 0 \qquad \text{and} \qquad u(x, t) \equiv 0$$

we could still find a nontrivial solution. For $T(t)$, no auxiliary conditions are prescribed.

Consequently we are led to the relation for the determination of the function $X(x)$ for the simplest eigenvalue problem:

Determine the values of λ for which a nontrivial solution of the problem

$$X'' + \lambda X = 0\,, \qquad X(0) = X(l) = 0 \tag{2-3.11}$$

exists and find the corresponding solutions. The λ value for which a solution exists is called an eigenvalue, and the corresponding solutions are called eigenfunctions. The problem just formulated is a special case of a Sturm-Liouville eigenvalue problem.

In the following considerations we will distinguish between three cases:

1. For $\lambda < 0$, the problem possesses no nontrivial solution. The general solution of this equation has the form

$$X(x) = C_1 e^{\sqrt{-\lambda}x} + C_2 e^{-\sqrt{-\lambda}x},$$

while the boundary conditions are

$$X(0) = C_1 + C_2 = 0,$$
$$X(l) = C_1 e^{\alpha} + C_2 e^{-\alpha} = 0, \qquad \alpha = l\sqrt{-\lambda},$$

i.e.,

$$C_1 = -C_2 \quad \text{and} \quad C_1(e^{\alpha} - e^{-\alpha}) = 0.$$

Since now α for $\lambda < 0$ is real and positive, we have $e^{\alpha} - e^{-\alpha} \neq 0$. Thus

$$C_1 = 0, \qquad C_2 = 0$$

and

$$X(x) \equiv 0.$$

2. For $\lambda = 0$ likewise, no nontrivial solutions exist, since here the general solution is

$$X(x) = ax + b,$$

while the boundary conditions are

$$X(0) = [ax + b]_{x=0} = b = 0,$$
$$X(l) = al = 0,$$

i.e., $a = 0$ and $b = 0$; thus

$$X(x) \equiv 0.$$

3. For $\lambda > 0$, the general solution possesses imaginary exponents and therefore can be represented in the form

$$X(x) = D_1 \cos \sqrt{\lambda}x + D_2 \sin \sqrt{\lambda}x.$$

The boundary conditions are

$$X(0) = D_1 = 0$$
$$X(l) = D_2 \sin \sqrt{\lambda}l = 0.$$

If $X(x)$ does not vanish identically, then $D_2 \neq 0$ so that

$$\sin \sqrt{\lambda}l = 0 \tag{2-3.12}$$

or

$$\sqrt{\lambda} = \frac{\pi n}{l},$$

where n is an arbitrary integer. A nontrivial solution is therefore possible only for the values

$$\lambda_n = \left(\frac{\pi n}{l}\right)^2 .$$

These eigenvalues correspond to the eigenfunctions

$$X_n(x) = D_n \sin \frac{\pi n}{l} x .$$

Hence for those values of λ which equal

$$\lambda_n = \left(\frac{\pi n}{l}\right)^2 \tag{2-3.13}$$

there exist only the nontrivial solutions

$$X_n(x) = \sin \frac{\pi n}{l} x , \tag{2.3.14}$$

which, except for arbitrary factors which we have set equal to unity in (2-3.14) throughout, are determined uniquely. The solutions of Eq. (2-3.9) corresponding to these λ values are

$$T_n(t) = A_n \cos \frac{\pi n}{l} at + B_n \sin \frac{\pi n}{l} at , \tag{2-3.15}$$

where A_n and B_n are coefficients yet to be defined.

With regard to the three problems above, we know that the functions

$$u_n(x, t) = X_n(x) T_n(t) = \left(A_n \cos \frac{\pi n}{l} at + B_n \sin \frac{\pi n}{l} at\right) \sin \frac{\pi n}{l} x \tag{2-3.16}$$

are specific solutions of Eq. (2-3.1) which satisfy the boundary conditions (2-3.2). They can be described by (2-3.4) as the product of two functions, of which one is dependent only on x and the other only on t. These solutions must satisfy the initial conditions (2-3.3) of our original problem only for prescribed functions $\varphi(x)$ and $\psi(x)$.

We turn now to the solution of the problem in the general case. Because of the linearity and homogeneity of (2-3.1) the sum of the particular solutions

$$u(x, t) = \sum_{n=1}^{\infty} u_n(x, t) = \sum_{n=1}^{\infty} \left(A_n \cos \frac{\pi n}{l} at + B_n \sin \frac{\pi n}{l} at\right) \sin \frac{\pi n}{l} x , \tag{2-3.17}$$

if it converges and is twice differentiable with respect to x and t, term by term, likewise satisfies this equation and the boundary conditions (2-3.2). We shall treat this question in greater detail later (see Section 2-3 § 3). The initial conditions yield

$$\begin{aligned} u(x, 0) &= \varphi(x) = \sum_{n=1}^{\infty} u_n(x, 0) = \sum_{n=1}^{\infty} A_n \sin \frac{\pi n}{l} x \\ u_t(x, 0) &= \psi(x) = \sum_{n=1}^{\infty} \frac{\partial u_n}{\partial t}(x, 0) = \sum_{n=1}^{\infty} \frac{\pi n}{l} a B_n \sin \frac{\pi n}{l} x . \end{aligned} \tag{2-3.18}$$

From the theory of Fourier series it is now known that an arbitrary piecewise continuous and piecewise differentiable function $f(x)$, which is defined in an interval $0 \leqq x \leqq l$, can be developed in a Fourier series

$$f(x) = \sum_{n=1}^{\infty} b_n \sin \frac{\pi n}{l} x \tag{2-3.19}$$

where[14]

$$b_n = \frac{2}{l} \int_0^l f(\xi) \sin \frac{\pi n}{l} \xi d\xi \,. \tag{2-3.20}$$

If $\varphi(x)$ and $\psi(x)$ can be developed in a Fourier series, we obtain

$$\varphi(x) = \sum_{n=1}^{\infty} \varphi_n \sin \frac{\pi n}{l} x \,, \qquad \varphi_n = \frac{2}{l} \int_0^l \varphi(\xi) \sin \frac{\pi n}{l} \xi d\xi \,, \tag{2-3.21}$$

$$\psi(x) = \sum_{n=1}^{\infty} \psi_n \sin \frac{\pi n}{l} x \,, \qquad \psi_n = \frac{2}{l} \int_0^l \psi(\xi) \sin \frac{\pi n}{l} \xi d\xi \,. \tag{2-3.22}$$

Comparison of these series with Eq. (2-3.18) shows that in order to satisfy the initial equations we must set

$$A_n = \varphi_n \,, \qquad B_n = \frac{l}{\pi n a} \psi_n \,. \tag{2-3.23}$$

Hence the function (2-3.17) which gives the solution to the problem under consideration is defined completely.

The solution can be determined in the form of an infinite series (2-3.17). If, however, series (2-3.17) diverges or the function determined by this series is not differentiable, then, of course, it is not the solution of our differential equation.

We shall limit ourselves at this point to the formal construction of the solution. The conditions under which the series (2-3.17) converges and represents a solution will be investigated in Section (2-3.3).

[14] Usually one considers the periodic functions of period $2l$

$$F(x) = \frac{a_0}{2} + \sum_{n=1}^{\infty} \left(a_n \cos \frac{\pi n}{l} x + b_n \sin \frac{\pi n}{l} x \right),$$

$$a_n = \frac{1}{l} \int_{-l}^{l} F(\xi) \cos \frac{\pi n}{l} \xi d\xi, \quad b_n = \frac{1}{l} \int_{-l}^{l} F(\xi) \sin \frac{\pi n}{l} \xi d\xi \,.$$

If $F(x)$ is odd then $a_n = 0$; thus

$$F(x) = \sum_{n=1}^{\infty} b_n \sin \frac{\pi n}{l} x \,,$$

$$b_n = \frac{1}{l} \int_{-l}^{l} F(\xi) \sin \frac{\pi n}{l} \xi d\xi = \frac{2}{l} \int_0^l F(\xi) \sin \frac{\pi n}{l} \xi d\xi \,.$$

If $F(x)$ is defined only in an interval $(0, l)$ then $F(x)$ can be continued oddly and developed in the interval from $-l$ to $+l$. This then leads to formulas (2-3.19) and (2-3.20).

2. Interpretation of the solution

We shall turn now to the interpretation of the solution obtained. The function $u_n(x, t)$ can be written in the form

$$u_n(x, t) = \left(A_n \cos\frac{\pi n}{l}at + B_n \sin\frac{\pi n}{l}at\right)\sin\frac{\pi n}{l}x$$

$$= \alpha_n \cos\frac{\pi n}{l}a(t + \delta_n) \sin\frac{\pi n}{l}x \qquad (2\text{-}3.24)$$

with

$$\alpha_n = \sqrt{A_n^2 + B_n^2}\,, \qquad \frac{\pi n}{l}a\delta_n = -\operatorname{arc\,tg}\frac{B_n}{A_n}\,. \qquad (2\text{-}3.25)$$

Each point x_0 of the string describes a harmonic vibration

$$u_n(x_0, t) = \alpha_n \cos\frac{\pi n}{l}a(t + \delta_n) \sin\frac{\pi n}{l}x_0$$

with the amplitude

$$a_n \sin\frac{\pi n}{l}x_0\,.$$

Each such motion of a string is designated as a standing wave. The point $x = m(l/n)$, where $m = 1, 2, \cdots, n-1$, in which $\sin(\pi n/l)x = 0$, remains fixed in the course of the entire process and is called a node of the standing wave. By contrast the point $x = (2m+1)/2n$, where $m = 0, 1, \cdots, n-1$, in which $\sin(\pi n/l)x = \pm 1$, vibrates with the maximum amplitude α_n. One designates this as the maximum of the standing wave.

The profile of the standing wave is described for arbitrary t by

$$u_n(x, t) = C_n(t) \sin\frac{\pi n}{l}x\,.$$

Thus

$$C_n(t) = \alpha \cos\omega_n(t + \delta_n)\,, \qquad \omega_n = \frac{\pi n}{l}a\,.$$

When $\cos\omega_n(t+\delta_n) = \pm 1$ at the time t, the displacement reaches its maximum value when the velocity equals zero. By contrast the displacement for those t values for which $\cos\omega_n(t+\delta_n) = 0$ is valid equals zero but the velocity is maximum. The frequencies of vibration of all points of the string coincide and have the values

$$\omega_n = \frac{\pi n}{l}a\,. \qquad (2\text{-}3.26)$$

The frequencies ω_n are called the eigenfrequencies of the vibrating string. For a transverse vibrating string $a^2 = T/\rho$, and accordingly

$$\omega_n = \frac{\pi n}{l}\sqrt{\frac{T}{\rho}}\,. \qquad (2\text{-}3.27)$$

The energy of the nth standing wave (the nth harmonic) for a transverse vibrating string equals

$$E_n = \frac{1}{2}\int_0^l \left[\rho\left(\frac{\partial u_n}{\partial t}\right)^2 + T\left(\frac{\partial u_n}{\partial x}\right)^2\right]dx$$

$$= \frac{\alpha_n^2}{2}\int_0^l \left[\rho\omega_n^2 \sin^2 \omega_n(t+\delta_n)\sin^2\frac{\pi n}{l}x + T\left(\frac{\pi n}{l}\right)^2 \cos^2 \omega_n(t+\delta_n)\cos^2\frac{\pi n}{l}x\right]dx$$

$$= \frac{\alpha_n^2}{2}\frac{l}{2}\left[\rho\omega_n^2 \sin^2 \omega_n(t+\delta_n) + T\left(\frac{\pi n}{l}\right)^2 \cos^2 \omega_n(t+\delta_n)\right] \tag{2-3.28}$$

and

$$\int_0^l \sin^2\frac{\pi n}{l}x dx = \int_0^l \cos^2\frac{\pi n}{l}x dx = \frac{l}{2}\,.$$

By using the expressions for α_m and ω_n as well as the relation $T = a^2\rho$, we obtain

$$E_n = \frac{\rho\alpha_n^2\omega_n^2}{4}l = \omega_n^2 M\cdot\frac{A_n^2 + B_n^2}{4}\,, \tag{2-3.29}$$

with $M = l\rho$, the mass of the string.

The vibrations of a string can usually be observed acoustically. Without going into the process of wave propagation in air and the observation of sound vibrations by ear we can say that the acoustical effect of a string is composed of simple tones. The splitting into simple tones is not only a mathematical operation; it can also be observed with the help of resonators.

The pitch of a tone depends on the frequency of the vibration corresponding to this tone. The strength of the tone, by contrast, is dependent on its energy, i.e. on its amplitude. The lowest tone which the string produces is determined by the lowest natural frequency, $\omega_1 = (\pi/l)(\sqrt{T/\rho})$, and is called the basic tone of the string. The rest of the tones whose frequencies are multiples of ω_1 are called overtones of the string. The tone color, finally, is obtained from the presence of the overtones in addition to the basic tone and the distribution of the energy of the individual overtones.

The lowest tone of a string and its tone color are dependent on the excitation of the string. The type of excitation is defined namely by the initial conditions

$$u(x,0) = \varphi(x)\,, \qquad u_t(x,0) = \psi(x)\,, \tag{2-3.3}$$

and these determine in turn the coefficients A_n and B_n. If $A_1 = B_1 = 0$, the lowest tone is that one which corresponds to the frequency ω_n where n is the smallest number for which A_n or B_n is different from zero.

Usually a string produces one and the same tone. In order to understand this, we start a string vibrating by striking it on one side, and neglect the initial velocity. Then

$$u_t(x,0) = 0\,, \qquad u(x,0) = \varphi(x) > 0$$

and

$$A_1 = \frac{2}{l}\int_0^l \varphi(\xi) \sin \frac{\pi}{l}\xi d\xi > 0$$

because

$$\sin \frac{\pi}{l}\xi > 0.$$

The resulting coefficients are generally significantly smaller than A_1, since the function $\sin (\pi n/l)\xi$ for $n \geqq 2$ changes its sign. If $\varphi(x)$ is in particular symmetrical with respect to the center of the interval, then $A_2 = 0$.

Consequently the lowest tone of a string which is set to vibrating by one-sided impulses, $\varphi(x) > 0$, is just that tone whose energy is in general larger than the energies of the other harmonics.

A string can also execute other types of vibration. For example, if the function $\varphi(x)$, occurring in the initial conditions with respect to the center of the interval, is odd, then

$$A_1 = 0,$$

and the lowest tone corresponding to the frequency

$$\omega = \omega_2 = \frac{2\pi}{l}\sqrt{\frac{T}{\rho}}$$

is obtained. If a tuning string is contacted exactly in the middle, then it vibrates an octave higher than its natural tone with changing tone color. This type of tone conversion is often used in playing violins, guitars, and other string instruments. The tones thus produced are called flageolet tones. From the standpoint of the theory of a vibrating string this phenomenon is completely understandable. At the moment in which the string touches exactly in the middle, those standing waves having displacement at this point are extinguished, and only those waves remain which possess a node at the point of contact. Thus, only the even harmonics remain, so that the lowest frequency is

$$\omega_2 = \frac{2\pi}{l}\sqrt{\frac{T}{\rho}}.$$

If the string $(0, l)$ is touched at the point $x = l/3$, it increases the pitch of the basic tones threefold, since here only those harmonics whose nodes lie at the point $x = l/3$ remain. The formula

$$\omega_1 = \frac{\pi}{\rho}\sqrt{\frac{T}{\rho}} \quad \text{or} \quad \tau_1 = \frac{2\pi}{\omega_1} = 2l\sqrt{\frac{\rho}{T}} \tag{2-3.30}$$

for the frequency or the period of the basic vibration explains the following rules which were first found experimentally. (1) For strings of uniform density and uniform tension, the vibration period is proportional to the length of the string. (2) In a prescribed length of string, the period is inversely proportional to the square root of the tension. (3) For prescribed lengths and tension, the period is proportional to the square root of the linear density of the string. These three can be easily demonstrated in a monocord.

In this section the existence of standing waves by the vibrations of a string with fixed ends is demonstrated. It must still be mentioned that the existence of solutions of the form

$$u(x, t) = X(x)T(t)$$

is equivalent to the existence of standing waves, since the profiles of such a solution at different times are proportional to each other.

3. Description of arbitrary vibrations by superposition of standing waves

Earlier, in Section 2-3 § 1, we treated the free vibrations of a string fixed at the ends. There we proved the existence of special solutions in the form of standing waves and presented a formal scheme for the representation of an arbitrary vibration as an infinite sum of the standing waves. We shall prove in this section that such a representation is possible. First of all, a generalization of the superposition principle, known for finite sums, will be applied to infinite series.

Let $L(u)$ be a linear differential operator. This means that $L(u)$, that is, L applied to a function u, is equal to the sum of the corresponding derivatives of the function u with coefficients which are independent of u. Therefore, both ordinary as well as partial derivatives are admissible.

Lemma (*generalized superposition principal*): If the functions u_i $(i = 1, 2, \cdots)$ are separately solutions of a linear and homogeneous differential equation $L(u) = 0$, then the series $u = \sum_{i=1}^{\infty} C_i u_i$ is likewise a solution of the differential equation, provided the derivatives of u appearing in $L(u)$ can be differentiated termwise.

Thus, if the derivatives of u occurring in $L(u) = 0$ can be differentiated termwise, we have

$$\frac{\partial^n u}{\partial x^m \partial t^{n-m}} = \sum_{i=1}^{\infty} C_i \frac{\partial_n u_i}{\partial x^m \partial t^{n-m}} ,$$

and because of the linearity of the equation we can write

$$L(u) = L(\sum_{i=1}^{\infty} C_i u_i) = \sum_{i=1}^{\infty} C_i L(u_i) = 0 ,$$

since a convergent series can be added termwise. Hence it is shown that u satisfies the differential equation. As a sufficient condition for the termwise differentiability, we shall use the uniform convergence of the series[15]

$$\sum_{i=1}^{\infty} C_i \frac{\partial^n u_i}{\partial x^m \partial t^{n-m}} . \tag{2-3.31}$$

We return now to our boundary-value problem. First we have to prove the continuity of the function

[15] See V. I. Smirnov, *Textbook of Higher Mathematics*, 2d ed., Part II, Berlin, 1958.

$$u(x,t)=\sum_{n=1}^{\infty}u_n(x,t)=\sum_{n=1}^{\infty}\left(A_n\cos\frac{\pi n}{l}at+B_n\sin\frac{\pi n}{l}at\right)\sin\frac{\pi n}{l}x\,. \tag{2-3.32}$$

From this it then follows that $u(x,t)$ depends continuously on the corresponding initial and boundary conditions. Here it is sufficient to prove the uniform convergence of the series which represents the function $u(x,t)$, since the general term of the series is a continuous function, and a uniformly convergent series of continuous functions represents a continuous function. Therefore we can proceed as follows: From the well-known inequality

$$|u_n(x,t)|\leqq|A_n|+|B_n|$$

we conclude that the series

$$\sum_{n=1}^{\infty}(|A_n|+|B_n|) \tag{2-3.33}$$

is a majorant of the series (2-3.32). If the series (2-3.33) converges, then the series (2-3.32) converges uniformly, and $u(x,t)$ is continuous.

Furthermore, in order to see that $u_t(x,t)$ depends continuously on the initial conditions, the continuity of this function must be demonstrated; therefore, it is sufficient to prove the uniform convergence of the series

$$u_t(x,t)\sim\sum_{n=1}^{\infty}\frac{\partial u_n}{\partial t}=\sum_{n=1}^{\infty}a\frac{\pi n}{l}\left(-A_n\sin\frac{\pi n}{l}at+B_n\cos\frac{\pi n}{l}at\right)\sin\frac{\pi n}{l}x \tag{2-3.34}$$

or the simple convergence of the majorant series

$$\frac{a\pi}{l}\sum_{n=1}^{\infty}n(|A_n|+B_n|)\,. \tag{2-3.35}$$

Finally, in order to show that the function $u(x,t)$ is an integral of the differential equation, it is sufficient to show by the use of the generalized superposition principle that the series representing $u(x,t)$ is twice differentiable termwise, which suffices for the proof of the uniform convergence of the series

$$u_{xx}\sim\sum_{n=1}^{\infty}\frac{\partial^2u_n}{\partial x^2}=-\left(\frac{\pi}{l}\right)^2\sum_{n=1}^{\infty}n^2\left(A_n\cos\frac{\pi n}{l}at+B_n\sin\frac{\pi n}{l}at\right)\sin\frac{\pi n}{l}x$$

$$u_{tt}\sim\sum_{n=1}^{\infty}\frac{\partial^2u_n}{\partial t^2}=-\left(\frac{\pi a}{l}\right)^2\sum_{n=1}^{\infty}n^2\left(A_n\cos\frac{\pi n}{l}at+B_n\sin\frac{\pi n}{l}at\right)\sin\frac{\pi n}{l}x\,.$$

This corresponds within constant factors to the common majorant

$$\sum_{n=1}^{\infty}n^2(|A_n|+|B_n|)\,. \tag{2-3.36}$$

Since

$$A_n=\varphi_n\,,\qquad B_n=\frac{l}{\pi na}\psi_n\,,$$

where

$$\varphi_n=\frac{2}{l}\int_0^l\varphi(x)\sin\frac{\pi n}{l}xdx\,,\qquad \psi_n=\frac{2}{l}\int_0^l\psi(x)\sin\frac{\pi n}{l}xdx\,,$$

our problem is solved, as soon as the convergence of the series

$$\sum_{n=1}^{\infty} n^k \,|\varphi_n|\,, \qquad k = 0, 1, 2$$
$$\sum_{n=1}^{\infty} n^k \,|\psi_n|\,, \qquad k = -1, 0, 1 \tag{2-3.37}$$

is demonstrated.

To demonstrate the convergence of (2-3.37) we use some well-known properties of Fourier series.[16]

If a periodic function $F(x)$ with period $2l$ possesses continuous derivatives up to and including the kth order, while the $(k+1)$th derivative is only piecewise continuous, then the series

$$\sum_{n=1}^{\infty} n^k(|a_n| + |b_n|) \tag{2-3.38}$$

converges, where a_n and b_n are the Fourier coefficients. If we are dealing with development of a function $f(x)$, which is given only in the interval $(0, l)$, in a series with respect to the functions in $\sin(\pi n/l)x$, we require that the conditions stated above hold for the odd continuation $F(x)$ of the function $f(x)$ in order to guarantee the convergence of this series. Further for the continuity of $F(x)$ it is necessary that $f(0) = 0$, since otherwise a discontinuity in the odd continuation would appear at the point $x = 0$; accordingly, $f(l)$ must also equal zero at the point $x = l$, since the continued function is continuous and has a period equal to $2l$. The continuity of the first derivative at $x = 0$, $x = l$, follows automatically for the odd continuation. In general, we must require that the even derivatives of the continued function satisfy

$$f^{(k)}(0) = f^{(k)}(l) = 0\,, \qquad k = 0, 2, 4, \cdots, 2n\,, \tag{2-3.39}$$

while for the continuity of the odd derivatives no auxiliary conditions are imposed.

For the convergence of the series

$$\sum_{n=1}^{\infty} n^k \,|\varphi_n|\,, \qquad k = 0, 1, 2$$

it is sufficient to require that the initial displacement $\varphi(x)$ satisfy the following requirements:

Condition 1. The derivatives of $\varphi(x)$ are continuous up to and including the second order, the third derivative is piecewise continuous, and moreover

$$\varphi(0) = \varphi(l) = 0\,, \qquad \varphi''(0) = \varphi''(l) = 0\,. \tag{2-3.40}$$

For the convergence of the series

$$\sum_{n=1}^{\infty} n^k \,|\psi_n|\,, \qquad k = -1, 0, 1$$

we require that the initial velocity $\psi(x)$ satisfy:

16 *Ibid.*, *cf.* footnote 14.

Condition 2. The function $\psi(x)$ is continuously differentiable and possesses a piecewise continuous second derivative, and

$$\psi(0) = \psi(l) = 0 . \tag{2-3.41}$$

In summary, we have demonstrated that an arbitrary wave $u(x, t)$ can be represented by the superposition of standing waves if the functions $\varphi(x)$ and $\psi(x)$ occurring in the initial conditions satisfy Conditions 1 and 2. Conditions 1 and 2 are sufficient for the method of proof used here.

An analogous problem was solved in Section 2-2 § 5 with the help of the method of wave propagation, and the solution was given by

$$u(x, t) = \frac{\Phi(x - at) + \Phi(x + at)}{2} + \frac{1}{2a}\int_{x-at}^{x+at} \Psi(\alpha)d\alpha , \tag{2-3.42}$$

where Φ and Ψ are the odd continuations with respect to 0 and l of the prescribed initial functions $\varphi(x)$ and $\psi(x)$ defined in the interval $(0, l)$. The functions Φ and Ψ are, as shown, periodic functions of period $2l$ and therefore can be represented by the series

$$\Phi(x) = \sum_{n=1}^{\infty} \varphi_n \sin\frac{\pi n}{l}x , \qquad \Psi(x) = \sum_{n=1}^{\infty} \psi_n \sin\frac{\pi n}{l}x ,$$

where φ_n and ψ_n are respectively the Fourier coefficients of the functions $\varphi(x)$ and $\psi(x)$. By insertion of this series in (2-3.42) we obtain, with the aid of the corresponding addition theorem for the trigonometric functions,

$$u(x, t) = \sum_{n=1}^{\infty}\left(\varphi_n \cos\frac{\pi n}{l}at + \frac{l}{\pi na}\psi_n \sin\frac{\pi n}{l}at\right)\sin\frac{\pi n}{l}x , \tag{2-3.43}$$

which is exactly the representation given by the method of separation of variables.

Formula (2-3.43) therefore is valid under the same assumptions as (2-3.42) (see Section 2-3 § 1), which was derived under the conditions that $\Phi(x)$ is twice and $\Psi(x)$ is once continuously differentiable.

With regard to the functions $\varphi(x)$ and $\psi(x)$, besides the differentiability conditions we still require that the following be satisfied:

$$\varphi(0) = \varphi(l) = 0 , \qquad \psi(0) = \psi(l) = 0 , \qquad \varphi''(0) = \varphi''(l) = 0 . \tag{2-3.44}$$

Thus Conditions 1 and 2 from the method of proof, while sufficient for the exact foundation of the method of separation of variables, depend on and contain additional conditions, in comparison with conditions which guarantee the existence of the solution.

For the foundation of the representation of the solution by a superposition of standing waves, we used the first method for the proof of the convergence of the series, since it did not depend on the special form of solution (2-3.42), which is applicable only for the solution of the simplest vibration problems. Furthermore, this method is carried over without difficulty to a series of other problems, although more stringent requirements are imposed on the initial functions.

4. Inhomogeneous equations

We shall now consider the inhomogeneous wave equation

$$u_{tt} = a^2 u_{xx} + f(x, t) , \qquad a^2 = \frac{k}{\rho} , \qquad 0 < x < l , \tag{2-3.45}$$

with the initial conditions

$$\begin{aligned} u(x, 0) &= \varphi(x) \\ u_t(x, 0) &= \psi(x) \end{aligned} \qquad 0 \leqq x \leqq l , \tag{2-3.46}$$

and the homogeneous boundary conditions

$$\begin{aligned} u(0, t) &= 0 \\ u(l, t) &= 0 \end{aligned} \qquad t > 0 . \tag{2-3.47}$$

We shall represent its solution as a Fourier series with respect to x:

$$u(x, t) = \sum_{n=1}^{\infty} u_n(t) \sin \frac{\pi n}{l} x , \tag{2-3.48}$$

in which t is considered as a parameter. For the determination of $u(x, t)$ we must determine $u_n(t)$. The function $f(x, t)$ and the initial conditions likewise can be written as a Fourier series:

$$\begin{aligned} f(x, t) &= \sum_{n=1}^{\infty} f_n(t) \sin \frac{\pi n}{l} x \qquad & f_n(t) &= \frac{2}{l} \int_0^l f(\xi, t) \sin \frac{\pi n}{l} \xi d\xi , \\ \varphi(x) &= \sum_{n=1}^{\infty} \varphi_n \sin \frac{\pi n}{l} x & \varphi_n &= \frac{2}{l} \int_0^l \varphi(\xi) \sin \frac{\pi n}{l} \xi d\xi , \\ \psi(x) &= \sum_{n=1}^{\infty} \psi_n \sin \frac{\pi n}{l} x & \psi_n &= \frac{2}{l} \int_0^l \psi(\xi) \sin \frac{\pi n}{l} \xi d\xi . \end{aligned} \tag{2-3.49}$$

If we insert (2-3.48) into the original Eq. (2-3.45) we obtain

$$\sum_{n=1}^{\infty} \sin \frac{\pi n}{l} x \left\{ - a^2 \left(\frac{\pi n}{l} \right)^2 u_n(t) - \ddot{u}_n(t) + f_n(t) \right\} = 0 .$$

This relation is satisfied if all the coefficients of the series development vanish, i.e., if

$$\ddot{u}_n(t) + \left(\frac{\pi n}{l} \right)^2 a^2 u_n(t) = f_n(t) . \tag{2-3.50}$$

Therefore, we have obtained for the determination of $u_n(t)$ an ordinary differential equation with constant coefficients. The initial conditions read

$$u(x, 0) = \varphi(x) = \sum_{n=1}^{\infty} u_n(0) \sin \frac{\pi n}{l} x = \sum_{n=1}^{\infty} \varphi_n \sin \frac{\pi n}{l} x ,$$

$$u_t(x, 0) = \psi(x) = \sum_{n=1}^{\infty} \dot{u}_n(0) \sin \frac{\pi n}{l} x = \sum_{n=1}^{\infty} \psi_n \sin \frac{\pi n}{l} x .$$

Hence it follows that

$$\begin{aligned} u_n(0) &= \varphi_n \\ \dot{u}_n(0) &= \psi_n . \end{aligned} \tag{2-3.51}$$

These auxiliary conditions completely define the solution of Eq. (2-3.50). Now $u_n(t)$ can be represented in the form

$$u_n(t) = u_n^{(I)}(t) + u_n^{(II)}(t) ,$$

where

$$u_n^{(I)}(t) = \frac{l}{\pi n a}\int_0^t \sin\frac{\pi n}{l}a(t-\tau)\cdot f_n(\tau)d\tau \tag{2-3.52}$$

represents a solution of the inhomogeneous equation with homogeneous initial conditions,[17] and

$$u_n^{(II)}(t) = \varphi_n \cos\frac{\pi n}{l}at + \frac{l}{\pi n a}\psi_n \sin\frac{\pi n}{l}at \tag{2-3.53}$$

is a solution of the homogeneous equation with the prescribed initial conditions. Consequently, the solution sought has the form

$$\begin{aligned} u(x,t) = &\sum_{n=1}^{\infty}\frac{l}{\pi n a}\int_0^t \sin\frac{\pi n}{l}a(t-\tau)\sin\frac{\pi n}{l}x\cdot f_n(\tau)d\tau \\ &+\sum_{n=1}^{\infty}\left(\varphi_n\cos\frac{\pi n}{l}at + \frac{l}{\pi n a}\psi_n\sin\frac{\pi n}{l}at\right)\sin\frac{\pi n}{l}x . \end{aligned} \tag{2-3.54}$$

The second sum solves the problem of a freely vibrating string with prescribed initial conditions and was completely investigated earlier. The first sum by contrast represents the forced vibrations of the string under the influence of an external force with homogeneous initial conditions. With the use of (2-3.49) for $f_n(t)$ we find

$$\begin{aligned} u^{(I)}(x,t) &= \int_0^t\int_0^l\left\{\frac{2}{l}\sum_{n=1}^{\infty}\frac{l}{\pi n a}\sin\frac{\pi n}{l}a(t-\tau)\sin\frac{\pi n}{l}x\sin\frac{\pi n}{l}\xi\right\}f(\xi,\tau)d\xi d\tau \\ &= \int_0^t\int_0^l G(x,\xi,t-\tau)f(\xi,\tau)d\xi d\tau \end{aligned} \tag{5-3.55}$$

with

$$G(x,\xi,t-\tau) = \frac{2}{\pi a}\sum_{n=1}^{\infty}\frac{1}{n}\sin\frac{\pi n}{l}a(t-\tau)\sin\frac{\pi n}{l}x\sin\frac{\pi n}{l}\xi . \tag{2-3.56}$$

To determine the physical significance of this solution, we first assume that the function $f(\xi,\tau)$, in a sufficiently small neighborhood

$$\xi_0 \leqq \xi \leqq \xi_0 + \Delta\xi , \qquad \tau_0 \leqq \tau \leqq \tau_0 + \Delta\tau$$

of a point $M_0(\xi_0, \tau_0)$, is different from zero and vanishes outside this neighborhood. The function $\rho f(\xi,\tau)$ represents the force density of the acting force; the force developed in the interval $(\xi_0, \xi_0+\Delta\xi)$ is therefore equal to

$$F(\tau) = \rho\int_{\xi_0}^{\xi_0+\Delta\xi} f(\xi,\tau)d\xi .$$

17 See the comments at the end of this section.

Then

$$I = \int_{\tau_0}^{\tau_0+\Delta\tau} F(\tau)d\tau = \rho\int_{\tau_0}^{\tau_0+\Delta\tau}\int_{\xi_0}^{\xi_0+\Delta\xi} f(\xi, \tau)d\xi d\tau$$

is the impulse of the force during the time $\Delta\tau$. By applying the mean-value theorem to the expression

$$u(x, t) = \int_0^t\int_0^l G(x, \xi, t-\tau) f(\xi, \tau)d\xi d\tau = \int_{\tau_0}^{\tau_0+\Delta\tau}\int_{\xi_0}^{\xi_0+\Delta\xi} G(x, \xi, t-\tau) f(\xi, \tau)d\xi d\tau$$

we obtain

$$u(x, t) = G(x, \bar{\xi}, t - \bar{\tau})\int_{\tau_0}^{\tau_0+\Delta\tau}\int_{\xi_0}^{\xi_0+\Delta\xi} f(\xi, \tau)d\xi d\tau \qquad (2\text{-}3.57)$$

with

$$\xi_0 \leqq \bar{\xi} \leqq \xi_0 + \Delta\xi\,, \qquad \tau_0 \leqq \bar{\tau} \leqq \tau_0 + \Delta\tau\,.$$

If in formula (2-3.57) we take the limit as $\Delta\xi \to 0$ and $\Delta\tau \to 0$, we obtain the function

$$u(x, t) = G(x, \xi_0, t - \tau_0)\frac{I}{\rho}\,, \qquad (2\text{-}3.58)$$

which can be regarded as the effect of an instantaneously concentrated impulse I.

If the function $(1/\rho)G(x, \xi, t-\tau)$, which represents the effect of a concentrated impulse, is known, then it is immediately clear that the effect of a continuously distributed force $f(x, t)$ can be represented by

$$u(x, t) = \int_0^l\int_0^t G(x, \xi, t-\tau) f(\xi, \tau)d\xi d\tau\,. \qquad (2\text{-}3.59)$$

This representation coincides with the representation (2-3.55) above.

The function describing the action of concentrated impulses was investigated for the case of the infinite straight line in the preceding paragraphs. We recall (see Figure 10) that it is piecewise constant, and within the upper angle for the point (ξ, τ) this function is equal to $(1/2a)(I/\rho)$; everywhere outside of this angle the function is equal to zero. From this the function describing the action of concentrated impulses for the bounded string $(0, l)$ can be found by the odd continuation with respect to the points $x = 0$ and $x = l$.

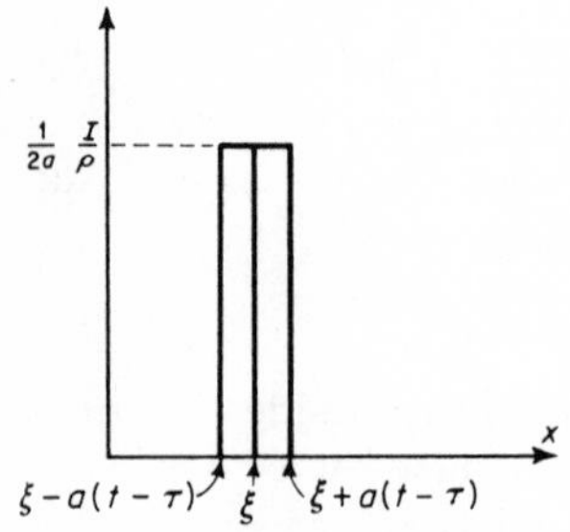

FIG. 23.

Let t be so near to τ that the influence of the reflection at $x = 0$ and $x = l$ still does not appear. At this time the influence function takes the form shown in Figure 23. If we develop it in a Fourier series with respect to $\sin(\pi n/l)x$, in which we set $I = \rho$, its Fourier coefficients are then equal to

$$A_n = \frac{2}{l}\int_0^l G(\alpha, \xi, t-\tau)\sin\frac{\pi n}{l}\alpha d\alpha = \frac{1}{al}\int_{\xi-a(t-\tau)}^{\xi+a(t-\tau)} \sin\frac{\pi n}{l}\alpha d\alpha$$

$$= \frac{1}{a\pi n}\left\{\cos\frac{\pi n}{l}[\xi - a(t-\tau)] - \cos\frac{\pi n}{l}[\xi + a(t-\tau)]\right\}$$

$$= \frac{2}{a\pi n}\sin\frac{\pi n}{l}\xi\,\sin\frac{\pi n}{l}a(t-\tau)\,.$$

From this we obtain the formula

$$G(x,\xi,t-\tau) = \frac{2}{\pi a}\sum_{n=1}^{\infty}\frac{1}{n}\sin\frac{\pi n}{l}a(t-\tau)\sin\frac{\pi n}{l}x\cdot\sin\frac{\pi n}{l}\xi\,. \qquad (2\text{-}3.60)$$

Thus it agrees with the formula (2-3.56) found by the method of separation of variables.

For values $t \geqq \tau$, where the influence of the fixed ends has already appeared, there are difficulties; in the construction of the influence function by means of characteristics its description by Fourier series remains to be obtained, even in this case.

We shall limit ourselves here to a formal scheme of solution, without going more precisely into the conditions for the applicability of the formulas obtained.

We shall now consider an ordinary inhomogeneous linear differential equation with constant coefficients

$$L(u) = u^{(n)} + p_1u^{(n-1)} + \cdots + p_{n-1}u^{(1)} + p_nu = f(t)\,, \qquad u^{(i)} = \frac{d^iu}{dt^i} \qquad (1^*)$$

with the initial conditions

$$u^{(i)}(0) = 0\,, \qquad i = 0, 1, \cdots, n-1\,. \qquad (2^*)$$

Its solution is given by

$$u(t) = \int_0^t U(t-\tau)f(\tau)d\tau\,, \qquad (3^*)$$

where $U(t)$ is the solution of the homogeneous equation

$$L(U) = 0\,,$$

with the initial conditions

$$U^{(i)}(0) = 0\,, \qquad i = 0, 1, \cdots, n-2$$
$$U^{(n-1)}(0) = 1\,. \qquad (4^*)$$

If we calculate the derivatives of $u(t)$ by differentiation of the right side of (3^*) with respect to t, we find

$$\begin{aligned}
u^{(1)}(t) &= \int_0^t U^{(1)}(t-\tau)f(\tau)d\tau + U(0)f(t)\,, && U(0) = 0\\
u^{(2)}(t) &= \int_0^t U^{(2)}(t-\tau)f(\tau)d\tau + U^{(1)}(0)f(t)\,, && U'(0) = 0\\
&\cdots\cdots\cdots && \qquad (5^*)\\
u^{(n-1)}(t) &= \int_0^t U^{(n-1)}(t-\tau)f(\tau)\,d\tau + U^{(n-2)}(0)f(t)\,, && U^{(n-2)}(0) = 0\\
u^{(n)}(t) &= \int_0^t U^{(n)}(t-\tau)f(\tau)d\tau + U^{(n-1)}(0)f(t)\,, && U^{(n-1)}(0) = 1\,.
\end{aligned}$$

If we substitute (5*) into (1*), we find

$$L(u) = \int_0^t L[U(t-\tau)]f(\tau)d\tau + f(t) = f(t)\,;$$

i.e., the differential equation is satisfied. Obviously, $u(t)$ also satisfies the initial conditions (2*).

For the function $U(t)$ and formula (3*) we can easily find a clear physical interpretation. Usually $u(t)$ designates the displacement of a given system and $f(t)$ is the force acting on this system. Our system is in a state of rest for $t < 0$. Let the displacement of the system be given by the non-negative function $f_\varepsilon(t)$; let $f_\varepsilon(t)$ be different from 0 only at the time $0 < t < \varepsilon$. We denote the impulse of this force by

$$I = \int_0^t f(\tau)d\tau\,.$$

Further let $u_\varepsilon(t)$ be the function corresponding to $f_\varepsilon(t)$. Therefore we can consider ε as a parameter and set $I = 1$. Obviously then, as $\varepsilon \to 0$, $\lim_{\varepsilon\to 0} u_\varepsilon(t)$ exists independent of the selection $f_\varepsilon(t)$. Also one easily recognizes that this limit value is equal to the function $U(t)$ defined above; namely

$$U(t) = \lim_{\varepsilon\to 0} u_\varepsilon(t)\,,$$

if $U(t) \equiv 0$ for $t < 0$. $U(t)$ is called the influence function of the instantaneous impulses.

If we apply the mean-value theorem to (3*) we obtain

$$u_\varepsilon(t) = U(t-\tau_\varepsilon^*)\int_0^\varepsilon f(\tau)d\tau = U(t-\tau_\varepsilon^*)\,, \qquad 0 \leqq \tau_\varepsilon^* \leqq \varepsilon < t\,.$$

By passage to the limit as $\varepsilon \to 0$ we then obtain the limit value

$$\lim_{\varepsilon\to 0} u_\varepsilon(t) = \lim_{\varepsilon\to 0} U(t-\tau_\varepsilon^*) = U(t)\,,$$

which therefore proves our assertion.

We now want to represent the solution of the inhomogeneous equation by $U(t)$, the influence function of the instantaneous impulses. For this purpose we divide the interval $(0, t)$ by points τ_i into equal intervals

$$\Delta\tau = \frac{t}{m}$$

and write $f(t)$ in the form

$$f(t) = \sum_{i=1}^m f_i(t)\,,$$

where

$$\begin{aligned} f_i(t) &= 0 \qquad \text{for} \quad t < \tau_i \quad \text{and} \quad t \geqq \tau_{i+1} \\ &= f(t) \qquad \text{for} \quad \tau_i \leqq t < \tau_{i+1}\,. \end{aligned}$$

Then

$$u(t) = \sum_{i=1}^{m} u_i(t),$$

where $u_i(t)$ is the solution of the equation $L(u_i) = f_i$ with homogeneous initial conditions.

If m is sufficiently large, $u_i(t)$ can be regarded as the influence function of the instantaneous impulse of intensity

$$I = f_i(\tau_i)\Delta\tau = f(\tau_i)\Delta\tau,$$

so that for $u(t)$ we have

$$u(t) = \sum_{i=1}^{m} U(t-\tau_i) f(\tau_i)\Delta\tau \underset{\Delta\tau\to 0}{\longrightarrow} \int_0^t U(t-\tau) f(\tau) d\tau$$

and arrive at the formula

$$u(t) = \int_0^t U(t-\tau) f(\tau) d\tau .$$

This shows that the influence of a continuously distributed force can be represented by the superposition of the influences caused by the instantaneous impulses.

In the case considered above, $u_n^{(1)}$ satisfies Eq. (2-3.50) and the conditions $u_n(0) = \dot{u}_n(0)$. For $U(t)$ we have

$$\ddot{U} + \left(\frac{\pi n}{l}\right)^2 a^2 U = 0, \qquad U(0) = 0, \qquad \dot{U}(0) = 1,$$

so that

$$U(t) = \frac{l}{\pi n a} \sin \frac{\pi n}{l} a t .$$

From this and from (3*) there results

$$u_n^{(1)}(t) = \int_0^t U(t-\tau) f_n(\tau) = \frac{l}{\pi n a} \int_0^t \sin \frac{\pi n}{l} a(t-\tau) f_n(\tau) d\tau .$$

The integral representation (3*) derived above for the solution of the ordinary differential Eq. (1*) has the same physical significance as formula (2-3.59), which gave the integral representation of the solution of the homogeneous wave equation.

5. The general first boundary-value problem

The general first boundary-value problem for the wave equation reads: Find a solution of the differential equation

$$u_{tt} = a^2 u_{xx} + f(x, t), \qquad 0 < x < l, \ t > 0 \tag{2-3.45}$$

with the auxiliary conditions

$$\begin{aligned} u(x, 0) &= \varphi(x) \\ u_t(x, 0) &= \psi(x) \end{aligned} \tag{2-3.46}$$

$$u(0, t) = \mu_1(t)$$
$$u(l, t) = \mu_2(t) \,. \tag{2-3.47}$$

First, by means of

$$u(x, t) = U(x, t) + v(x, t)$$

we introduce a new function $v(x, t)$. This then signifies the difference of the function $u(x, t)$ from a function $U(x, t)$ still to be determined.

The function $v(x, t)$ can be determined as a solution of the wave equation

$$v_{tt} = a^2 v_{xx} + \bar{f}(x, t) \,, \qquad \bar{f}(x, t) = f(x, t) - [U_{tt} - a^2 U_{xx}]$$

with the auxiliary conditions

$$v(x, 0) = \bar{\varphi}(x) \,, \qquad v_t(x, 0) = \bar{\psi}(x)$$
$$v(0, t) = \bar{\mu}_1(t) \,, \qquad v(l, t) = \bar{\mu}_2(t)$$
$$\bar{\varphi}(x) = \varphi(x) - U(x, 0) \,, \qquad \bar{\psi}(x) = \psi(x) - U_1(x, 0)$$
$$\bar{\mu}_1(t) = \mu_1(t) - U(0, t) \,, \qquad \bar{\mu}_2(t) = \mu_2(t) - U(l, t) \,.$$

Now we choose $U(x, t)$ such that

$$\bar{\mu}_1(t) = 0 \quad \text{and} \quad \bar{\mu}_2(t) = 0 \,.$$

Thus it suffices to set

$$U(x, t) = \mu_1(t) + \frac{x}{l}[\mu_2(t) - \mu_1(t)] \,.$$

Hence the general boundary-value problem for $u(x, t)$ has been reduced to a boundary-value problem for $v(x, t)$ with homogeneous boundary conditions which we have already solved (see Section 2-3 § 4).

6. Boundary-value problems with stationary inhomogeneities

A very important class of problems is formed by the boundary-value problems with stationary inhomogeneities. In these problems the boundary conditions and the right side of the equation are independent of the time t:

$$u_{tt} = a^2 u_{xx} + f_0(x) \tag{2-3.45'}$$

$$u(x, 0) = \varphi(x)$$
$$u_t(x, 0) = \psi(x) \tag{2-3.46}$$

$$u(0, t) = u_1$$
$$u(l, t) = u_2 \,. \tag{2-3.47'}$$

In this case we seek the solution of the problem in the form

$$u(x, t) = \bar{u}(x) + v(x, t)$$

where $\bar{u}(x)$, the stationary state (the static deflection) of the string is determined by the conditions

$$a^2\bar{u}''(x) + f_0(x) = 0$$
$$\bar{u}(0) = u_1$$
$$\bar{u}(l) = u_2$$

while $v(x, t)$ designates the displacement from the stationary state. It is easily seen that

$$\bar{u}(x) = u_1 + (u_2 - u_1)\frac{x}{l} + \frac{x}{l}\int_0^x d\xi_1 \int_0^{\xi_1} \frac{f_0(\xi_2)}{a^2} d\xi_2 - \int_0^x d\xi_1 \int_0^{\xi_1} \frac{f_0(\xi_2)}{a^2} d\xi_2 \,.$$

If, in particular, $f_0 = \text{const.}$, then

$$\bar{u}(x) = u_1 + (u_2 - u_1)\frac{x}{l} + \frac{f_0}{2a^2}(lx - x^2)\,.$$

The function $v(x, t)$ obviously satisfies the homogeneous equation

$$v_{tt} = a^2 v_{xx}$$

with the homogeneous boundary conditions

$$v(0, t) = 0$$
$$v(l, t) = 0$$

and the initial conditions

$$v(x, 0) = \bar{\varphi}(x)\,, \qquad \bar{\varphi}(x) = \varphi(x) - \bar{u}(x)\,, \qquad v_t(x, 0) = \psi(x)\,.$$

Hence v is the solution of the simplest boundary value problem treated in Section 2-3 § 1.

In the derivation of the equation of the vibrating string and for a series of other cases the influence of the force of gravity was not considered. From the above it follows that it is sufficient to assume the displacement from the stationary state instead of the direct influences of the force of gravity (and in general for time-independent forces).

We shall now give the solution of the simplest problem of this type with homogeneous initial conditions:

$$u_{tt} = a^2 u_{xx} + f_0(x) \tag{2-3.45''}$$
$$u(x, 0) = 0\,, \qquad u_t(x, 0) = 0 \tag{2-3.46''}$$
$$u(0, t) = u_1\,, \qquad u(l, t) = u_2\,. \tag{2-3.47''}$$

For $v(x, t)$ the problem then reads

$$v_{tt} = a^2 v_{xx} \qquad v(x, 0) = \varphi(x) = -\bar{u}(x)\,, \qquad v(0, t) = 0$$
$$v_t(x, 0) = 0\,, \qquad v(l, t) = 0\,.$$

We can easily see that for the solution of this problem it is not necessary to know the exact analytic expression for $\bar{u}(x)$.

According to formula (2-3.17), $v(x, t)$ has the form

$$v(x, t) = \sum_{n=1}^{\infty} (A_n \cos a\sqrt{\lambda_n}t + B_n \sin a\sqrt{\lambda_n}t) X_n(x)$$

where

$$X_n(x) = \sin \sqrt{\lambda_n} x , \quad \sqrt{\lambda_n} = \frac{\pi n}{l}$$

are the eigenfunctions of the boundary value problem defined by

$$X'' + \lambda X = 0 \tag{2-3.8}$$

$$X(0) = 0 , \quad X(l) = 0 . \tag{2-3.10}$$

From the initial conditions it follows that

$$B_n = 0$$

and

$$A_n = -\frac{2}{l}\int_0^l \bar{u}(x) X_n(x) dx .$$

The following method is appropriate for the calculation of these integrals. From (2-2.8) we find

$$X_n(x) = -\frac{1}{\lambda_n} X_n''(x) .$$

We introduce this expression into the formula for A_n and integrate twice by parts:

$$A_n = \frac{2}{l\lambda_n}\int_0^l \bar{u}(x) X_n''(x) dx = \frac{2}{l\lambda_n}\left\{ \bar{u} X_n'(x) \Big|_0^l - \bar{u}' X_n \Big|_0^l + \int_0^l \bar{u}'' X_n(x) dx \right\} ,$$

from which, by taking into consideration the differential equation and the boundary conditions for $\bar{u}(x)$, there follows

$$A_n = \frac{2}{l\lambda_n}\left[u_2 X_n'(l) - u_1 X_n'(0) - \int_0^l \frac{f_0(x)}{a^2} X_n(x) dx \right]$$

or

$$A_n = \frac{2}{\pi n}[u_2(-1)^n - u_1] - \frac{2l}{\pi n^2}\int_0^l \frac{f_0(x)}{a^2} X_n(x) dx .$$

In particular we find for the homogeneous equation ($f_0(x) = 0$)

$$A_n = \frac{2}{l\sqrt{\lambda_n}}[u_2(-1)^n - u_1] = \frac{2}{\pi n}[u_2(-1)^n - u_1] .$$

With the aid of this method it is possible to calculate the Fourier coefficients also for the boundary conditions of the second and third type and for the boundary-value problems of the inhomogeneous string

$$\frac{d}{dx}\left[k(x) \frac{dX}{dx} \right] + \lambda \rho(x) X = 0 ,$$

if the eigenfunctions and the eigenvalues are known.

7. Problems without initial conditions

As shown above, the general first boundary-value problem for the equation of the vibrating string can be reduced to the solution of an inhomogeneous equation with homogeneous boundary conditions. However, it often happens that the solution of a problem by this method is more difficult than by the direct solution.

Thus it is important in the investigation of the influences of boundary conditions to find some specific solution (of the homogeneous equation) which satisfies the prescribed boundary conditions, since the calculation of the necessary corrections owing to the initial conditions leads to the solution of the same equation with homogeneous boundary conditions.

A very important class of problems for the study of boundary influences is composed of the so-called problems without initial conditions.

That is, if the boundary conditions have acted sufficiently long, the influence of the initial conditions vanishes owing to the friction which occurs in every real physical system. We arrive quite naturally at the following problem (1) without initial conditions:

Find the solution of the equation

$$u_{tt} = a^2 u_{xx} - \alpha u_t \,, \qquad \alpha > 0 \tag{2-3.61}$$

with the prescribed boundary conditions

$$u(0, t) = \mu_1(t) \,, \qquad u(l, t) = \mu_2(t) \,.$$

The term αu_t on the right side corresponds to a frictional force proportional to the velocity.

We shall first investigate the consequences of periodic boundary influences:

$$u(l, t) = A \cos \omega t \qquad \text{or} \qquad u(l, t) = B \sin \omega t \,, \tag{2-3.62}$$

$$u(0, t) = 0 \,. \tag{2-3.63}$$

For the following, the complex representation of the boundary conditions is found to be advantageous:

$$u(l, t) = Ae^{i\omega t} \,. \tag{2-3.64}$$

If

$$u(x, t) = u^{(1)}(x, t) + iu^{(2)}(x, t)$$

satisfies Eq. (2-3.61) with the boundary conditions (2-3.62) and (2-3.63), then $u^{(1)}(x, t)$ and $u^{(2)}(x, t)$, the real and imaginary parts of $u(x, t)$, separately satisfy the same equation (since it is linear); the condition (2-3.63) and the boundary conditions at $x = l$ lead to

$$u^{(1)}(l, t) = A \cos \omega t \,, \qquad u^{(2)}(l, t) = A \sin \omega t \,.$$

We therefore seek the solution of the problem

$$\begin{aligned} u_{tt} &= a^2 u_{xx} - \alpha u_t \\ u(0, t) &= 0 \\ u(l, t) &= Ae^{i\omega t} \,. \end{aligned} \tag{2-3.65}$$

With the expression

$$u(x, t) = X(x)e^{i\omega t}$$

e following problem for $X(x)$:

$$X'' + k^2 X = 0\,, \qquad k^2 = \frac{\omega^2}{a^2} - i\alpha\frac{\omega}{a^2} \tag{2-3.66}$$

$$X(0) = 0 \tag{2-3.67}$$

$$X(l) = A\,. \tag{2-3.68}$$

From Eq. (2-3.66) and the boundary condition (2-3.67) we find

$$X(x) = C \sin kx\,.$$

The condition at $x = l$ gives

$$C = \frac{A}{\sin kl}\,. \tag{2-3.69}$$

Thus

$$X(x) = A\frac{\sin kx}{\sin kl} = X_1(x) + iX_2(x)\,, \tag{2-3.70}$$

where $X_1(x)$ and $X_2(x)$ are the real and imaginary parts of $X(x)$.

We can then represent the sought solution in the form

$$u(x, t) = [X_1(x) + iX_2(x)]e^{i\omega t} = u^{(1)}(x, t) + u^{(2)}(x, t)$$

with

$$u^{(1)}(x, t) = X_1(x)\cos\omega t - X_2(x)\sin\omega t$$
$$u^{(2)}(x, t) = X_1(x)\sin\omega t + X_2(x)\cos\omega t\,.$$

By passage to the limit as $\alpha \to 0$ we obtain

$$k = \lim_{\alpha\to 0} k = \frac{\omega}{a} \tag{2-3.71}$$

and correspondingly

$$\bar{u}^{(1)}(x, t) = \lim_{\alpha\to 0} u^{(1)}(x, t) = A\frac{\sin(\omega/a)x}{\sin(\omega/a)l}\cos\omega t\,, \tag{2-3.72}$$

$$\bar{u}^{(2)}(x, t) = \lim_{\alpha\to 0} u^{(2)}(x, t) = A\frac{\sin(\omega/a)x}{\sin(\omega/a)l}\sin\omega t\,. \tag{2-3.73}$$

The functions $\bar{u}^{(1)}(x, t)$ and $\bar{u}^{(2)}(x, t)$ are obviously solutions of the equation

$$u_{tt} = a^2 u_{xx}$$

with the boundary conditions (2)

$$\bar{u}^{(1)}(0, t) = 0 \qquad\qquad \bar{u}^{(2)}(0, t) = 0$$
$$\bar{u}^{(1)}(l, t) = A\cos\omega t \qquad \bar{u}^{(2)}(l, t) = A\sin\omega t\,.$$

A solution for $\alpha = 0$ does not always exist. Thus if the frequency ω of the forced vibrations coincides with a characteristic frequency ω_n of the vibrating string with fixed ends, that is,

$$\omega = \omega_n = \frac{\pi n}{l} a ,$$

then the denominator vanishes in the equation for $\bar{u}^{(1)}$ and $\bar{u}^{(2)}$ and no solution exists for the problem considered here.

This fact has a simple physical significance, namely: for $\omega = \omega_n$ there occurs a resonance. At a given time $t = t_0$ the amplitude grows without bound. With the existence of friction ($\alpha \neq 0$) a vibration process is possible for each ω.

If $f(t)$ is a periodic function which can be represented by the series

$$f(t) = \frac{A_0}{2} + \sum_{n=1}^{\infty} (A_n \cos \omega n t + B_n \sin \omega n t) , \tag{2-3.74}$$

where ω is the lowest frequency and A_n, B_n are the Fourier coefficients, then the solution of the equation for $\alpha = 0$ has the form

$$\bar{u}(x, t) = \frac{A_0}{2l} x + \sum_{n=1}^{\infty} (A_n \cos \omega n t + B_n \sin \omega n t) \frac{\sin (\omega n / a) x}{\sin (\omega n / a) l} ,$$

provided none of the frequencies ω_n coincides with the characteristic frequencies of the bounded string.

If $f(t)$ is a non-periodic function, we represent it by a Fourier integral and the solution is obtained in integral form in a corresponding manner.

We note that the solution of the problem without initial conditions for $\alpha = 0$ is not uniquely defined if no further additional conditions are furnished. Thus if one adds to any solution of this problem even an arbitrary linear combination of standing waves

$$\sum \left(A_n \cos \frac{\pi n}{l} a t + B_n \sin \frac{\pi n}{l} a t \right) \sin \frac{\pi n}{l} x ,$$

where A_n and B_n are arbitrary constants, then the sum so obtained likewise satisfies the equation and the boundary conditions.

In order that problem (1) for $\alpha = 0$ be uniquely solvable we introduce the additional condition on the vanishing friction:

We say a solution of the problem (2) has vanishing friction if it is the limit value of a solution of problem (1) as $\alpha \to 0$. The problem for a fixed end $x = l$ and with a prescribed boundary condition $u(0, t) = \mu(t)$ at $x = 0$ is solved in a similar manner.

The solution of the general problem without initial conditions

$$u(0, t) = \mu_1(t) , \qquad u(l, t) = \mu_2(t)$$

is calculated as the sum of two summands, each of which satisfies an inhomogeneous boundary condition.

We shall now prove the uniqueness of a bounded solution of the problem without initial conditions for Eq. (2-3.61). For this purpose we shall assume that the solution and its derivatives up to and including the second order are continuous in the region $0 \leqq x \leqq l$, $-\infty < t < t_0$ when the boundary values

$$u(0, t) = \mu_1(t)\,, \qquad u(l, t) = \mu_2(t)$$

are defined for $-\infty < t < t_0$.

Let $u_1(x, t)$ and $u_2(x, t)$ be two bounded solutions of problem (1) under consideration,

$$|u_1| < M\,, \qquad |u_2| < M\,,$$

where $M > 0$ is a fixed number.

The difference

$$v(x, t) = u_1(x, t) - u_2(x, t)$$

of these functions is likewise bounded ($|v| < 2M$) and satisfies Eq. (2-3.61) as well as the homogeneous boundary conditions

$$v(0, t) = 0\,, \qquad v(l, t) = 0\,.$$

The Fourier coefficients for v

$$v_n(t) = \frac{2}{l}\int_0^l v(x, t)\sin\frac{\pi n}{l}x dx$$

obviously satisfy the equation

$$\ddot{v}_n + \alpha\dot{v}_n + \omega_n^2 v_n = 0\,, \qquad \omega_n = \frac{\pi n}{l}a\,, \tag{*}$$

since the second derivatives of $v(x, t)$ for $0 \leqq x \leqq l$ are continuous.

The general solution of (*) reads

$$v_n(t) = A_n e^{-q_n^{(1)}t} + B_n e^{-q_n^{(2)}t}\,, \tag{**}$$

where

$$q_n^{(1)} = -\frac{\alpha}{2} + \sqrt{\frac{\alpha^2}{4} - \omega_n^2}\,, \qquad q_n^{(2)} = -\frac{\alpha}{2} - \sqrt{\frac{\alpha^2}{4} - \omega_n^2}\,, \qquad \alpha > 0$$

are the roots of the characteristic equation. There are now two possible cases:

1. The roots are real and negative.
2. The roots are complex and possess a negative real part. From this it follows that every solution (**) of Eq. (*) either is identically zero or is such that its absolute value as $t \to -\infty$ becomes arbitrarily large. Now, however, $|v_n| < 4M$ is valid for all n so that $v_n \equiv 0$ for all n.

Hence we must have

$$v(x, t) \equiv 0 \quad \text{and} \quad u_1(x, t) \equiv u_2(x, t)\,,$$

from which the unique solvability of the problem (I) is proved under the given assumptions.

8. Action of a concentrated force

A string is set to vibrating under the action of a concentrated force which acts at the point $x = x_0$. If the force is distributed in a given interval

$(x_0 - \varepsilon,\ x_0 + \varepsilon)$ then the solution is found from formula (2-3.55). By passage to the limit as $\varepsilon \to 0$ we obtain also the solution for a concentrated force.

On the other hand we have seen in the derivation of the wave equation that at the point x_0 at which the concentrated force acts, a point of discontinuity of the first derivative occurs, whereas the function itself remains continuous. The solution $u(x, t)$ can be represented for such a displacement of the string by two different functions:

$$\begin{aligned} u(x, t) &= u_1(x, t) \quad \text{for} \quad 0 \leqq x \leqq x_0 \\ u(x, t) &= u_2(x, t) \quad \text{for} \quad x_0 \leqq x \leqq l\,. \end{aligned} \tag{2-3.75}$$

These functions must satisfy the equation

$$u_{tt} = a^2 u_{xx}\,, \tag{2-3.76}$$

the boundary and initial conditions

$$\begin{aligned} u_1(0, t) &= 0 \qquad u(x, 0) = \varphi(x) \\ u_2(l, t) &= 0 \qquad u_t(x, 0) = \psi(x)\,, \end{aligned} \tag{2-3.77}$$

the continuity condition at the point $x = x_0$

$$u_1(x_0, t) = u_2(x_0, t)\,, \tag{2-3.78}$$

and the condition which determines the magnitude of the jump in the first derivative at the point x_0 at which the concentrated force $f(t)$ acts:

$$\left.\frac{\partial u}{\partial x}\right|_{x_0-0}^{x_0+0} = \frac{\partial u_2}{\partial x}(x_0, t) - \frac{\partial u_1}{\partial x}(x_0, t) = -\frac{f(t)}{k}\,. \tag{2-3.79}$$

If the initial conditions are satisfied we need not investigate further. Thus if we find a particular solution of Eq. (2-3.76) which satisfies both the boundary conditions of (2-3.77) and the relations (2-3.78) and (2-3.79), the prescribed initial conditions can also be satisfied only when the corresponding solution of the homogeneous equation is added to this solution.

We shall now seek a solution of the equation for the special case

$$f(t) = A \cos \omega t \qquad -\infty < t < +\infty\,.$$

Hence only the boundary conditions are to be fulfilled in which we assume that the force has been acting from $t = -\infty$ on, i.e., it is a problem without initial conditions. For the solution we set

$$\begin{aligned} u_1(x, t) &= X_1(x) \cos \omega t \quad \text{for} \quad 0 \leqq x \leqq x_0 \\ u_2(x, t) &= X_2(x) \cos \omega t \quad \text{for} \quad x_0 \leqq x \leqq l\,. \end{aligned}$$

Then there follows from (2-3.76)

$$\begin{aligned} X_1'' + \left(\frac{\omega}{a}\right)^2 X_1 &= 0 \quad \text{for} \quad 0 \leqq x \leqq x_0 \\ X_2'' + \left(\frac{\omega}{a}\right)^2 X_2 &= 0 \quad \text{for} \quad x_0 \leqq x \leqq l\,. \end{aligned} \tag{2-3.80}$$

The functions X_1 and X_2 on the other hand must satisfy the boundary conditions

$$X_1(0) = 0\,, \qquad X_2(l) = 0 \tag{2-3.81}$$

which results from (2-3.77) and also satisfy the continuity and jump conditions

$$X_1(x_0) = X_2(x_0)\,, \qquad X_1'(x_0) - X_2'(x_0) = \frac{A}{k}\,, \tag{2-3.82}$$

which are derived from (2-3.78) and (2-3.79).

From Eq. (2-3.80) and the condition (2-3.81) we find

$$X_1(x) = C\sin\frac{\omega}{a}x\,, \qquad X_2(x) = D\sin\frac{\omega}{a}(l-x)\,.$$

The connection conditions (2-3.82) give

$$C\sin\frac{\omega}{a}x_0 - D\sin\frac{\omega}{a}(l-x_0) = 0\,,$$

$$C\frac{\omega}{a}\cos\frac{\omega}{a}x_0 + D\frac{\omega}{a}\cos\frac{\omega}{a}(l-x_0) = \frac{A}{k}\,.$$

Therefore, when the coefficients C and D are determined, we obtain

$$\begin{aligned} u(x,t) = u_1 &= \frac{Aa}{k\omega}\,\frac{\sin(\omega/a)(l-x_0)}{\sin(\omega/a)l}\sin\frac{\omega}{a}x\cos\omega t \qquad \text{for} \quad 0 \leqq x \leqq x_0 \\ = u_2 &= \frac{Aa}{k\omega}\,\frac{\sin(\omega/a)x_0}{\sin(\omega/a)l}\sin\frac{\omega}{a}(l-x)\cos\omega t \qquad \text{for} \quad x_0 \leqq x \leqq l\,. \end{aligned}$$

The solution for $f(t) = A\sin\omega t$ is written similarly.

Thus the problem for the case $f(t) = A\cos\omega t$ and $F(t) = A\sin\omega t$ is solved. Now if $f(t)$ is a periodic function, say

$$f(t) = \frac{\alpha_0}{2} + \sum_{n=1}^{\infty}(\alpha_n\cos\omega nt + \beta_n\sin\omega nt)\,,$$

where ω is the lowest frequency, then obviously we have[18]

$$\begin{aligned} u(x,t) = u_1 &= \frac{1}{k}\left\{\frac{\alpha_0 x}{2}\left(1-\frac{x_0}{l}\right) + \sum_{n=1}^{\infty}\frac{a\sin(\omega n/a)(l-x_0)}{\omega n\sin(\omega n/a)l}\sin\frac{\omega nx}{a}\right. \\ &\qquad \times(\alpha_n\cos\omega nt + \beta_n\sin\omega nt)\,, \qquad 0 \leqq x \leqq x_0 \\ = u_2 &= \frac{1}{k}\left\{\frac{\alpha_0 x_0}{2}\left(1-\frac{x}{l}\right) + \sum_{n=1}^{\infty}\frac{a\sin(\omega n/a)x_0}{\omega n\sin(\omega n/a)l}\sin\frac{\omega n(l-x)}{a}\right. \\ &\qquad \times(\alpha_n\cos\omega nt + \beta_n\sin\omega nt)\,, \qquad x_0 \leqq x \leqq l\,. \end{aligned} \tag{2-3.83}$$

If by contrast $f(t)$ is a nonperiodic function then in a corresponding

[18] The first summand of these sums corresponds to the stationary deflection which is determined by the force $f(t) = \alpha_0/2 = \text{const.}$ through the functions

$$\begin{aligned} u = u_1(x,t) = u_1(x) &= \frac{1}{k}\frac{\alpha_0}{2}x\left(1-\frac{x_0}{l}\right) \qquad \text{for} \quad 0 \leqq x \leqq x_0 \\ = u_2(x,t) = u_2(x) &= \frac{1}{k}\frac{\alpha_0}{2}x_0\left(1-\frac{x}{l}\right) \qquad \text{for} \quad x_0 \leqq x \leqq l\,. \end{aligned}$$

manner, in which we represent $f(t)$ by a Fourier integral, we obtain the solution in integral form.

The resonance phenomena which can occur in the process described by the function (2-3.83) are easy to overlook. Resonance occurs when a denominator in these functions is zero:

$$\sin\frac{\omega n l}{a} = 0\,, \qquad \omega n = \frac{\pi m}{l} a = \omega_m\,,$$

i.e., if the frequency spectrum of the driving force contains one of the characteristic frequencies of the vibration.

If one of the nodes of the standing wave is found at the point x_0 of action of the force which corresponds to the free vibration with frequency ω_n, then

$$\sin\frac{\omega_m}{a} x_0 = 0\,, \qquad \sin\frac{\omega_m}{a}(l - x_0) = 0\,.$$

Here the numerators of the corresponding summands for u are equal to zero, and no resonance occurs. However, if a displacement of the corresponding standing wave of frequency ω_m is found at the point of action of the force which acts with the frequency ω_m, then

$$\sin\frac{\omega_m}{a} x_0 = 1\,,$$

and the resonance phenomena is pronounced.

From the above calculations, we can formulate the following rule: In order to stimulate to resonance a string which remains under the influence of a concentrated acting force, it is necessary that the frequency ω be equal to one of the characteristic frequencies of the string and that the point of action of the force coincide with one of the maxima of the corresponding standing waves.

9. A general scheme for the method of separation of variables

The method of separation of variables can be used not only for the wave equation of a homogeneous string, $u_{tt} = a^2 u_{xx}$, but also for the wave equation of the inhomogeneous string,

$$L[u] = \frac{\partial}{\partial x}\left[k(x)\frac{\partial u}{\partial x}\right] - q(x)u = \rho(x)\frac{\partial^2 u}{\partial t^2}\,, \tag{2-3.84}$$

where $k, q,$ and ρ depend on x and are positive ($k > 0,\ \rho > 0,\ q > 0$).[19]

For example, consider the first boundary-value problem for Eq. 2-3.84:

$$u(0, t) = 0\,, \qquad u(l, t) = 0 \tag{2-3.85}$$

$$u(x, 0) = \varphi(x)\,, \qquad u_t(x, 0) = \psi(x)\,. \tag{2-3.86}$$

We shall seek the solution of this problem by the method of separation of

[19] The case that $k(x)$ vanishes at some point must be considered separately.

variables. Therefore, in a search for specific solutions as we did earlier, we shall first turn to the following auxiliary problems.

Find a nontrivial solution of Eq. (2-3.84) which satisfies the boundary conditions

$$u(0, t) = 0\,, \qquad u(l, t) = 0$$

and is representable as a product

$$u(x, t) = X(x)T(t)\,.$$

If we substitute this product expression into the partial differential equation, we obtain, with consideration of the boundary conditions for $X(x)$ and $T(t)$, the two ordinary differential equations

$$\frac{d}{dx}\left[k(x)\frac{dX}{dx}\right] - qX + \lambda\rho X = 0$$

$$T'' + \lambda T = 0\,.$$

For the determination of the function $X(x)$ we are led to the following eigenvalue problem:

Find those values of the parameter λ for which the boundary-value problem

$$L[X] + \lambda\rho X = 0 \tag{2-3.87}$$

$$X(0) = 0\,, \qquad X(l) = 0 \tag{2-3.88}$$

possesses nontrivial solutions, the so-called eigenvalues of the boundary value problem, as well as the corresponding solutions—the so-called eigenfunctions of the boundary-value problem.[20]

Next we shall formulate the basic properties of the eigenfunctions and the eigenvalues of the boundary-value problems (2-3.87) and (2-3.88) which are necessary for the following investigations.

1. There exists a denumerably infinite number of eigenvalues $\lambda_1 < \lambda_2 < \cdots < \lambda_n < \cdots$, which correspond to the nontrivial solutions of the boundary-value problem, the so-called eigenfunctions $X_1(x), X_2(x), \cdots, X_n(x) \cdots$.
2. For $q \geqq 0$ all the eigenvalues λ_n are positive.
3. The eigenfunctions in the interval $0 \leqq x \leqq l$ are orthogonal to each other with respect to the density function $\rho(x)$:

$$\int_0^l X_m(x)X_n(x)\rho(x)dx = 0\,, \qquad m \neq n\,. \tag{2-3.89}$$

4. (Development theorem of V. A. Steklov.) An arbitrary function $F(x)$

[20] For $\rho = \rho_0 =$ const., $k = k_0 =$ const. we obtain the boundary-value problem for the characteristic vibrations of a string bounded on both sides:

$$X'' + \mu X = 0\,, \qquad \mu = \frac{\rho_0}{k_0}\lambda$$

$$X(0) = 0\,, \qquad X(l) = 0\,,$$

which we have already investigated.

which is twice continuously differentiable and satisfies the boundary conditions $F(0) = F(l) = 0$ can be developed in a uniformly and absolutely convergent series with respect to the eigenfunctions $X_n(x)$:

$$F(x) = \sum_{n=1}^{\infty} F_n X_n(x) , \qquad F_n = \frac{1}{N_n}\int_0^l F(x)X_n(x)\rho(x)dx$$

$$N_n = \int_0^l X_n^2(x)\rho(x)dx . \tag{2-3.90}$$

The proof for propositions 1 and 4 are usually given in the theory of integral equations. We shall limit ourselves to the proof of propositions 2 and 3.

Before we prove these properties we shall first derive Green's formula. Let $u(x)$ and $v(x)$ be two functions which are twice differentiable in the interval $a < x < b$ and possess continuous first derivatives in $a \leqq x \leqq b$. Next we consider the expression

$$uL[v] - vL(u) = u(kv')' - v(ku')' = [k(uv' - vu')]' .$$

If we integrate this equation with respect to x from a to b, we obtain Green's formula

$$\int_a^b (uL[v] - vL[u])dx = k(uv' - vu')\Big|_a^b . \tag{2-3.91}$$

Proof of the third proposition. Let $X_m(x)$ and $X_n(x)$ be two eigenfunctions with the corresponding eigenvalues λ_m and λ_n. Then if $u = X_m(x)$, $v = X_n(x)$ are inserted in the formula (2-3.91) we obtain, by consideration of the boundary conditions (2-3.88),[21]

$$\int_0^l \{X_m L[X_n] - X_n L[X_m]\}dx = 0 , \qquad a = 0, \qquad b = l ,$$

from which because of Eq. (2-3.87) we obtain

$$(\lambda_n - \lambda_m)\int_0^l X_m(x)X_n(x)\rho(x)dx = 0 .$$

Therefore provided that $\lambda_n \neq \lambda_m$, we obtain the following relation

$$\int_0^l X_m(x)X_n(x)\rho(x)dx = 0 , \tag{2-3.92}$$

i.e., the eigenfunctions $X_m(x)$ and $X_n(x)$ are orthogonal to each other with respect to the density function $\rho(x)$. We shall now prove that every eigen-

[21] The derivatives $X_m'(x)$ and $X_n'(x)$ are continuous throughout $0 \leqq x \leqq l$, including the points $x = 0$ and $x = l$. Eq. (2-3.87) gives

$$k(x)X_m'(x) = \int_x^{x_0}(q - \lambda_m\rho)X_m dx + C .$$

From this follows in particular the existence of the derivative $X_m'(x)$ for $x = 0$ and $x = l$.

value to within a constant factor corresponds to only one eigenfunction.[22] Thus it follows that each eigenfunction is uniquely defined as a solution of a differential equation of the second order by the value of the function itself and by its first derivative at $x=0$. Let us assume the existence of two functions $\bar{X}$ and $\bar{\bar{X}}$ which correspond to one and the same λ and vanish at $x=0$, and consider the function

$$X^*(x)=\frac{\bar{X}'(0)}{\bar{\bar{X}}'(0)}\bar{\bar{X}}(x)\,.$$

Then we see that this function satisfies the same equation of the second order (2-3.87) and the same initial conditions as the function $\bar{X}(x)$:

$$X^*(0)=\frac{\bar{X}'(0)}{\bar{\bar{X}}'(0)}\bar{\bar{X}}(0)=0$$

$$\frac{dX^*}{dx}(0)=\frac{\bar{X}'(0)}{\bar{\bar{X}}'(0)}\bar{\bar{X}}'(0)=\bar{X}'(0)\,.$$

Therefore, we have shown that $X^*(x)=\bar{X}(x)$ and that

$$\bar{X}(x)=A\bar{\bar{X}}(x)\,,\qquad A=\frac{\bar{X}'(0)}{\bar{\bar{X}}'(0)}$$

is valid.

Let it be noted that for the proof, the condition $\bar{\bar{X}}'(0)\neq 0$ was used. This, however, is not necessarily satisfied, since the solution of the linear equation (2-3.87) determined by the initial conditions

$$\bar{\bar{X}}(0)=0\,,\qquad \bar{\bar{X}}'(0)=0$$

is identically zero and, therefore, no eigenfunction can exist.

If $X_n(x)$ is an eigenfunction corresponding to the eigenvalue λ_n, then $A_nX_n(x)$, where A_n is an arbitrary constant, because of the linearity and the homogeneity of the equation and the boundary conditions, is likewise an eigenfunction corresponding to λ_n.

We proved earlier that the class of eigenfunctions has been completely exhausted. The eigenfunctions which differ from each other only by constant factors will appear as not essentially different. However, in order to avoid ambiguity in the selection of factors the eigenfunctions will be normalized by

$$N_n=\int_0^l X_n^2(x)\rho(x)dx=1\,.$$

If, at the outset, an arbitrary eigenfunction $\hat{X}_n(x)$ does not satisfy this normalizing condition, then it can be normalized by multiplication by a suitable coefficient A_n:

[22] This property of the first boundary-value problem therefore depends on the fact that two linearly independent solutions of a differential equation of the second order cannot be at one and the same point equal to 0. This assertion is based on the boundary-value problem with homogeneous boundary conditions. With other boundary conditions (for example, with $X(0)=X(l)$, $X'(0)=X'(l)$) two different characteristic functions can be given which correspond to one and the same characteristic value.

$$A_n\hat{X}_n(x) = X_n(x)\,, \qquad A_n = \frac{1}{\sqrt{\int_0^l \hat{X}_n^2(x)\rho(x)dx}}\,.$$

Consequently, the eigenfunctions $X_n(x)$ of our boundary-value problems (2-3.87), (2-3.88), form a normalized orthogonal system (orthonormal system)

$$\int_0^l X_m(x)X_n(x)\rho(x)dx = \begin{cases} 0\,, & m \neq n \\ 1\,, & m = n\,. \end{cases}$$

Proof of the second proposition. Let $X_n(x)$ be the eigenfunction corresponding to the eigenvalue λ_n. Then,

$$L[X_n] = -\lambda_n\rho(x)X_n(x)\,.$$

Multiplication of both sides of this equation with $X_n(x)$ and integration with respect to x from 0 to l yields

$$\lambda_n\int_0^l X_n^2(x)\rho(x)dx = -\int_0^l X_n(x)L[X_n]dx$$

or

$$\lambda_n = -\int_0^l X_n\frac{d}{dx}\left[k(x)\frac{dX_n}{dx}\right]dx + \int_0^l q(x)X_n^2(x)dx\,,$$

since the function $X_n(x)$ was assumed to be normalized. We then obtain by partial integration and by use of the boundary conditions (2-3.88)

$$\begin{aligned} \lambda_n &= -X_nkX_n'\Big|_0^l + \int_0^l k(x)[X_n'(x)]^2dx + \int_0^l q(x)X_n^2(x)dx \\ &= \int_0^l k(x)[X_n'(x)]^2dx + \int_0^l q(x)X_n^2(x)dx\,, \end{aligned} \tag{2-3.93}$$

from which it follows that

$$\lambda_n > 0$$

since by assumption $k(x) > 0$ and $q(x) \geqq 0$.

We soon arrive at the calculation of the development coefficients of $F(x)$, but not at the proof of the development theorem itself, which we shall use in this case. Obviously,

$$F_n = \frac{\int_0^l \rho(x)F(x)X_n(x)dx}{\int_0^l \rho(x)X_n^2(x)dx}\,. \tag{2-3.94}$$

Now if we multiply both sides of the equation

$$F(x) = \sum_{n=1}^{\infty} F_nX_n(x)$$

by $\rho(x)X_n(x)$, integrate this expression with respect to x from 0 to l, and bear in mind the orthogonality of the eigenfunctions, we obtain directly the expression shown above for F_n (the Fourier coefficients).

We turn again to the partial differential Eq. (2-3.84). For $T(t)$ we obtain the equation

$$T'' + \lambda_n T = 0 \tag{2-3.95}$$

without any auxiliary conditions. Since λ_n is positive, its solution has the form

$$T_n(t) = A_n \cos \sqrt{\lambda_n} t + B_n \sin \sqrt{\lambda_n} t\,,$$

where A_n and B_n are arbitrary coefficients. Our auxiliary problem therefore has infinitely many solutions of the form

$$u_n(x, t) = T_n(t) X_n(x) = (A_n \cos \sqrt{\lambda_n} t + B_n \sin \sqrt{\lambda_n} t) X_n(x)\,.$$

The solution of the problem with prescribed initial conditions, from which we started at the beginning of this section shall be introduced in the form

$$u(x, t) = \sum_{n=1}^{\infty} (A_n \cos \sqrt{\lambda_n} t + B_n \sin \sqrt{\lambda_n} t) X_n(x)\,. \tag{2-3.96}$$

The formal scheme for satisfying the initial conditions (2-3.86) depends on the Steklov theorem (4) above. It is completely analogous for the homogeneous string, and we find from the equations

$$u(x, 0) = \varphi(x) = \sum_{n=1}^{\infty} A_n X_n(x)\,, \qquad u_t(x, 0) = \psi(x) = \sum_{n=1}^{\infty} B_n \sqrt{\lambda_n} X_n(x)$$

the relation

$$A_n = \varphi_n\,, \qquad B_n = \frac{\psi_n}{\sqrt{\lambda_n}}\,. \tag{2-3.97}$$

Hence φ_n and ψ_n are Fourier coefficients of the functions $\varphi(x)$ and $\psi(x)$ which occur in the development of these functions with respect to the orthogonal system of functions $\{X_n(x)\}$ with the weight factor $\rho(x)$.

Since we have limited ourselves here to the general scheme of separation of variables, the conditions for the applicability of this method, with regard to both the coefficient of the equation and the initial functions, have not been discussed.

The basic ideas of this method are due to V. A. Steklov.[23]

Problems

1. Determine the function $u(x, t)$ which describes the vibrations of a string $(0, l)$ fixed at the ends, if the string is excited in such a way that at the point $x = c$ it has been displaced to a magnitude equal to h from the original position (see Figure 24), i.e., let $u(c, 0) = h$.

2. A string fixed at both ends has been displaced at the point $x = c$ by a force F_0. Determine the string vibrations if the force at the initial moment ceases to act.

[23] *Report of the Kharkov Mathematical Society*, second series, Vol. 5, nos. 1 and 2 (1896); also *Fundamental Problems of Mathematical Physics*, Vol. 1 (1922).

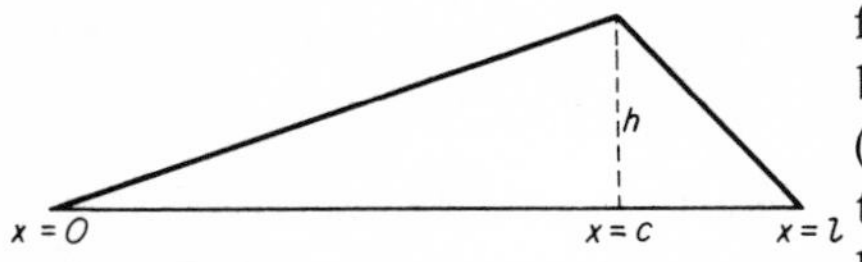

FIG. 24.

3. Determine the function $u(x, t)$ which describes the vibrations of a string $(0, l)$ fixed at both ends if the string is excited by an impulse K distributed in the interval $(c - \delta,\ c + \delta)$ for the case when the distribution is (a) uniform, (b) subject to the law $v_0 \cos (x - c)/2\delta$.

4. Determine the function $u(x, t)$ which describes the vibrations of a string fixed at both ends if the excitation results from impulse K acting at point $x = c$.

5. Prove the additivity of the energies of the individual harmonic vibrations for a vibration process with the boundary conditions $u = 0,\ u_x = 0$. Consider also the case of the boundary condition $u_x + hu = 0$ (all of the series occurring are assumed to be uniformly convergent). Calculate the energies of the individual harmonic vibrations in Problems 1, 2, 3, and 4.

6. A spring which is fastened on one side at the point $x = 0$ is stretched by a weight of mass M fastened at the point $x = l$. Determine the spring vibration if the weight is removed at time $t = 0$ and subsequently no force occurs again at $x = l$.

7. Let a rod be fastened at one end; at the other end acts a force F_0. What vibrations does the rod perform if the force ceases to act at the initial moment?

8. What vibrations are performed by a spring which is fastened at one end while at the other end a weight of mass M hangs at the initial moment? Let the initial conditions be homogeneous.

9. A mass M is fastened at the point $x = c$ on a homogeneous string with fixed ends $x = 0$ and $x = l$. Determine the displacement $u(x, t)$ of the string if (a) the string at the initial moment moves from its equilibrium state at $x = c$ to a value equal to h without losing its initial velocity; and (b) the initial displacement and the initial velocity are equal to zero.

10. Determine the course of vibration of a spring with free ends with uniform initial expansion (give a model of this problem).

11. Describe the vibrations of a spring which is fastened elastically at both ends as in Problem 10, if the initial conditions are arbitrary. The solution should be investigated for small h ("soft" attachment) and for a larger h ("rigid" attachment), and the corresponding correction to the eigenvalues of the spring with fixed and free ends should be calculated.

12. Find the displacement $u(x, t)$ of a string whose ends are rigidly fixed if the vibrations occur in a medium in which the resistance is proportional to the velocity. Let the initial conditions be arbitrary.

Solution:

$$u_{tt} = a^2 u_{xx} - 2\nu u_t\,, \qquad \nu > 0$$

$$u(x, t) = e^{-\nu t} \sum_{n=1}^{\infty} (a_n \cos \omega_n t + b_n \sin \omega_n t) \sin \sqrt{\lambda_n} x\,,$$

$$a_n = \frac{2}{l}\int_0^l \varphi(x)\sin\sqrt{\lambda_n}x dx\,, \qquad b_n = \nu\frac{a_n}{\omega_n} + \frac{2}{l\omega_n}\int_0^l \psi(x)\sin\sqrt{\lambda_n}x dx$$

$$\lambda_n = \left(\frac{\pi n}{l}\right)^2, \qquad \omega_n = \sqrt{a^2\lambda_n - \nu}\ .$$

13. Let an isolated electrical conductor of length l with characteristic coefficients L, R, C, and $G = 0$ be charged to a fixed potential v_0. One end of the conductor is grounded at the initial moment while the other remains isolated during the entire time of the process. Determine the voltage distribution in the conductor.

Solution:

$$v(x, t) = e^{-(R/2L)t}\sum_{n=0}^{\infty} a_n \sin\frac{2n+1}{2l}\pi x \cdot \sin(\omega_n t + \varphi_n)\,,$$

$$\omega_n = \frac{(2n+1)\pi}{2l\sqrt{LC}}\sqrt{1 - \frac{CR^2l^2}{L\pi^2(2n+1)^2}}\,,$$

$$a_n = \frac{4v_0}{\pi(2n+1)\sin\varphi_n}\,, \qquad \operatorname{tg}\varphi_n = 2\omega_n\frac{L}{R}\ .$$

14. A string which is rigidly fastened at the ends vibrates under the influence of a harmonic force which is distributed with density $f(x, t) = \Phi(x) \sin\omega t$. Determine the displacement $u(x, t)$ of the string with arbitrary initial conditions. When is resonance possible and what solution results in the case of resonance?

15. Solve Problem 14 under the assumption that the vibrations occur in a medium in which the resistance is proportional to the velocity. Find the vibrations which comprise the principal part of the solution for $t \to \infty$.

16. An elastic rod of length l is in a vertical position and at its upper end a free-falling elevator is fastened, which at the moment it is stopped, has attained a velocity v_0. What vibrations are performed by the rod if the other end is freely movable?

17. Solve the equation

$$u_{tt} = a^2u_{xx} + b^2u + A$$

with homogeneous initial conditions and the boundary conditions

$$u(0, t) = 0 \qquad u(l, t) = B\,,$$

where b, A, and B are constant.

18. Solve the differential equation

$$u_{tt} = a^2u_{xx} + A\sinh x$$

with homogeneous initial conditions and the boundary conditions

$$u(0, t) = B \qquad u(l, t) = C\,,$$

where A, B, and C are constant.

19. On a homogeneous string with rigidly fixed ends $x = 0$ and $x = l$ acts a harmonic force

$$F(t) = P_0 \sin \omega t ,$$

which starts acting at $t = 0$ at the point $x = c$ $(0 < c < l)$. Determine the displacement $u(x, t)$ of the string with homogeneous initial conditions.

20. Describe the vibrations of an inhomogeneous rod of length l with rigidly fixed ends, which consists of two homogeneous rods connected at the point $x = c$ $(0 < c < l)$, when the initial displacement has the form

$$u(x, 0) = \frac{h}{c} x \qquad \text{for} \quad 0 \leqq x \leqq c ,$$

$$= \frac{h}{l - c}(l - x) \qquad \text{for} \quad c \leqq x \leqq l$$

and the initial velocity is equal to zero.

21. Determine the vibrations of a spring which is fixed at one end while at the other acts a force given by

$$F(t) = A \sin \omega_1 t + B \sin \omega_2 t .$$

22. Describe the vibrations of an inhomogeneous rod which consists of two homogeneous rods connected at the point $x = c$ when one end of the rod is fixed and the other moves according to the law

$$u(l, t) = A \sin \omega t .$$

2-4. PROBLEMS WITH AUXILIARY CONDITIONS ON THE CHARACTERISTICS

1. Statement of the problem

In the following discussion, we shall consider a series of problems which are extensions of the first boundary-value problem for the equation of a vibrating string. For simplicity we shall investigate phenomena only in the neighborhood of boundary points where the other boundary point moves toward infinity, i.e., we proceed from the problem for the semi-infinite line.

The equation of the vibrating string $u_{t't'} = a^2 u_{xx}$ is symmetrical with respect to x and t if $a^2 = 1$, i.e., if the unit of time is changed by the introduction of the variable $t = at'$. Of course, the auxiliary conditions introduce an asymmetry in the mathematical interpretation of x and t; in the initial conditions (for $t = 0$) two functions $u(x, 0)$ and $u_t(x, 0)$ are prescribed, while in the boundary conditions (at $x = 0$) only one function $u(0, t)$ is prescribed.

As noted in 2-2 §7, between the derivatives of the displacement function at $t = 0$ and $x = 0$ the relation

$$u_t(0, z) + u_x(0, z) = u_t(z, 0) + u_x(z, 0) , \qquad a^2 = 1 ,$$

exists for an arbitrary z. Hence it follows that these functions at $x = 0$ and $t = 0$ cannot be prescribed independently of each other; only three relations can be prescribed arbitrarily, which proves that the auxiliary conditions cannot be arranged symmetrically.

The auxiliary conditions can be prescribed either on the straight lines $x = 0$, $t = 0$ (as in the problems considered hitherto), or on known curves in the phase plane. For example, if the boundary values are given on curve C_1 $(x = f_1(t))$, then this curve, in order to guarantee the solvability of the problem considered, must still satisfy the determined auxiliary conditions in addition to certain continuity and differentiability conditions.

We shall consider the vibration process of a gas in a tube in which a piston moves. The velocity of the piston whose law of motion is given by $x = f_1(t)$ cannot be prescribed arbitrarily: it must not exceed the velocity of sound a, $[df_1(t)/dt < a]$. Geometrically it follows that the curve C_1 $(x = f_1(t))$ from the straight line $t = 0$, which supports the initial value, must be separated from the characteristic $x = at$ (Figure 25). Also if only one point of C_1 were to lie below the characteristic $x = at$, then the value of the function $u(x, t)$ would be completely determined by the initial value and could not be arbitrarily prescribed. The physical significance of these relations is as follows: if the motion of a gas has a velocity which is larger than that of the velocity of sound, the equations of acoustics lose their sense and must be replaced by the non-linear equations of gas dynamics.[24]

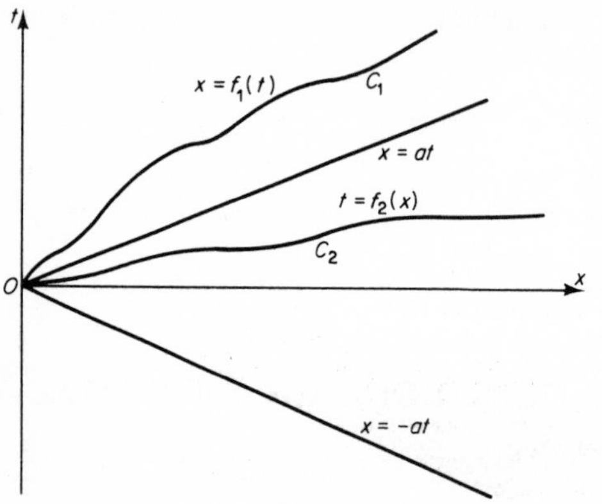

FIG. 25.

The initial conditions can be given on the straight line $t = 0$ and also on a curve C_2 $(t = f_2(x))$, which satisfies the inequality $|f_2'(x)| < 1/a$. Such problems can be easily solved with the aid of the integral vibration equation (see Section 2-2 §7).

Without going into a complete review of all the possible boundary-value problems, we shall now deal more precisely with the problem in which the auxiliary conditions are prescribed on the characteristics. This problem is known as the Goursat problem. Such problems are of extraordinary interest from the standpoint of the physical applications. They arise in problems of adsorption and absorption of gases, for example, (see Section 2-6 §5) with evaporation processes (see Problem 1, page 106) and many other problems.

2. The method of successive approximation

We shall first consider the simplest of the problems in which the auxiliary conditions are prescribed on the characteristics. It reads as follows:

$$\begin{aligned} u_{xy} &= f(x, y) \\ u(x, 0) &= \varphi_1(x) \\ u(0, y) &= \varphi_2(y)\,. \end{aligned} \tag{2-4.1}$$

[24] See Application, Section 2-6, 4.

The auxiliary conditions here are given on the straight lines $x = 0$ and $y = 0$, which represent the characteristics of Eq. (2-4.1). We assume the functions $\varphi_1(x)$ and $\varphi_2(y)$ to be differentiable and related to each other by the relationship $\varphi_1(0) = \varphi_2(0)$. If we integrate Eq. (2-4.1) with respect to x and then with respect to y, we obtain

$$u_y(x, y) = u_y(0, y) + \int_0^x f(\xi, y)d\xi$$

$$u(x, y) = u(x, 0) + u(0, y) - u(0, 0) + \int_0^y d\eta\int_0^x f(\xi, \eta)d\xi$$

or

$$u(x, y) = \varphi_1(x) + \varphi_2(y) - \varphi_1(0) + \int_0^y\int_0^x f(\xi, \eta)d\xi d\eta . \tag{2-4.2}$$

Therefore, the solution in this case, in which the differential equation contains neither the first derivatives nor the sought function itself, can be represented explicitly by the analytic expression (2-4.2). From (2-4.2) the uniqueness and the existence of the solution of our problem follows directly.

We shall now seek the solution of the linear hyperbolic differential equation

$$u_{xy} = a(x, y)u_x + b(x, y)\, u_y + c(x, y)u + f(x, y) , \tag{2-4.3}$$

with the auxiliary conditions given on the characteristics $x = 0$, $y = 0$

$$u(x, 0) = \varphi_1(x) , \qquad u(0, y) = \varphi_2(y) ,$$

where $\varphi_1(x)$ and $\varphi_2(y)$ satisfy the above cited conditions, differentiability and $\varphi_1(0) = \varphi_2(0)$. Let the coefficients a, b, and c be continuous functions of x and y.

From the differential Eq. (2-4.3) we know that the function $u(x, y)$ satisfies the integro-differential equation

$$\begin{aligned} u(x, y) = &\int_0^y\int_0^x [a(\xi, \eta)u_\xi + b(\xi, \eta)u_\eta + c(\xi, \eta)u]d\xi d\eta \\ &+ \varphi_1(x) + \varphi_2(y) - \varphi_1(0) + \int_0^y\int_0^x f(\xi, \eta)d\xi d\eta . \end{aligned} \tag{2-4.4}$$

We shall determine its solution with the help of the method of successive approximations. For the zero-th approximation we choose the function

$$u_0(x, y) = 0 .$$

Eq. (2-4.4) then gives for the successive approximations the expression

$$u_1(x, y) = \varphi_1(x) = \varphi_2(y) - \varphi_1(0) + \int_0^y\int_0^x f(\xi, \eta)d\xi d\eta$$

$$. \quad . \quad . \quad . \quad . \quad . \quad . \quad . \quad .$$

$$\begin{aligned} u_n(x, y) = &\, u_1(x, y) \\ &+ \int_0^y\int_0^x \left[a(\xi, \eta)\frac{\partial u_{n-1}}{\partial \xi} + b(\xi, \eta)\frac{\partial u_{n-1}}{\partial \eta} + c(\xi, \eta)u_{n-1}\right]d\xi d\eta . \end{aligned} \tag{2-4.5}$$

Incidentally we note the validity of the expressions

$$\begin{aligned}\frac{\partial u_n}{\partial x} &= \frac{\partial u_1}{\partial x} + \int_0^y \left[a(x,\eta)\frac{\partial u_{n-1}}{\partial x} + b(x,\eta)\frac{\partial u_{n-1}}{\partial \eta} + c(x,\eta)u_{n-1} \right] d\eta \\ \frac{\partial u_n}{\partial y} &= \frac{\partial u_1}{\partial y} + \int_0^x \left[a(\xi,y)\frac{\partial u_{n-1}}{\partial \xi} + b(\xi,y)\frac{\partial u_{n-1}}{\partial y} + c(\xi,y)u_{n-1} \right] d\xi \,.\end{aligned} \tag{2-4.6}$$

In order to demonstrate the uniform convergence of the following sequences

$$\{u_n(x,y)\}\,, \qquad \left\{\frac{\partial u_n}{\partial x}(x,y)\right\}, \qquad \left\{\frac{\partial u_n}{\partial y}(x,y)\right\},$$

we shall consider the differences

$$\begin{aligned} z_n(x,y) &= u_{n+1}(x,y) - u_n(x,y) \\ &= \int_0^y \int_0^x \left[a(\xi,\eta)\frac{\partial z_{n-1}}{\partial \xi} + b(\xi,\eta)\frac{\partial z_{n-1}}{\partial \eta} + c(\xi,\eta)z_{n-1}(\xi,\eta) \right] d\xi d\eta\,, \\ \frac{\partial z_n(x,y)}{\partial x} &= \frac{\partial u_{n+1}(x,y)}{\partial x} - \frac{\partial u_n(x,y)}{\partial x} \\ &= \int_0^y \left[a(x,\eta)\frac{\partial z_{n-1}}{\partial x} + b(x,\eta)\frac{\partial z_{n-1}}{\partial \eta} + c(x,\eta)z_{n-1}(x,\eta) \right] d\eta\,, \\ \frac{\partial z_n(x,y)}{\partial y} &= \frac{\partial u_{n+1}(x,y)}{\partial y} - \frac{\partial u_n(x,y)}{\partial y} \\ &= \int_0^x \left[a(\xi,y)\frac{\partial z_{n-1}}{\partial \xi} + b(\xi,y)\frac{\partial z_{n-1}}{\partial y} + c(\xi,y)z_{n-1}(\xi,y) \right] d\xi\,. \end{aligned}$$

Let M be an upper bound for the absolute values of the coefficients $a(x,y)$, $b(x,y)$, $c(x,y)$, and H an upper bound for the absolute values of the function $z_0(x,y)$ and its partial derivatives

$$|z_0| < H\,, \qquad \left|\frac{\partial z_0}{\partial x}\right| < H\,, \qquad \left|\frac{\partial z_0}{\partial y}\right| < H\,,$$

where x and y vary in a square $(0 \leqq x \leqq L,\ 0 \leqq y \leqq L)$. We shall now estimate the functions z_n, $\partial z_n/\partial x$, $\partial z_n/\partial y$ according to the above. First, the inequalities are valid;

$$\begin{aligned} |z_1| &< 3HMxy < 3HM\frac{(x+y)^2}{2!} \\ \left|\frac{\partial z_1}{\partial x}\right| &< 3HMy < 3HM(x+y) \\ \left|\frac{\partial z_1}{\partial y}\right| &< 3HMx < 3HM(x+y)\,, \end{aligned}$$

and the recursion relations

$$\begin{aligned} |z_n| &< 3HM^nK^{n-1}\frac{(x+y)^{n+1}}{(n+1)!} \\ \left|\frac{\partial z_n}{\partial x}\right| &< 3HM^nK^{n-1}\frac{(x+y)^n}{n!} \\ \left|\frac{\partial z_n}{\partial y}\right| &< 3HM^nK^{n-1}\frac{(x+y)^n}{n!} \end{aligned}$$

where $K > 0$ is a constant number whose value will be specified later. With these estimates and the formula for the $(n+1)$th approximation we obtain after a series of simplifications

$$|z_{n+1}| < 3HM^{n+1}K^{n-1}\frac{(x+y)^{n+2}}{(n+2)!}\left(\frac{x+y}{n+3}+2\right) <$$

$$< 3HM^{n+1}K^{n}\frac{(x+y)^{n+2}}{(n+2)!} < \frac{3H}{K^2M}\frac{(2KLM)^{n+2}}{(n+2)!}$$

$$\left|\frac{\partial z_{n+1}}{\partial x}\right| < 3HM^{n+1}K^{n-1}\frac{(x+y)^{n+1}}{(n+1)!}\left(\frac{x+y}{n+2}+2\right) <$$

$$< 3HM^{n+1}K^{n}\frac{(x+y)^{n+1}}{(n+1)!} < \frac{3H}{K}\frac{(2KLM)^{n+1}}{(n+1)!}$$

$$\left|\frac{\partial z_{n+1}}{\partial y}\right| < 3HM^{n+1}K^{n-1}\frac{(x+y)^{n+1}}{(n+1)!}\left(\frac{x+y}{n+2}+2\right) <$$

$$< 3HM^{n+1}K^{n}\frac{(x+y)^{n+1}}{(n+1)!} < \frac{3H}{K}\frac{(2KLM)^{n+1}}{(n+1)!}$$

where

$$K = 2L + 2 .$$

On the right sides of these inequalities we have, to within constant factors, the general term in the series development of e^{2KLM}. Thus the above estimates show that the sequences of functions

$$u_n = u_0 + z_1 + \cdots + z_{n-1}$$

$$\frac{\partial u_n}{\partial x} = \frac{\partial u_0}{\partial x} + \frac{\partial z_1}{\partial x} + \cdots + \frac{\partial z_{n-1}}{\partial x}$$

$$\frac{\partial u_n}{\partial y} = \frac{\partial u_0}{\partial y} + \frac{\partial z_1}{\partial y} + \cdots + \frac{\partial z_{n-1}}{\partial y}$$

converge uniformly. We shall denote their limit functions by

$$u(x, y) = \lim_{n\to\infty} u_n(x, y) ,$$

$$v(x, y) = \lim_{n\to\infty} \frac{\partial u_n}{\partial x}(x, y) ,$$

$$w(x, y) = \lim_{n\to\infty} \frac{\partial u_n}{\partial y}(x, y) .$$

By passage to the limit under the integral signs in (2-4.5) and (2-4.6) we then find

$$\begin{aligned} u(x, y) &= u_1(x, y) + \int_0^y\int_0^x [a(\xi, \eta)v + b(\xi, \eta)w + c(\xi, \eta)u]d\xi d\eta , \\ v(x, y) &= \frac{\partial u_1}{\partial x}(x, y) + \int_0^y [a(x, \eta)v + b(x, \eta)w + c(x, \eta)u]d\eta , \\ w(x, y) &= \frac{\partial u_1}{\partial y}(x, y) + \int_0^x [a(\xi, y)v + b(\xi, y)w + c(\xi, y)u]d\xi . \end{aligned} \tag{2-4.7}$$

Hence the following equations

$$v = u_x \qquad w = u_y$$

establish the fact that $u(x, y)$ satisfies the integrodifferential equation

$$u(x, y) = \varphi_1(x) + \varphi_2(y) - \varphi_1(0) + \int_0^y \int_0^x f(\xi, \eta) d\xi d\eta$$

$$+ \int_0^y \int_0^x [a(\xi, \eta) u_\xi + b(\xi, \eta) u_\eta + c(\xi, \eta) u] d\xi d\eta \tag{2-4.4}$$

and also the original differential Eq. (2-4.3). We verify this directly by differentiation of (2-4.4) with respect to x and y. Moreover, as one easily sees, $u(x, y)$ satisfies the auxiliary conditions.

The uniqueness of the solution of the stated problem will now be demonstrated. If we assume the existence of two solutions $u_1(x, y)$ and $u_2(x, y)$, we obtain for their difference

$$U(x, y) = u_1(x, y) - u_2(x, y)$$

the homogeneous integrodifferential equation

$$U(x, y) = \int_0^y \int_0^x (aU_x + bU_y + cU) d\xi d\eta \, .$$

Now if H_1 is a common upper bound of the magnitudes $|U|$, $|U_x|$ and $|U_y|$ for $0 \leqq x \leqq L$ and $0 \leqq y \leqq L$, then by a repetition of the estimates which led to those on the function $z_n(x, y)$, the correctness of the inequality

$$|U| < 3H_1 M^{n+1} K^n \frac{(x + y)^{n+2}}{(n + 2)!} < \frac{3H_1}{K^2 M} \frac{(2KLM)^{n+2}}{(n + 2)!}$$

for an arbitrary value of n follows easily. Hence it follows that

$$U(x, y) \equiv 0 \qquad \text{or} \qquad u_1(x, y) \equiv u_2(x, y) \, ,$$

whereby the uniqueness of our solution is shown.

If the coefficients a, b, and c are constant, then Eq. (2-4.3) with the help of the substitution

$$u = ve^{\lambda x + \mu y} \, ,$$

can be brought to the form

$$v_{xy} + C_1 v = f \, . \tag{2-4.8}$$

For $C_1 = 0$ we obtain the simple Eq. (2-4.1) whose solution was given by formula 2-4.2.

By contrast, if $C_1 \neq 0$ then we obtain for the solution of (2-4.8) an explicit analytic representation by the method given in Section 2-5.

Problems

1. Air with a velocity ν passes through a tube ($x > 0$) which is filled with a moist fluid. Let $v(x, t)$ be the concentration of the moisture in the saturated

substance and $u(x, t)$ be the concentration of the free vapor. What equations are satisfied by the functions $u(x, t)$ and $v(x, t)$ describing the drying process when (a) the process proceeds isothermally; and (b) the dry isotherm has the form $u = \gamma \cdot v$ where γ is the isothermal constant (see also Section 2-6, Application 5)?

2. Hot water with velocity ν flows through a tube $(x > 0)$. Let u be the temperature of the water in the tube, v the temperature of the walls of the tube, and u_0 the temperature of the environment. Derive the equations for u and v by neglecting the temperature distribution in the individual cross sections of the tube and the walls. Assume further that a temperature gradient exists at the boundaries of the water-tube wall and the wall environment, and that the flow of heat follows Newton's law (see Chapter 3-1).

2-5. SOLUTION OF GENERAL LINEAR HYPERBOLIC DIFFERENTIAL EQUATIONS

1. Adjoint differential operators

In order to represent the solutions of boundary-value problems in integral form we need some auxiliary formulas. Let

$$\boldsymbol{L}[u] = u_{xx} - u_{yy} + a(x, y)u_x + b(x, y)u_y + c(x, y)u \,, \tag{2-5.1}$$

where $a(x, y)$, $b(x, y)$, $c(x, y)$ are differentiable functions, be a linear differential operator corresponding to a linear hyperbolic differential equation. We multiply $\boldsymbol{L}[u]$ by a function v and write the individual summands in the form

$$\begin{aligned} vu_{xx} &= (vu_x)_x - (v_x u)_x + uv_{xx} \\ vu_{yy} &= (vu_y)_y - (v_y u)_y + uv_{yy} \\ vau_x &= (avu)_x - u(av)_x \\ vbu_y &= (bvu)_y - u(bv)_y \\ vcu &= ucv \,. \end{aligned}$$

By summation of the individual summands we obtain

$$v\boldsymbol{L}[u] - u\boldsymbol{M}[v] = \frac{\partial H}{\partial x} + \frac{\partial K}{\partial y} \,, \tag{2-5.2}$$

where

$$\boldsymbol{M}[v] = v_{xx} - v_{yy} - (av)_x - (bv)_y + cv \tag{2-5.3}$$

$$H = vu_x - v_x u + avu = (vu)_x - (2v_x - av)u \tag{2-5.4}$$

$$= - (vu)_x + (2u_x + au)v \tag{2-5.4'}$$

$$K = - vu_y + vu + bvu = - (vu)_y + (2v_y + bv)u \tag{2-5.5}$$

$$= (uv)_y - (2u_y - bu)v \,. \tag{2-5.5'}$$

Two differential operators $\boldsymbol{L}$ and $\boldsymbol{M}$ are said to be adjoint to each other if the difference

$$vL[u] - uM[v]$$

is equal to the sum of the partial derivatives of the expressions H and K with respect to x and y.

In particular, if $L[u] = M[u]$, then the operator L is called self-adjoint.

For the double integral, the difference $vL[u] - uM[v]$, where u and v are twice differentiable functions throughout a region G which is bounded by a piecewise smooth curve C, we have

$$\int_G\int (vL[u] - uM[v])d\xi d\eta = \int_C (Hd\eta - Kd\xi) \qquad (2\text{-}5.6)$$

(Green's formula).

2. Integral form of the solution

We shall apply Formula (2-5.6) for the solution of the following problem. Find a solution of a linear hyperbolic differential equation

$$L[u] = u_{xx} - u_{yy} + a(x, y)u_x + b(x, y)u_y + c(x, y)u = - f(x, y)\,, \qquad (2\text{-}5.7)$$

which satisfies the initial conditions

$$u|_C = \varphi(x)\,, \qquad u_n|_C = \psi(x)$$

on a curve C (u_n is the derivative in the direction of the normal to the curve C).

Obviously the operators L and M are adjoint to each other.

Hence let C be given by

$$y = f(x)\,,$$

where $f(x)$ is a differentiable function. On the curve C we impose the requirement that every pair of characteristics $y - x =$ const. and $y + x =$ const. intersects curve C at most once (therefore it is necessary that $|f'(x)| \leqq 1$). Formula (2-5.6) then yields for the curvilinear triangle MPQ which is bounded by the arc PQ of C and the segments of the characteristics MP and MQ (Figure 26).

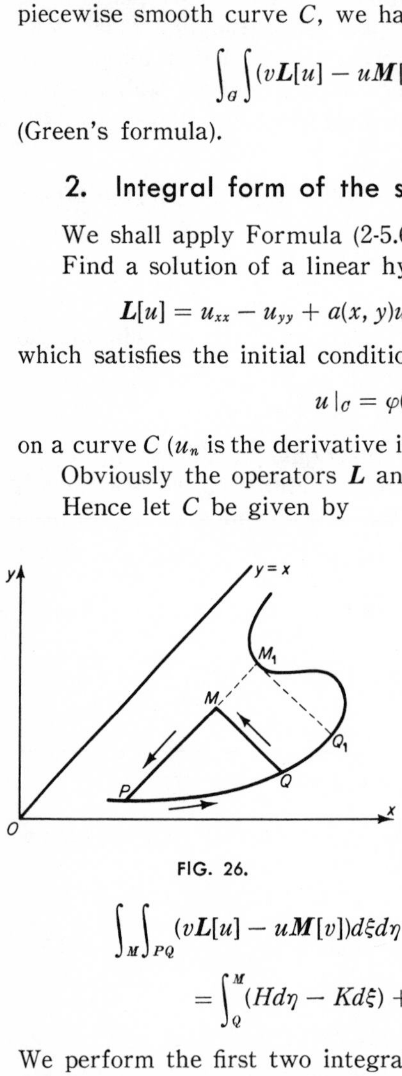

FIG. 26.

$$\int_M\int_{PQ} (vL[u] - uM[v])d\xi d\eta$$

$$= \int_Q^M (Hd\eta - Kd\xi) + \int_M^P (Hd\eta - Kd\xi) + \int_P^Q (Hd\eta - Kd\xi)\,.$$

We perform the first two integrals which are taken along the characteristics MQ and MP, and by taking into consideration the relations

$$d\xi = - d\eta = -\frac{ds}{\sqrt{2}} \qquad \text{on the characteristic } QM$$

$$d\xi = d\eta = -\frac{ds}{\sqrt{2}} \quad \text{on the characteristic } MP$$

(where ds is the element of the arc along QM and MP), and the formulas (2-5.4) and (2-5.5), we obtain

$$\int_Q^M (Hd\eta - Kd\xi) = -\int_Q^M d(uv) + \int_Q^M \left(2\frac{\partial v}{\partial s} - \frac{a+b}{\sqrt{2}}v\right)uds$$

$$= -(uv)_M + (uv)_Q + \int_Q^M \left(2\frac{\partial v}{\partial s} - \frac{a+b}{\sqrt{2}}v\right)uds$$

and correspondingly

$$\int_M^P (Hd\eta - Kd\xi) = -(uv)_M + (uv)_P + \int_P^M \left(2\frac{\partial v}{\partial s} - \frac{b-a}{\sqrt{2}}v\right)uds\,.$$

From this and from (2-5.6) it follows that

$$(uv)_M = \frac{(uv)_P + (uv)_Q}{2} + \int_P^M \left(\frac{\partial v}{\partial s} - \frac{b-a}{2\sqrt{2}}v\right)uds + \int_Q^M \left(\frac{\partial v}{\partial s} - \frac{a+b}{2\sqrt{2}}v\right)uds$$

$$+\frac{1}{2}\int_P^Q (Hd\eta - Kd\xi) - \frac{1}{2}\int_M\int_{PQ} (v\boldsymbol{L}[u] - u\boldsymbol{M}[v])d\xi d\eta\,. \tag{2-5.8}$$

This relation is an identity which is correct for arbitrary but sufficiently smooth functions u and v.

Now let u be a solution of the problem with above stated initial conditions, while v depends on the point M as a parameter and fulfills the requirements

$$\boldsymbol{M}[v] = v_{\xi\xi} - v_{\eta\eta} - (av)_\xi - (bv)_\eta + cv = 0 \quad \text{in the interior of } \Delta MPQ \tag{2-5.9}$$

and

$$\left.\begin{aligned} \frac{\partial v}{\partial s} &= \frac{b-a}{2\sqrt{2}}v \quad \text{on the characteristic } MP \\ \frac{\partial v}{\partial s} &= \frac{b+a}{2\sqrt{2}}v \quad \text{on the characteristic } MQ \\ v(M) &= 1\,. \end{aligned}\right\} \tag{2-5.9$'$}$$

From the conditions which must be fulfilled on the characteristics and the last condition we then find

$$v = e^{\int_{s_0}^{s} (b-a)/(2\sqrt{2})\,ds} \quad \text{on } MP$$

$$v = e^{\int_{s_0}^{s} (b+a)/(2\sqrt{2})\,ds} \quad \text{on } MQ$$

where s_0 denotes the value of s at the point M. As we saw in Section 2-4, Eq. (2-5.9) and the value of v on the characteristics MP and MG define the function v completely in the region MPQ. The function v is ordinarily called the Riemann function.

Consequently formula (2-5.8) for a function u which satisfies Eq. (2-5.7) takes the following definitive form:

$$u(M) = \frac{(uv)_P + (uv)_Q}{2}$$
$$+ \frac{1}{2}\int_P^Q [v(u_\xi d\eta + u_\eta d\xi) - u(v_\xi d\eta + v_\eta d\xi) + uv(ad\eta - bd\xi)]$$
$$+ \frac{1}{2}\iint_{MPQ} v(M, M')f(M')d\sigma_{M'}\,, \qquad d\sigma_{M'} = d\xi d\eta\,. \tag{2-5.10}$$

The stated problem is solved by this formula since the expression which stands under the integral extended along PQ contains only functions which are known along C. The function v has already been defined above while the functions

$$u\,|_C = \varphi(x)$$
$$u_x = u_s \cos(x, s) + u_n \cos(x, n) = \frac{\varphi'(x) - \psi(x) f'(x)\sqrt{1+f'^2(x)}}{1+f'^2(x)}$$
$$u_y = u_s \cos(y, s) + u_n \cos(y, n) = \frac{\varphi'(x) f'(x) + \psi(x)\sqrt{1+f'^2(x)}}{1+f'^2(x)}$$

can be calculated from the initial conditions.

If the initial conditions along the arc PQ are known, the function u in the triangle PMQ can be completely determined according to formula (2-5.10) when $f(x, y)$ is known in this region.[25]

Formula (2-5.10), obtained under the assumption of the existence of a solution, defines the solution from the initial conditions and the right side of Eq. (2-5.7). Most important, it also proves the uniqueness of the solution (compare it with the D'Alembert formula, Section 2-2).

It can also be shown that the function u defined by (2-5.10) satisfies the conditions of the problems.

3. The physical interpretation of the Riemann function

In order to clarify the physical meaning of the Riemann function $v(M, M')$ we shall first determine the solution of the inhomogeneous equation

$$L[u] = -2f_1\,, \qquad f = 2f_1$$

with homogeneous initial conditions on a curve C. We see from (2-5.10) that the desired solution has the form

$$u(M) = \iint_{MPQ} v(M, M')f_1(M')d\sigma_{M'} \tag{2-5.11}$$

If we now assume that $f_1(M)$, except in a small neighborhood S_ε of the point M_1, is everywhere equal to zero and satisfies the normalization condition

[25] If the characteristics intersect the curve C at the two points P and M_1 (Figure 26), the value $u(M_1)$ cannot be arbitrarily given. On the contrary, it is determined according to formula (2-5.10) by the initial value on the arc PQ_1 and the value of $f(x, y)$ in ΔPM_1Q_1.

$$\iint_{S_\varepsilon} f_1(M')d\sigma_{M'} = 1 . \tag{2-5.12}$$

Then the above formula for $u_\varepsilon(M)$ assumes the form

$$u_\varepsilon(M) = \iint_{S_\varepsilon} v(M, M')f_1(M')d\sigma_{M'} . \tag{2-5.13}$$

By use of the mean-value theorem we can write

$$u_\varepsilon(M) = v(M, M_1^*)\iint_{S_\varepsilon} f_1(M')d\sigma_{M'} = v(M, M_1^*) ,$$

where M_1^* is a determined point in S_ε.

If now the ε-neighborhood S_ε of the point M_1 shrinks ($\varepsilon \to 0$) then we obtain

$$u(M) = \lim_{\varepsilon \to 0} u_\varepsilon(M) = v(M, M_1) . \tag{2-5.14}$$

The function f_1, as we have already seen in a series of examples, represents a force density whereas y denotes the time. The expression

$$\iint_{S_\varepsilon} f_1(M')d\sigma_{M'} = \iint_{S_\varepsilon} f_1(\xi, \eta)d\xi d\eta \tag{2-5.15}$$

then denotes the impulse of the force. Hence, because of (2-5.11) we conclude that $v(M, M_1)$ is the influence function of the unit impulse acting at M_1.

The function $v(M, M_1) = v(x, y; \xi, \eta)$ can be defined as a function of the parameter $M(x, y)$, which with respect to the coordinates ξ, η of the point M_1 satisfies the equation

$$\boldsymbol{M}_{(\xi, \eta)}[v] = 0 \tag{2-5.16}$$

with the auxiliary conditions (2-5.9′).

We shall now consider the function

$$u = u(M, M_1) ,$$

which depends on the parameter $M_1(\xi, \eta)$ and with respect to the coordinates x, y of the point M satisfies the equation

$$\boldsymbol{L}_{(x, y)}[u] = 0 \tag{2-5.17}$$

with the auxiliary conditions

$$\begin{aligned} &\frac{\partial u}{\partial s} = \frac{b-a}{2\sqrt{2}}u \quad \text{on the characteristic } M_1Q_1 , \\ &\frac{\partial u}{\partial s} = \frac{b+a}{2\sqrt{2}}u \quad \text{on the characteristic } M_1P_1 , \\ &u(M_1, M_1) = 1 . \end{aligned} \tag{2-5.18}$$

From these conditions there results

$$u(M, M_1) = \begin{cases} e^{\int_{s_0}^{s} (b-a)/(2\sqrt{2})\, ds} & \text{on } M_1Q_1 \\ e^{\int_{s_0}^{s} (b+a)/(2\sqrt{2})\, ds} & \text{on } M_1P_1 \end{cases} \tag{2-5.19}$$

$$u(M_1, M_1) = 1 .$$

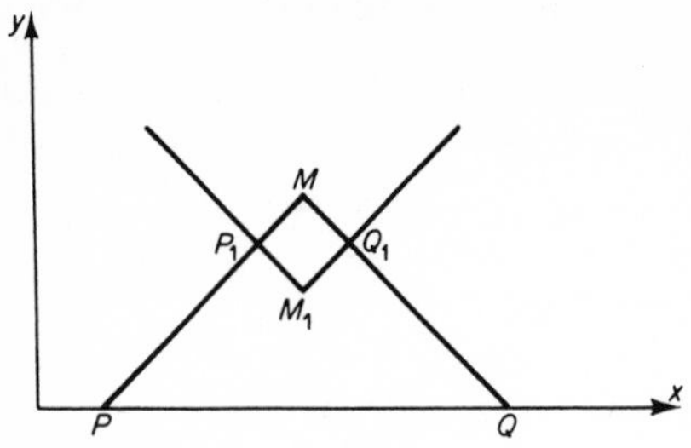

FIG. 27.

In the quadrangle $MP_1M_1Q_1$, which is bounded by the intersection of the characteristics MP_1, MQ_1, M_1P_1 and M_1Q_1 (Figure 27), u is completely determined by Eq. (2-5.17) and the conditions (2-5.18).

If we apply formula (2-5.6) to the quadrangle $MP_1M_1Q_1$ we obtain

$$\iint_{MP_1M_1Q_1} (vL[u] - uL[v])d\xi d\eta$$
$$= \int_M^{P_1} (Hd\eta - Kd\xi) + \int_{Q_1}^{M} + \int_{M_1}^{Q_1} + \int_{P_1}^{M_1} = 0 .$$

If we use formulas (2-5.4) and (2-5.5) for K and H and the conditions (2-5.9′), the first two integrals on the right side can be easily calculated

$$\int_M^{P_1} (Hd\eta - Kd\xi) = -(uv)_M + (uv)_{P_1} ,$$

$$\int_{Q_1}^{M} (Hd\eta - Kd\xi) = -(uv)_M + (uv)_{Q_1} ,$$

just as in the derivation of formula (2-5.10).

In a similar manner we find with the use of equations (2-5.4′) and (2-5.5′) as well as conditions (2-5.19)

$$\int_{P_1}^{M_1} (Hd\eta - Kd\xi) = \int_{P_1}^{M_1} [-(vu)_\xi d\eta - (uv)_\eta d\xi] + \int_{P_1}^{M_1} v[(2u_\xi d\eta + 2u_\eta d\xi) + (aud\eta - bud\xi)]$$
$$= \int_{P_1}^{M_1} d(uv) + \int_{P_1}^{M_1} 2\left(\frac{\partial u}{\partial s} - \frac{a+b}{2\sqrt{2}} u\right) vds = (uv)_{M_1} - (uv)_{P_1} ,$$

$$d\xi = -d\eta = \frac{ds}{\sqrt{2}} , \qquad \int_{M_1}^{Q_1} (Hd\eta - Kd\xi) = (uv)_{M_1} - (uv)_{Q_1} , \qquad d\xi = d\eta = \frac{ds}{\sqrt{2}} .$$

By addition of these equations, we obtain

$$2(uv)_M = 2(uv)_{M_1}$$

or

$$u(M, M_1) = v(M, M_1) , \tag{2-5.20}$$

since

$$(v)_{M_1} = (v)_M = 1 .$$

The influence function of the unit impulse acting at the point M_1 can also be defined as the solution of the equation

$$L_{(x,\, y)}[v(M, M_1)] = 0 ,$$

with auxiliary conditions (2-5.18).

4. Differential equations with constant coefficients

As the first example of application of formula (2-5.10) we shall consider the following initial-value problem for the equation of the vibrating string:

$$u_{yy} = u_{xx} + f_1(x, t)\,, \qquad y = at\,,\ f_1 = \frac{f}{a^2}\,,$$

$$u(x, 0) = \varphi(x)\,,$$

$$u_y = \psi_1(x)\,, \qquad \psi_1 = \frac{\psi}{a}\,.$$

As in (2-5.10) a strip of the axis $y = 0$ occurs as the arc PQ. The operator

$$\boldsymbol{L} = u_{xx} - u_{yy}$$

because of

$$\boldsymbol{M} = \boldsymbol{L} = u_{xx} - u_{yy}$$

is self-adjoint.

Because $a = 0$ and $b = 0$, v equals one on the characteristics MP and MQ. Hence it follows

$$v(M, M') \equiv 1$$

for every point M' which lies interior to the triangle PMQ.

Now in our case,

$$d\eta = 0 \quad \text{for} \quad PQ\,.$$

Thus we obtain

$$u(M) = \frac{u(P) + u(Q)}{2} + \frac{1}{2}\int_P^Q u_\eta d\xi + \frac{1}{2}\iint_{PMQ} f(\xi, \eta)d\xi d\eta\,.$$

If we bear in mind that $P = P(x - y, 0)$, $Q = Q(x + y, 0)$, where x and y are the coordinates of the point $M = M(x, y)$, we obtain by use of the initial conditions

$$u(x, y) = \frac{u(x - y) + u(x + y)}{2} + \frac{1}{2}\int_{x-y}^{x+y} \psi_1(\xi)d\xi + \frac{1}{2}\int_0^y\int_{x-(y-\eta)}^{x+(y-\eta)} f_1(\xi, \eta)d\xi d\eta\,.$$

For the variables x and t, therefore, we arrive at the formula

$$u(x, t) = \frac{u(x - at) + u(x + at)}{2} + \frac{1}{2a}\int_{x-at}^{x+at} \psi(\xi)d\xi + \frac{1}{2a}\int_0^t\int_{x-a(t-\tau)}^{x+a(t-\tau)} f(\xi, \tau)d\xi d\tau\,,$$

which we recognize from Section 2-3 §7.

As a second example we shall consider the following initial-value problem for differential equations with constant coefficients:

$$u_{xx} - u_{yy} + au_x + bu_y + cu = 0 \qquad (a, b, c \text{ are constants}) \tag{2-5.21}$$

$$u\,|_{y=0} = \varphi(x)\,, \tag{2-5.22}$$

$$u_y\,|_{y=0} = \psi(x)\,. \tag{2-5.23}$$

The substitution

$$U = ue^{\lambda x+\mu y} \tag{2-5.24}$$

transforms Eq. (2-5.21) into the simpler form

$$U_{xx} - U_{yy} + c_1 U = 0\,, \qquad c_1 = \frac{1}{4}(4c - a^2 - b^2) \tag{2-5.25}$$

with the auxiliary conditions

$$U|_{y=0} = \varphi(x)e^{(a/2)x} = \varphi_1(x) \tag{2-5.22$'$}$$

$$U_y|_{y=0} = \left(\psi(x) - \frac{b}{2}\varphi(x)\right)e^{(a/2)x} = \psi_1(x) \tag{2-5.23$'$}$$

only when the parameters λ and μ are suitably selected; that is

$$\lambda = \frac{a}{2}\,, \qquad \mu = -\frac{b}{2}\,. \tag{2-5.26}$$

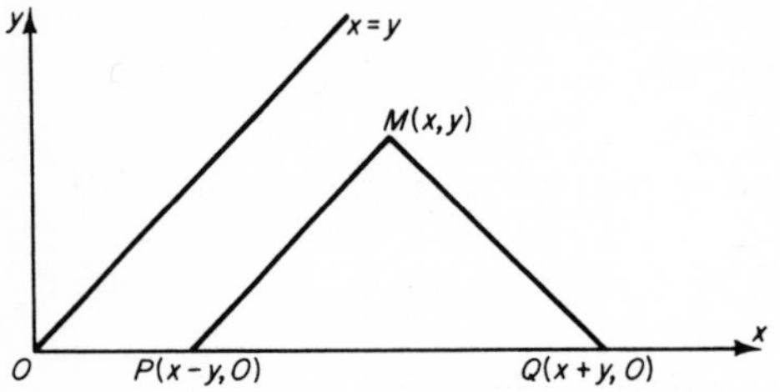

FIG. 28.

The determination of the function $U(x, y)$ from the initial conditions and Eq. (2-5.25) leads to the construction of the Riemann function $v(x, y; \xi, \eta)$.

The function v must satisfy the conditions (Figure 28)

$$v_{xx} - v_{yy} + c_1 v = 0 \tag{2-5.27}$$

$$\begin{aligned} v &= 1 \quad \text{on the characteristic } MP\,, \\ v &= 1 \quad \text{on the characteristic } MQ\,. \end{aligned} \tag{2-5.28}$$

We chose v in the form

$$v = v(z) \tag{2-5.29}$$

with

$$z = \sqrt{(x-\xi)^2 - (y-\eta)^2}$$

or (2-5.30)

$$z^2 = (x-\xi)^2 - (y-\eta)^2\,.$$

On the characteristics MP and MQ, z is equal to zero so that $v(0) = 1$. The left side of (2-5.27) can be brought to the form

$$v_{xx} - v_{yy} + c_1 v = v''(z)(z_x^2 - z_y^2) + v'(z)(z_{xx} - z_{yy}) + c_1 v = 0\,.$$

By differentiating twice the expression for z^2 (with respect to x and y), we obtain

$$\begin{aligned} zz_x &= x - \xi \\ zz_y &= -(y-\eta) \\ zz_{xx} + z_x^2 &= 1 \\ zz_{yy} + z_y^2 &= -1\,. \end{aligned}$$

From this and from (2-5.30) it follows

$$z_x^2 - z_y^2 = 1\,, \qquad z_{xx} - z_{yy} = \frac{1}{z}\,.$$

Consequently, the equation for v can be written in the form

$$v'' + \frac{1}{z}v' + c_1 v = 0$$

with the condition $v(0) = 1$. A solution of this equation is the Bessel function of the zero order (see Appendix)

$$v(z) = J_0(\sqrt{c_1}z)$$

or

$$v(x, y; \xi, \eta) = J_0(\sqrt{c_1[(x-\xi)^2 - (y-\eta)^2]})\,. \tag{2-5.31}$$

For the determination of $U(x, y)$ we shall now use formula (2-5.10) which in our case reads

$$U(M) = \frac{U(P) + U(Q)}{2} + \frac{1}{2}\int_P^Q (vU_\eta d\xi - Uv_\eta d\xi)\,, \qquad d\eta = 0\,. \tag{2-5.32}$$

First we calculate the integral along PQ $(\eta = 0)$:

$$\int_P^Q (vU_\eta - Uv_\eta)d\xi = \int_{x-y}^{x+y}\Big\{J_0(\sqrt{c_1[(x-\xi)^2 - y^2]})U_\eta(\xi, 0)$$
$$- \frac{U(\xi, 0)\sqrt{c_1}\,yJ_0'(\sqrt{c_1}\sqrt{(x-\xi)^2 - y^2})}{\sqrt{c_1[(x-\xi)^2 - y^2]}}\Big\}d\xi\,. \tag{2-5.33}$$

On the basis of the initial conditions (2-5.22′), (2-5.23′) we find

$$U(x, y) = \frac{\varphi_1(x-y) + \varphi_1(x+y)}{2} + \frac{1}{2}\int_{x-y}^{x+y} J_0(\sqrt{c_1}\sqrt{(x-\xi)^2 - y^2})\psi_1(\xi)d\xi$$
$$+ \frac{1}{2}\sqrt{c_1}\,y\int_{x-y}^{x+y}\frac{J_1(\sqrt{c_1}\sqrt{(x-\xi)^2 - y^2})\varphi_1(\xi)d\xi}{\sqrt{(x-\xi)^2 - y^2}} \tag{2-5.34}$$

from which because of (2-5.24), (2-5.22′) and (2-5.23′) there results the formula

$$u(x, y) = \frac{\varphi(x-y)e^{-((a-b)/2)y} + \varphi(x+y)e^{((a+b)/2)y}}{2}$$
$$- \frac{1}{2}e^{(b/2)y}\int_{x-y}^{x+y}\Big\{\frac{b}{2}J_0(\sqrt{c_1}\sqrt{(x-\xi)^2 - y^2})$$
$$+ \sqrt{c_1}\,y\frac{J_1(\sqrt{c_1}\sqrt{(x-\xi)^2 - y^2})}{\sqrt{(x-\xi)^2 - y^2}}\Big\}e^{-(a/2)(x-\xi)}\varphi(\xi)d\xi$$
$$+ \frac{1}{2}e^{(b/2)y}\int_{x-y}^{x+y} J_0(\sqrt{c_1}\sqrt{(x-\xi)^2 - y^2})\,e^{-(a/2)(x-\xi)}\psi(\xi)d\xi \tag{2-5.35}$$

which represents the solution of our problem.

We shall consider the special case $a = 0$, $b = 0$, i.e., the equation

$$u_{xx} - u_{yy} + cu = 0\,.$$

From (2-5.35) directly follows

$$u(x, y) = \frac{\varphi(x-y) + \varphi(x+y)}{2} + \frac{1}{2}\int_{x-y}^{x+y} J_0(\sqrt{c_1}\sqrt{(x-\xi)^2 - y^2})\psi(\xi)d\xi$$

$$-\frac{1}{2}\sqrt{c_1}\, y\int_{x-y}^{x+y} \frac{J_1(\sqrt{c_1}\sqrt{(x-\xi)^2 - y^2})}{\sqrt{(x-\xi)^2 - y^2}}\varphi(\xi)d\xi\,. \qquad (2\text{-}5.36)$$

If we put $c_1 = 0$ and $y = at$, we arrive at the D'Alembert formula

$$u(x, t) = \frac{\varphi(x-at) + \varphi(x+at)}{2} + \frac{1}{2a}\int_{x-at}^{x+at} \bar{\psi}(\xi)d\xi\,. \qquad (2\text{-}5.37)$$

This solves the equation of the vibrating string

$$u_{xx} - \frac{1}{a^2}u_{tt} = 0$$

with the initial conditions

$$u(x, 0) = \varphi(x)$$
$$u_t(x, 0) = \bar{\psi}(x)$$
$$\bar{\psi}(x) = a\psi(x) = au_y(x, 0)\,.$$

Problems

1. Solve Problem 1 from Section 2-4 under the assumption that at the initial moment the concentration of the liquid in the entire tube is constant and dry air streams in through an opening.

2. Solve Problem 2 from Section 2-4 under the assumption that the initial temperature of the system equals u_0 while the temperature at the ends of the tube during the entire time maintains a constant value $v_0 > u_0$.

3. Find a solution of the telegraphic system of equations (see Eq. (2-1.21)),

$$i_x + Cv_t + Gv = 0$$
$$v_x + Li_t + Ri = 0$$

for the infinite straight line with the initial conditions

$$i(x, 0) = \varphi(x)\,,$$
$$v(x, 0) = \psi(x)\,.$$

Hint: First reduce the equation system to an equation of the second order for one of the functions $i(x, t)$ or $v(x, t)$, then find, for example,

$$i_{xx} = CLi_{tt} + (CR + GL)i_t + GRi$$

with the initial conditions

$$i(x, 0) = \varphi(x)\,,$$

$$\left.\frac{\partial i}{\partial t}\right|_{t=0} = -\left(\frac{1}{L}v_x + \frac{R}{L}i\right)_{t=0} = -\frac{1}{L}\psi'(x) - \frac{R}{L}\varphi(x) = \psi_0(x)\,.$$

Then use formula (2-5.35). Investigate the solution of the telegraphic equation which is obtained for small G and R, formula (2-5.35). Consider the limiting case $G \to 0$, $R \to 0$ and obtain from (2-5.35) the D'Alembert formula for the solution of the equation of the vibrating string.

2-6. APPLICATIONS TO CHAPTER 2

1. The vibration of strings of musical instruments

A vibrating string produces vibrations in the air which the human ear perceives as the tone emitted from the string. The tone strength is determined by the energy or the amplitude of the vibrations, the tone pitch by the vibration period, and the tone color by the energy relation between the lowest tone and the overtones.[26]

We shall not go into the physiological process of sound perception and the propagation of sound in air; on the contrary the acoustic effect produced by a string is characterized by the energy, the period, and the distribution of the energy in the overtones.

Ordinarily in musical instruments transverse vibrations of the strings are generated. We can distinguish three types of string instruments, depending on whether the strings are stroked, plucked, or struck. Strings which are struck (for example, in a piano) are thus given a fixed initial velocity, but undergo no initial displacement. With the plucked instruments (for example, a harp or guitar) the strings are made to vibrate from a fixed initial displacement without initial velocity.

The free vibrations of a string excited in an arbitrary manner can be represented in the form (see Section 2-3)

$$u(x, t) = \sum_{n=1}^{\infty} (a_n \cos \omega_n t + b_n \sin \omega_n t) \sin \frac{\pi n}{l} x , \qquad \omega_n = \frac{\pi n}{l} a .$$

Problem 1 given in Section 2-3 as an exercise underlies the very simple theory of vibration of the stroked instrument. The solution of this problem shows that the above coefficients are given by

$$a_n = \frac{2hl^2}{\pi^2 n^2 c(l - c)} \sin \frac{\pi n c}{l} , \qquad b_n = 0 \tag{2-6.1}$$

provided that the initial displacement has the form of a triangle with the height h at the point $x = c$ (Figure 29). For the energy of the nth harmonic vibration we find

$$E_n = \frac{1}{4} \rho l \omega_n^2 a_n^2 = Mh^2 \frac{l^2 a^2}{\pi^2 n^2 c^2 (l-c)^2} \sin^2 \frac{\pi n c}{l} , \qquad M = \rho l \tag{2-6.2}$$

which is inversely proportional to n^2.

In Problem 4, Section 2-3, the simple theory of the struck string was investigated; that is, the string was excited by a concentrated blow with an impulse K at a point c. The solution of this problem has the form

[26] Rayleigh *Theory of Sound*, 2d ed., Vol. I, Ch. VI, London, 1894.

$$u(x,t)=\frac{2K}{\pi a\rho}\sum_{n=1}^{\infty}\frac{1}{n}\sin\frac{\pi nc}{l}\cdot\sin\frac{\pi n}{l}x\cdot\sin\omega_n t\,,\qquad \omega_n=\frac{\pi n}{l}a \tag{2-6.3}$$

$$E_n=\frac{K^2}{M}\sin^2\frac{\pi nc}{l}\,. \tag{2-6.4}$$

Consequently, for a string which is excited by a concentrated blow in a small interval of length δ, (for which δ is small in comparison with the diistance between the individual nodes) the energies of the different harmonics can differ only slightly, and the tone of a string thus excited produces overtones to a strong degree. This conclusion can be easily demonstrated experimentally as follows: If a stretched string (as in a monochord) is struck with the edge of a knife, then it rings very clearly, i.e., the overtones are very noticeable. In the piano, the strings are struck by hammers which are padded with felt or leather. Such an excitation of the string can be represented by the following scheme:

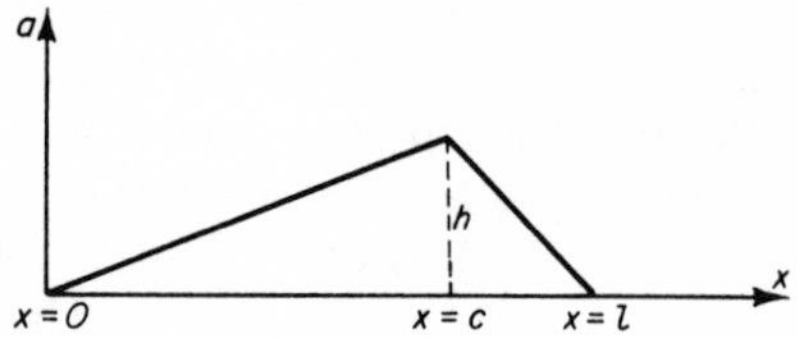

FIG. 29.

(1) Let the string under consideration be excited so that it obtains a constant initial velocity v_0 in the interval $(c-\delta,\ c+\delta)$. This case corresponds to a flat rigid hammer which has a width of 2δ and strikes at the point c. Here the vibrations are described by the function

$$u(x,t)=\frac{4v_0 l}{\pi^2 a}\sum_{n=1}^{\infty}\frac{1}{n^2}\sin\frac{\pi nc}{l}\sin\frac{\pi n}{l}\delta\sin\frac{\pi n}{l}x\sin\omega_n t$$

(see Section 2-3, Problem 3) while the energy of the individual harmonic vibrations is given by

$$E_n=\frac{4Mv_0^2}{n^2\pi^2}\sin^2\frac{\pi nc}{l}\sin^2\frac{\pi n\delta}{l}\,.$$

(2) The string is excited by an initial velocity of the form

$$\frac{\partial u}{\partial t}(x,0)=\begin{cases} v_0\cos\dfrac{x-c}{\delta}\cdot\dfrac{\pi}{2} & \text{for}\quad |x-c|<\delta \\ 0 & \text{for}\quad |x-c|>\delta\,. \end{cases}$$

This case corresponds to a rigid convex hammer of "width" 2δ. Such a hammer gives the string at the center of the interval 2δ the largest initial velocity described schematically by the last-mentioned function. The vibrations so produced have the form

$$u(x,t)=\frac{8v_0\delta}{\pi^2 a}\sum_{n-1}^{\infty}\frac{1}{n}\frac{\cos\frac{\pi n}{l}\delta\cdot\sin\frac{\pi n}{l}c}{1-\left(\frac{2\delta n}{l}\right)^2}\sin\frac{\pi n}{l}x\cdot\sin\omega_n t$$

(see Section 2-3, Problem 3). The energy of the nth harmonic vibration is

$$E_n = \frac{16v_0^2\delta^2\rho}{l\pi^2} \frac{1}{\left[1-\left(\frac{2\delta n}{l}\right)^2\right]^2} \cos^2\frac{\pi n\delta}{l}\sin^2\frac{\pi nc}{l}.$$

(3) A hammer which strikes a string is not ideally rigid. Then the vibrations are no longer determined by the initial velocity but by a time-varying force. Thus we arrive at an inhomogeneous equation with the function

$$F(x,t) = \begin{cases} F_0 \cos\dfrac{x-c}{\delta} \cdot \dfrac{\pi}{2}\sin\dfrac{\pi t}{\tau} & \text{for} \quad |x-c| < \delta, \quad 0 \leqq t \leqq \tau, \\ 0 & \text{for} \quad |x-c| > \delta, \quad t > \tau \end{cases}$$

in the right-hand member. The solution of this equation for $t > \tau$ reads

$$u(x,t) = \frac{16F_0\tau\delta}{\pi^3\rho a}\sum_{n=1}^{\infty}\frac{1}{n}\frac{\cos\dfrac{\pi n\delta}{l}\cos\dfrac{\omega_n\tau}{2}\sin\dfrac{\pi nc}{l}}{\left[1-\left(\dfrac{2\delta n}{l}\right)^2\right]\left[1-\left(\dfrac{na\tau}{l}\right)^2\right]}\sin\frac{\pi n}{l}x\sin\omega_n\left(t-\frac{\tau}{2}\right).$$

The above example shows that the width of the interval on which the blow acts as well as the duration of the blow has a substantial influence on the energies of the higher overtones. Moreover the appearance of the factor $\sin(\pi n/l)c$ shows that when the center of the blow lies at a node of the nth harmonic, the energy of the harmonics are equal to zero.

The appearance of higher overtones (from the seventh on) disturbs the harmonics of the sound and produces a dissonance phenomenon.[27] Conversely, the presence of lower overtones produces a greater sound volume. In order to reduce the energies, the striking point in the piano is chosen in the neighborhood of the point of attachment, between the nodes of the seventh and eighth overtones. By a suitable selection of the width of the hammers and the cushioning, an increase of the energy of the lower (the third and fourth) overtones is again obtained. With older types of pianos, the use of narrower and harder hammers produces a shriller and even a clinking tone.

2. Vibrations of rods

Differential equations of the second order occupy an important place in textbooks on methods of mathematical physics, although many vibration problems—for example, the vibration of rods, plates, etc.—lead to equations of higher order.

To exemplify an equation of the fourth order, we shall consider the natural vibrations of a tuning fork. This problem is equivalent to the problem of the vibration of a thin rectangular rod which is permanently

[27] When, for example, the basic frequency (the first harmonic) corresponds to 440 vibrations per second —A in the center octave—then at the sevenfold frequency the A, G of the fourth octave is produced. The interval A-G, the so-called minor seventh, is unpleasant to the ear and is felt as a dissonance.

fixed at its ends as in a vise. The determination of the form of the vibrations of a tuning fork and its frequencies leads to the equation of a transverse vibrating rod,

$$\frac{\partial^2 y}{\partial t^2} + a^2 \frac{\partial^4 y}{\partial x^4} = 0 . \qquad (2\text{-}6.5)$$

From this equation we are led to several problems in vibrations of rods, the calculation of the stability of rolling waves, and investigations of the vibration of vessels.[28]

To give an elementary derivation of (2-6.5) we shall consider a rectangular rod of length l $(0 \leqq x \leqq l)$ of height h and of width b (Figure 30). Let

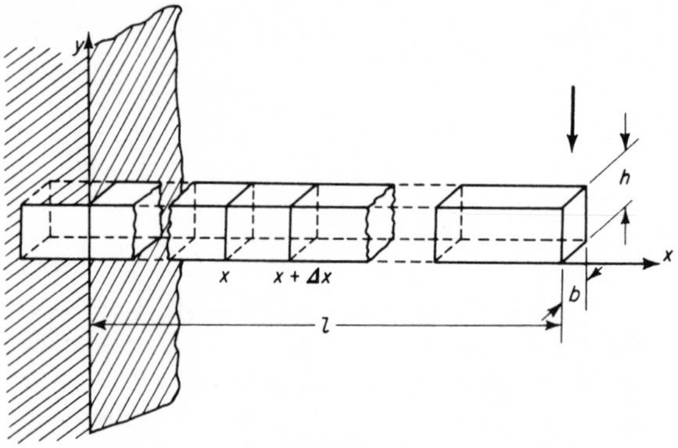

FIG. 30.

dx be the length of an element. The boundary surfaces of the chosen rod element, which is assumed as planar, after the deformation forms the angle $d\varphi$ as shown in the figure. If the deformation is small and the length of the rod axis does not change under the deformation $(dl = dx)$ then

$$d\varphi = \left.\frac{\partial y}{\partial x}\right|_x - \left.\frac{\partial y}{\partial x}\right|_{x+dx} = -\frac{\partial^2 y}{\partial x^2}\, dx$$

is valid. The section of the rod which is at a distance η from the rod axis $y = 0$ changes its length by an amount $\eta d\varphi$ (Figure 31). Therefore, according to Hooke's law the tension acting along the section is equal to

$$dN = E \cdot b d\eta \cdot \frac{\eta d\varphi}{dx} = -E \cdot b \frac{\partial^2 y}{\partial x^2} \eta d\eta ,$$

where E is the modulus of elasticity of the corresponding section. The complete moment of flexure of the force acting on the slice at x is

$$M = -E \frac{\partial^2 y}{\partial x^2} b \int_{-h/2}^{h/2} \eta^2 d\eta = -E \frac{\partial^2 y}{\partial x^2} J , \qquad (2\text{-}6.6)$$

where

[28] See for example, the monograph of A. N. Krylov, *The Vibrations of Vessels*, Moscow, [and] Leningrad, 1948.

$$J = b\int_{-h/2}^{h/2} \eta^2 d\eta = \frac{bh^3}{12}$$

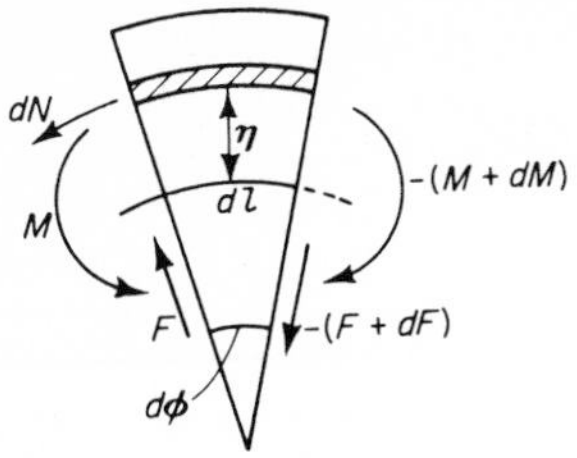

FIG. 31.

is the moment of inertia of the rectangular layer with respect to its horizontal axis. We denote by $M(x)$ the moment acting on the slice at x on the right side of the rod. Then obviously $(M + dM)$ is the moment of the force corresponding to the slice at $x + dx$.

The moment dM coincides with the moment of the tangential force

$$dM = F dx \,.$$

Hence, because of (2-6.6), we obtain

$$F(x, t) = \frac{\partial M}{\partial x} = -EJ\frac{\partial^3 y}{\partial x^3} \tag{2-6.7}$$

for the magnitude of the tangential force

If we set the resulting force on the element under consideration,

$$dF = \frac{\partial F}{\partial x} dx = -EJ\frac{\partial^4 y}{\partial x^4} dx \,,$$

equal to the product of the mass of the element by the acceleration

$$\rho S \frac{\partial^2 y}{\partial t^2} dx \,,$$

where ρ is the density of the rod and S is the area of the cross section (here we neglect the rotary motion arising from the distortion), we obtain the equation of a transverse vibrating rod:

$$\frac{\partial^2 y}{\partial t^2} + a^2 \frac{\partial^4 y}{\partial x^4} = 0 \,, \qquad a^2 = \frac{EJ}{\rho S} \,. \tag{2-6.5}$$

The boundary conditions at the fixed end $x = 0$ are the immovability of the rod and the horizontal position of the tangent:

$$y\Big|_{x=0} = 0 \,, \qquad \frac{\partial y}{\partial x}\Big|_{x=0} = 0 \,. \tag{2-6.8}$$

At the free end the moment of flexure (2-6.6) and the tangential force (2-6.7) must be equal to zero. This yields

$$\frac{\partial^2 y}{\partial x^2}\Big|_{x=l} = 0 \,, \qquad \frac{\partial^3 y}{\partial x^3}\Big|_{x=l} = 0 \,. \tag{2-6.9}$$

In order to completely define the motion of the rod even the initial conditions (the initial displacement and initial velocity) must be given in the form

$$y\Big|_{t=0} = f(x) \quad \text{and} \quad \frac{\partial y}{\partial t}\Big|_{t=0} = \varphi(x) \,, \qquad 0 \leq x \leq l \,. \tag{2-6.10}$$

The problem considered therefore leads to the solution of equation (2-6.5) with boundary conditions (2-6.8), (2-6.9), and the initial conditions (2-6.10).

We shall solve this problem by separation of variables with the aid of the expression

$$y = Y(x)\,T(t)\,. \tag{2-6.11}$$

By putting (2-6.11) into (2-6.5) we obtain

$$\frac{T''(t)}{a^2 T(t)} = -\frac{Y^{(4)}(x)}{Y(x)} = -\lambda\,,$$

from which the eigenvalue problem

$$Y^{(4)} - \lambda Y = 0 \tag{2-6.12}$$

$$Y\Big|_{x=0} = 0\,, \qquad \frac{dY}{dx}\Big|_{x=0} = 0\,, \qquad \frac{d^2Y}{dx^2}\Big|_{x=l} = 0\,, \qquad \frac{d^3Y}{dx^3}\Big|_{x=l} = 0 \tag{2-6.13}$$

results for $Y(x)$. The general solution of Eq. (2-6.12) reads

$$Y(x) = A\cosh\sqrt[4]{\lambda}\,x + B\sinh\sqrt[4]{\lambda}\,x + C\cos\sqrt[4]{\lambda}\,x + D\sin\sqrt[4]{\lambda}\,x\,.$$

From the conditions $Y(0) = 0$, $Y'(0) = 0$, we find $C = -A$ and $D = -B$. Hence it follows that

$$Y(x) = A(\cosh\sqrt[4]{\lambda}\,x - \cos\sqrt[4]{\lambda}\,x) + B(\sinh\sqrt[4]{\lambda}\,x - \sin\sqrt[4]{\lambda}\,x)\,.$$

From $Y''(l) = 0$ and $Y'''(l) = 0$, we find

$$A(\cosh\sqrt[4]{\lambda}\,l + \cos\sqrt[4]{\lambda}\,l) + B(\sinh\sqrt[4]{\lambda}\,l + \sin\sqrt[4]{\lambda}\,l) = 0\,,$$
$$A(\sinh\sqrt[4]{\lambda}\,l - \sin\sqrt[4]{\lambda}\,l) + B(\cosh\sqrt[4]{\lambda}\,l + \cos\sqrt[4]{\lambda}\,l) = 0\,.$$

This system of homogeneous equations possesses a nontrivial solution A and B, provided its determinant is equal to zero. If we set this determinant equal to zero then we obtain the eigenvalues from the transcendental equation

$$\sinh^2\sqrt[4]{\lambda}\,l - \sin^2\sqrt[4]{\lambda}\,l = \cosh^2\sqrt[4]{\lambda}\,l + 2\cosh\sqrt[4]{\lambda}\,l\cos\sqrt[4]{\lambda}\,l + \cos^2\sqrt[4]{\lambda}\,l\,.$$

Because $\cosh^2 x - \sinh^2 x = 1$, we can write

$$\cosh\mu\cdot\cos\mu = -1\,, \qquad \mu = \sqrt[4]{\lambda}\,l\,. \tag{2-6.14}$$

The roots of Eq. (2-6.14) can be calculated without difficulty[29], as, for example, graphically we find

$$\mu_1 = 1.875\,,$$
$$\mu_2 = 4.694\,,$$
$$\mu_3 = 7.854\,,$$
$$\cdots$$
$$\mu_n \approx \frac{\pi}{2}(2n-1) \qquad \text{for} \qquad n > 3\,.$$

[29] For the calculation of the roots of Eq. (2-6.14) see Rayleigh, *op. cit.*, fn. 26.

The last formula accurately gives the value of μ_n for $n = 3$ to the third decimal place and accurately for $n = 7$ up to the sixth place.

Now we shall consider the frequency of vibration of a tuning fork. The equation

$$T'' + a^2\lambda_n T = 0$$

is satisfied by the trigonometric functions

$$T_n(t) = a_n \cos 2\pi\nu_n t + b_n \sin 2\pi\nu_n t$$

with the frequencies

$$\nu_n = \frac{a\sqrt{\lambda_n}}{2\pi} = \frac{\sqrt{\lambda_n}}{2\pi}\sqrt{\frac{EJ}{\rho S}} = \frac{\mu_n^2}{2\pi l^2}\sqrt{\frac{EJ}{\rho S}} .$$

The frequencies μ_n of the eigenvibrations therefore behave as the square of μ_n. Because

$$\frac{\mu_2^2}{\mu_1^2} = 6.267 , \qquad \frac{\mu_3^2}{\mu_1^2} = 17.548$$

the second eigentone is more than two and one-half octaves higher than the base tone, i.e., higher than the sixth harmonic of the string with equal base tones, while the third eigenvibration is more than four octaves higher than the base tone. If the tuning fork, for example, has as a basic frequency of 440 vibrations per second (usually one takes for A′ the small A of the first octave) then the following eigenfrequency of the tuning fork equals 2757.5 vibrations per second (between C′′′′ = 2637.3 and F′′′′ = 2794.0, thus between the E and F of the fourth octave of uniformly tempered scale) while the third eigenfrequency of 7721.1 vibrations per second already is higher than those frequencies used in music.

If the tuning fork is set to vibrating by a blow, higher frequencies appear in addition to the first, which explains the initial metallic sound. The higher harmonics are nevertheless quickly damped so that the tuning fork soon rings out with the pure basic tone.

3. Vibrations of a string loaded by masses

1. *Statement of the problem.* In the following discussion, we shall limit ourselves to vibrations of a string $(0, l)$ fixed at the ends and loaded at fixed points $x = x_i$ $(i = 1, 2, \cdots, n)$ by concentrated masses M_i.

The conditions at point x_i can be of two different types. If a concentrated force $F_i(t)$ acts at point x_i $(i = 1, 2, \cdots, n)$, the conditions

$$u(x_i - 0, t) = u(x_i + 0, t) \tag{2-6.15}$$

$$ku_x \,\Big|_{x_i-0}^{x_i+0} = -F_i \tag{2-6.16}$$

must be satisfied. In the present case, F_i signifies an inertial force. If we substitute into (2-6.16) the following

$$F_i = -M_i u_{tt}(x_i , t) ,$$

then we obtain

$$M_i u_{tt}(x_i, t) = k u_x \mid_{x_i-0}^{x_i+0} . \tag{2-6.17}$$

The condition (2-6.17) can be derived by still another method. First we distribute the mass M_i in the interval $(x_i - \varepsilon, x_i + \varepsilon)$ with uniform density δ_i and then use the vibration equation for the inhomogeneous string

$$(\rho + \delta_i)\, u_{tt} = \frac{\partial}{\partial x}\left(k\frac{\partial u}{\partial x}\right) \qquad x_i - \varepsilon < x < x_i + \varepsilon , \tag{2-6.18}$$

where ρ is the density of the string. Let $u_\varepsilon(x, t)$ be a solution of this equation.

By integration of Eq. (2-6.18) with respect to x from $x_i - \varepsilon$ to $x_i + \varepsilon$ and passage to the limit as $\varepsilon \to 0$, the condition (2-6.17) results for the function $u(x, t) = \lim_{\varepsilon \to 0} u_\varepsilon(x, t)$. We shall not go into a more precise investigation of the passage to the limit.

The complete formulation of our problem then reads:

Find a solution of the equation

$$\rho\frac{\partial^2 u}{\partial t^2} = \frac{\partial}{\partial x}\left(k\frac{\partial u}{\partial x}\right) , \tag{2-6.19}$$

which satisfies the boundary conditions

$$\left.\begin{aligned} u(0, t) &= 0, \\ u(l, t) &= 0, \end{aligned}\right\} \tag{2-6.20}$$

the transition conditions

$$\begin{aligned} u(x_i - 0, t) &= u(x_i + 0, t) \\ M_i u_{tt}(x_i, t) &= k u_x \mid_{x_i-0}^{x_i+0} \end{aligned} \qquad i = 1, 2, \cdots, n \tag{2-6.21}$$

at the point $x = x_i$, and the initial conditions

$$\left.\begin{aligned} u(x, 0) &= \varphi(x) \\ u_t(x, 0) &= \psi(x) \end{aligned}\right\} \tag{2-6.22}$$

where $\varphi(x)$ and $\psi(x)$ are prescribed functions.

2. *Eigenvibrations of a string loaded by masses.* We shall first consider the eigenfrequencies and the profile of a standing wave for a loaded string. Therefore, we shall seek the solution of this problem in the form

$$u(x, t) = X(x)\, T(t) . \tag{2-6.23}$$

If we substitute (2-6.23) into (2-6.19) and use the boundary conditions, we obtain by separation of the variables

$$T'' + \lambda T = 0 \tag{2-6.24}$$

and

$$\left.\begin{aligned} &\frac{d}{dx}(kX') + \lambda\rho X = 0 , \\ &X(0) = 0 \qquad X(l) = 0 . \end{aligned}\right\} \tag{2-6.25}$$

The transition conditions yield

$$X(x_i - 0) = X(x_i + 0)$$
$$M_i X(x_i) T'' = kX' \mid_{x_i-0}^{x_i+0} T \, .$$

By consideration of (2-6.24) we can write this relation in the form

$$kX' \mid_{x_i-0}^{x_i+0} = -\lambda M_i X(x_i) \, .$$

In this manner we arrive at the following eigenvalue problem for $X(x)$:

$$\frac{d}{dx}(kX') + \lambda\rho X = 0 \, , \qquad X(0) = 0 \, , \qquad X(l) = 0 \tag{2-6.25}$$

$$X(x_i - 0) = X(x_i + 0) \, , \qquad i = 1, 2, \cdots, n \tag{2-6.26}$$

$$kX'(x_i + 0) - kX'(x_i - 0) + \lambda M_i X(x_i) = 0 \, . \tag{2-6.27}$$

The peculiarity of the boundary-value problem considered, which differs from the problems treated previously, lies in the occurrence of the parameter λ not only in the equation but also in an auxiliary condition.

It was shown in Section 2-3 that the eigenfunctions

$$X_1(x) \, , \qquad X_2(x), \cdots$$

of the problem

$$\frac{d}{dx}(kX') + \lambda\rho X = 0 \, , \qquad X(0) = 0 \, , \qquad X(l) = 0$$

are orthogonal in the interval $(0, l)$ with respect to the density function $\rho(x)$:

$$\int_0^l X_m(x) X_n(x) \rho(x) dx = 0 \, , \qquad m \neq n \, . \tag{2-6.28}$$

We now distribute each mass M_i with uniform density δ in the interval $x_i - \varepsilon < x < x_i + \varepsilon$, where $\varepsilon > 0$ is an arbitrarily small number. Hence we arrive at a corresponding vibration problem for the inhomogeneous string with density $\rho_\varepsilon(x)$. Let $\lambda_{\varepsilon n}$ and $X_n(x)$ be the eigenvalues and eigenfunctions respectively of this problem. The eigenfunctions must satisfy the orthogonality relation,

$$\int_0^l X_{\varepsilon m}(x) X_{\varepsilon n}(x) \rho_\varepsilon(x) dx = 0 \, . \tag{2-6.29}$$

If we break up the integral in (2-6.29) over $(0, l)$ into ranges from $(0, x_i - \varepsilon)$ plus the integral first from $(x_i - \varepsilon, \; x_i + \varepsilon)$ about the portion of the interval, then from $(x_i + \varepsilon, l)$, and take the limit as $\varepsilon \to 0$, we obtain the relation

$$\int_0^l X_m(x) X_n(x) \rho(x) dx + \sum_{i=1}^{n} M_i X_m(x_i) X_n(x_i) = 0 \qquad m \neq n \, , \tag{2-6.30}$$

the condition for the so-called weighted orthogonality.[30]

[30] R. Courant and D. Hilbert, *Methods of Mathematical Physics*, Vol. I, Ch. 6, Berlin, 1931.

We shall not go into the investigation of the question as to whether such passage to the limit is permissible.

The orthogonality condition (2-6.30) can also be derived by a purely formal method from the differential equation and the conditions (2-6.25) through (2-6.27). Let $X_m(x)$ and $X_n(x)$ be two eigenfunctions of the problem. Let λ_m and λ_n be the eigenvalues corresponding to it. These satisfy the conditions

$$\frac{d}{dx}\left(k\frac{dX_m}{dx}\right) + \lambda_m \rho X_m = 0 \quad \text{and} \quad \frac{d}{dx}\left(k\frac{dX_n}{dx}\right) + \lambda_n \rho X_n = 0 .$$

We multiply the first relation with $X_n(x)$, the second with $X_m(x)$, and subtract the resulting equations from each other. If we integrate this difference over $(0, x_1)$, (x_1, x_2), $\cdots$ (x_k, l) and add the results, we find

$$(\lambda_m - \lambda_n)\int_0^l X_m(x)X_n(x)\rho(x)dx - \sum_{i=0}^{k}\int_{x_i}^{x_i+1}\frac{d}{dx}[X_m kX'_n - X_n kX'_m]dx = 0 , \qquad (2\text{-}6.31)$$

where we have set $x_0 = 0$, $x_{k+1} = l$. If the integration is performed in each summand of the sum, and if the terms which correspond to the boundaries $x = x_i - 0$ and $x = x_i + 0$ are collected, we obtain

$$A_i = (X_m kX'_n - X_n kX'_m)_{x=x_i-0} - (X_m kX'_n - X_n kX'_m)_{x=x_i+0} .$$

Here the expression evaluated at $x = 0$ and $x = l$ on the basis of the boundary conditions equals zero.

For the calculation of A_i we use the transition conditions

$$\begin{aligned} X_j(x_i - 0) &= X_j(x_i + 0) \\ kX'_j(x_i + 0) - kX'_j(x_i - 0) &= -M_i\lambda_j X_j(x_i) \end{aligned} \qquad j = m, n . \qquad (2\text{-}6.27')$$

If we then write A_i in the form

$$A_i = X_m(x_i)\,[kX'_n(x_i - 0) - kX'_n(x_i + 0)] - X_n(x_i)\,[kX'_m(x_i - 0) - kX'_m(x_i + 0)]$$

and take (2-6.27) into consideration, we obtain

$$A_i = X_m(x_i)M_i\lambda_n X_n(x_i) - X_n(x_i)M_i\lambda_m X_m(x_i) = M_i X_m(x_i)X_n(x_i)(\lambda_n - \lambda_m) .$$

Equation (2-6.31) can now be written in the form

$$(\lambda_m - \lambda_n)\left\{\int_0^l X_m(x)X_n(x)\rho(x)dx + \sum_{i=1}^{k} M_i X_m(x_i)X_n(x_i)\right\} = 0 .$$

For $\lambda_m \neq \lambda_n$ the orthogonality condition (2-6.30) follows immediately.

The norm of the eigenfunction $X_n(x)$ is defined by

$$N_n = \int_0^l X_n^2(x)\rho(x)dx + \sum_{i=1}^{k} M_i X_n^2(x_i) . \qquad (2\text{-}6.32)$$

We shall not at this point go into the proof of the existence of infinitely many eigenvalues and eigenfunctions, the positiveness of the eigenvalues, and the corresponding development theorem. The boundary-value problem considered above, as also the problem investigated in Section 2-3, leads to an integral equation, in the present case to a weighted integral equation,[31] which is equivalent to an integral equation with Stieltjes integrals.

For the development of a function $f(x)$ in a series

$$f(x) = \sum_{n=1}^{\infty} f_n X_n(x)$$

the following formula for the coefficients holds:

$$f_n = \frac{\int_0^l f(x) X_n(x) \rho(x) dx + \sum_{i=1}^{k} M_i f(x_i) X_n(x_i)}{N_n} . \tag{2-6.33}$$

The initial-value problem described in Section 2-6 § 1 is solved according to the above method of separation of variables. We can treat analogously the vibrations of a rod (or a beam) which is loaded with a concentrated mass.

In physics and in technology vibration problems of a string loaded with a concentrated mass often occur. Poisson had already solved the problem of the motion of a weight hanging from an elastic string. Then A. N. Krylov[32] showed that the theory is applicable to the indicators of damping machines, the torsional vibrations to balance wheels, to valves of different types, etc., and that they lead back to this problem. Also of great significance for the theory of various measuring instruments is the study of the torsional vibrations of fibers with a mass fastened to one end (for example, a mirror).

A specific instance occurs with a similar problem in investigating the stability of vibrations of the air foils of airplanes. For the solution of this problem one must calculate the eigenfrequencies of the air foils (which can be considered as a beam of variable cross section) which are loaded by masses (say, the motor). Another example is the calculation of the eigenvibrations of antennas with lumped capacity and self-inductance.

We shall not concern ourselves here with the approximation methods for the determination of the eigenvalues and the eigenfunctions of these problems, since they are analogous to the approximation methods for the determination of the corresponding quantities for the inhomogeneous string.

3. *The vibrations of a string with a loaded end.* The vibration of a homogeneous string which is fastened at the end ($x = 0$) while at the other end ($x = l$) hangs a weight of mass M is, in practice, of special interest.

In this case the condition at $x = l$ assumes the form

$$M u_{tt}(l, t) = -k u_x(l, t) .$$

For the amplitudes of the standing waves we obtain the equation

$$X_n'' + \lambda_n X_n = 0$$

with the boundary conditions

[31] See A. Kneser, "*Integral Equations and the Representation of Arbitrary Functions of Two Variables,*" Rend. Palermo **27**, 117–147, 1908.

[32] A. N. Krylov, *Differential Equations of Mathematical Physics,* Ch. VII, Academy of Science of USSR, 1932.

$$X_n(0) = 0\,, \qquad X'_n(l) = \frac{M}{\rho}\lambda_n X_n(l)\,.$$

Hence we find

$$X_n(x) = \frac{\sin\sqrt{\lambda_n}x}{\sin\sqrt{\lambda_n}l}\,,$$

where λ_n is fixed by

$$\operatorname{ctg}\sqrt{\lambda_n}l = \frac{M}{\rho}\sqrt{\lambda_n}\,. \tag{2-6.34}$$

The orthogonality condition for the functions $X_n(x)$ assumes the form

$$\int_0^l X_n(x)X_m(x)\rho(x)dx + MX_n(l)X_m(l) = 0\,.$$

For the norms we have

$$N_n = \int_0^l X_n^2(x)\rho(x)dx + MX_n^2(l)\,.$$

From (2-6.34) we therefore obtain

$$N_n = \frac{l\rho}{2} + \frac{M}{2} + \frac{M^2}{2\rho}\lambda_n l\,.$$

The initial-value problem is solved here in the usual manner.

4. *Corrections on the eigenvalues.* We shall calculate the corrections to the eigenfrequencies for the case of smaller and larger loads M. For the sake of simplicity we shall consider the case in which the weight hangs at the end of the string. Both of the following limiting cases are possible:

(1) $M = 0$. The end $x = l$ is free. For the eigenvalues, then, we have

$$\sqrt{\lambda_n^{(1)}} = \frac{2n+1}{2}\frac{\pi}{l}\,.$$

(2) $M = \infty$. The end $x = l$ is rigidly fixed: $u(l, t) = 0$. Here the eigenvalues can be calculated from

$$\sqrt{\lambda_n^{(2)}} = \frac{\pi n}{l}\,.$$

Of interest to us now are the eigenvalues for small M ($M \to 0$) and large M ($M \to \infty$).

(*a*) M is small. In order to find the corrections to the eigenvalues $\lambda_n^{(1)}$ we set

$$\sqrt{\lambda_n} = \sqrt{\lambda_n^{(1)}} + \varepsilon M\,, \tag{2-6.35}$$

where ε is a fixed number. If we substitute (2-6.35) into Eq. (2-6.34) and neglect M^2 and the higher powers of M, we obtain

$$\lambda_n = \lambda_n^{(1)}\left(1 - \frac{2M}{\rho l}\right), \tag{2-6.36}$$

i.e., the eigenvalues of the weighted string increase as $M \to 0$ and approaches the eigenvalues of the string with a free end.

(*b*) M is large. Now we set

$$\sqrt{\lambda_n} = \sqrt{\lambda_n^{(2)}} + \varepsilon \frac{1}{M}\,.$$

Then (2-6.34) yields

$$\varepsilon = \frac{\rho}{\sqrt{\lambda_n^{(2)}}\,l}\,,$$

where the terms which contain $1/M^2$ and higher powers of $1/M$ can be neglected. Thus, there results

$$\sqrt{\lambda_n} = \sqrt{\lambda_n^{(2)}} + \frac{1}{\sqrt{\lambda_n^{(2)}}\,l}\frac{\rho}{M}\,, \qquad \lambda_n = \lambda_n^{(2)} + \frac{2\rho}{Ml}\,, \tag{2-6.37}$$

i.e., the eigenfrequencies with increasing loads becomes smaller and approaches uniformly the eigenvalues of the string with rigidly fastened ends.

4. Equations of gas dynamics and the theory of shock waves

1. *Equations of gas dynamics. The conservation of energy expression.* The equations of acoustics (see Section 2-6 §1) were derived under the assumption that the stream velocity of the gases and the pressure changes are small. Under these assumptions the equations of hydrodynamics assume a linear form.

On the other hand, one deals with hydrodynamic processes in problems which result from the investigation of rocket flights, the velocity of airplanes, ballistics, with detonation waves, etc., for which high velocities and large pressure differences are characteristic. In these cases, the linear approximation of acoustics is useless and instead we must use the nonlinear equations of hydrodynamics.

Since in practice such motions occur predominantly in gases, the hydrodynamics of high velocities are usually called gas dynamics.

The equations of gas dynamics have, for one-dimensional motion of the gas (in the direction of the x axis), the form

continuity equation: $$\frac{\partial \rho}{\partial t} + \frac{\partial}{\partial x}(\rho v) = 0 \tag{2-6.38}$$

momentum equation: $$\rho\frac{\partial v}{\partial t} + \rho v\frac{\partial v}{\partial x} = -\frac{\partial p}{\partial x} \tag{2-6.39}$$

equation of state: $$p = f(\rho, T)\,. \tag{2-6.40}$$

Therefore, the equations of gas dynamics represent the equations of motion of an ideal compressible fluid in the absence of external forces.

We shall now derive the conservation of energy law. The energy per unit of volume is equal to

$$\frac{\rho v^2}{2} + \rho \varepsilon\,, \tag{2-6.41}$$

where the first member signifies the kinetic energy and the second, the internal energy. Obviously, here ε is the internal energy per unit of mass.

For an ideal gas, $\varepsilon = c_v T$ where c_v is the specific heat at constant volume and T is the temperature. For the energy change in a unit of time we therefore have

$$\frac{\partial}{\partial t}\left(\frac{\rho v^2}{2} + \rho\varepsilon\right) = \frac{\partial}{\partial t}\left(\frac{\rho v^2}{2}\right) + \frac{\partial}{\partial t}(\rho\varepsilon)\,. \tag{2-6.42}$$

If we carry out the differentiation in the first summand, then on the basis of Eq. (2-6.38) and (2-6.39) we obtain

$$\frac{\partial}{\partial t}\left(\frac{\rho v^2}{2}\right) = \frac{v^2}{2}\frac{\partial \rho}{\partial t} + \rho v \frac{\partial v}{\partial t} = -\frac{v^2}{2}\frac{\partial}{\partial x}(\rho v) - \rho v \frac{\partial}{\partial x}\left(\frac{v^2}{2}\right) - v\frac{\partial p}{\partial x}\,. \tag{2-6.43}$$

To transform the derivative $(\partial/\partial t)(\rho\varepsilon)$ we apply the first law of thermodynamics which expresses the law of conservation of energy:

$$dQ = d\varepsilon + p d\tau\,. \tag{2-6.44}$$

Thus dQ is the amount of heat which the system obtains from the outside or gives to the outside, and $pd\tau$ is the work which must be performed in order to change the volume by an amount $d\tau$ ($\tau = 1/\rho$ is the specific volume).

If the process proceeds adiabatically (i.e., no heat exchange occurs with the surrounding medium) then

$$dQ = 0\,,$$

and

$$d\varepsilon = -pd\frac{1}{\rho} = \frac{p}{\rho^2}d\rho\,. \tag{2-6.45}$$

With the help of this expression we find

$$d(\rho\varepsilon) = \varepsilon d\rho + \rho d\varepsilon = \varepsilon d\rho + \frac{p}{\rho}d\rho = w d\rho \tag{2-6.46}$$

$$\frac{\partial}{\partial t}(\rho\varepsilon) = w\frac{\partial \rho}{\partial t} \tag{2-6.47}$$

where

$$w = \varepsilon + \frac{p}{\rho} \tag{2-6.48}$$

is the heat function (enthalpy), or the heat content per unit of mass.

The derivative $\partial w/\partial x$ on the basis of the expressions (2-6.46) and (2-6.48) satisfies the equation

$$\rho v\frac{\partial w}{\partial x} = v\frac{\partial p}{\partial x}\,. \tag{2-6.49}$$

By consideration of Eqs. (2-6.39), (2-6.42), (2-6.43), (2-6.47) and (2-6.49), we obtain the conservation of energy relation in the differential form

$$\frac{\partial}{\partial t}\left(\frac{\rho v^2}{2} + \rho\varepsilon\right) = -\frac{\partial}{\partial x}\left[\rho v\left(\frac{v^2}{2} + w\right)\right]. \tag{2-6.50}$$

To find the physical significance of this equation we integrate it over an interval (x_1, x_2):

$$\frac{\partial}{\partial t}\int_{x_1}^{x_2}\left(\frac{\rho v^2}{2} + \rho\varepsilon\right)dx = -\rho v\left(\frac{v^2}{2} + w\right)\Big|_{x_1}^{x_2}.$$

On the left side is the energy change per unit of time in the interval (x_1, x_2); on the right is the amount of energy which in a unit of time flows out from the considered volume.

If the heat conduction can not be ignored, the conservation of energy equation assumes the form

$$\frac{\partial}{\partial t}\left(\frac{\rho v^2}{2} + \rho\varepsilon\right) = -\frac{\partial}{\partial x}\left[\rho v\left(\frac{v^2}{2} + w\right) - \kappa\frac{\partial T}{\partial x}\right], \tag{2-6.51}$$

where κ is the coefficient of thermal conductivity.

2. *Shock waves: the Hugoniot conditions.* With high velocities motions are possible, which on certain surfaces can propagate discontinuities of the hydrodynamic quantities (pressure, velocity, density, etc.) in space. These surfaces of discontinuity are usually called shock waves.

On the surface supporting the discontinuity (the front of the shock wave), the conditions for the continuity of the streaming of the fluid (or of the gas), the energy, and the momentum (the Hugoniot conditions) must be satisfied.

To derive these conditions, we first transform Eq. (2-6.38) to a form suitable for our purpose. For this purpose we multiply (2-6.38) by v and add the result to (2-6.38). This gives

$$\frac{\partial}{\partial t}(\rho v) = -\frac{\partial}{\partial x}(p + \rho v^2). \tag{2-6.39$'$}$$

Further we write the continuity equation, the equation of motion, and the conservation of energy relation in the following form,

$$\frac{\partial \rho}{\partial t} = -\frac{\partial}{\partial x}(\rho v) \tag{2-6.38$'$}$$

$$\frac{\partial(\rho v)}{\partial t} = -\frac{\partial}{\partial x}(p + \rho v^2) \tag{2-6.39$'$}$$

$$\frac{\partial}{\partial t}\left(\frac{\rho v^2}{2} + \rho\varepsilon\right) = -\frac{\partial}{\partial x}\left[\rho v\left(\frac{v^2}{2} + w\right)\right]. \tag{2-6.50}$$

In the x, t plane we consider the "spur" $x = \alpha(t)$ of the shock front. Let AC be any arc of $x = \alpha(t)$. The points A and C must therefore have the coordinates x_1, t_1, or $x_2 = x_1 + \Delta x$, $t_2 = t_1 + \Delta t$. Further, let the points B and D be situated so that the sides of the rectangle $ABCD$ run parallel to the coordinate axes.

We write the law of the conservation of mass in the integral form

$$\int_{x_1}^{x_2}[(\rho)_{t_2}-(\rho)_{t_1}]\,dx=-\int_{t_1}^{t_2}[(\rho v)_{x_2}-(\rho v)_{x_1}]\,dt\,. \tag{2-6.52}$$

Here the left side is the change of mass in the interval (x_1, x_2) during the period of time (t_1, t_2); on the right side is the amount of fluid (the gas) which flows out from (x_1, x_2) during the time (t_1, t_2). If the functions ρ and ρv are continuous throughout and differentiable in $ABCD$, Eqs. (2-6.52) and (2-6.37′) are equivalent. In the present case, however, this does not occur.

We apply the mean-value theorem to each individual summand, with the result

$$[(\rho)_{\substack{t=t_2\\x=x^*}}-(\rho)_{\substack{t=t_1\\x=x^{**}}}]\frac{\Delta x}{\Delta t}=-(\rho v)_{\substack{x=x_2\\t=t^*}}+(\rho v)_{\substack{x=x_1\\t=t^{**}}}\,.$$

Here x^*, x^{**}, t^*, t^{**} signify the corresponding mean values of x and t.

If we pass to the limit as $\Delta x \to 0\,(x_2 \to x_1)$ and $\Delta t \to 0\,(t_2 \to t_1)$ and denote the value of the function above the curve $x=\alpha(t)$, behind the front of the shock wave, by the index 1 and the value of the function below this curve, before the front, by the index 2, we obtain

$$(\rho_2-\rho_1)U=-(\rho v)_1+(\rho v)_2\,, \tag{2-6.53}$$

where

$$U=\frac{d\alpha}{dt}=\lim_{\Delta t\to 0}\frac{\Delta x}{\Delta t}$$

is the velocity of the shock wave.

In the coordinate system moving with the shock wave we denote by

$$u_1=U-v_1\,,\ u_2=U-v_2$$

the velocity of the elements before and behind the front. Therefore (2-6.53) can be written in the form

$$\rho_1 u_1=\rho_2 u_2\,. \tag{2-6.53′}$$

This equation signifies the continuity of the matter flowing across the fronts of the shock wave.

The law of conservation of momentum in integral form reads

$$\int_{x_1}^{x_2}[(\rho v)_{t_2}-(\rho v)_{t_1}]dx=-\int_{t_1}^{t_2}[(p+\rho v^2)_{x_2}-(p+\rho v^2)_{x_1}]dt\,,$$

where the right side represents the sum of the acting forces produced by the impulses (pressure forces) and the flow of the momentum. As $\Delta x \to 0$ and $\Delta t \to 0$ we obtain

$$U[(\rho v)_2-(\rho v)_1]=-(p+\rho v^2)_1+(p+\rho v^2)_2$$

or

$$p_1+\rho_1 u_1^2=p_2+\rho_2 u_2^2\,, \tag{2-6.54}$$

the conservation law for the flow of the momentum across a front; and for the conservation of energy on the front we obtain the equation

$$\left(\frac{\rho v^2}{2}+\rho\varepsilon\right)_2 U-\left(\frac{\rho v^2}{2}+\rho\varepsilon\right)_1 U=-\rho_1 v_1\left(\frac{v^2}{2}+w\right)_1+\rho_2 v_2\left(\frac{v^2}{2}+w\right)_2,$$

which after a single simple transformation assumes the form

$$\rho_1 u_1\left(w_1+\frac{u_1^2}{2}\right)=\rho_2 u_2\left(w_2+\frac{u_2^2}{2}\right)$$

or according to (2-6.53)

$$w_1+\frac{u_1^2}{2}=w_2+\frac{u_2^2}{2}. \tag{2-6.55}$$

Thus, on the front of a shock wave, the following equations (the Hugoniot conditions) must be satisfied:

$$\rho_1 u_1=\rho_2 u_2 \tag{2-6.53'}$$

$$p_1+\rho_1 u_1^2=p_2+\rho_2 u_2^2 \tag{2-6.54}$$

$$w_1+\frac{u_1^2}{2}=w_2+\frac{u_2^2}{2}. \tag{2-6.55}$$

From both of the first Eqs. (2-6.53′) and (2-6.54) we can express u_1 and u_2 through p and ρ:

$$u_1^2=\frac{\rho_2}{\rho_1}\cdot\frac{p_1-p_2}{\rho_1-\rho_2}, \qquad u_2^2=\frac{\rho_1}{\rho_2}\cdot\frac{p_1-p_2}{\rho_1-\rho_2},$$

from which it follows that

$$u_1^2-u_2^2=-\frac{\rho_1+\rho_2}{\rho_1\rho_2}(p_1-p_2).$$

If we then insert this expression into (2-6.55), we find between the energy values on both sides of the wave front the relations

$$w_1-w_2=\frac{1}{2\rho_1\rho_2}(\rho_1+\rho_2)(p_1-p_2)$$

and

$$\varepsilon_1-\varepsilon_2=\frac{1}{2\rho_1\rho_2}(\rho_1-\rho_2)(p_1+p_2).$$

For an ideal gas we have

$$p=R\rho T, \qquad \varepsilon=c_v T, \qquad w=c_p T=\frac{c_p}{c_p-c_v}RT=\frac{\gamma}{\gamma-1}\cdot\frac{p}{\rho},$$

that is,

$$w=\frac{\gamma}{\gamma-1}\cdot\frac{p}{\rho}. \tag{2-6.56}$$

After a simple transformation we obtain from (2-6.56) the so-called Hugoniot adiabatic equation

$$\frac{\rho_2}{\rho_1} = \frac{(\gamma+1)p_2 + (\gamma-1)p_1}{(\gamma-1)p_2 + (\gamma+1)p_1} \tag{2-6.57}$$

or

$$\frac{p_2}{p_1} = \frac{(\gamma+1)\rho_2 - (\gamma-1)\rho_1}{(\gamma+1)\rho_1 - (\gamma-1)\rho_2}\,. \tag{2-6.58}$$

From this, the quantities t_1, ρ_1, t_2, ρ_2 can be calculated if the remaining three are known.

A shock wave can move continuously with respect to the gas from positions of high pressure to positions of lower pressure: $p_2 \to p_1$ (law of Zemplen). Hence it follows that the density of gas behind the front is larger than that before the front.

Formula (2-6.57) expresses the dependence between p_2 and ρ_2 for prescribed p_1 and ρ_1. For a given p_1 and ρ_1, $\rho_2 = \rho_2(p_2)$ is a monotone increasing function which for $p_2/p_1 \to \infty$ (shock wave of larger amplitude) tends towards a finite limit value

$$\frac{\rho_2}{\rho_1} = \frac{\gamma+1}{\gamma-1}\,. \tag{2-6.59}$$

This formula gives the maximum jump in the density which can occur on the front of the shock wave. For diatomic gases $\gamma = 7/5$, and the maximum density jump is then equal to 6:

$$\frac{\rho_2}{\rho_1} = 6\,.$$

From Eqs. (2-6.53′), (2-6.54), and (2-6.57), we find for $p_1 = 0$,

$$u_1 = \sqrt{\frac{\gamma+1}{2}\cdot\frac{p_2}{\rho_1}}\,, \qquad u_2 = \sqrt{\frac{(\gamma-1)^2}{2(\gamma+1)}\cdot\frac{p_2}{\rho_1}}\,.$$

If the motion of the shock wave with respect to the gas is considered as static ($v_1 = 0$), the velocity of propagation of the shock wave equals

$$U = \sqrt{\frac{\gamma+1}{2}\cdot\frac{p_2}{\rho_1}}\,,$$

i.e., it increases as the square root of p_2.

We shall now treat a quite simple problem in the theory of shock waves, whose solution can be given analytically. A cylindrical tube $x > 0$, which is unbounded on one side and enclosed by a piston at the other ($x = 0$) contains a static gas with constant density ρ_1 and constant pressure p_1. At the initial moment $t = 0$, the piston begins to move with a constant velocity "v" in the direction of the positive x axis. In front of the piston a shock wave forms, which at the initial moment is in the same position as the piston and then moves away from this position with a constant velocity $U > v$. Between the piston and the front of the shock wave a region 2 forms, in which the gas moves with the velocity of the piston. Before the front (region 1) the gas is found in the original state: $\rho = \rho_1$, $p = p_1$ $(v = 0)$.

With the conditions (2-6.53′), (2-6.54), and (2-6.55) for the front, we can easily determine its velocity, the magnitude of the jump, the density, and the pressure.

To this end we introduce the nondimensional quantities

$$\omega = \frac{\rho_1}{\rho_2} \qquad \tilde{U} = \frac{U}{c_1} \qquad \tilde{v} = \frac{v}{c_1} \qquad \tilde{p} = \frac{\gamma p_2}{\rho_1 c_1^2} \tag{2-6.60}$$

where $c_1 = \sqrt{\gamma p_1/\rho_1}$ is the velocity of sound before the front (in the non-excited region 1). Then the equation of state can be written in the form

$$\omega\tilde{U} = \tilde{U} - \tilde{v} \qquad \text{or} \qquad \tilde{U} = \frac{\tilde{v}}{1-\omega}\,, \tag{2-6.61}$$

$$\tilde{p} = 1 + \gamma\tilde{U}\tilde{v} \qquad \text{or} \qquad \tilde{p} = 1 + \gamma\frac{\tilde{v}^2}{1-\omega}\,, \tag{2-6.62}$$

$$\tilde{p}\omega = 1 + (\gamma - 1)\left(\tilde{U}\tilde{v} - \frac{1}{2}\tilde{v}^2\right). \tag{2-6.63}$$

Then, by elimination of $\tilde{p}$ and $\tilde{U}$, we obtain for the determination of ω the quadratic equation

$$2\omega^2 - \omega[4 + (\gamma+1)\tilde{v}^2] + [2 + (\gamma-1)\tilde{v}^2] = 0\,. \tag{2-6.64}$$

Since, obviously, $\omega < 1$, $(\rho_2 > \rho_1)$, the smallest root is given by

$$\omega^2 = 1 + \frac{(\gamma+1)}{4}\tilde{v}^2 - \tilde{v}\sqrt{1 + \frac{(\gamma+1)^2}{16}\tilde{v}^2}\,. \tag{2-6.65}$$

From (2-6.61) and (2-6.65) there results then

$$\tilde{U} = \frac{(\gamma+1)}{4}\tilde{v} + \sqrt{1 + \frac{(\gamma+1)^2}{16}\tilde{v}^2} \tag{2-6.66}$$

$$\tilde{p} = 1 + \frac{\gamma(\gamma+1)}{4}\tilde{v}^2 + \gamma\tilde{v}\sqrt{1 + \frac{(\gamma+1)^2}{16}\tilde{v}^2}\,. \tag{2-6.67}$$

In the old quantities, therefore,

$$\rho_2 = \rho_1 \frac{1 + \left(\frac{\gamma+1}{4}\cdot\frac{v^2}{c_1^2}\right) + \frac{v}{c_1}\sqrt{1 + \frac{(\gamma+1)^2}{16c_1^2}\cdot v^2}}{1 + \frac{(\gamma-1)v^2}{2c_1^2}} \tag{2-6.68}$$

$$U = \frac{\gamma+1}{4}v + c_1\sqrt{1 + \frac{(\gamma+1)^2}{16c_1^2}v^2}\,, \tag{2-6.69}$$

$$p_2 = p_1\left\{1 + \left(\frac{\gamma(\gamma+1)}{4}\frac{v^2}{c_1^2}\right) + \frac{\gamma v}{c_1}\sqrt{1 + \frac{(\gamma+1)^2}{16c_1^2}v^2}\right\}. \tag{2-6.70}$$

Since the velocity of the shock wave is constant there, we find for the position of the front at time t

$$x = \alpha(t) = \left\{\frac{(\gamma+1)}{4}v + c_1\sqrt{1+\frac{(\gamma+1)^2}{16c_1^2}v^2}\right\}t\,. \tag{2-6.71}$$

In the limiting case $v/c_1 \gg 1$ (shock wave of greater intensity) we find from the formulas (2-6.68) through (2-6.70) the limiting relations

$$\rho_2 = \rho_1\frac{\gamma+1}{\gamma-1}\,, \qquad U = \frac{\gamma+1}{2}v\,, \qquad p_2 = p_1\cdot\frac{\gamma(\gamma+1)}{2}\cdot\frac{v^2}{c_1^2}$$

obtained earlier.

If $v/c_1 \ll 1$ (shock wave of smaller intensity) then the term v^2/c_1^2 can be neglected:

$$\rho_2 = \rho_1\left(1+\frac{v}{c_1}\right)$$

$$U = c_1 + \frac{(\gamma+1)}{4}v$$

$$p_2 = p_1\left(1+\frac{\gamma v}{c_1}\right).$$

3. *Weak discontinuities.* We have hitherto considered the motion of a shock wave, on whose front the quantities ρ, p, v, and others change their values by jumps. Such discontinuities are called strong discontinuities.

However, there are also possible motions for which only the first derivatives of ρ, p, v, etc., are discontinuous on certain surfaces, while these quantities themselves are continuous. We call these weak discontinuities.

In Section 2-2 § 8, we investigated the motions of such discontinuities and determined that these discontinuities propagated along the characteristics. We shall therefore proceed from the equations of acoustics. Corresponding results can be obtained also from the nonlinear problems of gas dynamics.

We can easily see that a surface, on which weak discontinuities lie with respect to the gas, propagates with a velocity which is equal to the local velocity of sound. Therefore, if we consider a small neighborhood of the surface of discontinuity and take the average value of the hydrodynamic quantities in this neighborhood, then the weak discontinuities can obviously be considered as small disturbances which satisfy the equations of acoustics and propagate with the local velocity of sound.

As an example, we shall consider the flow of a gas in a vacuum. Let the gas which is enclosed in a semi-infinite body $x > 0$ be found in the rest state at time $t = 0$, and have in the entire region $x > 0$ the constant density ρ and constant pressure p_0. For $t = 0$ the external pressure which acts on the plane $x = 0$ vanishes, and the gas begins to move; hence, a weak discontinuity (the attenuation wave) arises, which propagates with the velocity of sound c_0 in the direction of the positive x axis. The density and the pressure for $t = 0$ have discontinuities on the interior side of the front

$x = x_1(t)$ of the gas. These discontinuities vanish however, immediately after the beginning of the motion.

From the conditions for the continuity of the flow of gases and the momentum for $x = x_1(t)$,

$$0 = \rho_1^-(v_1 - v_1^-) = \rho_1^+(v_1 - v_1^+)\,,$$
$$p_1^- + \rho_1^-(v_1 - v_1^-)^2 = p_1^+ + \rho_1^+(v_1 - v_1^+)^2\,,$$

where ρ_1^-, p_1^-, v_1^- are the left-hand and ρ_1^+, p_1^+, v_1^+ are the right-hand values at the point $x_1(t)$, we obtain

$$p_1^+ = 0 \qquad \text{and} \qquad \rho_1^+ = 0$$

because

$$\rho_1^- = p_1^- = v_1^- = 0\,.$$

For an adiabatic process the equation of state of an ideal gas reads

$$p = p_0\left(\frac{\rho}{\rho_0}\right)^\gamma\,. \tag{2-6.72}$$

For the solution of the problem we assume that

$$\rho = \rho(\xi)\,, \qquad p = p(\xi)\,, \qquad v = v(\xi)\,,$$

where

$$\xi = \frac{x}{t}\,.$$

If we then calculate the derivatives

$$\frac{\partial f}{\partial t} = -\frac{1}{t}\xi\frac{df}{d\xi}\,, \qquad \frac{\partial f}{\partial x} = \frac{1}{t}\frac{df}{d\xi}\,,$$

where $f = \rho$, v, or p, and substitute the found expression in (2-6.38) and (2-6.39) then we obtain

$$\begin{aligned}(v - \xi)\frac{d\rho}{d\xi} &= -\rho\frac{dv}{d\xi}\\ (v - \xi)\rho\frac{dv}{d\xi} &= \frac{dp}{d\xi}\,.\end{aligned} \tag{2-6.73}$$

Now if we multiply the first equation by $(v - \xi)$ and add the product to the second, we obtain

$$(v - \xi)^2\frac{d\rho}{d\xi} = \frac{dp}{d\xi}\,,$$

or

$$\frac{dp}{d\rho} = (v - \xi)^2\,.$$

Hence

$$v - \xi = \pm\sqrt{\frac{dp}{d\rho}} = \pm c\,,$$

where c is the velocity of sound for the adiabatic process.

Since the motion of the weak discontinuity was considered to be in the direction of the positive x axis, then in the last formula we take the minus sign, i.e., we have

$$v - \xi = -c\,. \tag{2-6.74}$$

If we put this solution into (2-6.73),

$$\frac{dv}{d\rho} = \frac{c}{\rho} \tag{2-6.75}$$

or

$$\frac{dv}{dp} = \frac{1}{\rho c}\,.$$

With the help of the equation of state (2-6.72) we find

$$c^2 = \gamma \frac{p}{\rho}$$

and after integration of Eq. (2-6.75)

$$v = \frac{2}{\gamma - 1} \cdot c_0 \left[\left(\frac{\rho}{\rho_0}\right)^{(\gamma-1)/2} - 1\right]. \tag{2-6.76}$$

By use of this formula ρ can be expressed through v:

$$\rho = \rho_0 \left(1 + \frac{\gamma - 1}{2} \cdot \frac{v}{c_0}\right)^{2/(\gamma-1)}. \tag{2-6.77}$$

Here we denote by

$$c_0 = \sqrt{\frac{\gamma p_0}{\rho_0}}$$

the velocity of sound for $v = 0$ (in the static gas). For (2-6.76) we can also write

$$v = \frac{2}{\gamma - 1}(c - c_0)\,. \tag{2-6.78}$$

By introduction of the expression (2-6.77) for ρ in the equation of state (2-6.72) we obtain

$$p = p_0 \left(1 + \frac{\gamma - 1}{2} \cdot \frac{v}{c_0}\right)^{2\gamma/(\gamma-1)}. \tag{2-6.79}$$

From (2-6.78) and (2-6.73) follows the formula

$$v = \frac{2}{\gamma + 1}\left(\frac{x}{t} - c_0\right), \tag{2-6.80}$$

which gives the dependence of the velocity v on x and t. Accordingly, if we insert expression (2-6.80) for v into (2-6.77) and (2-6.79), we obtain the explicit dependence of the quantities ρ and p on x and t. Hence, all the quantities are dependent only on x/t. Therefore, if the distance is measured in units which are proportional to t, the form of motion does not change.

We seek now the velocity of the forward front $v_1(t)$. If we set $p = 0$ in Eq. (2-6.79), we obtain

$$v_1 = -\frac{2}{\gamma - 1} c_0 . \tag{2-6.81}$$

From this it follows that the flow velocity of the gas in vacuum is finite. For diatomic gases $\gamma = 7/5$ and, therefore,

$$v_1 = -5c_0 .$$

We can also obtain the expression (2-6.81) for the velocity of the forward front $x = x_1(t)$ from the relation

$$\int_{x_1}^{x_2} \rho dx = \rho_0 x_2 = \rho_0 c_0 t , \tag{2-6.82}$$

which is the equation of conservation of mass. If, namely, we introduce

$$\xi = \frac{x}{t} ,$$

we obtain

$$\int_{v_1}^{c_0} \rho d\xi = \rho_0 c_0 .$$

Here we substitute the expression for ρ from (2-6.77). With

$$1 + \frac{\gamma - 1}{\gamma + 1} \cdot \frac{\xi - c_0}{c_0} = \lambda$$

it follows that

$$\int_{\lambda_1}^{\lambda_2} \lambda^{2/(\gamma-1)} d\lambda = \frac{\gamma - 1}{\gamma + 1} \tag{2-6.83}$$

with

$$\lambda_1 = 1 + \frac{\gamma - 1}{\gamma + 1} \cdot \frac{v_1 - c_0}{c_0} , \qquad \lambda_2 = 1 .$$

By calculating the integral (2-6.83) we obtain

$$\lambda_2^{(\gamma+1)/(\gamma-1)} - \lambda_1^{(\gamma+1)/(\gamma-1)} = 1 ,$$

i.e.,

$$\lambda_1 = 0 ,$$

where

$$v_1 = -\frac{2c_0}{\gamma - 1} .$$

The problem of the flow of a gas in a vacuum is therefore solved.

In the above considerations we have limited ourselves to the simplest problem of gas dynamics. For a detailed study of the questions occurring here we refer to the list of the corresponding special literature.[33]

5. Dynamics of gas absorption

1. *Equation of gas absorption.* We shall consider the problem of the absorption of a gas.[34] Let a gas-air mixture be passed through a tube (whose axis is directed along the x axis of our coordinate system) be filled with an absorbing substance. Further, we shall indicate by $a(x, t)$ the amount of gas which is absorbed per unit of volume of absorbent and by $u(x, t)$ the concentration of the gas in the pores of the absorbent in the layer x.

We first derive the condition for the conservation of mass assuming that the velocity ν is sufficiently large and that the diffusion for the passage of the gas plays no essential role. For the layer of absorption from x_1 to x_2 in the time from t_1 to t_2 there obviously holds the relation

$$[\nu u\,|_{x_1} - \nu u\,|_{x_2}]\,S\Delta t = [(a+u)\,|_{t_2} - (a+u)\,|_{t_1}]\,S\Delta x\,. \tag{2-6.84}$$

If we divide this by $\Delta x \Delta t$, as $\Delta x \to 0$ and $\Delta t \to 0$ we obtain

$$-\nu\frac{\partial u}{\partial x} = \frac{\partial}{\partial t}(a+u)\,. \tag{2-6.85}$$

The left side of this equation represents the amount of gas absorbed during the passage with respect to the volume and per unit of time, while the right side gives directly the amount of gas consumed in raising the concentration of the gases absorbed and found in the pores. To this equation one must still add the equation of the kinetic absorption

$$\frac{\partial a}{\partial t} = \beta(u - y)\,, \tag{2-6.86}$$

where β is the so-called kinetic coefficient and y is the concentration of the gas which exists in equilibrium with the amount of gas absorbed.

The quantities a and y are linked to each other by a relation

$$a = f(y)\,, \tag{2-6.87}$$

the so-called characteristic of the absorbent.

The curve $a = f(y)$ is called the absorption isotherm. If

[33] See N. E. Kochin, J. A. Kibel, and N. W. Rose, *Theoretical Hydromechanics*, Part II, Ch. I (trans. from Russian), Berlin, 1954; L. Landau and E. Lifschitz, *Mechanics of Deformable Media*, Ch. VII, Moscow, 1944; Ya. B. Zeldovich, *Theory of Shock Waves and Introduction to Gas Dynamics*, Moscow, 1946; L. I. Sedov, "Propagation of Strong Detonation Waves," *Applied Mathematics and Mechanics*, **10**: 2, 1946; R. Sauer, *Introduction to Theoretical Gas Dynamics*, 2d ed., Berlin, 1951; K. Oswatitsch, *Gas Dynamics*, Vienna, 1952.

[34] A. N. Tychonoff, A. A. Zhukhovitskii, and J. L. Zabezhinskii, "Absorption of Gases from an Airstream by the Layers of a Granulated Substance," *J. Phys. Chem., U.S.S.R.* **20**: 10, 1946.

$$f(y) = \frac{y}{u_0 + py},$$

then we speak of a Langmuir isotherm. A simpler form of the function f corresponds to the so-called Henry isotherm, which is accurate in regions of low concentration:

$$a = \frac{1}{\gamma} y, \tag{2-6.88}$$

where $1/\gamma$ is the Henry coefficient.

In this case the following problem arises: From the equations

$$-\nu \frac{\partial u}{\partial x} = \frac{\partial u}{\partial t} + \frac{\partial a}{\partial t} \tag{2-6.85}$$

$$\frac{\partial a}{\partial t} = \beta(u - \gamma a) \tag{2-6.89}$$

determine the functions $u(x, t)$ and $a(x, t)$ which satisfy the auxiliary conditions

$$\left.\begin{aligned} a(x, 0) &= 0 \\ u(x, 0) &= 0 \end{aligned}\right. \tag{2-6.90}$$

$$u(0, t) = u_0 \tag{2-6.91}$$

where u_0 is the concentration of the gas at the entrance of the tube.

By neglecting the derivative $\partial u/\partial t$ (the amount of gas necessary to increase the free concentration in the pores of the absorbent) compared with the derivative $\partial a/\partial t$ (the amount of gas necessary for the increase of the amount of absorbed gases) we obtain[35]

$$-\nu \frac{\partial u}{\partial x} = \frac{\partial a}{\partial t} \tag{2-6.85$'$}$$

$$\frac{\partial a}{\partial t} = \beta(u - \gamma a) \tag{2-6.89}$$

$$a(x, 0) = 0, \qquad u(0, t) = u_0 .$$

If we eliminate the function $a(x, t)$ by introducing the second equation into the first equation and differentiating with respect to t, then

$$-\nu u_{xt} = \beta u_t - \beta\gamma a_t = \beta u_t + \beta\nu\gamma u_x$$

or

$$u_{xt} + \frac{\beta}{\nu} u_t + \beta\gamma u_x = 0 .$$

If we set $t = 0$ in (2-6.85′), we obtain the initial value of u:

$$-\nu u_x(x, 0) = \beta u(x, 0), \qquad u(0, 0) = u_0 .$$

From this we find

$$u(x, 0) = u_0 e^{-(\beta/\nu)x} .$$

[35] For the system, Eqs. (2-6.85′) and (2-6.89) satisfy a single condition, since the axis $t = 0$ here is characteristic.

The determination of $u(x, t)$ thus leads to the problem of the integration of the equation

$$u_{xt} = \frac{\beta}{\nu} u_t + \beta\gamma u_x = 0 \tag{2-6.92}$$

with the auxiliary conditions

$$u(x, 0) = u_0 e^{-(\beta/\nu)x} \tag{2-6.93}$$

$$u(0, t) = u_0 \; . \tag{2-6.91}$$

The characteristics of this equation are the straight lines

$$x = \text{const.}\,, \qquad t = \text{const.}$$

The auxiliary conditions for this problem thus prescribe the values of the sought function $u(x, t)$ on the characteristics. Analogously, the problem for $a(x, t)$ reads:

$$a_{xt} = \frac{\beta}{\nu} a_t + \beta\gamma a_x = 0 \tag{2-6.94}$$

$$a(x, 0) = 0 \tag{2-6.90}$$

$$a(0, t) = \frac{u_0}{\gamma}(1 - e^{-\beta\gamma t}) \; . \tag{2-6.95}$$

Note that a similar problem occurs for a whole series of other questions (for example, with the process of drying in a stream of air, with the heating of a tube by flowing water, etc.).[36]

[36] In the transition to Eq. (2-6.85′) we have neglected u_t. Moreover, we can still show that we arrive at the same equation if we introduce the variables

$$\tau = t - \frac{x}{\nu}\,, \qquad t = \tau + \frac{\xi}{\nu}\,, \qquad \xi = x\,, \qquad x = \xi$$

(Figure 32) in which the time at the point x is measured from the moment $t^\circ = x/\nu$ at which the stream of the gas-air mixture has reached this point. We obtain

$$\frac{\partial u}{\partial x} = \frac{\partial u}{\partial \xi} - \frac{1}{\nu}\frac{\partial u}{\partial \tau}$$

$$\frac{\partial}{\partial t} = \frac{\partial}{\partial \tau}$$

so that Eq. (2-6.85) has the form

$$-\nu\frac{\partial u}{\partial \xi} = \frac{\partial a}{\partial \tau} \tag{2-6.85″}$$

$$\frac{\partial a}{\partial \tau} = \beta(u - \gamma a) \; . \tag{2-6.89}$$

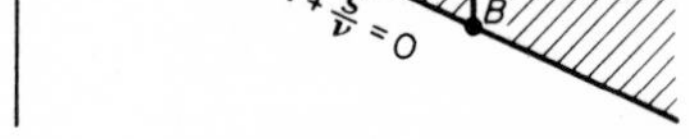

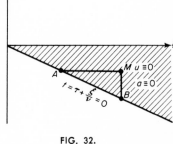

FIG. 32.

The initial conditions (2-6.90) and Eqs. (2-6.85) and (2-6.89) read

$$\begin{aligned} u(x, 0) &= 0 \\ u_t(x, 0) &= 0 \; . \end{aligned} \tag{2-6.90′}$$

The problem is therefore to determine the function u in the region between the straight lines $t = 0$ and the ξ axis corresponding to the initial conditions (2-6.90′) (Cauchy problem). Obviously, in this region $u(x, t) \equiv 0$ but also $a \equiv 0$). Further, from (2-6.85′) and (2-6.89) it is evident that the function $u(x, t)$ for $\tau = 0$ is discontinuous, while $a(x, t)$ remains continuous. Therefore, u for $\tau = 0$, as was shown above, is defined by Eq. (2-6.85′) for $a(x, 0) = 0$. As shown on pages 141–142 (see formulas (2-6.93) and (2-6.95)), when we define the value $u(x, 0)$ and $a(x, 0)$ we obtain for $u(x, t)$ and $a(x, t)$, problems with auxiliary conditions on the characteristics.

A solution of Eq. (2-6.92) can be obtained explicitly by the method investigated in Section 2-5, and we obtain

$$u(x_1, t_1) = u_0 e^{-x_1}\left[e^{-t_1} I_0(2\sqrt{x_1 t_1}) + \frac{1}{x_1}\int_0^{x_1 t_1} e^{-\tau/x_1} I_0(2\sqrt{\tau})d\tau\right], \tag{2-6.96}$$

where $x_1 = (\beta x/\nu)$, $t_1 = (\beta t/\gamma)$ are dimensionless variables and I_0 is the Bessel function of the first kind of zero-th order with imaginary argument.

If an asymptotic formula is used, for I_0, an asymptotic description of the solution for large values of the argument can easily be obtained.

2. *Asymptotic solution.* In the above we investigated the absorption process of a gas for the case of a Henry isotherm. This relates the amount a of the absorbed gases with the equilibrium concentration by the linear expression

$$a = \frac{1}{\gamma} y .$$

We now consider a general absorption isotherm

$$a = f(y) .$$

If we introduce the dimensionless variables

$$x_1 = \frac{x\beta}{\nu} \qquad t_1 = \frac{t\beta}{\gamma} \qquad \bar{u} = \frac{u}{u_0} \qquad z = \frac{y}{u_0} \qquad v = \frac{a}{u_0\gamma},$$

then the system of Eqs. (2-6.85), (2-6.89), (2-6.90), and (2-6.91) becomes

$$\frac{\partial \bar{u}}{\partial x_1} = -\frac{\partial v}{\partial t_1}, \qquad \frac{\partial v}{\partial t_1} = (\bar{u} - z) \tag{2-6.97}$$

$$v = f_1(z) = \frac{1}{u_0\gamma} f(zu_0) \tag{2-6.98}$$

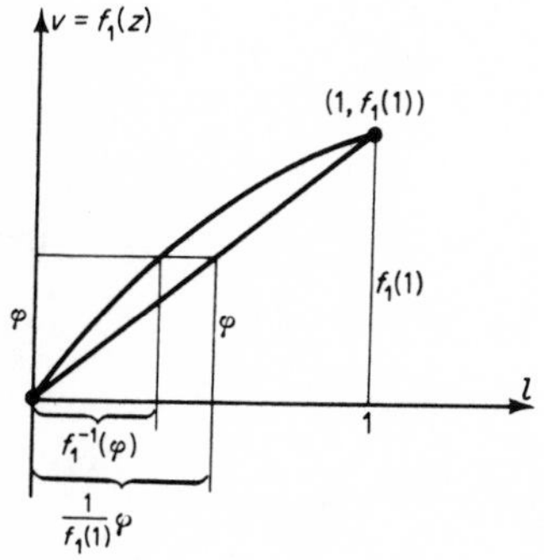

FIG. 33.

with the auxiliary conditions

$$\bar{u}(0, t) = 1 \tag{2-6.99}$$

$$v(x, 0) = 0 . \tag{2-6.100}$$

We are interested in the asymptotic forms of the solutions of (2-6.97).

To this end, with regard to the function $f_1(v)$, we impose the following conditions:

1. Let $f_1(z)$ be an increasing function and let $f_1(0) = 0$.
2. Let $f_1(z)$ possess, for all z with $0 \leqq z \leqq 1$, a continuous derivative.
3. Let the line leading from the origin of the coordinates to the point $(1, f_1(1))$ lie for $0 \leqq z \leqq 1$ below the curve $f_1(z)$ (Figure 33). This holds in particular for convex isotherms.

For the inverse function corresponding to $f_1(z)$ we introduce the relation

$$z = f_1^{-1}(v) = F(v)$$

and seek the asymptotic solutions in the form of propagating waves

$$\tilde{u} = \psi(\xi) \qquad \tilde{v} = \varphi(\xi) \qquad \xi = x - \sigma t\ , \tag{2-6.101}$$

where τ is the velocity of propagation of the waves still to be determined.

This means that for large distances (as $x \to \infty$) or for large times (as $t \to \infty$)

$$v(x,\, t) = \tilde{v} = \varphi(x - \sigma t)\ , \qquad \bar{u}(x,\, t) = \tilde{u} = \psi(x - \sigma t)\ .$$

The concentration $\bar{u}$ and a for $x = \infty$ or $t = \infty$ must satisfy the equilibrium condition

$$v = f_1(\bar{u}) \qquad \text{or} \qquad \bar{u} = F(v)\ .$$

From (2-6.99) it follows

$$\bar{u}\Big|_{\substack{x=0\\t=\infty}} = \psi(-\infty) = 1\ , \qquad \varphi(-\infty) = v\Big|_{\substack{x=0\\t=\infty}} = f_1(1) \tag{2-6.102}$$

and from (2-6.100)

$$v\Big|_{\substack{x=\infty\\t=0}} = \varphi(+\infty) = 0\ , \qquad \psi(+\infty) = \bar{u}\Big|_{\substack{x=\infty\\t=0}} = F(0) = 0\ . \tag{2-6.103}$$

The condition (2-6.102) states that as $t \to \infty$ ($\xi \to -\infty$) saturation must occur throughout.

If we insert (2-6.101) into (2-6.97), we obtain

$$\psi' = \sigma\varphi' = 0\ , \tag{2-6.104}$$

$$-\sigma\varphi' = \psi - F(\varphi)\ . \tag{2-6.105}$$

From (2-6.104) and (2-6.105) we derive the relation

$$\psi(\xi) - \sigma\varphi(\xi) = 0\ . \tag{2-6.106}$$

Hence it follows from (2-6.102) that

$$\sigma = \frac{\psi(\xi)}{\varphi(\xi)}\Bigg|_{\xi=-\infty} = \frac{1}{f_1(1)} \tag{2-6.107}$$

or (in the dimensionless quantities)

$$\sigma = \gamma\frac{u_0}{a_0}\ . \tag{2-6.107$'$}$$

From (2-6.105) and (2-6.106) we find

$$-\,\sigma\frac{d\varphi}{\sigma\varphi - F(\varphi)} = d\xi \tag{2-6.108}$$

and hence after integration

$$\omega(\varphi) = \xi - \xi_0\ , \tag{2-6.109}$$

where $\omega(\varphi)$ is an integral of the left side and ξ_0 is the integration constant. The sought function $\varphi(\xi)$ is defined by this relation to within the unknown constant ξ_0 :

$$\varphi = \omega^{-1}(\xi - \xi_0) \tag{2-6.110}$$

$$\psi = \sigma\omega^{-1}(\xi - \xi_0) . \tag{2-6.111}$$

We want now to determine whether the function ω^{-1} is defined at all and whether the functions φ and ψ as $\xi \to \infty$ and $\xi \to -\infty$ for the inverse function satisfy the required conditions. Therefore we show that

$$\frac{d\omega}{d\varphi} = -\sigma \frac{1}{\sigma\varphi - f_1^{-1}(\varphi)} < 0 \tag{2-6.112}$$

i.e.,

$$\xi - \xi_0 = \omega(\varphi)$$

is a monotone decreasing function of φ. For the denominator in (2-6.112) the following relation holds,

$$\sigma\varphi - f_1^{-1}(\varphi) = \frac{1}{f_1(1)}\varphi - f_1^{-1}(\varphi) .$$

The first summand represents the abscissa of points on the line corresponding to the ordinate φ which runs from the origin of the coordinates to the point $(1, f_1(1))$, (Figure 33). Since by hypothesis the curve $\varphi = f_1(z)$ lies above these lines, we have

$$f_1^{-1}(\varphi) < \frac{1}{f_1(1)}\varphi , \qquad 0 < \varphi < f_1(1)$$

and consequently

$$\sigma\varphi - f_1^{-1}(\varphi) > 0 .$$

Moreover,

$$\sigma\varphi - f_1^{-1}(\varphi) = 0 \qquad \text{for } \varphi = 0 \text{ and } \varphi = f_1(1) .$$

From this it follows that

$$\xi - \xi_0 = \omega(\varphi) = \infty \qquad \text{for} \qquad \varphi = 0$$

$$\xi - \xi_0 = \omega(\varphi) = -\infty \qquad \text{for} \qquad \varphi = f_1(1) .$$

For the inverse function we therefore obtain

$$\varphi = \omega^{-1}(\xi - \xi_0) = f_1(1) \qquad \text{for} \qquad \xi = -\infty$$

$$\varphi = \omega^{-1}(\xi - \xi_0) = 0 \qquad \text{for} \qquad \xi = \infty .$$

Further because of (2-6.112) we also find

$$\psi = \sigma\varphi = \frac{1}{f_1(1)}\varphi = 1 \qquad \text{for} \qquad \xi = -\infty$$

$$\psi = \sigma\varphi = \frac{1}{f_1(1)}\varphi = 0 \qquad \text{for} \qquad \xi = \infty .$$

The conditions (2-6.102) and (2-6.103) are therefore satisfied. Besides this it is shown that our system of equations permits a solution in the form of a propagating wave which still contains an arbitrary constant ξ_0.

In order to determine ξ_0 we integrate the first equation of (2-6.97) from 0 to t_0 and 0 to x_0:

$$\left[\int_0^{t_0} \bar{u}(x_0, \tau)d\tau - \int_0^{t_0} \bar{u}(0, \tau)d\tau\right] + \left[\int_0^{x_0} v(x, t_0)dx - \int_0^{x_0} v(x, 0)dx\right] = 0 . \quad (2\text{-}6.113)$$

This relation expresses the law of conservation of mass. By passage to the limit as $x_0 \to \infty$ we find by using the initial condition for $\bar{u}$ and v that

$$\int_0^{\infty} v(x, t_0)dx = \int_0^{t_0} \bar{u}(0, \tau)d\tau = t_0 .$$

We now assume that the solution of our problem for large values of t approximates the functions $\tilde{u}$ and $\tilde{v}$ which we have found above as propagating waves.

If then we determine ξ_0 according to the condition

$$\int_0^{\infty} v(x, t_0)dx - t_0 \to 0 \qquad (t_0 \to \infty) \quad (2\text{-}6.114)$$

then this is just the ξ_0-value which corresponds to the functions $\tilde{u}(x, t)$ and $\tilde{v}(x, t)$.

We form our integral in the following manner:

$$\int_0^{\infty} \tilde{v}(x, t_0)dx = \int_0^{\infty} \varphi(x - \sigma t_0)dx = \int_0^{\infty} \omega^{-1}(x - \sigma t_0 - \xi_0)dx$$
$$= \int_{-\sigma t_0 - \xi_0}^{\infty} \omega^{-1}(\xi)d\xi = \int_{\zeta_1}^{\infty} \omega^{-1}(\zeta)d\zeta$$
$$\zeta = x - \sigma t_0 - \xi_0 \qquad \zeta_1 = - \sigma t_0 - \xi_0 .$$

We denote by φ^* the value of $\omega^{-1}(\zeta)$ for $\zeta = 0$:

$$\omega^{-1}(0) = \varphi^* .$$

Then it is easy to see that

$$\int_{\zeta_1}^{\infty} \omega^{-1}(\zeta)d\zeta = \int_{\zeta_1}^{0} \omega^{-1}(\zeta)d\zeta + \int_0^{\infty} \omega^{-1}(\zeta)d\zeta$$
$$= \left[-\zeta_1\omega^{-1}(\zeta_1) + \int_{\varphi^*}^{\omega^{-1}(\zeta_1)} \omega(\varphi)d\varphi + \int_0^{\varphi^*} \omega(\varphi)d\varphi\right] \quad (2\text{-}6.115)$$

is valid when $\varphi = \omega^{-1}(\zeta)$ which is the inverse function corresponding to $\zeta = \omega(\varphi)$ (Figure 34). Hence it follows that instead of the conditions (2-6.114)

$$\int_{-\sigma t_0 - \xi_0} \omega^{-1}(\zeta)d\zeta - t_0 = \left\{(\sigma t_0 + \xi_0)\varphi(-\sigma t_0 - \xi_0) + \int_0^{\varphi(-\sigma t_0 - \xi_0)} \omega(\varphi)d\varphi\right\} - t_0 \to 0$$
$$(2\text{-}6.115')$$

can also be written as $t_0 \to \infty$.

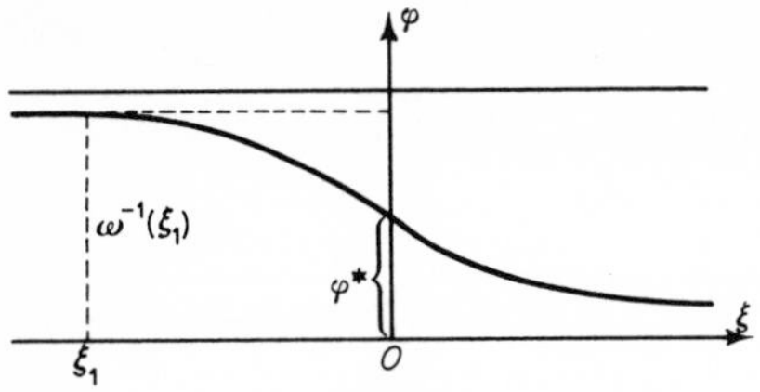

FIG. 34.

As $t \to \infty$,

$$\sigma\varphi(-\sigma t_0 - \xi_0) \to \sigma\varphi(-\infty) = \sigma f_1(1) = 1 . \tag{2-6.115''}$$

In order to calculate the limit values of the expression

$$\sigma t_0\varphi(-\sigma t_0 - \xi_0) - t_0$$

we use Eq. (2-6.108). By developing $f^{-1}(\varphi) = F(\varphi)$ in a series in the neighborhood of the point $\varphi_0 = f_1(1)$ we obtain

$$\begin{aligned}\sigma\varphi - F(\varphi) &= \sigma(\varphi - \varphi_0) + 1 - F(\varphi)\\ &= \sigma(\varphi - \varphi_0) - [F(\varphi) - F(\varphi_0)]\\ &= [\sigma - F'(\varphi_0)]\,(\varphi - \varphi_0) + \cdots,\end{aligned}$$

where

$$-\sigma\frac{d\varphi}{[\sigma - F'(\varphi_0)]\,(\varphi - \varphi_0) + \cdots} = d\xi . \tag{2-6.116}$$

The dots here denote the terms of higher order with respect to $(\varphi - \varphi_0)$.

From the requirement 3 for f_1 it follows that

$$F'(\varphi_0) > \sigma = \frac{1}{f_1(1)} .$$

From (2-6.116), the order of magnitude of φ as $\xi \to -\infty$ results:

$$\varphi = Ae^{k\xi} + \varphi_0 , \tag{2-6.117}$$

where A and $k > 0$ are constant.

The expression (2-6.117) gives

$$\lim_{t_0\to\infty} t_0\,[\sigma\varphi(-\sigma t_0 - \xi_0) - 1] = \lim_{t_0\to\infty} t_0 A\sigma e^{-k(\sigma t_0+\xi_0)} = 0 . \tag{2-6.115'''}$$

If now in (2-6.115') we still let $t_0 \to \infty$ and bearing in mind (2-6.115'') and (2-6.115'''), we obtain

$$\xi_0 = -\frac{1}{f_1(1)}\int_0^{f_1(1)} \omega(\varphi)d\varphi . \tag{2-6.118}$$

Therefore the profile of the wave $\{u, v\}$ is completely determined.

Of particular interest is the case of the Langmuir isotherm. For this we seek now an asymptotic solution of the absorption process.

Eq. (2-6.108) here assumes the form

$$-\sigma\frac{d\varphi}{\sigma\varphi - \varphi/(1 - p\varphi)} = d\xi \tag{2-6.119}$$

where $\sigma = 1/f_1(1) = 1 + p$ is the wave velocity. From (2-6.119) we find

$$\xi - \xi_0 = \omega(\varphi)$$

with

$$\omega(\varphi) = \sigma \int \frac{(1 - p\varphi)d\varphi}{\varphi - \sigma\varphi(1 - p\varphi)} + A = \frac{\sigma}{\sigma - 1}\left[\frac{1}{\sigma}\ln(\sigma - 1 - p\sigma\varphi) - \ln\varphi\right] + A\,.$$

If φ varies from 0 to $f_1(1)$, then obviously $\omega(\varphi)$ varies from $-\infty$ to $+\infty$. We choose A so that

$$\varphi^* = \frac{1}{2} f_1(1)\,,$$

i.e.,

$$\omega(\varphi^*) = 0 \qquad \text{for} \qquad \varphi^* = \frac{1}{2} f_1(1) = \frac{1}{2}\frac{1}{1 + p}\,.$$

The conditions for it are

$$A = -\frac{\sigma}{\sigma - 1}\left[\frac{1}{\sigma}\ln\left(\frac{1}{2}p\right) - \ln\left(\frac{1}{2}\frac{1}{1 + p}\right)\right]$$

and

$$\omega(\varphi) = \frac{\sigma}{\sigma - 1}\left[\frac{1}{\sigma}\ln 2(1 - \sigma\varphi) - \ln 2(1 + p)\varphi\right].$$

The value of ξ_0 can be calculated from

$$\xi_0 = \frac{1}{f_1(1)}\int_0^{f_1(1)} \omega(\varphi)d\varphi = -(\ln 2 - 1)$$

and does not depend on $p = u_0/y$, the prescribed concentration.

The sought asymptotic solution then has the form

$$\begin{aligned} \tilde{v}(x, t) &= \omega^{-1}(x - \sigma t - \xi_0) \\ \tilde{u}(x, t) &= \sigma\omega^{-1}(x - \sigma t - \xi_0) \end{aligned} \tag{2-6.120}$$

where $\omega^{-1}(\xi)$ is the inverse function of $\omega(\varphi)$.

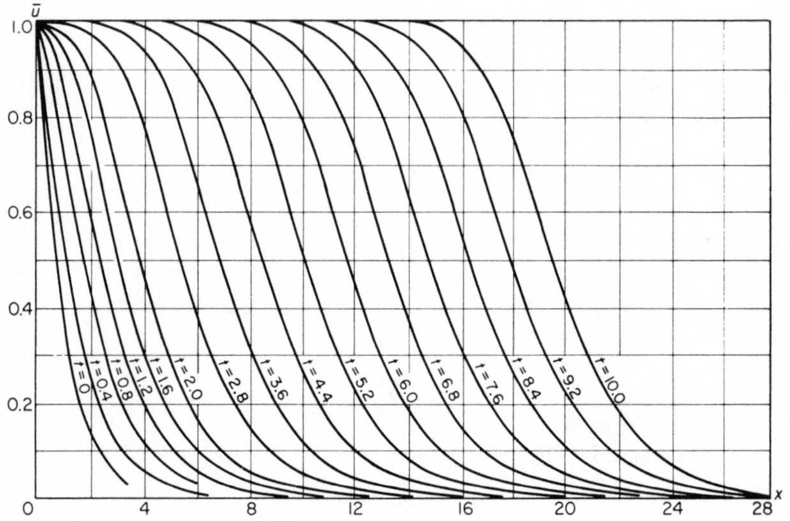

FIG. 35.

Figure 35 shows the results of the numerical integration of Eq. (2-6.97) for the Langmuir isotherm (by means of difference equations). We considered here the range of values $0 < t \leqq t_1 = 10$. For $t = t_1$ the results of the numerical integration agree with the asymptotic solution to within 1 per cent. For $t > t_1$ we can use the asymptotic formula.

6. Physical analogies

In the investigations of phenomena in different branches of physics one often establishes a common characteristic. This then leads in the mathematical formulation of the corresponding problems to one and the same equation which describes simultaneously different physical phenomena. The following equation serves as a simple example:

$$a\frac{d^2x}{dt^2} + bx = 0 \,,$$

which describes different vibration processes of a simple system: vibrations of a mathematical pendulum, a weight under the influence of an elastic spring, electrical vibrations in a simple conductor with inductance and capacity, etc. The fact that the different physical processes can be described by the same mathematical equation permits us, on the basis of the investigation of one of these processes, to reach conclusions about the properties of the other (less accurately investigated) processes.

The propagation of electric vibrations in systems with distributed constants can be given by the telegraphic equations

$$\begin{aligned} -\frac{\partial I}{\partial x} &= C\frac{\partial V}{\partial t} + GV \\ -\frac{\partial V}{\partial x} &= L\frac{\partial I}{\partial t} + RI \end{aligned} \tag{2-6.121}$$

where C, G, L, R are coefficients of capacity, the loss, the induction, and the resistance of the system. If we can neglect R and G, the voltage V and the current density I satisfy the ordinary wave equations

$$\frac{\partial^2 V}{\partial x^2} - LC\frac{\partial^2 V}{\partial t^2} = 0$$

$$\frac{\partial^2 I}{\partial x^2} - LC\frac{\partial^2 I}{\partial t^2} = 0$$

while Eqs. (2-6.121) become

$$\begin{aligned} -\frac{\partial I}{\partial x} &= C\frac{\partial V}{\partial t} \\ -\frac{\partial V}{\partial x} &= L\frac{\partial I}{\partial t} \end{aligned} \tag{2-6.122}$$

On the other hand, in the investigation of the propagation of sound in a unique direction, we arrive—for example, for the motion of air in a tube—

at the equations

$$-\frac{\partial p}{\partial x} = \rho\frac{\partial v}{\partial t}$$
$$-\frac{\partial v}{\partial x} = \frac{1}{\tau}\frac{\partial p}{\partial t} \tag{2-6.123}$$

where v is the velocity of the vibrating particles, ρ is the density, p is the pressure, and $\tau = p_0\gamma$ is the elastic coefficient of air.

The similarity of Eqs. (2-6.122) and (2-6.123) point to the analogy between the acoustic and the electrical quantities. The potential difference corresponds to the pressure, the current density to the displacement velocity of the particles. Further, the induction of the electrical system corresponds to the density which determines the inertia properties of the gas, and the capacity corresponds to the quantity $1/\tau$, i.e., the reciprocal of the elastic coefficient. This analogy can also be determined from the expressions for the kinetic and potential energy of the electrical and acoustical systems.

By a glance at Eqs. (2-6.121) we can, by analogy with the corresponding electrical quantities, introduce an acoustic resistance and loss. The magnitude of the acoustic resistance is then to be considered if, in the motion, the friction of the gas on the side of the vessel plays an essential role. By analogy with electrical resistance, which is defined as the ratio of the voltage to the current density, we define the acoustic resistance as the ratio of the pressure to the current in the medium which is proportional to the displacement velocity of the gas particles:

$$R_A = \frac{p}{uv}\,.$$

In those cases in which the motion of a gas in a porous medium is considered, one has to introduce a quantity which corresponds to the loss in an electrical system. This quantity (which we designate by P) is called the porosity and is defined per unit volume for those materials which are filled with air.

The mechanical analogy of telegraphic equations are the equations of a longitudinal vibrating rod. These can be written, similar to Eqs. (2-6.122), as

$$-\frac{\partial v}{\partial x} = \frac{1}{k}\frac{\partial T}{\partial t}$$
$$-\frac{\partial T}{\partial x} = \rho\frac{\partial v}{\partial t}$$

where T is the tension of the rod, v is the velocity of the vibrating points, ρ is the density, and k is the elastic coefficient of the rod.

By comparison of these equations with Eqs. (2-6.122) we can define further analogies, this time between mechanical and electrical quantities. If the electrical voltage can correspond to the tension of the rod and the current density to the motion velocity of the particles, then the reciprocal of the elastic coefficient is known to correspond to the capacity and the density to the induction.

The consideration of similar dynamic problems leads thus to an analogy between a series of electrical, acoustic, and mechanical quantities. This is illustrated in the following table.[37]

Electric systems	Acoustic systems	Mechanical systems
Variables		
Voltage V	Pressure, p	Tension, T
Current density, I	Particle velocity, v	Particle velocity, $\dot{x}$
Charge, e	Displacement, u	Displacement, x
Parameter		
Inductance, L	Inertia (density), ρ	Mass density, ρ_m
Capacity, C	Acoustic capacity, $C_A = 1/\tau$	Rigidity, elastic modulus $C_M = 1/k$
Resistance, R	Acoustic resistance, R_A	Mechanical resistance, R_M

The above table is based on the results of acoustic problems about the character of the phenomena and gives an insight for the solution of the problem.

Thus the problem of motion of air in a porous material for simple harmonic waves leads to the equations[38]

$$-i\omega\rho_m u + ru = -\operatorname{grad} p$$

$$\Delta p + i\frac{\gamma P\omega}{\rho c^2}(r - i\omega\rho_m)p = 0$$

where u is the spatial velocity of air through the pores, p is the pressure, ρ is the density, ρ_m is the effective density of air in the pores (ρ_m can be larger than ρ, since the material particles and the air can also vibrate in the pores), P is the porosity, c is the velocity, ω is the frequency of sound, and r is the flow resistance. The latter can be characterized by prescribing the pressure in the material. If we put $r = R_A$, $\rho_m = L_A$, $\gamma P/\rho c^2 = C_A$, then the above equations take the form

$$L_A\frac{\partial u}{\partial t} + R_A u = -\operatorname{grad} p$$

$$C_A L_A\frac{\partial^2 p}{\partial t^2} + C_A R_A\frac{\partial p}{\partial t} = \Delta p\,.$$

These equations are completely analogous to the equations for the propagation of electrical vibrations in a conductor. Therefore, by analogy with the wave impedance in conductors,

$$Z = \sqrt{\frac{R + i\omega L}{G + i\omega C}}\,, \qquad G = 0$$

[37] See, for example, H. F. Olson, *Dynamic Analogies*, New York, Toronto, London, 1944.

[38] W. Furduev, *Electroacoustics*, Moscow, 1948.

we can write the expression

$$Z = c\sqrt{\rho}\sqrt{\frac{\rho_m - i(r/\omega)}{\gamma P}}$$

for the so-called characteristic impedence of porous materials. The characteristic impedence causes a dampening of the waves propagating in a porous material.

With the help of these analogies between electrical and acoustic phenomena, the investigation of many acoustic problems can be replaced by the consideration of equivalent electrical systems. These methods of analogy have in recent times found many applications with analog computers, in which an equivalent electrical circuit is constructed for the solution of an equation which corresponds to a physical process.

3

PARABOLIC DIFFERENTIAL EQUATIONS

Partial differential equations of the second order of the parabolic type occur principally in problems connected with heat conduction and diffusion. The simplest parabolic differential equation

$$u_{xx} - u_y = 0$$

is usually denoted as the heat-conduction equation.

3-1. SIMPLE PROBLEMS WHICH LEAD TO PARABOLIC DIFFERENTIAL EQUATIONS

1. The linear problem of heat propagation

We shall consider a homogeneous rod of length l which can be heat insulated and is sufficiently thin so that at an arbitrary time the temperature at all points of the cross section can be regarded as equal. If the ends of the rod are held at the constant temperatures u_1 and u_2, then, as is known, along the rod a linear temperature distribution occurs (Figure 36):

$$u(x) = u_1 + \frac{u_2 - u_1}{l} x . \qquad (3\text{-}1.1)$$

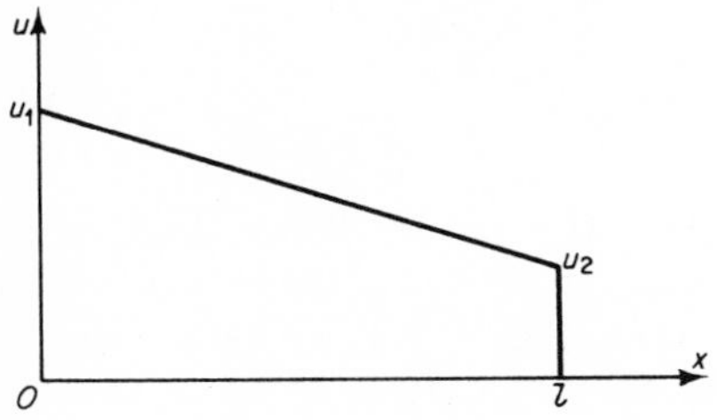

FIG. 36.

Here the heat flows from the warmer to the colder end of the rod, that is, in the direction in which the temperature decreases. The amount of heat which, in a unit of time, flows through a cross section of area S is given by the experimentally determined formula

$$Q = -k \frac{u_2 - u_1}{l} S = -k \frac{\partial u}{\partial x} S . \qquad (3\text{-}1.2)$$

The coefficient k, the so-called thermal conductivity, depends on the material of the rod. The magnitude of the heat flow is taken to be positive if the heat flows in the positive x direction.

The course of the temperature distribution in a rod can be described by a function $u(x, t)$, which gives the temperature in the cross section at x at time t. What equation must $u(x, t)$ now satisfy? For the derivation of this equation we formulate first the physical laws which govern heat conduction.

1. *The Fourier law* If the temperature of a body is distributed non-uniformly, then there arises in the body a heat flow in the direction of temperature decrease.

The amount of heat which flows through the cross section at x during an interval of time $(t, t+dt)$ is equal to

$$dQ = qS\,dt\,, \tag{3-1.3}$$

where

$$q = -\,k(x)\frac{\partial u}{\partial x} \tag{3-1.4}$$

is the density of the heat flow. This is equal to the amount of heat flowing through an area of $1\,\text{cm}^2$ per unit of time. This law represents a generalization of formula (3-1.2). It can also be written in the integral form

$$Q = -\,S\int_{t_1}^{t_2} k\frac{\partial u}{\partial x}(x, t)\,dt\,. \tag{3-1.5}$$

Then Q is the amount of heat flowing in the time interval (t_1, t_2) through the cross section at x. If the rod is inhomogeneous, k is a function of x.

2. The amount of heat which must be added to a homogeneous body in order to raise its temperature by an amount Δu, is equal to

$$Q = cm\,\Delta u = c\rho V\,\Delta u\,, \tag{3-1.6}$$

where c is the specific heat capacity, m is the mass of the body, ρ is its density, and V is the volume of the body.

If the temperature change differs at different places of the rod or the rod can be treated as inhomogeneous, then

$$Q = \int_{x_1}^{x_2} c\rho S\Delta u(x)\,dx\,. \tag{3-1.7}$$

3. Within a rod, heat can arise or vanish (for example, by the flow of an electric current, because of chemical reaction, etc.). The occurrence of heat can be completely described by a function $F(x, t)$, which is a measure of the heat source at the point x at time t.[39] The effect of these sources on an element of the rod $(x, x + dx)$ during an interval of time $(t, t + dt)$ induces an amount of heat given by

$$dQ = SF(x, t)\,dx\,dt\,. \tag{3-1.8}$$

By integration we find

$$Q = S\int_{t_1}^{t_2}\int_{x_1}^{x_2} F(x, t)\,dx\,dt\,, \tag{3-1.9}$$

[39] For example, if heat is produced by an electric current of strength I in a rod, whose resistance per unit length is equal to R, then $F = 0.24\cdot I^2\cdot R$.

which is the amount of heat which exists in the interval (x_1, x_2) of the rod in the time interval (t_1, t_2).

We obtain the equation of heat conduction from the law of conservation of energy for an interval (x_1, x_2) in a time interval (t_1, t_2) and with the use of formulas (3-1.5), (3-1.7), and (3-1.9) for the energy balance, we can write

$$\begin{aligned}\int_{t_1}^{t_2}\left[k\frac{\partial u}{\partial x}(x,\tau)\Big|_{x=x_2} - k\frac{\partial u}{\partial x}(x,\tau)\Big|_{x=x_1}\right]d\tau + \int_{x_1}^{x_2}\int_{t_1}^{t_2} F(\xi,\tau)\,d\xi\,d\tau \\ = \int_{x_1}^{x_2} c\rho[u(\xi,t_2) - u(\xi,t_1)]\,d\xi\,. \end{aligned} \tag{3-1.10}$$

This is the equation of heat conduction in integral form.

In order to derive the differential form we shall assume that the function $u(x, t)$ possesses the continuous derivatives u_{xx} and u_t.[40]

Then from the mean-value theorem of integral calculus we obtain

$$\begin{aligned}\left[k\frac{\partial u}{\partial x}(x,\tau)\Big|_{x=x_2} - k\frac{\partial u}{\partial x}(x,\tau)\Big|_{x=x_1}\right]_{\tau=t_3}\Delta t + F(x_4, t_4)\Delta x\Delta t \\ = \{c\rho[u(\xi,t_2) - u(\xi,t_1)]\}_{\xi=x_3}\Delta x\end{aligned} \tag{3-1.11}$$

and hence with the help of the mean-value theorem of differential calculus

$$\frac{\partial}{\partial x}\left[k\frac{\partial u}{\partial x}(x,t)\right]_{\substack{x=x_5\\ t=t_3}}\Delta t\Delta x + F(x_4, t_4)\Delta x\Delta t = \left[c\rho\frac{\partial u}{\partial t}(x,t)\right]_{\substack{x=x_3\\ t=t_5}}\Delta x\Delta t\,, \tag{3-1.12}$$

where t_3, t_4, t_5 and x_3, x_4, x_5 are suitable intermediate values in the intervals (t_1, t_2) and (x_1, x_2).

If we divide the last equation by $\Delta x\Delta t$, we find

$$\frac{\partial}{\partial x}\left(k\frac{\partial u}{\partial x}\right)\Big|_{\substack{x=x_5\\ t=t_3}} + F(x,t)\Big|_{\substack{x=x_4\\ t=t_4}} = c\rho\frac{\partial u}{\partial t}\Big|_{\substack{t=t_5\\ x=x_3}}\,. \tag{3-1.13}$$

All these considerations hold for arbitrary intervals (x_1, x_2) and (t_1, t_2). Accordingly if x_1, x_2 tend towards x and t_1, t_2 tend towards t, there results

$$\frac{\partial}{\partial x}\left(k\frac{\partial u}{\partial x}\right) + F(x,t) = c\rho\frac{\partial u}{\partial t}\,, \tag{3-1.14}$$

the so-called equation of heat conduction.

We shall next consider a special case.

1. If the rod is homogeneous then k, c, ρ can be taken as constant, and the heat-conduction equation takes the form

$$u_t = a^2 u_{xx} + f(x,t)$$

$$a^2 = \frac{k}{c\rho}\,, \qquad f(x,t) = \frac{F(x,t)}{c\rho}$$

40 Through these restrictions on the function $u(x, t)$, in general, we will lose a class of solutions, namely those which satisfy the integral equation but not the differential equation. In the case of the heat conduction equation, however, these requirements do not exclude any possible solutions. That is, we can show that a function which satisfies Equation (3-1.10) must be differentiable.

where a^2 is the coefficient of temperature conductivity. If there are no sources present, i.e., if $F(x, t) = 0$, then the equation simplifies:

$$u_t = a^2 u_{xx} . \tag{3-1.14'}$$

2. The density of the heat sources are dependent on the temperature. If heat exchange with the surroundings exists which obeys Newton's law, the amount of heat emanating from the rod per unit of length and time equals

$$F_0 = h(u - \theta) ,$$

where $\theta(x, t)$ is the temperature of the surrounding medium and h is the heat exchange coefficient.[41] Therefore the density of the heat sources at the point x at time t is equal to

$$F = F_1(x, t) - h(u - \theta) ,$$

where $F_1(x, t)$ is the density of other heat sources.

If we are dealing with an inhomogeneous rod, then the heat conduction equation considering heat exchange with the surroundings takes the form

$$u_t = a^2 u_{xx} - \alpha u + f(x, t) , \tag{3-1.15}$$

where $\alpha = h/c\rho$ and $f(x, t) = \alpha\theta(x, t) + F_1(x, t)/c\rho$ is a known function.

3. The coefficients k and c as a rule are slowly varying functions of temperature. Therefore, from the above cited assumption, these coefficients can now be assumed as constant, which is valid for small temperature fluctuations. The consideration of the course of temperature for large temperature fluctuations leads to a quasilinear heat-conduction equation, which for an inhomogeneous medium can be written in the form

$$\frac{\partial}{\partial x}\left(k(u, x)\frac{\partial u}{\partial x}\right) + F(x, t) = C(u, x)\rho(u, x)\frac{\partial u}{\partial t}$$

(see Application 3).

2. Diffusion equation

If a medium is filled nonuniformly with a gas, then a diffusion occurs from the places of higher concentration to places of lower concentration. This phenomenon also occurs in solutions when the concentration of the dissolved material is not everywhere equal.

We shall now consider the diffusion in the interior of a hollow tube or in a tube which is filled with a porous substance, under the assumption that at any arbitrary moment the concentration of the gas (the solution) in any cross section of the tube is constant. Then the diffusion process can be de-

[41] Since with our approximation the temperature distribution inside an individual cross section was not considered, the influence of the surface sources is equivalent to the influence of the heat sources in the interior.

scribed by a function $u(x, t)$, which gives the concentration in the cross section at x at time t.

According to the Nernst law, the mass of the gas passing through the cross section at x during the time interval $(t, t + \Delta t)$ equals

$$dQ = -D\frac{\partial u}{\partial x}(x, t)S\,dt\,, \tag{3-1.16}$$

where D is the diffusion coefficient and S is the area of the tube cross section.

From the definition of concentration,

$$Q = uV$$

results for the amount of gas found in the volume V. Here we know that the change of mass of the gas in the interval (x_1, x_2) of the tube equals

$$\Delta Q = \int_{x_1}^{x_2} c(x)\,\Delta u\cdot S\,dx$$

when the concentration changes by an amount Δu. Here $c(x)$ denotes the coefficient of porosity.[42]

The condition for the conservation of mass in the interval (x_1, x_2) during the time interval (t_1, t_2) reads

$$S\int_{t_1}^{t_2}\left[D(x_2)\frac{\partial u}{\partial x}(x_2, \tau) - D(x_1)\frac{\partial u}{\partial x}(x_1, \tau)\right]d\tau = S\int_{x_1}^{x_2} c(\xi)[u(\xi, t_2) - u(\xi, t_1)]\,d\xi\,.$$

Hence, as in Section 1 we arrive at the equation

$$\frac{\partial}{\partial x}\left(D\frac{\partial u}{\partial x}\right) = c\frac{\partial u}{\partial t}\,, \tag{3-1.17}$$

the so-called diffusion equation. It is completely analogous to the heat-conduction equation. For its derivation we assume that in the tube no material sources exist, and no diffusion takes place through the tube walls. If we take into consideration also the sources, then we arrive at equations which correspond to Eqs. (3-1.14) and (3-1.15).

If the diffusion coefficient is constant, the diffusion equation assumes the form

$$u_t = a^2 u_{xx}$$

with

$$a^2 = \frac{D}{c}\,.$$

If $c = 1$ and the diffusion coefficient is constant, the diffusion equation reads

$$u_t = Du_{xx}\,.$$

42 The porosity coefficient we understand to be the relation between the volume of the pores and the total volume V_0, which in this case is equal to $S\,dx$.

3. Spatial heat propagation

Spatial heat propagation can be characterized by the temperature $u(x, y, z, t)$ as a function of the point (x, y, z) and the time t.

If the temperature is not constant, a heat flow occurs which again proceeds from places of higher temperature to places of lower temperature. The amount of heat flowing through the surface element $d\sigma$ at the point (x, y, z) during the time interval $(t, t + \Delta t)$ is given, according to the Fourier law, by the formula

$$dQ = -k\frac{\partial}{\partial n}u(x, y, z, t)\,d\sigma\,dt\,.$$

Here k is the heat conductivity of the body[43] and n is the normal to the surface element $d\sigma$ in the direction of the heat flow. As is known,

$$\frac{\partial u}{\partial n} = \frac{\partial u}{\partial x}\cos(n, x) + \frac{\partial u}{\partial y}\cos(n, y) + \frac{\partial u}{\partial z}\cos(n, z) = \operatorname{grad} u\cdot\boldsymbol{N}\,,$$

so that we can write

$$dQ = -k\operatorname{grad} u\cdot\boldsymbol{N}\,d\sigma\,dt$$

where $\boldsymbol{N}$ is the exterior normal. Hence it follows that the heat flow per unit of time and area is equal to

$$q_n = \boldsymbol{q}\cdot\boldsymbol{N} \tag{3-1.18}$$

where $\boldsymbol{q} = -k\operatorname{grad} u$ is the vector density of the heat flow.

For the amount of heat which flows through a surface S in the time interval (t_1, t_2), we have

$$Q_1 = -\int_{t_1}^{t_2}\int_S\int k\frac{\partial u}{\partial n}dt\,d\sigma$$

or

$$Q_1 = -\int_{t_1}^{t_2}\int_S\int k\operatorname{grad} u\cdot\boldsymbol{N}\,d\sigma\,dt = \int_{t_1}^{t_2}\int_S\int \boldsymbol{q}\cdot\boldsymbol{N}\,d\sigma\,dt\,. \tag{3-1.19}$$

Further, the amount of heat necessary to raise the temperature of a point of the body by

$$\Delta u(x, y, z) = u(x, y, z, t_2) - u(x, y, z, t_1)$$

is equal to

$$Q_2 = \iint_V\int c\rho[u(\xi, \eta, \zeta, t_2) - u(\xi, \eta, \zeta, t_1)]\,dV\,. \tag{3-1.20}$$

Finally, if we denote the density of the heat sources by $F(x, y, z, t)$, then for the amount of heat freed in the volume V in the time interval (t_1, t_2) we obtain

[43] In this case, a homogeneous isotropic body.

$$Q_3 = \int_{t_1}^{t_2}\iiint_V F(\xi, \eta, \zeta, t)\, dV dt\,. \tag{3-1.21}$$

We shall now formulate the law of conservation of energy for a volume V whose surface will be denoted by S. Obviously, we must have

$$Q_2 = Q_3 - Q_1\,. \tag{3-1.22}$$

Under the assumption that the function u, in the region considered, with respect to the variables x, y, z, is twice continuously differentiable, and with respect to t, is once continuously differentiable, we now form the relations (3-1.19), (3-1.20), and (3-1.21). By applying Green's theorem[44]

$$\int_S \boldsymbol{q}\cdot\boldsymbol{N}\, d\sigma = \int_V \operatorname{div}\boldsymbol{q}\, dV$$

and the mean-value theorem of integral and differential calculus for functions of several variables, we obtain

$$Q_1 = \operatorname{div}\boldsymbol{q}(x_1, y_1, z_1, t_3)V\Delta t$$

$$Q_2 = c\rho[u(x_2, y_2, z_2, t_2) - u(x_2, y_2, z_2, t_1)]V = c\rho\frac{\partial u}{\partial t}(x_2, y_2, z_2, t_4)V\Delta t$$

$$Q_3 = F(x_3, y_3, z_3, t_5)V\Delta t$$

or, after division by $V\Delta t$ follows

$$c\rho\frac{\partial u}{\partial t}(x_2, y_2, z_2, t_4) = -\operatorname{div}\boldsymbol{q}(x_1, y_1, z_1, t_3) + F(x_3, y_3, z_3, t_5)\,. \tag{3-1.23}$$

Here all the values of the argument lie within the region considered, i.e., they are the coordinates of certain interior points of V for a certain value of time in the interval (t_1, t_2).

Equation (3-1.23) holds for any volume V within the body. If we shrink the volume to the point with coordinates x, y, z, and carry out the passage to the limit $t_1, t_2 \to t$, we obtain[45]

$$c\rho\frac{\partial u}{\partial t}(x, y, z, t) = -\operatorname{div}\boldsymbol{q}(x, y, z, t) + F(x, y, z, t) \tag{3-1.24}$$

because of continuity of the derivatives.

If now $\boldsymbol{q}$ is replaced according to (3-1.18), we obtain the heat-conduction equation

$$c\rho u_t = \operatorname{div}(k \operatorname{grad} u) + F$$

or

$$c\rho u_t = \frac{\partial}{\partial x}\left(k\frac{\partial u}{\partial x}\right) + \frac{\partial}{\partial y}\left(k\frac{\partial u}{\partial y}\right) + \frac{\partial}{\partial z}\left(k\frac{\partial u}{\partial z}\right) + F\,. \tag{3-1.25}$$

If the body is homogeneous, we usually write this in the form

[44] In this formula as in (3-1.19) the exterior normal is assumed.

[45] $F(x, y, z, t)$ is assumed to be continuous in the region considered.

$$u_t = a^2(u_{xx} + u_{yy} + u_{zz}) + \frac{F}{c\rho}, \tag{3-1.26}$$

where $a^2 = k/c\rho$ is the temperature conductivity, or also

$$u_t = a^2 \Delta u + f, \qquad f = \frac{F}{c\rho}, \tag{3-1.26'}$$

where

$$\Delta = \frac{\partial^2}{\partial x^2} + \frac{\partial^2}{\partial y^2} + \frac{\partial^2}{\partial z^2}$$

is the Laplace operator.

4. Formulation of boundary-value problems

In order to determine the solution of the heat-conduction equation in a unique manner in each case we must still consider the initial and boundary conditions along with the equation itself.

In contrast to the differential equations of the hyperbolic type, only the initial conditions arise here in the prescription of the values of the function $u(x, t)$ at the initial time t_0.

The boundary conditions can assume different forms, according to the temperature conditions considered on the boundary. We thus distinguish three principal types of boundary conditions.

1. At the end of a rod ($x = 0$ or $x = l$) the temperature is prescribed, e.g.,

$$u(0, t) = \mu(t), \tag{3-1.27}$$

where $\mu(t)$ is a function defined in the interval $t_0 \leqq t \leqq T$. Here T characterizes the time interval in which the process is considered.

2. At one end, the value of the derivative is prescribed, e.g.,

$$\frac{\partial u}{\partial x}(l, t) = \nu(t). \tag{3-1.28}$$

We arrive at this condition when the heat flow $Q(l, t)$ occurring at the end of the rod is given by

$$Q(l, t) = -k\frac{\partial u}{\partial x}(l, t).$$

From this there results $(\partial u(l, t)\partial x) = \nu(t)$, where $\nu(t)$ is a known function; then we obtain

$$\nu(t) = -\frac{Q(l, t)}{k}.$$

3. At one end a linear relation exists between the derivative and the function given by

$$\frac{\partial u}{\partial x}(l, t) = -\lambda[u(l, t) - \theta(t)].$$

This boundary condition corresponds to Newton's heat exchange of the surface of the body with the surroundings whose temperature θ is known. Therefore, if for the flow of heat which flows through the cross section at $x = l$ we use the two expressions

$$Q = h(u - \theta)$$

and

$$Q = -k\frac{\partial u}{\partial x},$$

we obtain the mathematical formulation of the third boundary condition in the form

$$\frac{\partial u}{\partial x}(l, t) = -\lambda[u(l, t) - \theta(t)], \tag{3-1.29}$$

where $\lambda = h/k$ is the heat-exchange coefficient and $\theta(t)$ is a prescribed function. For the cross section at $x = 0$ of the rod $(0, l)$ the third boundary condition reads

$$\frac{\partial u}{\partial x}(0, t) = +\lambda[u(0, t) - \theta(t)]. \tag{3-1.29'}$$

Naturally, the boundary conditions for $x = 0$ and $x = l$ can be different so that the number of possible boundary conditions is large.

If the system considered is inhomogeneous and the coefficients of the differential equation are discontinuous functions, we divide up, in a suitable manner, the interval $(0, l)$ in which the solution is sought, by the points of discontinuity, and the coefficients into several subintervals, in such a way that the function u within these subintervals satisfies the heat-conduction equation and at the points of discontinuity satisfies the corresponding transition conditions.

In the simplest case these conditions are the continuity of the temperature and the continuity of the heat flow,

$$u(x_i - 0, t) = u(x_i + 0, t)$$

$$k(x_i - 0)\frac{\partial u}{\partial x}(x_i - 0, t) = k(x_i + 0)\frac{\partial u}{\partial x}(x_i + 0, t)$$

where x_i are the points of discontinuity of the coefficients.

Besides the problems discussed here, limiting cases also arise. We shall consider the heat conductivity in a very long rod. In the course of a sufficiently small time interval, then, the influence of the temperature conditions prescribed at the end points on the middle portions of the rod is very small, so that the temperature of these parts alone are determined by the initial temperature distribution. In this case the exact consideration of the rod length is of no significance, since a change in the rod length has no essential influence on the temperature of the portions of the rod of interest to us; for such problems we usually assume the rod to be of infinite length. Thus we have an initial-value problem (the Cauchy problem) for the temperature distribution in an infinite straight line, i.e.:

Find a solution of the heat-conduction equation in the region $-\infty < x < \infty$, $t \geqq t_0$, which satisfies the equation

$$u(x, t_0) = \varphi(x), \qquad -\infty < x < +\infty,$$

where $\varphi(x)$ is a prescribed function.

Correspondingly, the temperature in an element of the rod which lies nearer to one end and far from the other end is determined in practice by the temperature condition of the near end and the initial conditions. In such cases, we at least assume the rod to be bounded on one side and the coordinates from the bounded end to lie within the region defined by $0 \leqq x \leqq \infty$. As an example we shall formulate the first boundary-value problem for a one-sided bounded rod:

Find a solution of the heat-conduction equation in the region $0 < x < \infty$, $t_0 \leqq t$ which satisfies the conditions

$$\begin{aligned} u(x, t_0) &= \varphi(x), \qquad 0 < x < \infty \\ u(0, t) &= \mu(t), \qquad t \geqq t_0 \end{aligned} \tag{3-1.30}$$

where $\varphi(x)$ and $\mu(t)$ are prescribed functions.

The above formulated problems represent limiting cases (degenerate) of the fundamental boundary-value problems. A different limiting case of the fundamental boundary-value problem occurs when the exact initial conditions are not taken into consideration. Obviously, the influence of the initial conditions on the temperature propagation along a rod weakens in the course of time. If the time point of interest is sufficiently long from the initial time, the temperature of the rod is determined primarily by the boundary conditions, since a change of the initial conditions shows no change in the temperature condition of the rod (within the limits of accuracy of observation). In this case we must also assume that the process continues indefinitely and the effect of the initial conditions has ceased.

In this manner we arrive at boundary-value problems without initial conditions: Find a solution of the heat-conduction equation for $0 \leqq x \leqq l$ and $t > -\infty$ which satisfies the conditions

$$\begin{aligned} u(0, t) &= \mu_1(t) \\ u(l, t) &= \mu_2(t). \end{aligned} \tag{3-1.31}$$

According to the nature of the boundary conditions, other types of problems without initial conditions are also possible. Of great importance is the problem without initial conditions for a one-sided bounded rod ($l = \infty$): Find a solution of the heat-conduction equation for $0 < x < \infty$, $t > -\infty$ which satisfies the condition

$$u(0, t) = \mu(t), \tag{3-1.27}$$

where $\mu(t)$ is a prescribed function.

Often one encounters problems without initial conditions but with periodic boundary conditions,

$$\mu(t) = A \cos \omega t \tag{3-1.32}$$

(see Section 3-5 § 1).

Naturally we presume that the temperature of the rod varies after a sufficiently long time and, similarly, periodically with the same frequency. However, if the influence of the initial conditions were taken into consideration exactly, we could never obtain a periodic solution; since the influence of the initial conditions is continuously decaying, it completely vanishes; indeed the consideration of such cases, because of unavoidable errors of observations, are senseless. The investigation of a periodic solution is analogous, therefore, to a neglect of the initial conditions.

Finally, the above formulation of the boundary-value problem does not refer only to equations with constant coefficients. Under the "heat-conduction equation" we can subsume each of the equations of the preceding sections.

In addition to the linear boundary-value problems cited above we also have to investigate problems with nonlinear boundary conditions, for example, of the form

$$k \frac{\partial u}{\partial x}(0, t) = \sigma[u^4(0, t) - \theta^4(0, t)] \; . \tag{3-1.33}$$

This boundary condition corresponds to the Stefan-Boltzmann law underlying heat radiation from the point $x = 0$ in a medium with the temperature $\theta(t)$.

We shall now consider the formulation of boundary value problems in some detail and begin with the first boundary-value problem for a bounded region.

A function $u(x, t)$ is called a solution of the first boundary-value problem if it has the following properties:

1. It is defined and continuous in the closed region

$$0 \leqq x \leqq l \, , \qquad t_0 \leqq t \leqq T \, .$$

2. It satisfies the heat conduction equation in the region

$$0 < x < l \, , \qquad t_0 < t < T \, .$$

3. It satisfies the prescribed initial and boundary conditions, i.e.,

$$u(x, t_0) = \varphi(x) \, , \qquad u(0, t) = \mu_1(t) \, , \qquad u(l, t) = \mu_2(t) \, ,$$

where $\varphi(x)$, $\mu_1(t)$ and $\mu_2(t)$ are continuous functions which satisfy the transition conditions

$$\varphi(0) = \mu_1(t_0) \qquad [= u(0, t_0)]$$

and

$$\varphi(l) = \mu_2(t_0) \qquad [= u(l, t_0)]$$

which are necessary for the continuity of $u(x, t)$ in the closed region.

We consider now the x, t phase plane (Figure 37). In our problem we seek a function $u(x, t)$, which is defined in the interior of a rectangle $ABCD$. This region is already determined by the statement of the problem, since the course of the heat propagation in the rod $0 \leqq x \leqq l$ during the time interval $t \leqq t = T$, in which the heat behavior of the boundary is known, was already investigated. Let $t_0 = 0$; we assume that $u(x, t)$ satisfies the heat-conduction equation only for $0 < x < l, 0 < t \leqq T$, i.e., not for $t = 0$ (the side AB) or for $x = 0$, $x = l$ (the sides AD and BC). For $t = 0$, as well as $x = 0$ and $x = l$, the value of this function is given directly by the initial and boundary conditions. To require that the heat-conduction equation, for example, be satisfied also for $t = 0$ would imply that the derivative $\varphi'' = u_{xx}(x, 0)$ in this equation exists. Therefore, the generality of the physical phenomena to be investigated is limited, and thus the basic functions which do not satisfy this requirement are eliminated from consideration. The condition (3-1.3) loses its meaning when it is not required that $u(x, t)$ in the region $0 \leqq x \leqq l, 0 \leqq t \leqq T$ (i.e., in the closed rectangle $ABCD$) be continuous or this requirement must be replaced by another appropriate assumption.[46] To understand the significance of this requirement we consider the function $v(x, t)$ defined by the following conditions:

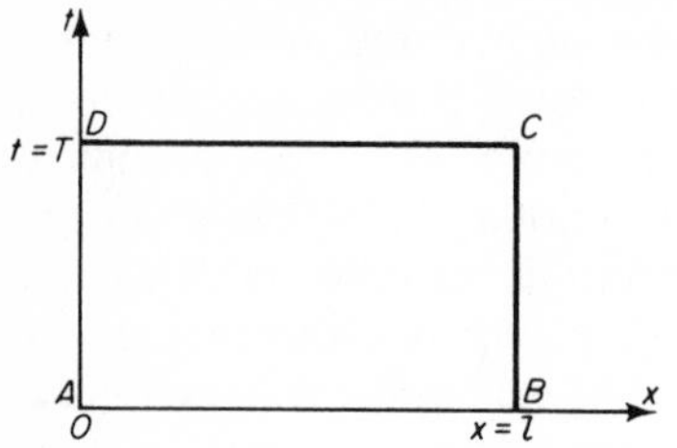

FIG. 37.

$$
\begin{aligned}
&& v(x, t) &= C\,, && 0 < x < l\,, \quad 0 < t \leqq T \\
&& v(x, 0) &= \varphi(x)\,, && 0 \leqq x \leqq l \\
v(0, t) &= \mu_1(t)\,, & v(l, t) &= \mu_2(t)\,, && 0 \leqq t \leqq T
\end{aligned}
$$

where C is an arbitrary constant. The function v obviously satisfies both condition (3-1.2) and the boundary conditions. However, this function in no case describes the course of the heat distribution in the rod with an initial temperature $\varphi(x) \neq C$ and boundary temperatures $\mu_1(t) \neq C$ and $\mu_2(t) \neq C$, since it is discontinuous for $t = 0$, $x = 0$, $x = l$.

The continuity of $u(x, t)$ for $0 < x < l, 0 < t < T$ directly follows in that $u(x, t)$ satisfies the differential equation. Therefore, the requirement that $u(x, t)$ be continuous in $0 \leqq x \leqq l$, $0 \leqq t \leqq T$, is based essentially only on those points at which the boundary and the initial values are prescribed. In the following, by a solution of the equation which satisfies the boundary conditions, we shall always mean a function which satisfies the requirements (3-1.1), (3-1.2), and (3-1.3) and hence not repeat these each time, unless there are special conditions.

Correspondingly, this is the case for other boundary-value problems, in particular for problems of an infinite rod and problems without initial conditions.

[46] Later, boundary-value problems with discontinuous boundary and initial conditions will be considered. For these, the problems will be properly defined so that the boundary conditions are fulfilled.

For problems with several independent geometric variables the above statements remain valid. In these problems, an initial temperature and boundary conditions determined on the surface of the body are prescribed for $t = 0$. We can also investigate problems for infinite domains.

With regard to all the problems discussed, the following problems exist[47]:

1. Are the solutions of the problems discussed uniquely determined?
2. Does a solution exist?
3. Do the solutions depend continuously on the auxiliary conditions?

If a problem admits of many solutions, then we naturally cannot speak of "the solution of the problem," and we must first prove the uniqueness. In practice, the second question above is the most important, since generally in proving the existence of a solution, we simultaneously find methods for its calculation.

As noted earlier (see Section 2–2 §3) we speak of a physically determined process when a small change in the initial or boundary conditions causes a small change in the solution. In the following, it will be shown that heat propagation is determined physically by the initial and boundary conditions, i.e., a small change in the initial or boundary conditions implies a small change in the solution.

5. The principle of the maximum

In the following we shall investigate differential equations with constant coefficients,

$$v_t = a^2 v_{xx} + \beta v_x + \gamma v \,. \tag{3-1.34}$$

As already shown, these equations, by the substitution of

$$v = e^{\mu x + \lambda t} u \qquad \text{with} \qquad \mu = -\frac{\beta}{2a^2}\,, \qquad \lambda = \gamma - \frac{\beta^2}{4a^2}$$

can be brought to the form

$$u_t = a^2 u_{xx} \,. \tag{3-1.35}$$

The solutions of this equation have the following properties which will be denoted as the principle of the maximum.

A function $u(x, t)$ defined and continuous in the closed region $0 \leqq t \leqq T$, $0 \leqq x \leqq l$ and satisfying the heat-conduction equation

$$u_t = a^2 u_{xx} \tag{3-1.35}$$

in the region $0 < t < T$, $0 < x < l$ assumes its maximum or minimum at the initial moment $t = 0$ or at the boundary points $x = 0$ or $x = l$.

Before we prove this, note that the function $u(x, t) = \text{const.}$ obviously satisfies the heat-conduction equation and assumes a maximum (minimum) at each point. However, this does not contradict our assertion, because it means only that when a maximum (minimum) is assumed in the interior of the region it is also (but not only) assumed for $t = 0$ or for $x = 0$ or $x = l$.

[47] *Cf.* Section 2–2.

The physical significance of this statement is immediately clear: if the temperature on the boundary and at the initial moment does not exceed a value M, then in the interior of the body no temperature higher than M can be attained. We shall limit ourselves to the proof of the statement of the maximum and give an indirect proof. We shall designate by M the maximum value of $u(x, t)$ for $t = 0$ $(0 \leqq x \leqq l)$ or for $x = 0$ or $x = l$ $(0 \leqq t \leqq T)$ and assume that the function $u(x, t)$ assumes its maximum at an interior point (x_0, t_0), $(0 < x_0 < l, 0 < t_0 \leqq T)$:[48]

$$u(x_0, t_0) = M + \varepsilon .$$

We now compare the signs in Eq. (3-1.35) at the point (x_0, t_0). Since the function at (x_0, t_0) assumes its maximum,[49] then necessarily

$$\frac{\partial u}{\partial x}(x_0, t_0) = 0 \qquad \text{and} \qquad \frac{\partial^2 u}{\partial x^2}(x_0, t_0) \leqq 0 . \tag{3-1.36}$$

Also, since $u(x_0, t)$ for $t = t_0$ has a maximum,[50] then

$$\frac{\partial u}{\partial t}(x_0, t_0) \geqq 0 . \tag{3-1.37}$$

By comparison of the signs on the left and right sides of (3-1.35) it follows that both sides can be different. These considerations, however, still do not prove the correctness of our theorem; since the right and the left sides can simultaneously equal zero, it would signify no contradiction. We bring forth this consideration simply to emphasize the fundamental concepts of our proof. For the completion of the proof we shall seek more than one point (x_1, t_1) at which $\partial^2 u/\partial x^2 \leqq 0$ and $\partial u/\partial t > 0$. Therefore, we consider the auxiliary function

$$v(x, t) = u(x, t) + k(t_0 - t) , \tag{3-1.38}$$

where k is a constant. Obviously then

$$v(x_0, t_0) = u(x_0, t_0) = M + \varepsilon$$

and

$$k(t_0 - t) \leqq kT .$$

[48] If the continuity of $u(x, t)$ were assumed in the bounded region $0 \leqq x \leqq l$, $0 \leqq t \leqq T$, then the function $u(x, t)$ could not exceed its maximum, and further considerations would be contradictory. On the basis of the theorem that every continuous function in a bounded region attains its maximum, then (a) the function $u(x, t)$ attains a maximum within or on the boundaries which will be denoted by M; (b) if $u(x, t)$ also were to exceed M only at a point, then a point (x_0, t_0) would exist at which the function $u(x, t)$ assumes a maximum which is larger than M: $u(x_0, t_0) = M + \varepsilon$ $(\varepsilon > 0)$, where $0 < x_0 < l$, $0 < t_0 \leqq T$.

[49] As is known from analysis, for the existence of a relative minimum of a function $f(x)$ at an interior point x_0 of an interval $(0, l)$, the conditions

$$\left.\frac{\partial f}{\partial x}\right|_{x=x_0} = 0, \left.\frac{\partial^2 f}{\partial x^2}\right|_{x=x_0} > 0$$

are sufficient. If, therefore, at the point x_0 the function $f(x)$ has a maximum value, then (a) $f'(x_0) = 0$, and (b) $f''(x_0) > 0$ cannot hold; therefore $f''(x_0) = 0$.

[50] Obviously, $\partial u/\partial t = 0$, in case $t_0 < T$, whereas for $t_0 = T$, then $\partial u/\partial t = 0$ must hold.

We now select $k > 0$ so that $kT < \varepsilon/2$, i.e., let $k < \varepsilon/2T$; then the maximum of $v(x, t)$ for $t = 0$ or for $x = 0, x = l$ does not exceed the value $M + \varepsilon/2$, i.e.,

$$v(x, t) \leqq M + \frac{\varepsilon}{2} \qquad \text{for } t = 0 \text{ or } x = 0, x = l\,, \tag{3-1.39}$$

since for this argument the first summand of (3-1.38) is not larger than M, and the second is not larger than $\varepsilon/2$.

Now, $v(x, t)$ is a continuous function. Thus a point (x_1, t_1) exists at which it assumes its maximum. Then we have

$$v(x_1, t_1) \geqq v(x_0, t_0) = M + \varepsilon\,.$$

Therefore, $t_1 > 0$ and $0 < x_1 < l$, since for $t = 0$ or $x = 0$, $x = l$ the inequality (3-1.39) is valid. It follows that

$$v_{xx}(x_1, t_1) = u_{xx}(x_1, t_1) \leqq 0$$

and

$$v_t(x_1, t_1) = u_t(x_1, t_1) - k \geqq 0 \qquad \text{or} \qquad u_t(x_1, t_1) \geqq k > 0\,.$$

By comparison of the signs on the right and the left sides in (3-1.35) at the point (x_1, t_1) we conclude that Eq. (3-1.35) at the point (x_1, t_1) cannot be satisfied, since the quantities on the right and left sides have different signs. Therefore, the first part of our proposition is proved. The statement for the minimum can be proved analogously, and it is sufficient to apply the first part to $u_1 = -u$.

6. The uniqueness theorem

We turn now to a series of consequences of the principle of the maximum. First, we prove the uniqueness theorem for the first boundary-value problem. If the functions $u_1(x, t)$ and $u_2(x, t)$, which are defined and continuous in a region $0 \leqq x \leqq l, 0 \leqq t \leqq T$, and which satisfy the heat-conduction equation

$$u_t = a^2 u_{xx} + f(x, t) \qquad \text{for} \qquad 0 < x < l, t > 0 \tag{3-1.35$'$}$$

as well as the same initial and boundary conditions

$$\begin{aligned} u_1(x, 0) &= u_2(x, 0) = \varphi(x) \\ u_1(0, t) &= u_2(0, t) = \mu_1(t) \\ u_1(l, t) &= u_2(l, t) = \mu_2(t)\,, \end{aligned}$$

then necessarily[51]

$$u_1(x, t) \equiv u_2(x, t)\,.$$

For the proof of this theorem we consider the function

51 Previously this theorem was refined and the continuity requirement at $t = 0$ was dropped.

$$v(x, t) = u_2(x, t) - u_1(x, t) .$$

Since $u_1(x, t)$ and $u_2(x, t)$ for

$$0 \leqq x \leqq l , \qquad 0 \leqq t \leqq T$$

are continuous, their difference $v(x, t)$ in the same region is continuous. Further, $v(x, t)$ as the difference of two solutions of the heat-conduction equation for $0 < x < l$, $t > 0$ is similarly a solution of the heat-conduction equation in that region. Consequently, the principle of the maximum can also be applied to this function, and the maximum and the minimum of $v(x, t)$ for $t = 0$ or $x = 0$ or $x = l$ is assumed. According to the hypothesis we obtain

$$v(x, 0) = 0 , \qquad v(0, t) = 0 , \qquad v(l, t) = 0 .$$

Therefore, also

$$v(x, t) \equiv 0 ,$$

i.e.,

$$u_1(x, t) \equiv u_2(x, t) ,$$

from which the uniqueness of the solution of the first boundary-value problem follows.

We shall now prove a series of direct conclusions from the principle of the maximum. In the following discussion we shall refer to "the solution of the heat-conduction equation," instead of enumerating the properties of the function in detail which also satisfy the initial and boundary conditions.

1. If two solutions $u_1(x, t)$ and $u_2(x, t)$ of the heat-conduction equation satisfy the conditions

$$u_1(x, 0) \leqq u_2(x, 0) , \qquad u_1(0, t) \leqq u_2(0, t) , \qquad u_1(l, t) \leqq u_2(l, t) ,$$

then

$$u_1(x, t) \leqq u_2(x, t)$$

for all $0 \leqq x \leqq l, 0 \leqq t \leqq T$.

The difference $v(x, t) = u_2(x, t) - u_1(x, t)$ satisfies the conditions on which the principal of the maximum is based; also

$$v(x, 0) \geqq 0 \qquad v(0, t) \geqq 0 \qquad v(l, t) \geqq 0 .$$

Therefore

$$v(x, t) \geqq 0 \qquad \text{for} \qquad 0 < x < l,\ 0 < t \leqq T ,$$

since $v(x, t)$ in the region

$$0<x<l , \qquad 0<t\leqq T$$

would otherwise have a negative value.

2. If three solutions

$$u(x, t) , \qquad \underline{u}(x, t) , \qquad \bar{u}(x, t)$$

of the heat-conduction equation satisfy the conditions

$$\underline{u}(x, t) \leqq u(x, t) \leqq \bar{u}(x, t) \qquad \text{for} \qquad t = 0\,, \qquad x = 0\,, \qquad x = l\,,$$

then this inequality is fulfilled for all x in $0 \leqq x \leqq l$ and all t in $0 \leqq t \leqq T$.

This assertion represents an application of conclusion (1) to the functions

$$u(x, t)\,, \qquad \bar{u}(x, t) \qquad \text{and} \qquad u(x, t)\,, \qquad \underline{u}(x, t)\,.$$

3. If, for two solutions $u_1(x, t)$ and $u_2(x, t)$ of the heat conduction equation, the inequality

$$|\, u_1(x, t) - u_2(x, t)\,| \leqq \varepsilon\,, \qquad \text{for} \qquad t = 0\,, \qquad x = 0\,, \qquad x = l$$

is valid, then

$$|\, u_1(x, t) - u_2(x, t)\,| \leqq \varepsilon$$

for all x, t in

$$0 \leqq x \leqq l\,, \qquad 0 \leqq t \leqq T$$

is satisfied.

This assertion results from conclusion (2), when we apply the heat-conduction equation to the solutions

$$\underline{u}(x, t) = -\,\varepsilon$$
$$u(x, t) = u_1(x, t) - u_2(x, t)$$
$$\bar{u}(x, t) = \varepsilon\,.$$

The question regarding the continuous dependence of the solution of the first boundary-value problem on the initial and boundary conditions is answered completely by conclusion (3). To understand this, we consider a solution $u(x, t)$ which satisfies other initial and boundary conditions, instead of the solution of the heat-conduction equation which corresponds to the initial and boundary conditions

$$u(x, 0) = \varphi(x)\,, \qquad u(0, t) = \mu_1(t)\,, \qquad u(l, t) = \mu_2(t)\,.$$

Let these be given by functions $\varphi^*(x)$, $\mu_1^*(t)$ and $\mu_2^*(t)$ which differ by less than ε from the functions $\varphi(x)$, $\mu_1(t)$, and $\mu_2(t)$:

$$|\,\varphi(x) - \varphi^*(x)\,| \leqq \varepsilon\,, \qquad |\,\mu_1(t) - \mu_1^*(t)| \leqq \varepsilon\,, \qquad |\,\mu_2(t) - \mu_2^*(t)\,| \leqq \varepsilon\,.$$

However, the function $u_1(x, t)$ according to conclusion (3) differs by less than ε from the function $u(x, t)$:

$$|\, u(x, t) - u_1(x, t)\,| \leqq \varepsilon\,.$$

Here the principle of the physical determination of a problem arises directly.

We have investigated in detail the question of the uniqueness and the physical determination of a problem in the case of the first boundary-value problem for a bounded interval. The uniqueness theorem for the first boundary-value problem for a two- or three-dimensional bounded region can be proven by a verbatim repetition of these deliberations.

Similar questions arise in the investigation of other problems, an entire series of which was discussed in the preceding paragraphs. These problems, however, require certain changes in the method of proof.

The solution of the problem for an unbounded region (see Section 7) or a problem without initial conditions is uniquely determined only if the sought functions are still subjected to certain auxiliary conditions.

7. The uniqueness theorem for the infinite straight line

For the solution of a problem on the infinite straight line it is essential to require the boundedness of the sought function in the entire region, i.e., there exists an M such that $|u(x, t)| < M$ holds for all $-\infty < x < +\infty$ and $t = 0$.

If $u_1(x, t)$ and $u_2(x, t)$ are two continuous and bounded functions for all values of the variables x and t considered, and if they satisfy the heat-conduction equation

$$u_t = a^2 u_{xx}\,, \qquad -\infty < x < \infty,\ t > 0 \tag{3-1.35}$$

and the conditions

$$u_1(x, 0) = u_2(x, 0)\,, \qquad -\infty < x < \infty$$

then

$$u_1(x, t) \equiv u_2(x, t)\,, \qquad -\infty < x < \infty,\ t \geqq 0\,.$$

We consider, as before, the difference

$$v(x, t) = u_1(x, t) - u_2(x, t)\,.$$

The function $v(x, t)$ is continuous, satisfies the heat-conduction equation, is bounded in the entire region

$$|v(x, t)| \leqq |u_1(x, t)| + |u_2(x, t)| < 2M\,, \qquad -\infty < x < \infty,\ t \geqq 0\,,$$

and satisfies the condition

$$v(x, 0) = 0\,.$$

The principle of the maximum, which was used for the proof of uniqueness for the case of a bounded interval, is not directly applicable here, since the function $v(x, t)$ in an unbounded region need not assume its maximum at any point. In order to use this principle we consider a region

$$|x| \leqq L\,,$$

where L is a parameter which is permitted to increase unboundedly, and a function

$$V(x, t) = \frac{4M}{L^2}\left(\frac{x^2}{2} + a^2 t\right), \tag{3-1.40}$$

which is continuous, satisfies the heat-conduction equation (which we can easily verify by differentiation), and also satisfies the inequalities

$$V(x, 0) \geqq |v(x, 0)| = 0$$
$$V(\pm L, t) \geqq 2M \geqq v(\pm L, t)\,.$$

If we apply the principle of maximum to the region $|x| \leqq L$, we obtain

$$-\frac{4M}{L^2}\left(\frac{x^2}{2}+a^2t\right) \leqq v(x, t) \leqq \frac{4M}{L^2}\left(\frac{x^2}{2}+a^2t\right). \tag{3-1.41}$$

If we now consider any fixed pair of values (x, t) and let L increase unboundedly, we obtain

$$v(x, t) \equiv 0 ,$$

and thus our theorem is proved.

3-2. THE METHOD OF SEPARATION OF VARIABLES

1. The homogeneous boundary-value problem

We turn now to the solution of the first boundary-value problem for the heat-conduction equation

$$u_t = a^2 u_{xx} + f(x, t) \tag{3-2.1}$$

with the initial conditions

$$u(x, 0) = \varphi(x) \tag{3-2.2}$$

and the boundary conditions

$$u(0, t) = \mu_1(t) , \qquad u(l, t) = \mu_2(t) . \tag{3-2.3}$$

For the investigation of the general first boundary-value problem we begin with the solution for the simplest case.

Problem 1. Find the solution of the homogeneous differential equation

$$u_t = a^2 u_{xx} , \tag{3-2.4}$$

which satisfies the initial conditions

$$u(x, 0) = \varphi(x) \tag{3-2.2}$$

and the homogeneous boundary conditions

$$u(0, t) = 0 , \qquad u(l, t) = 0 . \tag{3-2.5}$$

For the solution of this problem we shall first consider, as is customary in the method of separation of variables, the following general auxiliary problem:

Find a nonidentically vanishing solution of the differential equation

$$u_t = a^2 u_{xx} ,$$

which satisfies the homogeneous boundary conditions

$$u(0, t) = 0 , \qquad u(l, t) = 0 \tag{3-2.5}$$

and is representable in the form

$$u(x, t) = X(x)T(t) , \tag{3-2.6}$$

where $X(x)$ is a function dependent only on x and $T(t)$ depends only on t.

If we put (3-2.6) into (3-2.4) and divide both sides of the equation so obtained by a^2XT, then we obtain

$$\frac{1}{a^2}\frac{T'}{T} = \frac{X''}{X} = -\lambda\,, \tag{3-2.7}$$

where $\lambda = \text{const.}$, since the left side of the equation depends only upon t and the right only on x.

Hence, we obtain the equations

$$X'' + \lambda X = 0 \tag{3-2.8}$$

$$T' + a^2\lambda T = 0\,, \tag{3-2.8$'$}$$

whereas the boundary conditions (3-2.5) become

$$X(0) = 0\,, \qquad X(l) = 0\,. \tag{3-2.9}$$

For the determination of $X(x)$ we obtain the eigenvalue problem

$$X'' + \lambda X = 0\,, \qquad X(0) = 0\,, \qquad X(l) = 0\,, \tag{3-2.10}$$

which has already been investigated for the solution of the wave equation (Section 2–3 § 1), where it was shown that only for the value of the parameters

$$\lambda_n = \left(\frac{\pi n}{l}\right)^2, \qquad n = 1, 2, 3, \cdots \tag{3-2.11}$$

do nontrivial solutions of Eq. (3-2.8) exist which are then equal to

$$X_n(x) = \sin\frac{\pi n}{l}x\,. \tag{3-2.12}$$

These values λ_n correspond for Eq. (3-2.8′) to the solutions

$$T_n(t) = C_n e^{-a^2\lambda_n t}\,, \tag{3-2.13}$$

where C_n are still arbitrary constants.

For the auxiliary problem, therefore, the functions

$$u_n(x, t) = X_n(x)T_n(t) = C_n e^{-a^2\lambda_n t}\sin\frac{\pi n}{l}x \tag{3-2.14}$$

are particular integrals of Eq. (3-2.4) which satisfy the homogeneous boundary conditions (3-2.5).

To solve Problem 1, we formally construct the series

$$u(x, t) = \sum_{n=1}^{\infty} C_n e^{-(\pi n/l)^2 a^2 t}\sin\frac{\pi n}{l}x\,. \tag{3-2.15}$$

The function $u(x, t)$ satisfies the boundary conditions since these are satisfied by every member of the series. If the initial conditions are to be satisfied also, then we must have

$$\varphi(x) = u(x, 0) = \sum_{n=1}^{\infty} C_n \sin\frac{\pi n}{l}x\,, \tag{3-2.16}$$

i.e., C_n are the Fourier coefficients of the function $\varphi(x)$ when these are developed in the interval (0, l) in a sine series:

$$C_n = \varphi_n = \frac{2}{l}\int_0^l \varphi(\xi)\sin\frac{\pi n}{l}\xi\cdot d\xi\,. \tag{3-2.17}$$

The coefficients C_n of the series (3-2.15) must now have the value defined by (3-2.17). To show that this series then satisfies all the conditions of Problem 1, we must prove that the function defined by (3-2.15) is differentiable, satisfies Eq. (3-2.4) in the region $0 < x < l$, $t > 0$, and at the boundary points of this region (for $t = 0$, $x = 0$ and $x = l$) is continuous.

Because of the linearity of Eq. (3-2.4), a series consisting of particular integrals, according to the superposition principle, is also a solution if this series converges and is termwise twice differentiable with respect to x and once with respect to t (see the auxiliary theorem in Section 2–3 § 3). We show next that the series arising by termwise differentiation

$$\sum_{n=1}^{\infty}\frac{\partial u_n}{\partial t} \quad \text{and} \quad \sum_{n=1}^{\infty}\frac{\partial^2 u_n}{\partial x^2}$$

for $t \geqq \bar{t} > 0$ ($\bar{t}$ is a fixed number) converges uniformly. Therefore, we consider the expression

$$\left|\frac{\partial u_n}{\partial t}\right| = \left|-C_n\left(\frac{\pi}{l}\right)^2 a^2n^2e^{-(\pi n/l)^2a^2t}\sin\frac{\pi n}{l}x\right| < |C_n|\left(\frac{\pi}{l}\right)^2\cdot a^2n^2e^{-(\pi n/l)^2a^2t}\,.$$

In the following we shall formulate the additional conditions which the function $\varphi(x)$ must satisfy. First, let $\varphi(x)$ be bounded $|\varphi(x)| < M$; then

$$|C_n| = \left|\frac{2}{l}\right|\left|\int_0^l \varphi(\xi)\sin\frac{\pi n}{l}\xi\,d\xi\right| < 2M\,,$$

from which

$$\left|\frac{\partial u_n}{\partial t}\right| < 2M\left(\frac{\pi}{l}\right)^2 a^2n^2e^{-(\pi n/l)^2a^2\bar{t}} \quad \text{for} \quad t \geqq \bar{t}\,,$$

and correspondingly there follows

$$\left|\frac{\partial^2 u_n}{\partial x^2}\right| < 2M\left(\frac{\pi}{l}\right)^2 n^2e^{-(\pi n/l)^2a^2\bar{t}} \quad \text{for} \quad t \geqq \bar{t}\,.$$

In general, we find

$$\left|\frac{\partial^{k+l}u_n}{\partial t^k\partial x^l}\right| < 2M\left(\frac{\pi}{l}\right)^{2k+l} n^{2k+l}a^{2k}e^{-(\pi n/l)^2a^2\bar{t}} \quad \text{for} \quad t \geqq \bar{t}\,.$$

The convergence of the majorant $\Sigma\alpha_n$ with

$$\alpha_n = Nn^qe^{-(\pi n/l)^2a^2\bar{t}} \tag{3-2.15'}$$

results from the D'Alembert criterion, since

$$\lim_{n\to\infty}\left|\frac{\alpha_{n+1}}{\alpha_n}\right| = \lim_{n\to\infty}\frac{(n+1)^q}{n^q}\,\frac{e^{-(\pi/l)^2a^2(n^2+2n+1)\bar{t}}}{e^{-(\pi/l)^2a^2n^2\bar{t}}} = \lim_{n\to\infty}\left(1+\frac{1}{n}\right)^q e^{-(\pi/l)^2a^2(2n+1)\bar{t}} = 0\,.$$

Hence, it follows that the series (3-2.15) for $t \geqq \bar{t} > 0$ is arbitrarily often termwise differentiable. Further, we conclude from the superposition principle that the function defined by this series satisfies Eq. (3-2.4). Since t is arbitrary it holds for all $t > 0$. Consequently, the series (3-2.15) for $t > 0$ represents a function which is arbitrarily often differentiable and satisfies Eq. (3-2.4).[52]

If the function $\varphi(x)$ is continuous, possesses piecewise continuous derivatives, and satisfies the conditions $\varphi(0) = 0$ and $\varphi(l) = 0$, then the series

$$u(x, t) = \sum_{n=1}^{\infty} C_n e^{-(\pi n/l)^2 a^2 t} \sin \frac{\pi n}{l} x \tag{3-2.15}$$

defines a continuous function for $t \geqq 0$.

From the inequality

$$| u_n(x, t) | < | C_n | \qquad \text{for} \qquad t \geqq 0, 0 \leqq x \leqq l$$

follows directly the uniform convergence of the series (3-2.15) for $t \geqq 0, 0 \leqq x \leqq l$. Since for a continuous and piecewise smooth function $\varphi(x)$ the series of the absolute values of the Fourier coefficients converges uniformly in case $\varphi(0) = \varphi(l) = 0$, we have proved the proposition.[53] We have, therefore, completely solved the first boundary-value problem for the homogeneous equation with homogeneous boundary conditions with continuous, piecewise smooth initial conditions.

2. Green's function

We turn to Eq. (3-2.15) obtained above in which we introduce the corresponding values for C_n:

$$\begin{aligned} u(x, t) &= \sum_{n=1}^{\infty} C_n e^{-(\pi n/l)^2 a^2 t} \sin \frac{\pi n}{l} x \\ &= \sum_{n=1}^{\infty} \left[\frac{2}{l} \int_0^l \varphi(\xi) \sin \frac{\pi n}{l} \xi \, d\xi \right] \cdot e^{-(\pi n/l)^2 a^2 t} \sin \frac{\pi n}{l} x \\ &= \int_0^l \left[\frac{2}{l} \sum_{n=1}^{\infty} e^{-(\pi n/l)^2 a^2 t} \sin \frac{\pi n}{l} x \cdot \sin \frac{\pi n}{l} \xi \right] \varphi(\xi) \, d\xi \, . \end{aligned}$$

Summation and integration can be interchanged for $t > 0$, since the series for $t > 0$ in the brackets converges uniformly with respect to ξ.[54]

We now set

$$G(x, \xi, t) = \frac{2}{l} \sum_{n=1}^{\infty} e^{-(\pi n/l)^2 a^2 t} \sin \frac{\pi n}{l} x \cdot \sin \frac{\pi n}{l} \xi \, . \tag{3-2.18}$$

With the use of this function $G(x, \xi, t)$, $u(x, t)$ can be written in the form

[52] In proving that the series (3-2.15) satisfies the equation $u_t = a^2 u_{xx}$ for $t > 0$, only the boundedness of the Fourier coefficients C_n was used. This, however, is the case for bounded $\varphi(x)$.

[53] See Section 2-3 § 3.

[54] The series $\Sigma \alpha_n$, where α_n is taken according to formula (3-2.15′), represents a majorant corresponding to the series, standing for $q = 0$, in the brackets.

$$u(x, t) = \int_0^l G(x, \xi, t)\varphi(\xi)\,d\xi\,. \tag{3-2.19}$$

The function $G(x, \xi, t)$ is known as Green's function (source function). We shall investigate its significance.

We shall show that $G(x, \xi, t)$, considered as a function of x, represents the temperature distribution in the rod $0 \leqq x \leqq l$ at time t, provided (1) the temperature at the initial moment $t = 0$ is equal to 0, and (2) at this time at the point $x = \xi$ a certain amount of heat (whose magnitude we shall determine later) is free while at the boundary ($x = 0$, $x = l$ of the rod) in the course of the total process the temperature remains equal to 0.

By the term "amount of heat Q free at the point ξ" we shall mean as usual that an amount of heat exists which is freed in a sufficiently small interval about the point ξ considered. The temperature change $\varphi_\varepsilon(\xi)$ which is produced by the appearance of the amount of heat about the point ξ outside of the interval $(\xi - \varepsilon, \xi + \varepsilon)$ is equal to zero; by contrast $\varphi_\varepsilon(\xi)$ inside of this interval can be regarded as a positive, continuous, and differentiable function and is such that

$$c\rho \int_{\xi-\varepsilon}^{\xi+\varepsilon} \varphi_\varepsilon(\xi)\,d\xi = Q\,, \tag{3-2.20}$$

since the left side of this equation precisely represents the amount of heat producing the temperature change of amount $\varphi_\varepsilon(\xi)$. The temperature distribution in this case is given by formula (3-2.19)

$$u_\varepsilon(x, t) = \int_0^l G(x, \xi, t)\varphi_\varepsilon(\xi)\,d\xi\,. \tag{3-2.21}$$

Now we let ε tend toward 0. From the continuity of $G(x, \xi, t)$ for $t > 0$ as well as Eq. (3-2.20) we obtain next by use of the mean-value theorem for fixed x, t

$$u_\varepsilon(x, t) = \int_{\xi-\varepsilon}^{\xi+\varepsilon} G(x, \xi, t)\varphi_\varepsilon(\xi)\,d\xi = G(x, \xi^*, t)\int_{\xi-\varepsilon}^{\xi+\varepsilon} \varphi_\varepsilon(\xi)\,d\xi = G(x, \xi^*, t)\frac{Q}{c\rho}\,, \tag{3-2.21'}$$

where ξ^* is a determined point in the interval $(\xi - \varepsilon, \xi + \varepsilon)$ and the integral of $\varphi_\varepsilon(\xi)$ exists as $\varepsilon \to 0$ and is equal to $Q/c\rho$. Because of the continuity of $G(x, \xi, t)$ with respect to ξ for $t > 0$ there then results

$$\lim_{\varepsilon\to 0} u_\varepsilon(x, t) = \frac{Q}{c\rho} G(x, \xi, t) = \frac{Q}{c\rho} \cdot \frac{2}{l} \sum_{n=1}^{\infty} e^{-(\pi n/l)^2 a^2 t} \sin\frac{\pi n}{l}x \cdot \sin\frac{\pi n}{l}\xi\,. \tag{3-2.22}$$

Hence, it follows that $G(x, \xi, t)$ represents the influence of the temperature of a heat pole of intensity $Q = c\rho$ occurring instantaneously, which is found at time $t = 0$ at the point ξ in the interval $(0, l)$.

We shall now prove the following property of the function $G(x, \xi, t)$: For arbitrary x, ξ and $t > 0$, $G(x, \xi, t) \geqq 0$. For the proof we consider the initially given function $\varphi_\varepsilon(x)$ with the above stated properties and the corresponding solution (3-2.21). Since the initial conditions and the boundary conditions are nonnegative, it follows from the maximum principle that

$$u_\varepsilon(x, t) \geqq 0$$

for all $0 \leqq x \leqq l$ and $t > 0$. Hence, it follows by consideration of (3-2.21)

$$u_\varepsilon(x, t) = G(x, \xi^*, t)\frac{Q}{c\rho} \geqq 0 \qquad \text{for} \qquad t > 0 \tag{3-2.21''}$$

as $\varepsilon \to 0$, and from (3-2.21′) we obtain

$$G(x, \xi, t) \geqq 0 \qquad \text{for} \qquad 0 \leqq x\,, \qquad \xi \leqq l\,, \qquad t > 0\,.$$

This result has a simple physical significance which, however, can be recognized directly only from (3-2.19), since $G(x, \xi, t)$ can be represented there by an alternating series.

3. Boundary-value problems with discontinuous initial conditions

The theory treated above was based on solutions of the heat-conduction equation which are continuous in a bounded region $0 \leqq x \leqq l$, $0 \leqq t \leqq T$. This requirement is a significant restriction. We consider, for example, the simple problem of the cooling of a uniformly heated rod on whose boundaries the temperature is equal to 0. Here the auxiliary conditions read

$$u(x, 0) = u_0\,, \qquad u(0, t) = u(l, t) = 0\,.$$

If $u_0 \neq 0$ then the solution of this problem at the points (0, 0) and (0, l) must be discontinuous. This example shows that the continuity of the initial condition required above and its compatibility as defined above are caused by the boundary conditions—a fact which, in practice, excludes very important cases from consideration. However, formula (3-2.19) also yields the solution of the boundary-value problem in this case.

If we wish to use the results of the above theory without neglecting its domain of applicability, we must concern ourselves with an extension of this theory that also encompasses the fundamental problems. There are numerous formulas used in applications outside their domains of validity in addition to those which are, in general, stated according to the conditions for their applicability. The consistent basis of all formulas would be too time consuming and would deviate from the quantitative and qualitative aspects of those processes which are characteristic for these physical methods.

On the other hand, we retain what is necessary, at least with respect to the simplest examples, to give a basis of the mathematical apparatus sufficient for the solution of the fundamental problem.

We shall consider boundary-value problems with piecewise continuous initial conditions without assuming that the initial function in the above-defined sense is compatible with the boundary conditions. This class of auxiliary conditions is, in practice, sufficiently general and for the explanation of the theory sufficiently simple. Our goal, therefore, is to show that formula (3-2.19) still gives the solution of the problem described. The necessary investigations will be carried out in single steps. First, we shall prove the theorem:

The solution of the heat-conduction equation

$$u_t = a^2 u_{xx}\,, \qquad 0 < x < l\,, \qquad t > 0\,, \tag{3-2.4}$$

which is continuous in the closed region $0 \leqq x \leqq l$, $0 \leqq t \leqq T$ and satisfies the conditions

$$u(0, t) = u(l, t) = 0 \tag{3-2.5}$$

$$u(x, 0) = \varphi(x) \tag{3-2.2}$$

where $\varphi(x)$ is an arbitrary continuous function vanishing at $x = 0$ and $x = l$, is determined uniquely and is represented by

$$u(x, t) = \int_0^l G(x, \xi, t)\varphi(\xi)\,d\xi\,. \tag{3-2.19}$$

We have already proved this theorem under the assumption that $\varphi(\xi)$ possesses a piecewise continuous derivative.

We shall now prove the theorem without this assumption. Therefore we consider a sequence of piecewise continuous differentiable functions $\varphi_n(x)$, $\varphi_n(0) = \varphi_n(l) = 0$, which converges uniformly towards $\varphi(x)$, since $\varphi_n(x)$, for example, can be chosen as the function which represents the step function which coincides with $\varphi(x)$ at the points $l\cdot k/n$, $k = 0, 1, 2, \cdots, n$. The functions $u_n(x, t)$ defined by (3-2.19) through $\varphi_n(x)$ then satisfy all the assumptions of the theorem, since the $\varphi_n(x)$ are piecewise differentiable. The functions $u_n(x, t)$ converge uniformly towards a continuous limit function $u(x, t)$. To each $\varepsilon \to 0$, therefore, we can find an $n(\varepsilon)$ such that

$$|\varphi_{n_1}(x) - \varphi_{n_2}(x)| < \varepsilon\,, \qquad 0 \leqq x \leqq l$$

when $n_1, n_2 \geqq n(\varepsilon)$, since these functions, by hypothesis converge uniformly. From this, on the basis of the principle of the maximum it also follows that

$$|u_{n_1}(x, t) - u_{n_2}(x, t)| < \varepsilon\,, \qquad 0 \leqq x \leqq l\,, \qquad 0 \leqq t \leqq T$$

when $n_1, n_2 \geqq n(\varepsilon)$. Therefore, the uniform convergence of a sequence of functions $u_n(x, t)$ toward a continuous limit function $u(x, t)$ is demonstrated.

If now for fixed x and t we pass to the limit under the integral sign, it follows that the function

$$u(x, t) = \lim_{n\to\infty} u_n(x, t) = \lim_{n\to\infty} \int_0^l G(x, \xi, t)\varphi_n(\xi)\,d\xi = \int_0^l G(x, \xi, t)\varphi(\xi)\,d\xi$$

exists in the closed region $0 \leqq x \leqq l$, $0 \leqq t \leqq T$, is continuous, and satisfies the conditions (3-2.2). Referring to footnote 52 we see that this function also satisfies Eq. (3-2.4) and hence the theorem is proved.

As the following deliberations will show, the function $u(x, t)$ defined by (3-2.19) is a uniquely determined continuous solution of our problem.

We turn now to the proof of the uniqueness theorem for the case of a piecewise continuous initial function $\varphi(x)$ without assuming that this function is compatible with the boundary conditions and we prove:

A function which is continuous in the region $t > 0$ and for $0 < x < l$, $t > 0$

satisfies the heat-conduction equation

$$u_t = a^2 u_{xx} , \tag{3-2.4}$$

the homogeneous boundary conditions

$$u(0, t) = u(l, t) = 0 , \tag{3-2.5}$$

and the initial condition

$$u(x, 0) = \varphi(x) \tag{3-2.2}$$

is uniquely determined when
1. It is continuous at the points of continuity of the function $\varphi(x)$;
2. It is bounded in the closed region $0 \leqq x < l, 0 \leqq t \leqq \bar{t}_0$ ($\bar{t}_0$ is an arbitrary positive number).

We assume that such a function exists, and on the basis of the preceding theorem for $t > \bar{t}$ this can be represented by

$$u(x, t) = \int_0^l G(x, \xi, t - \bar{t})\varphi_{\bar{t}}(\xi) d\xi , \qquad t > \bar{t} > 0 \tag{3-2.19'}$$

for arbitrary $\bar{t}$ $(0 < \bar{t} \leqq t, \varphi_{\bar{t}}(x) = u(x, \bar{t}))$.

In (3-2.19′) we now carry out the passage to the limit $\bar{t} \to 0$ where x and t are fixed. We shall show[55] that the passage to the limit under the integral sign is possible, and therefore the function $u(x, t)$ is represented uniquely by

$$u(x, t) = \int_0^l G(x, \xi, t)\varphi(\xi) d\xi , \qquad \varphi(\xi) = u(\xi, 0) . \tag{3-2.19}$$

Let $x_1, x_2, \cdots, x_n$ be the points of discontinuity of the function $\varphi(x)$. Then, if we set $x_0 = 0$ and $x_{n+1} = l$ (Figure 38) and consider the closed intervals

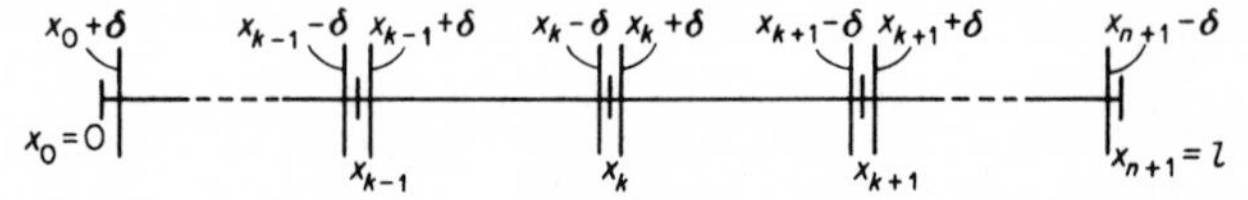

FIG. 38.

I_k $(x_k + \delta \leqq x \leqq x_{k+1} - \delta)$, $k = 0, 1, \cdots, n$, where δ is an arbitrarily small positive number, then we know that the integrand in (3-2.19′) in each of I_k, $k =$

[55] The theorem proven in the following is a special case of a theorem of Lebesgue, which states that the passage to the limit under the integral sign is possible in case the sequence of functions $F_n(x)$ converges almost everywhere toward a summable limit function $F(x)$ and if this sequence is bounded by a summable function. This proof can be carried out without the use of the notions of measure theory. If measure theory is used, one can prove completely analogously that a solution of the heat-conduction equation $u(x, t)$ which satisfies the homogeneous boundary conditions is defined uniquely when the following conditions hold: (1) $u(x, t) \leqq F(x)$, where $F(x)$ is a summable function; (2) if, almost everywhere

$$\lim_{t \to 0} u(x, t) = \varphi(x) ,$$

where $\varphi(x)$ is a prescribed summable initial function.

$0, 1, 2, \cdots, n$, converges uniformly towards the integrand in (3-2.19). In the intervals $\bar{I}_k$ $(x_k - \delta \leqq x \leqq x_k + \delta)$, $k = 1, 2, \cdots, n$, on the other hand, the integrands of (3-2.19) and (3-2.19′) are bounded by a fixed number M for each $\bar{t}$ $(0 \leqq \bar{t} \leqq \bar{t}_0)$, since $u(x, t)$ was assumed to be bounded and $G(x, \xi, t)$, for $0 \leqq \xi \leqq l$, $t > 0$, is continuous. If we split up the difference of the integrals (3-2.19) and (3-2.19′) into the $2n + 3$ integrals which correspond to the intervals I_k, $k = 0, 1, \cdots, n$, and $\bar{I}_k$, $k = 0, 1, \cdots, n + 1$, then we see that this difference can be made smaller than an arbitrary prescribed number ε if

$$\delta \leqq \frac{\varepsilon}{2n+3}\frac{1}{4N}$$

so that

$$\left| \int_{\bar{I}_k} [G(x, \xi, t - \bar{t})\varphi_{\bar{t}}(\xi) - G(x, \xi, t)\varphi(\xi)]\, d\xi \right| \leqq \frac{\varepsilon}{2n+3},$$

and if $\bar{t}$ is sufficiently small so that

$$| G(x, \xi, t - \bar{t})\varphi_{\bar{t}}(\xi) - G(x, \xi, t)\varphi(\xi) |$$
$$\leqq \frac{1}{l}\frac{\varepsilon}{2n+3} \quad \text{for} \quad t \leqq \bar{t} \text{ in } I_k, \quad k = 0, 1, \cdots, n.$$

Therefore,

$$\int_{I_k} | G(x, \xi, t - \bar{t})\varphi_{\bar{t}}(\xi) - G(x, \xi, t)\varphi(\xi) |\, d\xi$$
$$< \frac{\varepsilon}{2n+3} \quad \text{for} \quad t \leqq \bar{t}, \quad k = 0, 1, \cdots, n.$$

Hence follows the inequality

$$\left| \int_0^l [G(x, \xi, t - \bar{t})\varphi_{\bar{t}}(\xi) - G(x, \xi, t)\varphi(\xi)]\, d\xi \right| < \varepsilon \quad \text{for} \quad t \leqq \bar{t}.$$

Therefore, the passage to the limit under the integral signs is permissible, and if a function $u(x, t)$ exists which satisfies the assumptions of our theorem, it can be represented by the formula (3-2.19), from which also the unique determination of such a function is proved.

We shall now show that formula (3-2.19) represents a bounded solution of Eq. (3-2.4) which satisfies the conditions (3-2.2) for an arbitrary piecewise continuous function $\varphi(x)$ and is continuous everywhere that $\varphi(x)$ is continuous.

We shall prove this theorem in two steps. First, to show that it is true in case $\varphi(x)$ is a linear function

$$\varphi(x) = cx, \tag{3-2.2′}$$

we consider the sequence of auxiliary functions (Figure 39)

$$\varphi_n(x) = cx \qquad \text{for} \quad 0 \leqq x \leqq l\left(1 - \frac{1}{n}\right)$$
$$= \alpha(l - x) \qquad \text{for} \quad l\left(1 - \frac{1}{n}\right) \leqq x \leqq l.$$

The number α is determined so that $\varphi_n(x)$ at the point $x = l(1 - 1/n)$ shall be continuous:

$$cl\,\frac{n-1}{n} = \alpha\frac{l}{n} \qquad \text{i.e., } \alpha = (n-1)c\,.$$

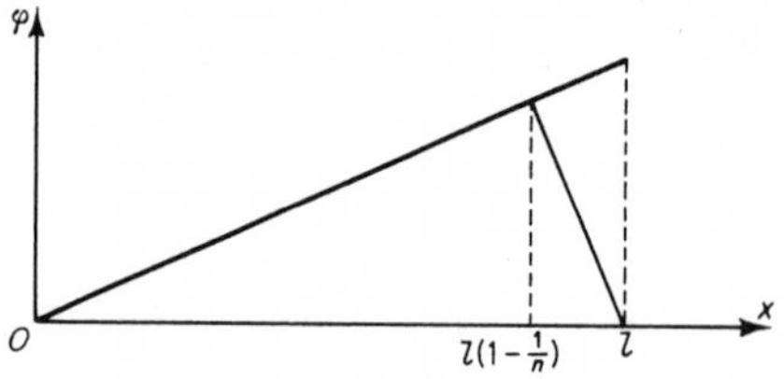

FIG. 39.

The functions $u_n(x, t)$, which for the $\varphi_n(x)$ are defined by formula (3-2.19), then are known continuous solutions of the heat-conduction equation with homogeneous boundary conditions and the initial conditions

$$u_n(x, 0) = \varphi_n(x)\,.$$

Since

$$\varphi_n(x) \leqq \varphi_{n+1}(x)\,, \qquad 0 \leqq x \leqq l\,,$$

then on the basis of the principle of the maximum

$$u_n(x, t) \leqq u_{n+1}(x, t)\,.$$

The function $U_0(x) = cx$ is a continuous solution of the heat-conduction equation. It follows from the principle of the maximum that necessarily

$$u_n(x, t) \leqq U_0(x)\,,$$

since this inequality is valid for $x = 0$, $x = l$, and $t = 0$. The sequence $\{u_n(x, t)\}$ is therefore monotonic, nondecreasing, and is bounded above by the function $U_0(x)$; consequently, it converges. We can now easily recognize the validity of the relations

$$u(x, t) = \lim_{n\to\infty} u_n(x, t) = \lim_{n\to\infty}\int_0^l G(x, \xi, t)\varphi_n(\xi)\,d\xi = \int_0^l G(x\ \xi, t)\varphi(\xi)\,d\xi \leqq U_0(x)$$

and pass to the limit under the integral sign. On the basis of footnote 52 this function satisfies Eq. (3-2.4) and the homogeneous boundary conditions (3-2.5) for $t > 0$. Moreover, it is continuous at $t = 0$ and $0 \leqq x < 1$, as we now prove. Let $x_0 < l$. We choose n such that $x_0 < l(1 - 1/n)$. In this case, $\varphi_n(x_0) = U_0(x_0)$. If we bear in mind that

$$u_n(x, t) \leqq u(x, t) \leqq U_0(x)$$

and

$$\lim_{\substack{x\to x_0\\ t\to 0}} u_n(x, t) = \lim_{x\to x_0} U_0(x) = \varphi(x_0)\,,$$

then we can conclude that the double limit exists, namely

$$\lim_{\substack{x\to x_0\\ t\to 0}} u(x, t) = \varphi(x_0)\,,$$

which is independent of the order of passage to the limit $x \to x_0$ and $t \to 0$. However, this implies the continuity of $u(x, t)$ at the point $(x_0, 0)$. This function is also bounded since it does not exceed $U_0(x)$. Therefore, the theorem for $\varphi(x) = cx$ is demonstrated.

If x is replaced by $l - x$, we see that the theorem holds also for

$$\varphi(x) = b(l - x)\,. \tag{3-2.2''}$$

Hence, each function of the form

$$\varphi(x) = B + Ax$$

is valid, since such a function can be obtained by addition of (3-2.2′) and (3-2.2″). Further, it follows that the theorem is also true for an arbitrary continuous function without the assumption $\varphi(0) = \varphi(l) = 0$. Every function of this type can therefore be represented in the form

$$\varphi(x) = \left[\varphi(0) + \frac{x}{l}(\varphi(l) - \varphi(0))\right] + \psi(x)\,,$$

where the sum in the brackets represents a linear function and $\psi(x)$ is a continuous function which vanishes at the ends of the interval: $\psi(0) = \psi(l) = 0$. However, we have already seen that the theorem is true for both summands; therefore, it is also true for $\varphi(x)$.

We turn now to the proof of the theorem for an arbitrary piecewise continuous function $\varphi(x)$. In this case, formula (3-2.19) also determines a solution which satisfies Eq. (3-2.4) and the homogeneous boundary conditions (3-2.5).

Let x_0 denote any point of continuity of the function $\varphi(x)$. To every positive ε, a $\delta(\varepsilon)$ can be found such that $|\, u(x, t) - \varphi(x_0)\,| < \varepsilon$ holds when $|\, x - x_0\,| < \delta(\varepsilon)$ and $t < \delta(\varepsilon)$. In order to understand this we first note that because of the continuity of the function $\varphi(x)$ at the point x_0, an $\eta(\varepsilon)$ exists such that

$$|\, \varphi(x) - \varphi(x_0)\,| \leqq \frac{\varepsilon}{2} \qquad \text{for} \qquad |\, x - x_0\,| < \eta(\varepsilon)\,,$$

from which results

$$\varphi(x_0) - \frac{\varepsilon}{2} \leqq \varphi(x) \leqq \varphi(x_0) + \frac{\varepsilon}{2} \qquad \text{for} \qquad |\, x - x_0\,| < \eta(\varepsilon)\,. \tag{3-2.23}$$

We now construct the following continuous differentiable functions $\bar{\varphi}(x)$ and $\underline{\varphi}(x)$:

$$\left.\begin{aligned} \bar{\varphi}(x) &= \varphi(x_0) + \frac{\varepsilon}{2} && \text{for} \quad |\, x - x_0\,| < \eta(\varepsilon) \\ \bar{\varphi}(x) &\geqq \varphi(x) && \text{for} \quad |\, x - x_0\,| > \eta(\varepsilon) \end{aligned}\right\} \tag{a}$$

$$\left.\begin{aligned} \underline{\varphi}(x) &= \varphi(x_0) - \frac{\varepsilon}{2} && \text{for} \quad |\, x - x_0\,| < \eta(\varepsilon) \\ \underline{\varphi}(x) &\leqq \varphi(x) && \text{for} \quad |\, x - x_0\,| > \eta(\varepsilon)\,. \end{aligned}\right\} \tag{b}$$

In the interval $|\, x - x_0\,| > \eta(\varepsilon)$, $\bar{\varphi}$ and $\underline{\varphi}$ must satisfy only the requirements (a) and (b), but are otherwise arbitrary. On the basis of the inequality (3-2.23) we already have

$$\underline{\varphi}(x) \leqq \varphi(x) \leqq \bar{\varphi}(x) . \tag{3-2.24}$$

We consider now the functions

$$\bar{u}(x, t) = \int_0^l G(x, \xi, t)\bar{\varphi}(\xi)\,d\xi$$

$$\underline{u}(x, t) = \int_0^l G(x, \xi, t)\underline{\varphi}(\xi)\,d\xi .$$

Because of the continuity of $\bar{\varphi}(x)$ and $\underline{\varphi}(x)$, $\bar{u}(x, t)$ and $\underline{u}(x, t)$ are also continuous at the point x_0, i.e., a $\delta(\varepsilon)$ exists such that

$$\left.\begin{aligned} |\,\bar{u}(x, t) - \bar{\varphi}(x)\,| &\leqq \frac{\varepsilon}{2} \\ |\,\underline{u}(x, t) - \underline{\varphi}(x)\,| &\leqq \frac{\varepsilon}{2} \end{aligned}\right\} \quad \text{for} \quad |\,x - x_0\,| < \delta(\varepsilon) , \quad t < \delta(\varepsilon)$$

and it then follows that

$$\left.\begin{aligned} \bar{u}(x, t) &\leqq \bar{\varphi}(x) + \frac{\varepsilon}{2} = \varphi(x_0) + \varepsilon \\ \underline{u}(x, t) &\geqq \underline{\varphi}(x) - \frac{\varepsilon}{2} = \varphi(x_0) - \varepsilon . \end{aligned}\right\} \quad \text{for} \quad |\,x - x_0\,| < \delta(\varepsilon) , \quad t < \delta(\varepsilon)$$

Since $G(x, \xi, t)$ is nonnegative, formula (3-2.24) gives the relation

$$\underline{u}(x, t) \leqq u(x, t) \leqq \bar{u}(x, t) , \tag{3-2.25}$$

and hence follows the inequality

$$\varphi(x_0) - \varepsilon \leqq u(x, t) \leqq \varphi(x_0) + \varepsilon \quad \text{for} \quad |\,x - x_0\,| < \delta(\varepsilon),\ t < \delta(\varepsilon) ,$$

i.e.,

$$|\,u(x, t) - \varphi(x_0)\,| < \varepsilon \quad \text{for} \quad |\,x - x_0\,| < \delta(\varepsilon),\ t < \delta(\varepsilon) ,$$

which was to be proved. The boundedness of the function $|\,u(x, t)\,|$ follows from (3-2.25) and from the boundedness of the functions $\bar{u}(x, t)$ and $\underline{u}(x, t)$. Thus the theorem is proved.

4. The inhomogeneous heat-conduction equation

We shall consider the inhomogeneous heat-conduction equation

$$u_t = a^2 u_{xx} + f(x, t) \tag{3-2.1}$$

with the initial condition

$$u(x, 0) = 0 \tag{3-2.26}$$

and the boundary conditions

$$\begin{aligned} u(0, t) &= 0 \\ u(l, t) &= 0 . \end{aligned} \tag{3-2.5}$$

The solution $u(x, t)$ of this problem is sought in the form of a Fourier series in terms of the functions $\sin (\pi n/l)x$:

$$u(x, t) = \sum_{n=1}^{\infty} u_n(t) \sin\frac{\pi n}{l} x\,. \tag{3-2.27}$$

Thus, we consider t as a parameter. In order to find $u(x, t)$ we must determine the functions $u_n(t)$. To this end we use for $f(x, t)$ the series representation

$$f(x, t) = \sum_{n=1}^{\infty} f_n(t) \sin\frac{\pi n}{l} x\,,$$

with

$$f_n(t) = \frac{2}{l}\int_0^l f(\xi, t) \sin\frac{\pi n}{l}\xi\, d\xi\,. \tag{3-2.28}$$

If we substitute this solution expression in the initial Eq. (3-2.1), we obtain

$$\sum_{n=1}^{\infty} \sin\frac{\pi n}{l} x \left\{\left(\frac{\pi n}{l}\right)^2 a^2 u_n(t) + \dot{u}_n(t) - f_n(t)\right\} = 0\,.$$

This equation will be satisfied if all the development coefficients are equal to 0, i.e., if

$$\dot{u}_n(t) = -a^2\left(\frac{\pi n}{l}\right)^2 u_n(t) + f_n(t)\,. \tag{3-2.29}$$

From the initial condition for $u(x, t)$

$$u(x, 0) = \sum_{n=1}^{\infty} u_n(0) \sin\frac{\pi n}{l} x = 0\,,$$

we find the initial condition for $u_n(t)$

$$u_n(0) = 0\,. \tag{3-2.30}$$

If we solve the ordinary differential Eq. (3-2.29) with the homogeneous initial conditions (3-2.30)[56] then we find

$$u_n(t) = \int_0^t e^{-(\pi n/l)^2 a^2 (t-\tau)} f_n(\tau)\, d\tau\,. \tag{3-2.31}$$

If we introduce this expression for $u_n(t)$ into (3-2.27) we obtain a solution of our problem in the form

$$u(x, t) = \sum_{n=1}^{\infty}\left[\int_0^t e^{-(\pi n/l)^2 a^2 (t-\tau)} f_n(\tau)\, d\tau\right] \sin\frac{\pi n}{l} x\,. \tag{3-2.32}$$

With the expression (3-2.28) for $f_n(\tau)$, (3-2.32) is transformed into

$$\begin{aligned} u(x, t) &= \int_0^t\int_0^l \left\{\frac{2}{l}\sum_{n=1}^{\infty} e^{-(\pi n/l)^2 a^2 (t-\tau)} \sin\frac{\pi n}{l} x \cdot \sin\frac{\pi n}{l}\xi\right\} f(\xi, \tau)\, d\xi\, d\tau \\ &= \int_0^t\int_0^l G(x, \xi, t-\tau) f(\xi, \tau)\, d\xi\, d\tau \end{aligned} \tag{3-2.33}$$

where

[56] See footnote 17.

$$G(x, \xi, t-\tau) = \frac{2}{l}\sum_{n=1}^{\infty} e^{-(\pi n/l)^2 a^2 (t-\tau)} \sin\frac{\pi n}{l}x \cdot \sin\frac{\pi n}{l}\xi \tag{3-2.34}$$

coincides with Green's function given by formula (3-2.18).

To determine the physical significance of the solution

$$u(x, t) = \int_0^t\int_0^l G(x, \xi, t-\tau) f(\xi, \tau)\, d\xi\, d\tau \tag{3-2.33}$$

we assume that $f(\xi, \tau)$ differs only from 0 in a sufficiently small neighborhood

$$\xi_0 \leqq \xi \leqq \xi_0 + \varDelta\xi\,, \qquad \tau_0 \leqq \tau \leqq \tau_0 + \varDelta\tau_0$$

of a point $M_0(\xi_0, \tau_0)$. The function

$$F(\xi, \tau) = c\rho f(\xi, \tau)$$

denotes the density of the heat source. The total amount of heat which is set free in the interval $(0, l)$ during the time of the action of the source (i.e., during $\varDelta\tau$) is then equal to

$$Q = \int_{\tau_0}^{\tau_0+\varDelta\tau}\int_{\xi_0}^{\xi_0+\varDelta\xi} c\rho f(\xi, \tau)\, d\xi\, d\tau\,. \tag{3-2.35}$$

If we use the mean-value theorem, we arrive at the expression

$$\begin{aligned} u(x, t) &= \int_0^t\int_0^l G(x, \xi, t-\tau) f(\xi, \tau)\, d\xi\, d\tau \\ &= \int_{\tau_0}^{\tau_0+\varDelta\tau}\int_{\xi_0}^{\xi_0+\varDelta\xi} G(x, \xi, t-\tau) f(\xi, \tau)\, d\xi\, d\tau = G(x, \bar{\xi}, t-\bar{\tau})\cdot\frac{Q}{c\rho} = \bar{u}(x, t) \end{aligned}$$

where

$$\xi_0 < \bar{\xi} < \xi_0 + \varDelta\xi\,, \qquad \tau_0 < \bar{\tau} < \tau_0 + \varDelta\tau\,.$$

Hence, as $\varDelta\xi \to 0$ and $\varDelta\tau \to 0$ we obtain the function

$$u(x, t) = \lim_{\substack{\varDelta\xi\to 0\\ \varDelta\tau\to 0}} \bar{u}(x, t) = \frac{Q}{c\rho} G(x, \xi_0, t-\tau_0)\,. \tag{3-2.36}$$

Consequently, this can be interpreted as an influence function of an instantaneous heat source which appears at the point ξ_0 at time τ_0.

When the function $(Q/c\rho)G(x, \xi, t-\tau)$ representing the action of an instantaneous unit source at a point is known, the action of a continuously distributed source of density $F(x, t) = c\rho f(x, t)$ can be represented by formula (3-2.33). This follows directly from the physical significance of the function $G(x, \xi, t-\tau)$.

Therefore, the influence of the temperature of the heat source occurring in the region $(\xi_0, \xi_0 + \varDelta\xi)$, $(\tau_0, \tau_0 + \varDelta\tau)$ can be represented by the expression

$$G(x, \xi, t-\tau) f(\xi, \tau)\varDelta\xi\varDelta\tau\,, \qquad \frac{Q}{c\rho} = f(\xi, \tau)\varDelta\xi\varDelta\tau\,.$$

For the case of a continuous distribution of heat sources in the entire region $0 \leqq \xi \leqq l$, $0 \leqq \tau \leqq t$ we obtain

$$u(x, t) = \int_0^t \int_0^l G(x, \xi, t - \tau) f(\xi, \tau) \, d\xi \, d\tau$$

by a passage to the limit as $\Delta\xi \to 0$ and $\Delta\tau \to 0$.

Therefore, proceeding from the physical significance of Green's function $G(x, \xi, t)$ one can immediately write the expression (3-2.33) for the solution of the inhomogeneous equation.

Since we know the form in which the solution of our problem must be represented, we can investigate the conditions which the function $f(\xi, \tau)$ must satisfy for this formula to be applicable. We shall not go into this now.

We have considered the inhomogeneous equation with homogeneous initial conditions. If, however, the prescribed initial condition is inhomogeneous, the solution obtained with the homogeneous initial condition must be added to the solution of the homogeneous equation with initial condition $u(x, 0) = \varphi(x)$ which we found in Section 3–1.

5. The general first boundary-value problem

For the heat-conduction equation, the first boundary-value problem reads as follows: Find the solution of the equation

$$u_t = a^2 u_{xx} + f(x, t) \tag{3-2.1}$$

with the auxiliary conditions

$$u(x, 0) = \varphi(x) \tag{3-2.2}$$

$$\left.\begin{aligned} u(0, t) &= \mu_1(t) \\ u(l, t) &= \mu_2(t) \,. \end{aligned}\right\} \tag{3-2.3}$$

In order to find the solution we introduce a new function $v(x, t)$ by

$$u(x, t) = U(x, t) + v(x, t) \,, \tag{3-2.37}$$

which represents the difference between $u(x, t)$ and a known function $U(x, t)$.

We define $v(x, t)$ as the solution of the equation

$$v_t - a^2 v_{xx} = \bar{f}(x, t)$$
$$\bar{f}(x, t) = f(x, t) - [U_t - a^2 U_{xx}]$$

with the auxiliary conditions

$$\begin{aligned} v(x, 0) &= \bar{\varphi}(x) \,, & \bar{\varphi}(x) &= \varphi(x) - U(x, 0) \\ v(0, t) &= \bar{\mu}_1(t) \,, & \bar{\mu}_1(t) &= \mu_1(t) - U(0, t) \\ v(l, t) &= \bar{\mu}_2(t) \,, & \bar{\mu}_2(t) &= \mu_2(t) - U(l, t) \,. \end{aligned}$$

Further we choose the auxiliary function $U(x, t)$ such that

$$\bar{\mu}_1(t) = 0 \quad \text{and} \quad \bar{\mu}_2(t) = 0 \,.$$

Obviously for this purpose it is sufficient to set[57]

$$U(x, t) = \mu_1(t) + \frac{x}{l}[\mu_2(t) - \mu_1(t)] \,.$$

[57] See Chapter 2, Section 3 § 5.

Consequently, the determination of the function $u(x, t)$ as a solution of the general boundary-value problem is based on the determination of a function $v(x, t)$, which represents the solution of the above boundary-value problem with homogeneous boundary conditions. A method of determination of $v(x, t)$ was given in Section 3-2 §4. To be sure, the "solution scheme" described there is not always suitable for the representation of the function $u(x, t)$ when inhomogeneities exist in the equation itself and in the boundary conditions. The degree of difficulty in determining the auxiliary function $v(x, t)$ depends on the function $U(x, t)$. In particular, for a problem with stationary inhomogeneities it is appropriate to distinguish a stationary solution and to find the difference between it and $u(x, t)$.[58]

As an example, consider the following problem for a bounded rod $(0, l)$ whose ends are held at the constant temperatures u_0 and u_1:

$$\begin{aligned} u_t &= a^2 u_{xx} \\ u(x, 0) &= \varphi(x) \\ u(0, t) &= u_0 \\ u(l, t) &= u_1 \,. \end{aligned}$$

We establish the solution in the form

$$u(x, t) = \bar{u}(x) + v(x, t) \,,$$

where $\bar{u}(x)$ is the stationary temperature and $v(x, t)$ is the deviation of the function $u(x, t)$ from $\bar{u}(x)$.

Then the conditions

$$\begin{aligned} &\bar{u}'' = 0 \,, &&v_t = a^2 v_{xx} \\ &\bar{u}(0) = u_0 \,, &&v(x, 0) = \varphi(x) - \bar{u}(x) = \varphi_1(x) \\ &\bar{u}(l) = u_1 \,, &&v(0, t) = 0 \,, \quad v(l, t) = 0 \end{aligned}$$

hold for $\bar{u}(x)$ and $v(x, t)$.

Hence we find

$$\bar{u}(x) = u_0 + \frac{x}{l}(u_1 - u_0) \,.$$

The function $v(x, t)$, determined by the initial condition and the homogeneous boundary conditions, is then easily found by separation of variables.

Problems

1. Derive the equation for the heating of a homogeneous thin wire due to a constant electrical current when heat exchange with the environment takes place on the surface of the wire.
Solution:

$$u_t = a^2 u_{xx} - hu + q \,,$$

where h and q are fixed constants.

[58] See Chapter 2, Section 3 §6.

2. Derive the diffusion equation in a medium which moves in the direction of the x axis uniformly with a velocity w. Consider the case of one independent variable.

Solution:

$$u_t = Du_{xx} - wu_x ,$$

(where D is the diffusion coefficient).

3. Proceeding from Maxwell's equations under the assumptions $E_x = E_z = 0$, $H_z = 0$ and disregarding the displacement current, prove that in a homogeneous conducting medium the resulting electromagnetic field E_y satisfies the differential equation

$$\frac{\partial^2 E_y}{\partial z^2} = \frac{4\pi\sigma}{c^2}\frac{\partial E_y}{\partial t} ,$$

where σ is the conductivity of the medium and c is the velocity of light. What equation does H_x satisfy?

4. Give a physical interpretation of the following boundary conditions in problems of the theory of heat conduction and diffusion:

(a) $u(0, t) = 0$ (b) $u_x(0, t) = 0$ (c) $u_x(0, t) - hu(0, t) = 0$, $u_x(l, t) + hu(l, t) = 0$ $h > 0$.

5. Solve the problem of the cooling of a uniformly heated homogeneous rod at whose ends the temperature is equal to 0, under the assumption that no heat loss occurs on the lateral surface.

Solution:

$$u(x, t) = \frac{4U_0}{\pi}\sum_{k=1}^{\infty}\frac{e^{-(a^2(2k-1)^2\pi^2/l^2)t}}{(2k-1)}\sin\frac{(2k-1)\pi}{l}x , \qquad u(x, 0) = U_0 .$$

6. Let the initial temperature of a rod be given by $u(x, 0) = u_0 = \text{const.}$ for $0 < x < l$. The temperature of the ends are held constant: $u(0, t) = u_1$, $u(l, t) = u_2$ for $0 < t < \infty$. Find the temperature of the rod when no heat exchange occurs on the lateral surface. Determine the stationary temperature.

7. Solve Problem 6 under the boundary conditions that one end has a constant temperature and that the other is heat-insulated.

8. Solve the problem of the heating of a thin homogeneous conductor due to a constant electrical current when the initial temperature, the temperature of the boundary, and the temperature of the environment are equal to 0.

9. A cylinder of length l is filled with air and has the same pressure and temperature as the exterior environment. At the initial moment, the cylinder is opened, and a diffusion of gases into the cylinder commences from the surrounding atmosphere in which the concentration of a known gas is equal to u_0. Find the amount of gas diffused into the cylinder during the time t when the initial concentration of the gases in the cylinder is equal to 0.

10. Solve Problem 9 under the assumption that the left end of the cylinder is closed by a semipermeable membrane.

11. Solve the problem of the cooling of a homogeneous rod whose lateral surface is heat-insulated; its initial temperature is $u(x, 0) = \varphi(x)$, and at the ends a heat exchange occurs with the environment whose temperature is 0. Consider the special case $\varphi(x) = u_0$.

12. Solve Problem 11 under the assumption that the temperature of the environment is equal to u_0.

13. Solve Problem 11 under the assumption that on the lateral surface a temperature exchange occurs with the environment whose temperature (a) equals 0, (b) is constant and equals u_1.

14. What temperature does a rod assume when one end is heat-insulated and through the other end passes a heat current changing harmonically with time, if the heat exchange on the lateral surface is neglected?

15. Solve Problem 11 now assuming that the temperature at one end of the rod is 0 while the temperature at the second end of the rod changes harmonically with time.

16. Let a rod $(0, l)$ be composed of two homogeneous pieces of equal cross section which touch at the point $x = x_0$ and are characterized by a_1, k_1 and a_2, k_2 respectively. What temperature is assumed in such a rod when the temperature at one end of the rod, $x = 0$, tends continuously toward the value 0 while the temperature at the other end changes sinusoidally with time?

17. The left end of the combined rods in Problem 16 has a constant temperature of 0; the right end, by contrast, has the temperature $u(l, t) = u_1$. Let the initial temperature of the rod be 0. Determine the temperature of the rod (taking into consideration only the first term in the series development).

18. Find the temperature $u(x, t)$ of a rod whose initial temperature is equal to 0 when the boundary conditions have the form

$$u(0, t) = Ae^{-\alpha t}, \qquad u(l, t) = B.$$

A, B, and $\alpha > 0$ are constant.

3-3. PROBLEMS FOR THE INFINITE STRAIGHT LINE

1. Green's function for the unbounded straight line

In the preceding paragraphs for the Green's function of a bounded interval $(0, l)$, we obtained the expression[59]

$$G_l(x, \xi, t) = \frac{2}{l} \sum_{n=1}^{\infty} e^{-(\pi n/l)^2 a^2 t} \sin \frac{\pi n}{l} x \cdot \sin \frac{\pi n}{l} \xi. \tag{3-3.1}$$

If the heat pole possesses the intensity Q, the temperature distribution is described by the function

[59] Here we introduce the symbol l to the function $G_l(x, \xi, t)$ in order to distinguish it from Green's function $G(x, \xi, t)$ for the unbounded region to which we shall limit ourselves in these paragraphs.

$$u(x, t) = \frac{Q}{c\rho} G_l(x, \xi, t) . \tag{3-3.2}$$

From our observations in the formulation of the heat-conduction problem for an infinite straight line, it follows that the sought function $G(x, \xi, t)$ is considered as the limit value of the corresponding function (3-3.1) for a finite interval when both ends tend towards infinity. In order to calculate this limit value we transform (3-3.1) so that the ends of the given intervals contain the coordinates $-l/2$, $l/2$. This is accomplished by the introduction of new coordinates x' and ξ'

$$x' = x - \frac{l}{2} , \qquad \xi' = \xi - \frac{l}{2} .$$

The Green's function of an instantaneous point-forming source of intensity $Q = c\rho$ which is found at the point ξ' of the interval $(-l/2, l/2)$ then has the form

$$G_l(x', \xi', t) = \frac{2}{l} \sum_{n=1}^{\infty} e^{-(\pi n/l)^2 a^2 t} \sin \frac{\pi n}{l}\left(x' + \frac{l}{2}\right) \cdot \sin \frac{\pi n}{l}\left(\xi' + \frac{l}{2}\right) . \tag{3-3.1'}$$

We transform the product of both sine functions. If n is even, i.e., $n = 2m$, then

$$\sin \frac{2\pi m}{l}\left(x' + \frac{l}{2}\right) \cdot \sin \frac{2\pi m}{l}\left(\xi' + \frac{l}{2}\right) = \sin \frac{2\pi m}{l} x' \cdot \sin \frac{2\pi m}{l} \xi' .$$

If n is odd, then $n = 2m + 1$, and

$$\sin \frac{(2m+1)\pi}{l}\left(x' + \frac{l}{2}\right) \cdot \sin \frac{(2m+1)\pi}{2}\left(\xi' + \frac{1}{2}\right)$$
$$= \cos \frac{(2m+1)\pi}{l} x' \cdot \cos \frac{(2m+1)\pi}{l} \xi' .$$

Consequently,

$$G_l(x', \xi', t) = \frac{2}{l} \sum_{n=0}^{\infty}{}'' \, e^{-(\pi n/l)^2 a^2 t} \sin \frac{\pi n}{l} x' \sin \frac{\pi n}{l} \xi'$$
$$+ \frac{2}{l} \sum_{n=1}^{\infty}{}' \, e^{-(\pi n/l)^2 a^2 t} \cos \frac{\pi n}{l} x' \cos \frac{x n}{l} \xi' \tag{3-3.1''}$$

where $\sum''$ ranges over the even and $\sum'$ over the odd n.

We shall next determine the limit value of the first sum as $l \to \infty$. It can be written in the form

$$\frac{2}{l} \sum_{n=0}^{\infty}{}'' \, e^{-\lambda_n^2 a^2 t} \sin \lambda_n x' \cdot \sin \lambda_n \xi' = \frac{1}{\pi} \sum_{n=0}^{\infty}{}'' \, f_1(\lambda_n) \Delta\lambda \tag{3-3.3}$$

with

$$f_1(\lambda) = e^{-\lambda^2 a^2 t} \sin \lambda x' \sin \lambda \xi' , \qquad \Delta\lambda = \frac{2\pi}{l} \qquad \text{and} \qquad \lambda_n = \frac{n\pi}{l} .$$

The sum (3-3.3) suggests the corresponding sums for the integral of the function $f_1(\lambda)$ over the interval $0 \leqq \lambda < \infty$. As $l \to \infty$ then $\Delta\lambda \to 0$. By passage to the limit we obtain for the integral[60]

$$\lim_{\Delta\lambda \to 0} \frac{1}{\pi} \sum_{n=0}^{\infty}{}'' f_1(\lambda_n)\Delta\lambda = \frac{1}{\pi}\int_0^\infty f_1(\lambda)d\lambda = \frac{1}{\pi}\int_0^\infty e^{-\lambda^2 a^2 t} \sin \lambda x' \cdot \sin \lambda\xi' d\lambda . \quad (3\text{-}3.4)$$

Analogously we can write the second sum in the form

$$\frac{2}{l} \sum_{n=1}^{\infty}{}' e^{-\lambda_n^2 a^2 t} \cos \lambda_n x' \cos \lambda_n \xi' = \frac{1}{\pi} \sum_{n=1}^{\infty}{}' f_2(\lambda_n)\Delta\lambda \quad (3\text{-}3.5)$$

with

$$f_2(\lambda) = e^{-\lambda^2 a^2 t} \cos \lambda x' \cos \lambda\xi' \qquad \Delta\lambda = \frac{2\pi}{l} \qquad \text{and} \qquad \lambda_n = \frac{\pi n}{l} .$$

60 In formula (3-3.4) we obtain an improper integral on the left side as the limit value of the integral sum is extended throughout the infinite interval $(0, \infty)$. For the justification of this passage to the limit, one must show that it does not contradict the usual definition

$$\int_0^\infty f(\lambda)d\lambda = \lim_{L \to \infty} \int_0^L f(\lambda)d\lambda$$

of an improper integral. Therefore, we shall prove that if for $0 \leqq \lambda < \infty$ we consider a continuous function $f(\lambda)$ such that for any subdivision of the integral $(0, \infty)$ into equal subintervals $(\alpha \leqq \Delta\lambda_i \leqq \beta)$ the integral sum

$$\sum_{i=1}^{\infty} f(\lambda_i)(\lambda_i - \lambda_{i-1}), \qquad \lambda_{i-1} \leqq \overset{*}{\lambda_i} \leqq \lambda_i$$

converges for an arbitrary choice of λ_i^*, then the integral

$$\int_0^\infty f(\lambda)d\lambda$$

exists.

We show that the limit value

$$\lim_{\mu_k \to \infty} \int_0^{\mu_k} f(\lambda)d\lambda$$

exists, independent of the manner in which μ_k approaches infinity. First, we shall consider the case $\mu_k = \lambda_k$. Then

$$(*) \qquad \int_0^{\lambda_{k+h}} f(\lambda)d\lambda - \int_0^{\lambda_k} f(\lambda)d\lambda = \int_{\lambda_k}^{\lambda_{k+h}} f(\lambda)d\lambda \leqq \sum_{i=k}^{k+h-1} \overline{f(\lambda_i)}(\lambda_{i+1} - \lambda_i)$$

and correspondingly,

$$(**) \qquad \int_{\lambda_k}^{\lambda_{k+h}} f(\lambda)d\lambda \geqq \sum_{i=k}^{k+h-1} \underline{f(\lambda_i)}(\lambda_{i+1} - \lambda_i) ,$$

where $\overline{f(\lambda_i)}$ and $\underline{f(\lambda_i)}$ denote the largest and smallest values of $f(\lambda)$ in the interval $(\lambda_i, \lambda_{i+1})$. From the convergence of the integral sums with respect to the chosen sequence of λ_k, it then follows that for every ε an $N(\varepsilon)$ exists such that for $k > N(\varepsilon)$,

$$\left| \sum_{i=k}^{k+h} f(\lambda_i)(\lambda_i - \lambda_{i-1}) \right| < \varepsilon$$

holds. From this and from the expressions (*) and (**) we obtain

$$\left| \int_{\lambda}^{\lambda_{k+h}} f(\lambda)d\lambda \right| < \varepsilon \qquad \text{for} \qquad k > N(\varepsilon) .$$

(Next page)

As $\Delta\lambda \to 0$, we obtain the limit value of the second sum

$$\lim_{\Delta\lambda \to 0} \frac{1}{\pi} \sum_{n=1}^{\infty}{}' f_2(\lambda_n)\Delta\lambda = \frac{1}{\pi}\int_0^\infty f_2(\lambda)d\lambda = \frac{1}{\pi}\int_0^\infty e^{-\lambda^2a^2t}\cos\lambda x'\cos\lambda\xi' d\lambda\,. \qquad (3\text{-}3.6)$$

The integrals for f_1 and f_2 are formed by splitting the interval $(0,\ l)$ into equal subintervals of length $\Delta\lambda = 2\pi/l$. In this way it can be seen that the intermediate point is the right end point of the interval in the first sum and the middle point in the second sum.

Summarizing the results, we obtain

(Cont'd footnote 60)

From the convergence of each integral sum with respect to a given subdivision it follows that $f(\lambda)$ approaches 0 for $\lambda \to 0$, and, therefore, that

$$\left|\int_{\mu_k}^{\mu_{k+l}} f(\lambda)d\lambda - \int_{\lambda_k}^{\lambda_{k+h}} f(\lambda)d\lambda\right| < \varepsilon \qquad \text{for} \qquad k > N(\varepsilon)\,,$$

where λ_k and λ_{k+h} are those points of the subdivision that lie nearest to the points μ_k and μ_{k+1}.

This proves the existence of the improper integral

$$\int_0^\infty f(\lambda)d\lambda\,.$$

We show now the existence of a limit value

$$\lim_{\Delta\lambda_i \to 0} \sum_{i=0}^{\infty} f(\lambda_i^*)\Delta\lambda_i = \int_0^\infty f(\lambda)d\lambda\,.$$

For the difference there holds

$$\left|\int_0^\infty f(\lambda)d\lambda - \sum_{i=0}^{\infty} f(\lambda_i^*)\Delta\lambda\right|$$

$$\leqq \left|\int_0^{\lambda_k} f(\lambda)d\lambda - \sum_{0}^{\lambda_k} f(\lambda_i^*)\Delta\lambda_i\right| + \left|\int_{\lambda_k}^\infty f(\lambda)d\lambda\right| + \left|\sum_{\lambda_k}^{\infty} f(\lambda_i^*)\Delta\lambda_i\right|$$

and by a suitable selection of $\Delta\lambda_i$ and λ_k each of the sums on the right side can be made less than $\varepsilon/3$. Therefore, our proposition is valid and our lemma is proved. (However, the definition of the improper integral arising from the lemma is not suitable, since an example can be found of a function which satisfies the ordinary definition but not the definition given here.)

In our case

$$f(\lambda) = e^{-\lambda^2a^2t}\cos\lambda x\cos\lambda\xi \qquad \text{or} \qquad f(\lambda) = e^{-\lambda^2a^2t}\sin\lambda x\sin\xi\lambda\,.$$

For the integral sum arising from the subdivision by equidistant points $\lambda_i - \lambda_{i-1} = \Delta\lambda$, it follows that

$$\left|\sum_{i=0}^{\infty} f(\lambda_i^*)\Delta\lambda\right| \leq \sum_{i=0}^{\infty} \bar{f}(\lambda_{i-1})\Delta\lambda = \sum_{i=0}^{\infty} e^{-\lambda_{i-1}^2a^2t}\Delta\lambda < \Delta\lambda\sum_{i=0}^{\infty} e^{-(i-1)^2(\Delta\lambda)^2a^2t}\,.$$

The convergence of this sum is easily shown by using the D'Alembert criterion in which we investigate the ratio of the ith term of the $(i-1)$th term

$$\frac{e^{-i^2\Delta\lambda^2a^2t}}{e^{-(i-1)^2\Delta\lambda^2a^2t}} = e^{-(2i-1)(\Delta\lambda)^2a^2t}\,.$$

$$
\begin{aligned}
G(x, \xi, t) &= \lim_{l\to\infty} G_l(x, \xi, t) \\
&= \frac{1}{\pi}\int_0^\infty e^{-\lambda^2 a^2 t} \sin\lambda x \sin\lambda\xi d\lambda + \frac{1}{\pi}\int_0^\infty e^{-\lambda^2 a^2 t} \cos\lambda x \cos\lambda\xi d\lambda \\
&= \frac{1}{\pi}\int_0^\infty e^{-\lambda^2 a^2 t} \cos\lambda(x-\xi)\, d\lambda \, .
\end{aligned}
$$

Green's function for the infinite straight line therefore has the form

$$G(x, \xi, t) = \frac{1}{\pi}\int_0^\infty e^{-\lambda^2 a^2 t} \cos\lambda(x-\xi) d\lambda \, . \tag{3-3.7}$$

We now evaluate the integral

$$I = \int_0^\infty e^{-\lambda^2 \alpha} \cos\lambda\beta d\lambda \, , \qquad \alpha > 0 \, , \tag{3-3.8}$$

which depends on both parameters α and β. To this end we fix α and denote the integral by $I(\beta)$. Here, obviously, in order to calculate the derivative we must differentiate under the integral sign:

$$\frac{dI}{d\beta} = -\int_0^\infty e^{-\lambda^2\alpha}\lambda \sin\lambda\beta\, d\lambda \, .$$

By partial integration it follows that

$$\frac{dI}{d\beta} = \sin\lambda\beta \frac{1}{2\alpha} e^{-\lambda^2\alpha}\Big|_0^\infty - \frac{\beta}{2\alpha}\int_0^\infty e^{-\lambda^2\alpha}\cos\lambda\beta\, d\lambda = -\frac{\beta}{2\alpha} I(\beta) \, .$$

In this manner we obtain for $I(\beta)$ a differential equation with separated variables

$$\frac{I'}{I} = -\frac{\beta}{2\alpha} \, ,$$

whose solution is

$$I(\beta) = Ce^{-\beta^2/4\alpha} \, .$$

The value of the constant is obtained from $\beta = 0$, and indeed is

$$C = I(0) = \int_0^\infty e^{-\lambda^2\alpha} d\lambda = \frac{1}{\sqrt{\alpha}}\int_0^\infty e^{-z^2} dz = \frac{1}{\sqrt{\alpha}} \cdot \frac{\sqrt{\pi}}{2}$$

because

$$\int_0^\infty e^{-z^2} dz = \frac{\sqrt{\pi}}{2} \, .$$

Hence we obtain

$$I(\beta) = \int_0^\infty e^{-\lambda^2\alpha} \cos\lambda\beta\, d\lambda = \frac{1}{2}\frac{\sqrt{\pi}}{\sqrt{\alpha}} e^{-\beta^2/4\alpha} \, . \tag{3-3.9}$$

Now, if we substitute (3-3.9) into Eq. (3-3.7), we arrive at the expression

$$G(x, \xi, t) = \frac{1}{2\sqrt{\pi a^2 t}} e^{-(x-\xi)^2/4a^2 t} \tag{3-3.10}$$

for the Green's function for the infinite straight line. This function is usually called the fundamental solution of the heat-conduction equation. We can verify directly that the function

$$G(x, \xi, t - t_0) = \frac{Q}{c\rho 2\sqrt{\pi a^2(t - t_0)}} e^{-(x-\xi)^2/4a^2(t-t_0)} \tag{3-3.10'}$$

represents the temperature at the point x at time t, when at the initial moment $t = t_0$ and at the point ξ the amount of heat $Q = c\rho$ is set free:

1. The function $G(x, \xi, t - t_0)$ satisfies the heat-conduction equation with respect to the variables x and t which is proved directly by differentiation.

In fact,

$$G_x = -\frac{1}{2\sqrt{\pi}} \cdot \frac{x - \xi}{2[a^2(t - t_0)]^{3/2}} e^{-(x-\xi)^2/4a^2(t-t_0)}$$

$$G_{xx} = \frac{1}{2\sqrt{\pi}}\left[-\frac{1}{2}\frac{1}{[a^2(t - t_0)]^{3/2}} + \frac{(x - \xi)^2}{4[a^2(t - t_0)]^{5/2}}\right] e^{-(x-\xi)^2/4a^2(t-t_0)}$$

$$G_t = \frac{1}{2\sqrt{\pi}}\left[-\frac{a^2}{2[a^2(t - t_0)]^{3/2}} + \frac{a^2(x - \xi)^2}{4[a^2(t - t_0)]^{5/2}}\right] e^{-(x-\xi)^2/4a^2(t-t_0)}$$

i.e.,

$$G_t = a^2 G_{xx} .$$

2. The amount of heat found on the x axis at time $t > t_0$ is equal to

$$c\rho \int_{-\infty}^{\infty} G(x, \xi, t - t_0)\, dx = \frac{Q}{\sqrt{\pi}} \int_{-\infty}^{\infty} e^{-(x-\xi)^2/4a^2(t-t_0)} \frac{dx}{2\sqrt{a^2(t-t_0)}}$$

$$= \frac{Q}{\sqrt{\pi}} \int_{-\infty}^{\infty} e^{-\alpha^2} d\alpha = Q = c\rho$$

since

$$\int_{-\infty}^{\infty} e^{-\alpha^2} d\alpha = \sqrt{\pi}, \qquad \left(\alpha = \frac{x - \xi}{2\sqrt{a^2(t - t_0)}}, \qquad d\alpha = \frac{dx}{2\sqrt{a^2(t - t_0)}}\right).$$

Therefore, the amount of heat on the straight line does not change with time. The function $G(x, \xi, t - t_0)$ depends only on the time through the argument $\theta = a^2(t - t_0)$, and therefore we can write

$$G = \frac{1}{2\sqrt{\pi}} \frac{1}{\sqrt{\theta}} e^{-(x-\xi)^2/4\theta} . \tag{3-3.10}$$

Figure 40 shows the graphic representation of G with respect to x for different θ values. Almost the entire area which is bounded by this curve lies in the interval

$$(\xi - \varepsilon, \ \xi + \varepsilon) ,$$

where ε is an arbitrarily small number when $\theta = a^2(t - t_0)$ is sufficiently small. The magnitude of this area when multiplied by $c\rho$ coincides with the amount of heat present at the initial moment. Therefore, for small values of $t - t_0 > 0$ almost the entire amount of heat is concentrated in a small neighbourhood of the point ξ. From what has been said it also follows that the entire amount of heat at time t_0 is found at the point ξ.

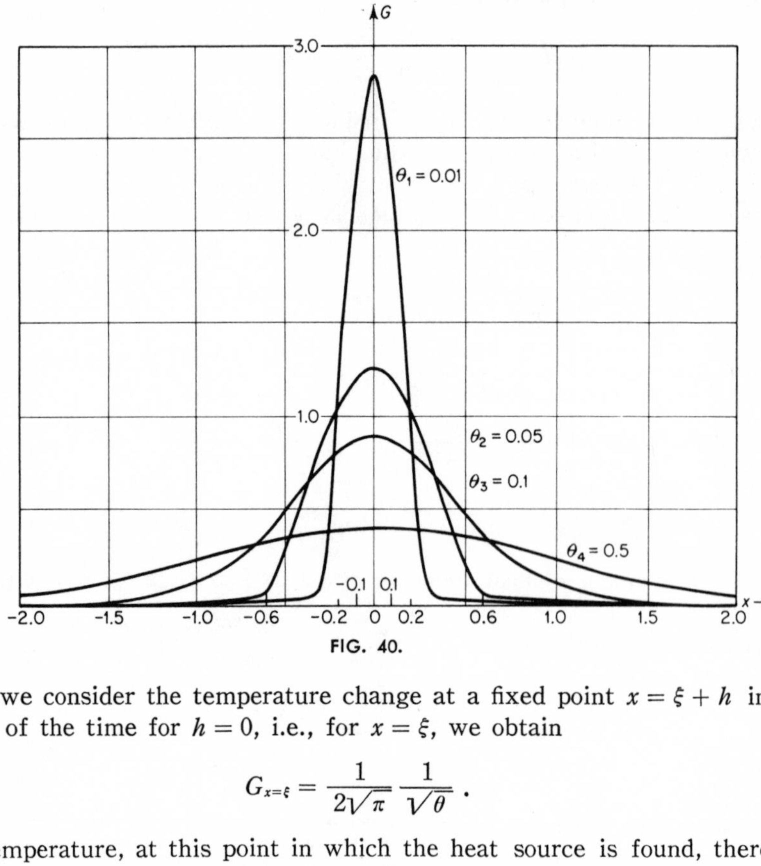

FIG. 40.

If we consider the temperature change at a fixed point $x = \xi + h$ in the course of the time for $h = 0$, i.e., for $x = \xi$, we obtain

$$G_{x=\xi} = \frac{1}{2\sqrt{\pi}} \frac{1}{\sqrt{\theta}} \, .$$

The temperature, at this point in which the heat source is found, therefore becomes unbounded for sufficiently small θ.

If $x \neq \xi$, i.e., $x = \xi + h$ with $h \neq 0$, then G is represented by the product of two factors:

$$G_{x \neq \xi} = \left[\frac{1}{2\sqrt{\pi}} \frac{1}{\sqrt{\theta}}\right] e^{-h^2/4\theta} \, .$$

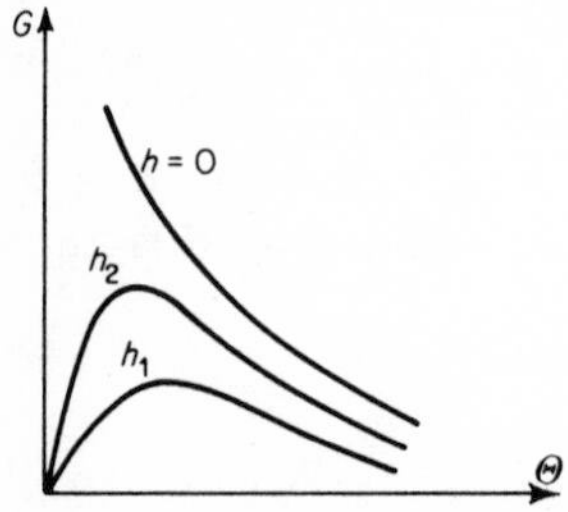

FIG. 41.

The second factor is smaller than 1: for large θ it is ≈ 1; for small θ, by contrast, it is ≈ 0. Hence, it follows that $G_{x \neq \xi} \approx G_{x=\xi}$ for large θ and $G_{x \neq \xi} \ll G_{x=\xi}$ for small θ. The smaller h is—that is, the closer x lies to ξ—the larger is the second factor. Figure 41 shows the course of $G_{x=\xi}$ and $G_{x \neq \xi}$ for $h_2 < h_1$. It is easy to see that

$$\lim_{\theta\to 0} G_{x\neq\xi} = 0\,.$$

By application of de l'Hôpital's rule we find,

$$\lim_{\theta\to 0}\left[\frac{1}{2\sqrt{\pi}}\frac{1}{\sqrt{\theta}}\right]e^{-h^2/4\theta} = \frac{1}{2\sqrt{\pi}}\lim_{\theta\to 0}\frac{-\frac{1}{2}\theta^{-3/2}}{(h^2/4\theta^2)e^{h^2/4\theta}} = 0\,.$$

From formula (3-3.10′) it follows that at each point x the temperature produced by an instantaneous point-forming source acting at the initial time $t=0$ is different from 0 for any small interval of time. This phenomenon can be considered the result of an infinitely fast temperature propagation (propagation with an unbounded velocity). This, however, contradicts the molecular-kinetic concept of the nature of heat. This contradiction is connected with the concept of heat flow used in the derivation of the heat conduction equation and with the neglect of the inertia of molecular motion.

2. Heat Conduction in the Infinite Straight Line. The problem of heat conduction in this case reads as follows: Find a bounded function $u(x, t)$, where $-\infty < x < \infty$, $t \geqq 0$, which satisfies the heat-conduction equation

$$u_t = a^2 u_{xx}\,, \qquad -\infty < x < \infty,\ t > 0 \tag{3-3.11}$$

and the initial condition

$$u(x, 0) = \varphi(x)\,. \tag{3-3.12}$$

As previously stated, since the initial condition is satisfied, the function $u(x, t)$ for $t=0$ not only satisfies the condition but also is continuous.[61]

In order to derive an analytical representation of the sought solution, we introduce an auxiliary function $\bar{\varphi}(x)$, which we set equal to 0 everywhere outside of a small interval $(\xi_0 - \delta,\ \xi_0 + \delta)$, and inside it coincides with $\varphi(x)$. In order to increase the initial temperature from 0 to the value $\varphi(x)$, an initial amount of heat is introduced into the interval $(\xi_0 - \delta,\ \xi_0 + \delta)$ which is given by

$$Q = c\rho\int_{\xi_0-\delta}^{\xi_0+\delta}\varphi(x)dx \approx c\rho\varphi(\bar{\xi})\Delta\xi\,, \qquad \Delta\xi = 2\delta\,.$$

The temperature at the point x at time t is then equal to

$$\frac{Q}{c\rho}G(x, \xi, t) = G(x, \xi, t)\varphi(\bar{\xi})\Delta\xi\,, \tag{3-3.13}$$

where $\bar{\xi}$ is a suitable average value in $(\xi_0 - \delta,\ \xi + \delta)$.

By splitting up the entire straight line into small intervals we can represent $u(x, t)$ on the basis of the superposition principle as the sum of summands of the form (3-3.13). More precisely, we are concerned with an integral sum which as $\delta\to 0$ is transformed into

$$u(x, t) = \int_{-\infty}^{\infty} G(x, \xi, t)\varphi(\xi)d\xi \tag{3-3.14}$$

61 As we saw in Section 3-1 § 7, the solution of the heat-conduction equation is determined uniquely by the initial conditions if it is bounded. Therefore, the requirement that $u(x, t)$ be bounded enters into the formulation of the theorem.

or

$$u(x, t) = \frac{1}{2\sqrt{\pi}} \int_{-\infty}^{\infty} \frac{1}{\sqrt{a^2 t}} e^{-(x-\xi)^2/4a^2 t} \varphi(\xi)\, d\xi \,. \qquad (3\text{-}3.14')$$

Obviously, the first function represents the solution of our problem.

These assertions do not constitute a proof; consequently we seek conditions for the applicability of this formula.

We shall show that in the case of a bounded function $\varphi(\xi), |\varphi(\xi)| < M$ for $t > 0$, the so-called Poisson's integral

$$u(x, t) = \frac{1}{2\sqrt{\pi}} \int_{-\infty}^{\infty} \frac{1}{\sqrt{a^2 t}} e^{-(x-\xi)^2/4a^2 t} \varphi(\xi) d\xi$$

represents a bounded solution of the heat-conduction equation which for $t = 0$ at all points of continuity of this function $u(x, t)$ is continuously connected with $\varphi(x)$.

Therefore, we shall prove the following lemma (generalized superposition principle). If the function $U(x, t, \alpha)$ for each fixed value of the parameter α, and with respect to the variables x and t satisfies a linear differential equation

$$L(U) = 0 \,,$$

then

$$u(x, t) = \int U(x, t, \alpha)\varphi(\alpha)\, d\alpha$$

is also a solution of the differential equation $L(U) = 0$, provided the derivatives occurring in the linear differential operator L can be obtained by differentiation under the integral sign.

The proof of this lemma is very simple. A linear differential operator $L(U)$ represents a linear combination of derivatives of the function U where the coefficients depend on x and t. Now by hypothesis the differentiation of u can be carried out under the integral sign. The coefficients obviously can also be brought under the integral sign. From this it follows that

$$L(u) = \int L(U(x, t, \alpha))\varphi(\alpha) d\alpha = 0 \,,$$

i.e., the function $u(x, t)$ satisfies the differential equation $L(u) = 0$.

Finally, let us consider the sufficient conditions for differentiability under the integral sign when the integral occurring depends on a parameter. A function

$$F(x) = \int_a^b f(x, \alpha) d\alpha \,,$$

in which a and b are finite limits of integration, can be differentiated under the integral signs when $\partial f(x, \alpha)/\partial x$, in the closed region of x and α, is a continuous function of these variables.[62]

[62] See V. I. Smirnov, *Textbook of Higher Mathematics*, 2d. ed. Part II, Ch. III, § 3, no. 80, Berlin, 1958.

We also easily see that

$$F_1(x) = \int_a^b f(x, \alpha)\varphi(\alpha)d\alpha ,$$

in which a and b once more are finite, similarly can be differentiated under the integral sign if $f(x, \alpha)$ satisfies the above stated conditions and $\varphi(\alpha)$ is a bounded (or absolutely integrable) function. If the limits of integration are infinite then in this case we must require the uniform convergence of those integrals which are obtained by differentiation of the integrands with respect to the parameter. This observation holds also for multiple integrals which depend on parameters.

For linear differential equations $L(u) = 0$ the superposition principle holds; that is, the function

$$u(x, t) = \sum_{i=1}^{n} C_i u_i(x, t) ,$$

which is a linear combination of several particular solutions, again represents a solution. If the functions $u(x, t, \alpha)$ are solutions which depend on a parameter, then the integral sum

$$\sum u(x, t, \alpha_n)C_n , \qquad C_n = \varphi(\alpha_n)\Delta\alpha \tag{3-3.15}$$

is also a solution of $L(u) = 0$. The proven lemma, similar to the one above, gives the conditions under which the limit value of the sum (3-3.15), i.e., here

$$u(x, t) = \int U(x, t, \alpha)\varphi(\alpha)d\alpha ,$$

is also a solution of equation $L(u) = 0$. Therefore, it is natural from the viewpoint of the proven lemma, as with the first, to designate it as a generalized superposition principle.

We shall now investigate the integral in (3-3.14′), first by showing that the definite integral in (3-3.14′) converges and represents a bounded function provided $\varphi(x)$ is bounded, $|\varphi(x)| < M$. In this case

$$|u(x, t)| < M\frac{1}{2\sqrt{\pi}}\int_{-\infty}^{\infty} \frac{1}{\sqrt{a^2t}}\, e^{-(x-\xi)^2/4a^2t}d\xi$$

$$= M\frac{1}{\sqrt{\pi}}\int_{-\infty}^{\infty} e^{-\alpha^2}d\alpha = M , \qquad \alpha = \frac{\xi - x}{2\sqrt{a^2t}} ,$$

since

$$\int_{-\infty}^{\infty} e^{-\alpha^2}d\alpha = \sqrt{\pi} .$$

Further, we shall prove that the integral in (3-3.14′) for $t > 0$ satisfies the heat-conduction equation. Therefore, it is sufficient to show that the derivatives of this integral for $t > 0$ can be calculated by differentiation under the integral sign.

In the case of finite integration limits, this is certainly permissible since the derivatives of the function

$$\frac{1}{2\sqrt{\pi a^2 t}}\, e^{-(x-\xi)^2/4a^2 t}$$

for $t > 0$ are continuous functions. To prove the possibility of differentiation under the integral signs for infinite integration limits it is sufficient to show the uniform convergence of the integral arising by differentiation under the integral sign. We carry out this proof, for example, for the first derivative with respect to x.

The differentiability of function (3-3.14) with respect to x and the validity of the equation

$$\frac{\partial u}{\partial x} = \int_{-\infty}^{\infty} \frac{\partial}{\partial x}(G(x, \xi, t))\varphi(\xi)d\xi$$

are proven when we have shown that the integral standing on the right side converges uniformly; in particular, for the proof of the differentiability at the point (x_0, t_0) it is sufficient to show the uniform convergence of the integral in a fixed region

$$t_1 \leqq t_0 \leqq t_2 , \qquad |x - x_0| \leqq \bar{x}$$

of that point.

Sufficient for the uniform convergence of an integral (an analogous criterion holds for the uniform convergence of a series) is the existence of a positive function $F(\xi)$ which does not depend on the parameters x and t and which majorizes the function

$$\left|\frac{\partial}{\partial x} G(x, \xi, t)\varphi(\xi)\right| \leqq F(\xi) , \qquad \xi - x_0 > \bar{x} , \qquad \xi - x_0 < - \bar{x} , \tag{3-3.15$'$}$$

such that

$$\int_{x_1}^{\infty} F(\xi)d\xi < \infty, \qquad \int_{-\infty}^{x_1} F(\xi)d\xi < \infty . \tag{3-3.15$''$}$$

Therefore, let x_1 be a number which satisfies the inequality (3-3.15$'$).

First of all we seek an upper bound for the magnitude of the integrands in the formula for $\partial u/\partial x$. It is

$$\begin{aligned} \left|\frac{\partial}{\partial x} G(x, \xi, t)\right| \cdot |\varphi(\xi)| &= \frac{1}{2\sqrt{\pi}} \frac{|\xi - x|}{2[a^2 t]^{3/2}}\, e^{-(x-\xi)^2/4a^2 t} |\varphi(\xi)| \\ &\leqq \frac{M}{2\sqrt{\pi}} \frac{|\xi - x_0| + \bar{x}}{2[a^2 t_1]^{3/2}}\, e^{-(|\xi - x_0| - \bar{x})^2/4a^2 t_2} = F(\xi) \end{aligned} \tag{3-3.16}$$

for $\xi - x_0 < \bar{x}$, $|x - x_0| \leqq \bar{x}$, and $t_1 \leqq t \leqq t_2$. For this function $F(\xi)$, however, (3-3.15$''$) is valid, and

$$\begin{aligned} \int_{x_1}^{\infty} F(\xi)\, d\xi &= \int_{x_1}^{\infty} \frac{1}{2\sqrt{\pi}} \frac{|\xi - x_0| + \bar{x}}{2[a^2 t_1]^{3/2}}\, e^{-(|\xi - x_0| - \bar{x})^2/4a^2 t_2} d\xi \\ &= \int_{x_1 - \bar{x}}^{\infty} \frac{1}{2\sqrt{\pi}} \frac{\xi_1 + 2\bar{x}}{2[a^2 t_1]^{3/2}} e^{-(\xi_1^2/4a^2 t_2)} d\xi_1 , \\ \xi_1 &= |\xi - x_0| - \bar{x} , \end{aligned}$$

and this integral converges, since a factor of the form $(a\xi + b)e^{-c\xi^2}$ appears under the integral sign. Therefore

$$\frac{\partial u}{\partial x} = \int_{-\infty}^{\infty} \frac{\partial}{\partial x} G(x, \xi, t)\varphi(\xi)d\xi . \tag{3-3.17}$$

By a completely analogous method, we can also prove that all the above derivatives can be calculated by differentiation under the integral sign. Therefore, we have proved that the function (3-3.14′) satisfies the heat-conduction equation.

We turn now to an important property of the integral (3-3.14), and indeed we shall show that at all the points of continuity x_0 of the function $\varphi(x)$, the following limit

$$u(x, t) \to \varphi(x_0) \qquad \text{for } t \to 0 \text{ and } x \to x_0$$

is valid.

Let $\varphi(x)$ be continuous at x_0. Then we have to show that

$$\lim_{\substack{t\to 0\\ x\to x_0}} u(x, t) = \varphi(x_0) .$$

For each $\varepsilon > 0$ we must therefore find a $\delta(\varepsilon)$ such that

$$| u(x, t) - \varphi(x_0) | < \varepsilon$$

holds when

$$| x - x_0 | < \delta(\varepsilon) \qquad \text{and} \qquad | t | < \delta(\varepsilon) .$$

On the basis of the assumed continuity of $\varphi(x)$ at x_0, an $\eta(\varepsilon)$ exists with

$$| \varphi(x) - \varphi(x_0) | < \frac{\varepsilon}{6} \tag{3-3.18}$$

for

$$| x - x_0 | < \eta .$$

We now split up the integration interval and represent $u(x, t)$ as the sum of three summands:

$$\begin{aligned} u(x, t) &= \frac{1}{2\sqrt{\pi}} \int_{-\infty}^{x_1} \frac{1}{\sqrt{a^2 t}} e^{-(x-\xi)^2/4a^2 t} \varphi(\xi) d\xi + \frac{1}{2\sqrt{\pi}} \int_{x_1}^{x_2} \cdots d\xi + \frac{1}{2\sqrt{\pi}} \int_{x_2}^{\infty} \cdots d\xi \\ &= u_1(x, t) + u_2(x, t) + u_3(x, t) , \end{aligned} \tag{3-3.19}$$

where

$$x_1 = x_0 - \eta \qquad \text{and} \qquad x_2 = x_0 + \eta . \tag{3-3.20}$$

For the second summand we can then write

$$\begin{aligned} u_2(x, t) &= \frac{\varphi(x_0)}{2\sqrt{\pi}} \int_{x_1}^{x_2} \frac{1}{\sqrt{a^2 t}} e^{-(x-\xi)^2/4a^2 t} d\xi \\ &+ \frac{1}{2\sqrt{\pi}} \int_{x_1}^{x_2} \frac{1}{\sqrt{a^2 t}} e^{-(x-\xi)/4a^2 t} [\varphi(\xi) - \varphi(x_0)] d\xi = I_1 + I_2 . \end{aligned}$$

The integral I_1 can be calculated directly, and we therefore obtain

$$I_1 = \frac{\varphi(x_0)}{2\sqrt{\pi}} \int_{x_1}^{x_2} \frac{e^{-(x-\xi)^2/4a^2t}}{\sqrt{a^2t}} d\xi = \frac{\varphi(x_0)}{\sqrt{\pi}} \int_{(x_1-x)/2\sqrt{a^2t}}^{(x_2-x)/2\sqrt{a^2t}} e^{-\alpha^2} d\alpha$$

with

$$\alpha = \frac{\xi - x}{2\sqrt{a^2t}}, \qquad d\alpha = \frac{d\xi}{2\sqrt{a^2t}}. \tag{3-3.21}$$

Now if $|x - x_0| < \eta$, then the upper limit is positive and the lower, negative, and as $t \to 0$ the upper limit tends towards $+\infty$ and the lower limit toward $-\infty$. It then follows, however, that

$$\lim_{\substack{t \to 0 \\ x \to x_0}} I_1 = \varphi(x_0).$$

Consequently a δ_1 can be prescribed such that

$$|I_1 - \varphi(x_0)| < \frac{\varepsilon}{6} \tag{3-3.22}$$

when

$$|x - x_0| < \delta_1 \qquad \text{and} \qquad |t| < \delta_1.$$

We shall now prove that the remaining integrals, that is, I_2, u_1 and u_3, can be made arbitrarily small. First we estimate I_2 as follows:

$$|I_2| \leqq \frac{1}{2\sqrt{\pi}} \int_{x_1}^{x_2} \frac{1}{\sqrt{a^2t}} e^{-(x-\xi)^2/4a^2t} |\varphi(\xi) - \varphi(x_0)| \, d\xi.$$

From (3-3.20) it is seen that for

$$x_1 < \xi < x_2$$

the inequality

$$|\xi - x_0| < \eta$$

is valid. If we use the inequality (3-3.18) and the relation

$$\frac{1}{\sqrt{\pi}} \int_{x'}^{x''} e^{-\alpha^2} d\alpha < \frac{1}{\sqrt{\pi}} \int_{-\infty}^{\infty} e^{-\alpha^2} d\alpha = 1,$$

we obtain for arbitrarily chosen x' and x''

$$|I_2| \leqq \frac{\varepsilon}{6} \cdot \frac{1}{2\sqrt{\pi}} \int_{x_1}^{x_2} \frac{1}{\sqrt{a^2t}} e^{-(x-\xi)^2/4a^2t} d\xi = \frac{\varepsilon}{6} \frac{1}{\sqrt{\pi}} \int_{(x_1-x)/2\sqrt{a^2t}}^{(x_2-x)/2\sqrt{a^2t}} e^{-\alpha^2} d\alpha < \frac{\varepsilon}{6}, \tag{3-3.23}$$

where the new variable α is defined by (3-3.21). Further,

$$|u_3(x, t)| = \frac{1}{2\sqrt{\pi}} \left| \int_{x_2}^{\infty} \frac{1}{\sqrt{a^2t}} e^{-(x-\xi)^2/4a^2t} \varphi(\xi) \, d\xi \right| < \frac{M}{\sqrt{\pi}} \int_{(x_2-x)/2\sqrt{a^2t}}^{\infty} e^{-\alpha^2} d\alpha \to 0$$

$$\text{for } x \to x_0 \text{ and } t \to 0 \tag{3-3.24}$$

and analogously

$$|u_1(x,t)| = \frac{1}{2\sqrt{\pi}}\left|\int_{-\infty}^{x_1} \frac{1}{\sqrt{a^2t}} e^{-(x-\xi)^2/4a^2t} \varphi(\xi)\,d\xi\right| < \frac{M}{\sqrt{\pi}}\int_{-\infty}^{(x_1-x)/2\sqrt{a^2t}} e^{-\alpha^2}\,d\alpha \to 0$$

$$\text{for } x \to x_0 \text{ and } t \to 0\,. \tag{3-3.25}$$

As $x \to x_0$, then $x_2 - x > 0$ and $x_1 - x < 0$. As $t \to 0$, the lower limit in the last member of (3-3.24) tends toward $+\infty$ and the upper limit in (3-3.25) tends toward $-\infty$. Consequently, there exists a δ_2 such that

$$|u_3(x,t)| < \frac{\varepsilon}{3} \quad \text{and} \quad |u_1(x,t)| < \frac{\varepsilon}{3} \tag{3-3.26}$$

holds when

$$|x - x_0| < \delta_2 \quad \text{and} \quad |t| < \delta_2\,.$$

With the use of the estimates (3-3.24) and (3-3.25) obtained above, we find

$$|u(x,t) - \varphi(x_0)| \leqq |u_1| + |I_1 - \varphi(x_0)| + |I_2| + |u_3|$$

$$< \frac{\varepsilon}{3} + \frac{\varepsilon}{6} + \frac{\varepsilon}{6} + \frac{\varepsilon}{3} = \varepsilon\,, \tag{3-3.27}$$

provided

$$|x - x_0| < \delta \quad \text{and} \quad |t| < \delta\,,$$

where δ denotes the smaller of the numbers δ_1 and δ_2.

Therefore we have shown that the function

$$u(x,t) = \frac{1}{2\sqrt{\pi}}\int_{-\infty}^{\infty} \frac{1}{\sqrt{a^2t}} e^{-(x-\xi)^2/4a^2t} \varphi(\xi)\,d\xi \tag{3-3.14$'$}$$

is bounded and satisfies the heat-conduction equation as well as the initial condition.

If the initial value is given not for $t = 0$ but for $t = t_0$, then the expression for $u(x,t)$ assumes the form

$$u(x,t) = \frac{1}{2\sqrt{\pi}}\int_{-\infty}^{\infty} \frac{1}{\sqrt{a^2(t-t_0)}} e^{-(x-\xi)^2/4a^2(t-t_0)} \varphi(\xi)\,d\xi\,. \tag{3-3.14$''$}$$

The uniqueness of this solution for a continuous function $\varphi(x)$ results from the theorem proven in 3-2§3. If the initial function $\varphi(x)$ possesses a finite number of points of discontinuity, then (3-3.14′) represents a bounded solution of Eq. (3-3.1), which is continuous everywhere with the exception of the points of discontinuity of $\varphi(x)$.[63]

We shall consider as an example the following problem: Find a solution of the heat-conduction equation when the initial temperatures (at $t = t_0 = 0$) for $x > 0$ and $x < 0$ are constant but have different values, i.e.,

$$u(x,0) = \varphi(x) = T_1 \quad \text{for} \quad x > 0$$
$$= T_2 \quad \text{for} \quad x < 0\,.$$

[63] With the aid of the method described in 3-3§3, we know that the function $u(x,t)$ is uniquely defined by the enumerated properties.

For the solution, formula (3-3.14′) yields

$$u(x,t)=\frac{1}{2\sqrt{\pi}}\int_{-\infty}^{\infty}\frac{1}{\sqrt{a^2t}}\,e^{-(x-\xi)^2/4a^2t}\varphi(\xi)\,d\xi$$

$$=\frac{T_2}{\sqrt{\pi}}\int_{-\infty}^{0}e^{-(x-\xi)^2/4a^2t}\frac{d\xi}{2\sqrt{a^2t}}+\frac{T_1}{\sqrt{\pi}}\int_{0}^{\infty}e^{-(x-\xi)^2/4a^2t}\frac{d\xi}{2\sqrt{a^2t}}$$

$$=\frac{T_2}{\sqrt{\pi}}\int_{-\infty}^{-x/2\sqrt{a^2t}}e^{-\alpha^2}d\alpha+\frac{T_1}{\sqrt{\pi}}\int_{-x/2\sqrt{a^2t}}^{\infty}e^{-\alpha^2}d\alpha$$

$$=\frac{T_1+T_2}{2}+\frac{T_1-T_2}{\sqrt{\pi}}\int_{0}^{x/2\sqrt{a^2t}}e^{-\alpha^2}d\alpha \qquad (3\text{-}3.28)$$

since

$$\frac{1}{\sqrt{\pi}}\int_{-\infty}^{-z}e^{-\alpha^2}d\alpha=\frac{1}{\sqrt{\pi}}\int_{-\infty}^{0}e^{-\alpha^2}d\alpha-\frac{1}{\sqrt{\pi}}\int_{0}^{z}e^{-\alpha^2}d\alpha=\frac{1}{2}-\frac{1}{\sqrt{\pi}}\int_{0}^{z}e^{-\alpha^2}d\alpha$$

and

$$\frac{1}{\sqrt{\pi}}\int_{-z}^{\infty}e^{-\alpha^2}d\alpha=\frac{1}{2}+\frac{1}{\sqrt{\pi}}\int_{-z}^{0}e^{-\alpha^2}d\alpha=\frac{1}{2}+\frac{1}{\sqrt{\pi}}\int_{0}^{z}e^{-\alpha^2}d\alpha,\qquad z=\frac{x}{2\sqrt{a^2t}}.$$

In particular,

$$u(x,t)=\frac{1}{2}\left(1+\frac{2}{\sqrt{\pi}}\int_{0}^{z}e^{-\alpha^2}d\alpha\right),\qquad z=\frac{x}{2\sqrt{a^2t}}$$

holds for

$$T_2=0\,,\qquad T_1=1\,.$$

The temperature profile at time t is given by the curve

$$f(z)=\frac{1}{2}+\frac{1}{\sqrt{\pi}}\int_{0}^{z}e^{-\alpha^2}d\alpha\,.$$

Here z is the abscissa of the point at which the temperature is considered when the value $2\sqrt{a^2t}$ dependent on t is chosen as the unit of length. The construction of this curve is not difficult, since the integral

$$\Phi(z)=\frac{2}{\sqrt{\pi}}\int_{0}^{z}e^{-\alpha^2}d\alpha\,,$$

the so-called error integral, occurs often and has been tabulated many times in probability calculations.[64]

For arbitrary T_1 and T_2, formula (3-3.28) can also be written in the form

$$u(x,t)=\frac{T_1+T_2}{2}+\frac{T_1-T_2}{2}\,\Phi\left(\frac{x}{2\sqrt{a^2t}}\right). \qquad (3\text{-}3.29)$$

[64] See, for example, A. A. Markov, *Text Book of Probability Calculations*, where this integral is tabulated to six places. At the end of this book, likewise, are given values of this integral.

Here we recognize that the temperature at the point $x = 0$ during the entire time is constant, and therefore is equal to half of the sum from the right and left sides of the initial value, since $\Phi(0) = 0$.

Finally, the solution of the inhomogeneous equation

$$u_t = a^2 u_{xx} + f(x, t), \qquad -\infty < x < \infty,\ t > 0$$

with the homogeneous initial condition

$$u(x, 0) = 0$$

obviously can be expressed by the formula

$$u(x, t) = \int_0^t \int_{-\infty}^{\infty} G(x, \xi, t - \tau) f(\xi, \tau) d\xi\, d\tau. \tag{3-3.29'}$$

This results from the meaning of the Green's function $G(x, \xi, t)$ (see Section 3-2 §4). At this point, however, we shall not investigate this formula and the conditions imposed on $f(x, t)$ for its applicability.

3. Boundary-value problems for the semi-infinite line

As we have already noted in 3-1 §4, when we are interested in the distribution of heat in the neighborhood of one end of a rod, while the influence at the other end of the rod is unessential, we make the assumption the latter end lies at infinity. This then leads to the problem of determining those solutions of the heat-conduction equation

$$u_t = a^2 u_{xx} \tag{3-3.11}$$

on the semi-infinite line $x > 0$ for $t > 0$ which satisfies the initial condition

$$u(x, 0) = \varphi(x), \qquad x > 0$$

and a prescribed boundary condition. This depends on the character of the boundary influence and can be given in one of the following forms:

first boundary-value problem $\quad u(0, t) = \mu(t)$;

second boundary-value problem $\quad \dfrac{\partial u}{\partial x}(0, t) = \nu(t)$;

or

third boundary-value problem $\quad \dfrac{\partial u}{\partial x}(0, t) = \lambda[u(0, t) - \theta(t)]$.

In the following investigations we shall consider only the first boundary-value problem, i.e., the determination of a solution of the heat-conduction equation with the auxiliary conditions

$$u(x, 0) = \varphi(x), \qquad u(0, t) = \mu(t). \tag{3-3.30}$$

Therefore, if the problem is to have a unique solution certain conditions must still be met at infinity. Thus we require that the solution $u(x, t)$ is bounded everywhere:

$$|u(x, t)| < M \qquad \text{for } 0 < x < \infty \text{ and } t \geqq 0,$$

where M is a constant. From this it follows that the initial function $\varphi(x)$ must also satisfy the condition

$$|\varphi(x)| < M.$$

The solution of this problem can be represented in the form

$$u(x, t) = u_1(x, t) + u_2(x, t),$$

where $u_1(x, t)$ refers to the influence of the initial condition and $u_2(x, t)$ to the influence of the boundary condition. These functions can be defined as those solutions of Eq. (3-3.11) which satisfy the conditions

$$u_1(x, 0) = \varphi(x), \qquad u_1(0, t) = 0 \tag{3-3.30'}$$

or

$$u_2(x, 0) = 0, \qquad u_2(0, t) = \mu(t). \tag{3-3.30''}$$

The sum of these functions then satisfy conditions (3-3.30).

We shall next prove two lemmas for the function defined by Poisson's integral

$$u(x, t) = \frac{1}{2\sqrt{\pi}} \int_{-\infty}^{\infty} \frac{1}{\sqrt{a^2 t}} e^{-(x-\xi)^2/4a^2 t} \psi(\xi) d\xi. \tag{3-3.31}$$

1. If $\psi(x)$ is an odd function, i.e.,

$$\psi(x) = -\psi(-x),$$

then the function

$$u(x, t) = \frac{1}{2\sqrt{\pi}} \int_{-\infty}^{\infty} \frac{1}{\sqrt{a^2 t}} e^{-(x-\xi)^2/4a^2 t} \psi(\xi) d\xi$$

vanishes for $x = 0$:

$$u(0, t) = 0.$$

Here, it must be assumed that the integral defining $u(x, t)$ converges; this is the case when $\psi(x)$ is bounded. The integrand in

$$u(0, t) = \frac{1}{2\sqrt{\pi}} \int_{-\infty}^{\infty} \frac{1}{\sqrt{a^2 t}} e^{-(\xi^2/4a^2 t)} \psi(\xi) d\xi$$

is odd with respect to ξ since it is the product of an odd function and an even function. Now, however, the integral of an odd function between the limits which lie symmetrical to the origin of the coordinates, is equal to 0; consequently

$$u(0, t) = 0,$$

which proves our lemma.

2. If $\psi(x)$ is an even function, i.e.,

$$\psi(x) = \psi(-x),$$

the derivative of the function $u(x, t)$ from (3-3.31) for $x = 0$ and all $t > 0$ is equal to 0:

$$\frac{\partial u}{\partial x}(0, t) = 0 .$$

That is,

$$\left.\frac{\partial u}{\partial x}\right|_{x=0} = -\frac{1}{2\sqrt{\pi}}\int_{-\infty}^{+\infty}\frac{(x-\xi)}{2(a^2t)^{3/2}}e^{-(x-\xi)^2/4a^2t}\psi(\xi)d\xi\Big|_{x=0} = 0 ,$$

since the integrand at $x = 0$ represents an odd function when $\psi(x)$ is even.

The determination of the function $u(x, t)$ now presents no further difficulty. First, we introduce an auxiliary function $U(x, t)$, which is defined on the entire straight line $-\infty < x < \infty$, and which satisfies Eq. (3-3.11) and the conditions

$$U(0, t) = 0 ,$$
$$U(x, 0) = \varphi(x) \qquad \text{for } x > 0 .$$

This function can be defined by use of the first lemma and an initial function $\Psi(x)$, which for $x > 0$ coincides with $\varphi(x)$ and for $x < 0$ represents the odd continuation of $\varphi(x)$, i.e.,

$$\Psi(x) = \varphi(x) \qquad \text{for } x > 0$$
$$\qquad - \varphi(-x) \qquad \text{for } x < 0$$

so that

$$U(x, t) = \frac{1}{2\sqrt{\pi}}\int_{-\infty}^{\infty}\frac{1}{\sqrt{a^2t}}e^{-(x-\xi)^2/4a^2t}\Psi(\xi)d\xi .$$

In the region of interest, $x \geqq 0$, we then obtain

$$u(x, t) = U(x, t) \qquad \text{for } x \geqq 0 .$$

Introduction of the function $\Psi(x)$ results in

$$U(x, t) = \frac{1}{2\sqrt{\pi}}\int_{-\infty}^{0}\frac{1}{\sqrt{a^2t}}e^{-(x-\xi)^2/4a^2t}\Psi(\xi)\,d\xi + \frac{1}{2\sqrt{\pi}}\int_{0}^{\infty}\frac{1}{\sqrt{a^2t}}e^{-(x-\xi)^2/4a^2t}\Psi(\xi)d\xi$$
$$= -\frac{1}{2\sqrt{\pi}}\int_{0}^{\infty}\frac{1}{\sqrt{a^2t}}e^{-(x+\xi)^2/4a^2t}\varphi(\xi)d\xi + \frac{1}{2\sqrt{\pi}}\int_{0}^{\infty}\frac{1}{\sqrt{a^2t}}e^{-(x-\xi)^2/4a^2t}\varphi(\xi)d\xi$$

where the substitution $\xi' = -\xi$ is introduced in the first integral and the relation

$$\Psi(\xi) = -\varphi(-\xi) = -\varphi(\xi')$$

is also used. By combining both integrals we arrive at the sought function

$$u_1(x, t) = \frac{1}{2\sqrt{\pi}}\int_{0}^{\infty}\frac{1}{\sqrt{a^2t}}\{e^{-(x-\xi)^2/4a^2t} - e^{-(x+\xi)^2/4a^2t}\}\varphi(\xi)d\xi \qquad (3\text{-}3.32)$$

in a form which no longer contains auxiliary functions. We also note that for $x = 0$ the expression in braces vanishes and $u_1(0, t) = 0$.

With the help of the second lemma one can see that the solution of the heat-conduction equation with the homogeneous boundary condition of the second type $(\partial\bar{u}_1(0, t)/\partial x) = 0$ and an initial condition $\bar{u}_1(x, 0) = \varphi(x)$ is representable in the form

$$\bar{u}_1(x, t) = \frac{1}{2\sqrt{\pi}}\int_0^\infty \frac{1}{\sqrt{a^2t}}\{e^{-(x-\xi)^2/4a^2t} + e^{-(x+\xi)^2/4a^2t}\}\varphi(\xi)\,d\xi\,. \tag{3-3.32'}$$

We now apply the formula so obtained to the problem of cooling a uniformly heated rod whose boundaries are held at a constant temperature. Let this temperature equal zero. The problem leads to the determination of those solutions v_1 of the heat-conduction equation for which the conditions

$$v_1(x, t_0) = T\,, \qquad v_1(0, t) = 0$$

are fulfilled.

Since the initial condition is prescribed not for $t = 0$ but for $t = t_0$, in place of (3-3.32) we obtain

$$v_1(x, t) = \frac{T}{2\sqrt{\pi}}\int_0^\infty \{e^{-(x-\xi)^2/4a^2(t-t_0)} - e^{-(x+\xi)^2/4a^2(t-t_0)}\}\frac{d\xi}{\sqrt{a^2(t-t_0)}}\,. \tag{3-3.33}$$

If we now split up the integral into two summands and introduce the variables

$$\alpha = \frac{\xi - x}{2\sqrt{a^2(t-t_0)}}\,, \qquad \alpha_1 = \frac{\xi + x}{2\sqrt{a^2(t-t_0)}}$$

we obtain

$$v_1(x, t) = \frac{T}{\sqrt{\pi}}\left[\int_{-x/2\sqrt{a^2(t-t_0)}}^\infty e^{-\alpha^2}\,d\alpha - \int_{x/2\sqrt{a^2(t-t_0)}}^\infty e^{-\alpha_1^2}\,d\alpha_1\right]$$

$$= \frac{T}{\sqrt{\pi}}\int_{-x/\sqrt{a_2(t-t_0)}}^{x/2\sqrt{a^2(t-t_0)}} e^{-\alpha^2}\,d\alpha = T\frac{2}{\sqrt{\pi}}\int_0^{x/2\sqrt{a^2(t-t_0)}} e^{-\alpha^2}\,d\alpha$$

or

$$v_1(x, t) = T\Phi\left(\frac{x}{2\sqrt{a^2(t-t_0)}}\right), \tag{3-3.33'}$$

where

$$\Phi(z) = \frac{2}{\sqrt{\pi}}\int_0^z e^{-\alpha^2}\,d\alpha$$

is the error integral.

We turn now to the determination of $u_2(x, t)$—that is, the second part of the solution of the first boundary-value problem.

Let

$$\mu(t) = \mu_0 = \text{const.}$$

The function

$$\bar{v}(x, t) = \mu_0\Phi\left(\frac{x}{2\sqrt{a^2(t-t_0)}}\right) \tag{3-3.34}$$

then represents those solutions of the heat-conduction equation which correspond to the conditions

$$\bar{v}(x, t_0) = \mu_0\,, \qquad \bar{v}(0, t) = 0\,.$$

From this it follows that

$$v(x, t) = \mu_0 - \bar{v}(x, t) = \mu_0\left[1 - \Phi\left(\frac{x}{2\sqrt{a^2(t - t_0)}}\right)\right] \tag{3-3.35}$$

is the sought function, since it satisfies the same equation and the conditions

$$v(x, t_0) = 0\,, \qquad x > 0 \qquad \text{and} \qquad v(0, t) = \mu_0\,, \qquad t > t_0\,.$$

For $v(x, t)$ we write

$$v(x, t) = \mu_0 U(x, t)\,,$$

where

$$U(x, t) = 1 - \Phi\left(\frac{x}{2\sqrt{a^2(t - t_0)}}\right) = \frac{2}{\sqrt{\pi}}\int_{x/2\sqrt{a^2(t-t_0)}}^{\infty} e^{-\alpha^2}\,d\alpha \tag{3-3.36}$$

is the solution of the same problem in the case of $\mu_0 = 1$.

By definition, the function $U(x, t)$ is defined at first only for $t \geqq t_0$. We now extend the region of definition in which we set

$$U(x, t) \equiv 0 \qquad \text{for} \qquad t < t_0\,.$$

Obviously this definition is compatible with the function values of $U(x, t)$ for $t = 0$. Also, the function so defined satisfies the heat-conduction equation for all t and $x > 0$. The boundary value of this function (for $x = 0$) forms a step function which for $t < t_0$ is equal to 0 and which for $t > t_0$ is equal to 1. The function $U(x, t)$ occurs frequently in applications and is an aid in the determination of $u_2(x, t)$.

We consider now a second auxiliary problem, namely to solve the heat-conduction equation with the initial and boundary conditions

$$v(x, t_0) = 0, \qquad v(0, t) = \mu(t) = \begin{cases} \mu_0 & \text{for } t_0 < t < t_1 \\ 0 & \text{for } t > t_1\,. \end{cases}$$

We can verify directly that

$$v(x, t) = \mu_0[U(x, t - t_0) - U(x, t - t_1)]\,.$$

By similar reasoning we find that:

If the boundary function $\mu(t)$ is given as a step function

$$\begin{aligned} \mu(t) &= \mu_0 && \text{for} && t_0 < t \leqq t_1 \\ &= \mu_1 && \text{for} && t_1 < t \leqq t_2 \\ &= \cdots && \cdots && \cdots \\ &= \mu_{n-1} && \text{for} && t_{n-1} < t \leqq t_n\,, \end{aligned}$$

then with the help of the function $\mu(t)$ the solution of the second boundary-value problem can be represented in the form

$$u(x, t) = \sum_{i=0}^{n-2} \mu_i[U(x, t - t_i) - U(x, t - t_{i+1})] + \mu_{n-1}U(x, t - t_{n-1})\,. \tag{3-3.37}$$

The mean-value theorem then yields

$$u(x, t) = \sum_{i=0}^{n-2} \mu_i \frac{\partial U(x, t-\tau)}{\partial t}\bigg|_{\tau_i} \Delta\tau + \mu_{n-1} U(x, t - t_{n-1}) \quad \text{with} \quad t_i \leqq \tau_i \leqq t_{i+1}\,. \tag{3-3.38}$$

We shall now determine the solution $u(x, t)$ of the heat-conduction equation with homogeneous initial conditions and the boundary condition

$$u(0, t) = \mu(t)\,, \qquad t > 0\,,$$

where $\mu(t)$ is a piecewise continuous function. An approximate solution is easily obtained in the form (3-3.37) when we replace $\mu(t)$ by a piecewise constant function. Now when we make arbitrarily small the interval in which the auxiliary functions are constant, we recognize that the limit value of the sum (3-3.38) is equal to

$$\int_0^t \frac{\partial U}{\partial t}(x, t-\tau)\mu(\tau)dt\,,$$

since for $x > 0$

$$\lim_{t-t_{n-1}-0} \mu_{n-1} U(x, t - t_{n-1}) = 0\,.$$

Obviously, the sought solution $u_2(x, t)$ of the second problem must satisfy

$$u_2(x, t) = \int_0^t \frac{\partial U}{\partial t}(x, t-\tau)\mu(\tau)d\tau\,. \tag{3-3.39}$$

We shall not consider here whether a passage to the limit is permissible, or the requirements that must be placed on the function $\mu(\tau)$ in order that this passage to the limit be applicable.

As we easily see, we have

$$\frac{\partial U}{\partial t}(x, t) = \frac{\partial}{\partial t}\left(\frac{2}{\sqrt{\pi}}\int_{x/2\sqrt{a^2t}}^{\infty} e^{-\alpha^2} d\alpha\right) = \frac{1}{2\sqrt{\pi}} \frac{a^2 x}{[a^2 t]^{3/2}} e^{-x^2/4a^2t}$$

$$= -2a^2 \frac{\partial G}{\partial x}(x, 0, t) = 2a^2 \frac{\partial G}{\partial \xi}\bigg|_{\xi=0}\,, \qquad G = \frac{1}{2\sqrt{\pi}} \frac{1}{\sqrt{a^2 t}} e^{-(x-\xi)^2/4a^2t}\,.$$

Consequently the sought solution in the case of an arbitrary function $\mu(t)$ can be represented in the form[65]

$$u_2(x, t) = \frac{a^2}{2\sqrt{\pi}} \int_{t_0}^t \frac{x}{[a^2(t-\tau)]^{3/2}} e^{-x^2/4a^2(t-\tau)} \mu(\tau)\, d\tau$$

or

$$u_2(x, t) = 2a^2 \int_{t_0}^t \frac{\partial G}{\partial \xi}(x, 0, t-\tau)\mu(\tau)\, d\tau\,. \tag{3-3.40}$$

We note further that in the derivation of formula (3-3.40), besides the linearity no further special properties of the heat conduction equation were

[65] This representation of the solution of the first boundary-value problem with homogeneous initial conditions was mentioned here so that it can be compared to an alternative solution in Chapter 5, Section 4.

used. Further, we never used the analytical expression of the function $U(x, t)$ but only the property that it satisfies the boundary and initial conditions

$$U(0, t) = 1 \qquad \text{for } t > 0$$
$$U(x, 0) = 0 \qquad \text{for } x > 0$$

or

$$U(0, t) = \begin{cases} 1 & \text{for } t > 0 \\ 0 & \text{for } t < 0 . \end{cases}$$

If a linear differential equation exists with a boundary condition

$$u(0, t) = \mu(t) , \qquad t > 0 ,$$

homogeneous initial conditions, and auxiliary homogeneous boundary conditions (when such are present, for example, where $x = l$), then the solution of this problem can be expressed in the form

$$u(x, t) = \int_0^t \frac{\partial U}{\partial t}(x, t - \tau)\mu(\tau)d\tau , \tag{3-3.41}$$

where $U(x, t)$ is the solution of the corresponding boundary-value problem for

$$U(0, t) = 1 .$$

The principle formulated here, the so-called Duhamel principle, shows that the constant boundary value causes the principal difficulty in the solution of boundary-value problems. If a boundary-value problem for a constant boundary value has already been solved, then one can immediately determine the solution of the same problem with variable boundary conditions by use of formula (3-3.41). This principle is often used for the solution of several boundary-value problems in which the solution is determined only for a constant boundary value, and it is assumed that the solution for a variable boundary condition $\mu(t)$ then can be represented by formula (3-3.41).

The sum

$$u_1(x, t) + u_2(x, t)$$

gives the solution of the first boundary-value problem for the semi-infinite line in the case of the homogeneous equation.

By the use of formula (3-3.29) and the method of odd continuation, it follows easily that the solution of the inhomogeneous equation

$$u_t = a^2 u_{xx} + f(x, t) , \qquad 0 < x < \infty,\ t > 0 ,$$

when the initial and the boundary conditions are homogeneous ($u(0, t) = 0$), can be represented by the formula

$$u_3(x, t) = \frac{1}{2\sqrt{\pi}} \int_0^\infty \int_0^t \frac{1}{\sqrt{a^2(t - \tau)}} \left\{ e^{-(x-\xi)^2/4a^2(t-\tau)} - e^{-(x+\xi)^2/4a^2(t-\tau)} \right\} f(\xi, \tau)\, d\xi\, d\tau . \tag{3-3.42}$$

The sum

$$u_1(x, t) + u_2(x, t) + u_3(x, t) = u(x, t) \tag{3-3.43}$$

is then the solution of the first boundary-value problem

$$u_t = a^2 u_{xx} + f(x, t)\,, \qquad u(0, t) = \mu(t)\,, \qquad u(x, 0) = \varphi(x)\,.$$

3-4. PROBLEMS WITHOUT INITIAL CONDITIONS

If one investigates the process of heat conduction at a time which is sufficiently long from the initial moment, the influence of the initial conditions on the temperature distribution at the time of the observation is practically negligible. In this case, then, there arises the problem of determining a solution of the heat-conduction equation which satisfies one of the three types of boundary conditions for all $t > -\infty$. If the rod is bounded on two sides then the boundary conditions are prescribed on both ends of the rod. By contrast, for a one-sided bounded rod one uses only a single boundary condition. We shall consider the first boundary-value problem for a one-sided bounded rod:

Find a bounded solution of the heat-conduction equation in the region $x > 0$ which satisfies the boundary condition

$$u(0, t) = \mu(t)\,, \tag{3-4.1}$$

where $\mu(t)$ is a prescribed function. We assume that the functions $u(x, t)$ and $\mu(t)$ are bounded everywhere, i.e.,

$$|u(x, t)| < M$$
$$|\mu(t)| < M\,.$$

It will be shown later that the function $u(x, t)$ is uniquely defined. Often we deal with the boundary condition

$$\mu(t) = A \cos \omega t\,. \tag{3-4.2}$$

Fourier has treated this problem, and it was applied to determine the temperature variation of the earth.[66]

We write the boundary condition in the form

$$\mu(t) = Ae^{i\omega t}\,. \tag{3-4.2'}$$

From the linearity of the heat-conduction equation it follows that the real and imaginary parts of a complex solution of the heat-conduction equation separately satisfy this equation.

If one also finds a solution of the heat-conduction equation which satisfies the condition (3-4.2′), then its real part satisfies condition (3-4.2) and its imaginary part satisfies the condition

$$u(0, t) = \mu_1(t) = A \sin \omega t\,.$$

We consider therefore the problem

[66] See Section 3-5 § 1.

$$u_t = a^2 u_{xx} ,\quad u(0, t) = Ae^{i\omega t} . \tag{3-4.3}$$

We seek its solution in the form

$$u(x, t) = Ae^{\alpha x+\beta t} , \tag{3-4.4}$$

where α and β are constants to be determined.

If we insert (3-4.4) into Eq. (3-4.3) and into the boundary conditions we find

$$\alpha^2 = \frac{1}{a^2}\beta , \qquad \beta = i\omega ,$$

from which there results

$$\alpha = \pm\sqrt{\frac{\beta}{a^2}} = \pm\sqrt{\frac{\omega}{a^2}}\sqrt{i} = \pm\sqrt{\frac{\omega}{a_2}}\,\frac{(1+i)}{\sqrt{2}} = \pm\left[\sqrt{\frac{\omega}{2a^2}} + i\sqrt{\frac{\omega}{2a^2}}\right] .$$

Hence we have

$$u(x, t) = Ae^{\pm\sqrt{(\omega/2a^2)}x + i(\pm\sqrt{(\omega/2a^2)}x+\omega t)} . \tag{3-4.5}$$

The real part of this solution, namely

$$u(x, t) = Ae^{\pm\sqrt{(\omega/2a^2)}x} \cos\left(\pm\sqrt{\frac{\omega}{2a^2}}x + \omega t\right) , \tag{3-4.6}$$

satisfies the heat-conduction equation as well as the boundary condition (3-4.2). Formula (3-4.6) first of all defines not only one but two functions, since there are both plus and minus signs in the exponents before the roots. If we observe that only the functions corresponding to the minus sign are bounded then we obtain as a solution of our problem:

$$u(x, t) = Ae^{-\sqrt{(\omega/2a^2)}x} \cos\left(-\frac{\omega}{2a^2}x + \omega t\right) . \tag{3-4.7}$$

The problem without initial conditions for a bounded interval is treated similarly:

$$u_t = a^2 u_{xx} ,\quad u(0, t) = A\cos\omega t ,\quad u(l, t) = 0 . \tag{3-4.8}$$

If we write the boundary conditions in the form

$$\hat{u}(0, t) = Ae^{-i\omega t} , \qquad \hat{u}(l, t) = 0$$

and seek the solution in the form

$$\hat{u}(x, t) = X(x)e^{-i\omega t} \tag{3-4.9}$$

then we obtain from (3-4.8) for $X(x)$ the differential equation

$$X'' + \frac{i\omega}{a^2}X = 0 \quad \text{or} \quad X'' + \gamma^2 X = 0 ,\qquad \gamma = \sqrt{\frac{i\omega}{a^2}} = \sqrt{\frac{\omega}{2a^2}}(1+i) \tag{3-4.10}$$

and the auxiliary conditions

$$X(0) = A\,, \qquad X(l) = 0\,. \tag{3-4-11}$$

Consequently, for $X(x)$ we find

$$X(x) = A\frac{\sin \gamma(l-x)}{\sin \gamma l} = X_1(x) + iX_2(x)\,, \tag{3-4.12}$$

where X_1 and X_2 are the real and imaginary parts of $X(x)$. Therefore, for $\hat{u}(x, t)$ we obtain the representation

$$\hat{u}(x, t) = A\frac{\sin \gamma(l-x)}{\sin \gamma l}e^{-i\omega t}\,. \tag{3-4.13}$$

By separating out the real parts of $\hat{u}(x, t)$, we finally find the solution of the original problem without initial conditions in the form

$$u(x, t) = X_1(x)\cos \omega t + X_2(x)\sin \omega t\,. \tag{3-4.14}$$

From the above, the explicit determination of X_1 and X_2 gives no difficulty.

If the boundary function is a combination of harmonic vibrations of different frequencies, the solution of such a problem can be represented by a superposition of the solutions corresponding to the individual harmonics.

We shall now prove the unique solvability of problems without initial conditions for the semi-infinite line. We proceed from the formula

$$\begin{aligned} u(x, t) &= \frac{a^2}{2\sqrt{\pi}}\int_{t_0}^{t}\frac{x}{[a^2(t-\tau)]^{3/2}}e^{-(x^2/4a^2(t-\tau))}u(0, \tau)\,d\tau \\ &\quad + \frac{1}{2\sqrt{\pi}}\int_0^\infty \frac{1}{\sqrt{a^2(t-t_0)}}\{e^{-(x-\xi)^2/4a^2(t-t_0)} - e^{-(x+\xi)^2/4a^2(t-t_0)}\}u(\xi, t_0)\,d\xi \\ &= I_1 + I_2\,, \qquad t \geqq t_0 \end{aligned} \tag{3-4.15}$$

which represents every bounded solution of the heat-conduction equation through its initial function $u(x, t_0)$ and its boundary function $u(0, t) = \mu(t)$ in the region $x \geqq 0$, $t \geqq t_0$.

We show next that the limit

$$\lim_{t_0 \to -\infty} I_2(x, t) = 0 \tag{3-4.16}$$

exists if the following holds for all t:

$$|u(x, t)| < M\,.$$

In fact, we have

$$\begin{aligned} |I_2| &< \frac{M}{\sqrt{\pi}}\left\{\int_{-x/2\sqrt{a^2(t-t_0)}}^{\infty} e^{-\alpha_1^2}d\alpha_1 - \int_{x/2\sqrt{a^2(t-t_0)}}^{\infty} e^{-\alpha_2^2}d\alpha_2\right\} \\ &= \frac{M}{\sqrt{\pi}}2\int_0^{x/2\sqrt{a^2(t-t_0)}} e^{-\alpha^2}d\alpha\,, \end{aligned}$$

where

$$\alpha_1 = \frac{\xi - x}{2\sqrt{a^2(t-t_0)}} \quad \text{and} \quad \alpha_2 = \frac{\xi + x}{2\sqrt{a^2(t-t_0)}} .$$

From this (3-4.16) follows, since as $t_0 \to \infty$ both x and t remain fixed. If in (3-4.15) the variables x and t remain fixed and t_0 tends towards $-\infty$, then $u(x, t)$ is equal to the limit value of the first summand. We therefore obtain

$$u(x, t) = \frac{a^2}{2\sqrt{\pi}} \int_{-\infty}^{t} \frac{x}{[a^2(t-\tau)]^{3/2}} e^{-(x^2/4a^2(t-\tau))} \mu(\tau) d\tau , \tag{3-4.17}$$

which shows that there cannot be two different solutions of our problem. We can also prove that formula (3-4.17), for every bounded piecewise continuous function $\mu(t)$, represents the solution of the corresponding problems.

We can proceed analogously for problems without initial conditions for a finite interval $0 \leqq x \leqq l$. Here if the boundedness of the solution is not required these problems would not be uniquely solvable, since the function

$$u_n(x, t) = Ce^{-(\pi n/l)^2 a^2 t} \sin \frac{\pi n}{l} x$$

for arbitrary n produces a solution of the problem in question with homogeneous boundary conditions. These solutions as $t \to -\infty$ become unbounded. The uniqueness of a bounded solution can be shown immediately.

Problems

1. Determine the Green's function for (*a*) a one-sided bounded rod for boundary conditions of the first and second type when no heat exchange results on the lateral surface; (*b*) a two-sided unbounded rod when there is heat exchange on the lateral surface; (*c*) a one-sided bounded rod in the presence of a heat exchange on the lateral surface and with boundary conditions of the first or second type.

2. Find the Green's function for a one-sided bounded rod with heat insulated lateral surface for the third boundary value problem, where the boundary conditions have the form

$$\frac{\partial u}{\partial x} - hu(0, t) = f(t) .$$

Solution:

$$G(x, \xi, t-\tau) = \frac{1}{2\sqrt{\pi a^2(t-\tau)}} \Big\{ e^{-(x-\xi)^2/4a^2(t-\tau)} + e^{-(x+\xi)^2/4a^2(t-\tau)}$$

$$- 2h \int_0^{\infty} e^{-hz-(\alpha+\xi+x)^2/4a^2(t-\tau)} d\alpha \Big\} .$$

3. Solve the heat-conduction equation for (*a*), (*b*), and (*c*) of Problem 1 when (1) a heat source $Q = Q(t)$ develops at the point $x = \xi_0$ ($Q = Q_0 = \text{const.}$); (2) an initial temperature distribution $u(x, 0) = \varphi(x)$ is prescribed, where

$$\varphi(x) = \begin{cases} u_0 & \text{for } 0 < x < l \\ 0 & \text{outside of the interval } (0,l) ; \end{cases}$$

(3) the heat sources are distributed throughout the entire rod with the density $f(x, t)$ while the initial temperature is equal to zero, where $f(x, t) = q_0 = \text{const.}$ (stationary sources).

4. A one-sided bounded rod with heat-insulated lateral surface is uniformly heated up to a temperature

$$u(x, 0) = u_0 = \text{const.}, \qquad x > 0 .$$

Let the ends of the rod be held at the time $t = 0$ at the constant temperature zero

$$u(0, t) = 0 , \qquad t > 0 .$$

Determine the temperature $u(x, t)$ of the rod and use the tables for the error integral

$$\Phi(z) = \frac{2}{\sqrt{\pi}} \int_0^z e^{-\alpha^2} d\alpha$$

to construct the graphic representation of $u(x, t)$ with respect to x in the interval

$$0 \leqq x \leqq l \quad \text{for} \quad t = \frac{l^2}{16a^2} , \qquad t = \frac{l^2}{2a^2} , \qquad t = \frac{l^2}{a^2} .$$

Hint: In a suitable manner introduce the dimensionless variables

$$x' = \frac{x}{l} , \qquad \theta = \frac{a^2 t}{l^2} , \qquad v = \frac{u}{u_0} .$$

5. The end of a one-sided bounded cylinder is opened at the initial moment $t = 0$. The surrounding atmosphere contains a gas whose concentration is u_0.

Find the concentration $u(x, t)$ of the gas in the cylinder for $t > 0$ and $x > 0$ when the initial concentration in the cylinder is equal to zero. Use the tables of the error integral to determine how much time must pass until the concentration of the gas in the cross section at the distance l from the end of the cylinder has reached 95 per cent of the exterior concentration. Further, determine the law of motion of the layers of constant concentration.

6. Let a heat flow $ku_x(0, t) = q(t)$ be directed toward the end of a one-sided bounded rod whose initial temperature is equal to zero. What temperature $u(x, t)$ does the rod attain when (*a*) the lateral surface of the rod is heat insulated; (*b*) on the lateral surface the rod undergoes a heat exchange (according to Newton's law) with the environment whose temperature is equal to zero? Consider the special case $q = q_0 = \text{const.}$

7. The end of a one-sided bounded rod is maintained at the constant temperature u_0; on the lateral area of the rod there occurs a heat exchange with the surroundings which is at the constant temperature u_1. The initial temperature of the rod is zero. Find the rod temperature $u(x, t)$.

8. Solve problems 6 (*a*) and (*b*) under the assumption that $u(x, 0)$ equals $u_0 = \text{const.}$

9. Determine the temperature distribution in a one-sided bounded rod with heat-insulated lateral areas at whose ends (*a*) a temperature $u(0, t) = A \cos \omega t$

exists; (*b*) a heat flow $Q(t) = B \sin \omega t$ occurs; (*c*) Newtonian heat exchange with the environment exists, whose temperature changes according to the law $v(t) = C \sin \omega t$.

10. By using the method of reflections construct the Green's function for a two-sided bounded rod with heat-insulated lateral surfaces for boundary conditions of the first and second types.

11. Let a two-sided unbounded rod be comprised of two homogeneous rods which are brought together at a point $x = 0$ and are characterized by a_1, k_1 and a_2, k_2 respectively. Let the initial temperature be

$$u(x, 0) = \varphi(x) = \begin{cases} T_1 & \text{for } x < 0 \\ T_2 & \text{for } x > 0 . \end{cases}$$

Determine the temperature $u(x, t)$ in the rod when the lateral surface is heat-insulated.

3-5. APPLICATIONS TO CHAPTER 3

1. Temperature waves

The treatment of the problems of propagation of temperature waves in the earth is one of the first examples of the application of the mathematical theory of heat conduction developed by Fourier for the investigation of natural phenomena.

As is known, the temperature of the earth's surface changes very distinctly in a daily (day-night) and a yearly (summer-winter) period. We shall treat the propagation of the periodic temperature distribution in the earth which we assume to be a homogeneous half-space $0 \leqq x < \infty$ (from the surface to the interior). This problem is a characteristic example of problems without initial conditions. After several temperature variations on the earth's surface, therefore, the influence of the initial temperature is small in comparison with the influence of other factors which we likewise disregard (for example, the inhomogeneity of the earth). In this way we then arrive at the following problem:[67]

Determine a bounded solution of the heat-conduction equation

$$\frac{\partial u}{\partial t} = a^2 \frac{\partial^2 u}{\partial x^2}, \qquad 0 \leqq x < \infty, \ -\infty < t, \tag{3-5.1}$$

which satisfies the condition

$$u(0, t) = A \cos \omega t . \tag{3-5.2}$$

We have already considered this problem earlier in this chapter. Its solution has the form (see Section 3-4 §7)

$$u(x, t) = A e^{\sqrt{(\omega/2a^2)}x} \cos\left(-\sqrt{\frac{\omega}{2a^2}}x - \omega t\right). \tag{3-5.3}$$

[67] H. S. Carslaw, *Mathematical Theory of the Conduction of Heat in Solids*, London, 1921.

On the basis of this solution the temperature waves in the earth can be described in the following manner: When the temperature of the surface changes periodically over a long period of time, then a temperature fluctuation with the same period is developed in the earth. Therefore:

1. The amplitude of the distribution decreases exponentially with the depth: $A(x) = Ae^{-\sqrt{(\omega/2a^2)}x}$, i.e., an arithmetic increase in the depth corresponds to a geometric decrease of the amplitude (Fourier's first law).

2. The temperature distribution in the earth takes place with a phase displacement. The time δ between the occurrence of the temperature maximum (minimum) in the earth and the corresponding time point on the earth surface is proportional to the depth:

$$\delta = \sqrt{\frac{1}{2\omega a^2}}x$$

(Fourier's second law).

3. The depth of penetration of the temperature in the earth depends on the amplitude of the temperature distribution on the surface. The relative change of the temperature amplitude is equal to

$$\frac{A(x)}{A} = e^{-\sqrt{(\omega/2a^2)}\,x} .$$

This formula shows that the depth of penetration of the temperature is smaller when the period is smaller. For two temperature distributions with periods T_1 or T_2, the corresponding depths x_1 and x_2 in which the relative temperature changes coincide, are connected by the relation

$$x_2 = \sqrt{\frac{T_2}{T_1}}x_1$$

(Fourier's third law). For example, it shows the comparison between the daily and the yearly variations ($T_2 = 365T_1$):

$$x_2 = \sqrt{365}\,x_1 = 19.1\,x_1$$

that is, the depth of penetration of the yearly distributions with equal amplitude on the surface is 19.1 times as great as the depth of penetration of the daily distribution.

For example we shall give the results of observations of the yearly temperature distributions of the station Gosch (Amur):[68]

Depth (m)	*Amplitude* (°C)
1	11.5
2	6.8
3	4.2
4	2.6

These values show that the amplitude of the yearly distributions at 4 m

[68] M. I. Sumgin, S. P. Kachurin, N. I. Topspikhin, V. F. Tumel, *General Ground Frost Science*, Moscow, 1940, Ch. V.

depth has diminished to 13.3 per cent of its value on the earth's surface, which is equal to 19.5 degrees.

On the basis of these values one can determine the thermal conductivity of the earth:

$$\ln \frac{A(x)}{A} = -\sqrt{\frac{\omega}{2a^2}}x, \qquad a^2 = \frac{\omega x^2}{2\ln^2(A(x)/A)}.$$

From this we find the thermal conductivity,

$$a^2 = 4\cdot 10^{-3}\,\frac{\text{cm}^2}{\text{sec}}.$$

The maximum temperature at 4 m depth four months later would therefore reach that of earth's surface.

However it should be noted that this theory holds only for heat conduction in dry soil or rocky terrain. With moist soils the temperature phenomena are more complicated; with frozen ground a latent amount of heat would be freed which this theory does not consider.

The thermal conductivity of a body is one of the characteristic quantities which is of importance in the investigation of its physical properties and also for different technical calculations. The investigation of the propagation of temperature waves in rods depends on one of the laboratory methods for the determination of the thermal conductivity.[69]

Let the end of a sufficiently long rod be heated and cooled periodically as $\mu(t)$. If we develop this function in a Fourier series,

$$\mu(t) = \frac{a_0}{2} + \sum_{n=1}^{\infty}\left(a_n \cos\frac{2\pi n}{T}t + b_n \sin\frac{2\pi n}{T}t\right) = \frac{a_0}{2} + \sum_{n=1}^{\infty} A_n \cos\left(\frac{2\pi n}{T}(t - \delta_n^0)\right)$$

$$A_n = \sqrt{a_n^2 + b_n^2}, \qquad \delta_n^0 = \frac{T}{2\pi n}\left(\pi + \operatorname{arctg}\frac{b_n}{a_n}\right),$$

(T is the period) and determine the temperature waves corresponding to the individual summands, then we find that the temperature $u(x, t)$ for an arbitrary x is a periodic function of time; hence for its nth harmonic vibration we have

$$\begin{aligned} u_n(x, t) &= a_n(x)\cos\frac{2\pi n}{T}t + b_n(x)\sin\frac{2\pi n}{T}t \\ &= A_n e^{-\sqrt{(\pi n/Ta^2)}x}\cos\left(\sqrt{\frac{\pi n}{Ta^2}}x - \frac{2\pi n}{T}t + \delta_n^0\right) \end{aligned}$$

or

$$\frac{\sqrt{a_n^2(x_1) + b_n^2(x_1)}}{\sqrt{a_n^2(x_2) + b_n^2(x_2)}} = e^{-\sqrt{(\pi n/Ta^2)}(x_1 - x_2)}.$$

This formula shows the following: If one measures the temperature changes at any two points x_1 and x_2 during an entire period, then by deter-

[69] *Special Physical Practices*, vol. I, Prob. 35, Moscow, 1945; V. I. Iveronova, *Physical Practice*, Prob. 23, p. 117, Berlin, 1957.

mination of the coefficients $a_n(x_1), b_n(x_1), a_n(x_2), b_n(x_2)$ by means of harmonic analysis, one can determine the thermal conductivity a^2 of the rod.

The periodic temperature variations (temperature waves) in a rod, for example, can be generated in the following manner. One end of the rod is placed in an electric furnace and a repeated pulsed current passed through. Because of this periodic warming in the rod, a periodic temperature fluctuation can result after a certain time. Now by means of a thermostat, we can measure the temperatures $u(x_1, t)$ and $u(x_2, t)$ at any two points x_1 and x_2 during a complete period of change of the boundary influence and thus obtain u_1 and u_2 as described above; in this manner the thermal conductivity a^2 of the material of the rod can be determined. There are two conditions necessary for application of this theory. First, the rod must be heat-insulated on the lateral surface; and second, the temperature at the other end of the rod must be controlled, if we are to be justified in using here the theory of temperature waves in a one-sided bounded rod. Therefore, we have to prove that the temperature at the free end of the rod is constant, and this is accomplished with the help of another thermostat.

2. The influence of radioactive decay on the temperature of the earth's crust

For the estimation of the state of temperature in the earth's interior some hint can be obtained from observations on the earth's surface. The importance of this lies in the fact that the daily and the yearly temperature variations take place only in a relatively thin layer of the surface (approximately 10—20 m for the yearly variations), while the temperature below this layer changes very slowly in the course of time.

It has been observed in ravines and caves which lie 2—3 km beneath the earth's surface that the temperature increases with increasing depth on the average of 3°C per 100 m.

The first test, carried out at the end of the 1800's, to give a theoretical explanation for the observed geometric gradient, met with insurmountable difficulties.[70] It was concluded that earlier the earth must have been radiating heat and that it cooled gradually. The initial temperature characterizing this cooling process must have been of the order of magnitude of $T_0 =$ 1200°C (the melting temperature of rock); the surface temperature is of the order of magnitude of 0°. Further, the surface temperature may not have changed essentially (not more than 100°) from the period when vegetable or animal organisms first occurred on the earth. The cooling process, considered in this sense as purely quantitative, leads then to the solution of the heat-conduction equation

$$\frac{\partial u}{\partial t} = a^2 \frac{\partial^2 u}{\partial z^2}$$

[70] H. S. *Carslaw*, *Mathematical Theory of the Conduction of Heat in Solids*, London, 1921, Ch. 3.

in the half space $0 < z < \infty$ with the initial and boundary conditions

$$u(z, 0) = T_0$$
$$u(0, t) = 0 .$$

The solution of this problem was treated in Section 3-3; we obtained it in the form

$$u(z, t) = T_0 \frac{2}{\sqrt{\pi}} \int_0^{z/2\sqrt{a^2 t}} e^{-\alpha^2} d\alpha .$$

The gradient of this function at $z = 0$ is given by

$$\left. \frac{\partial u}{\partial z} \right|_{z=0} = \frac{T_0}{\sqrt{\pi}\sqrt{a^2 t}} e^{-(z^2/4a^2 t)} \Bigg|_{z=0} = \frac{T_0}{\sqrt{\pi}\sqrt{a^2 t}} .$$

If we substitute in this expression the value of the geothermal gradient $\gamma = 3 \cdot 10^{-4}$ degrees/cm, $T_0 = 1200°$C, and the value $a^2 = 0.006\,\text{cm}^2/\text{sec}$ (the average value of the experimentally found coefficients of the thermal conductivity of granite and basalt), then for the time duration of the cooling process we obtain the value $t = 0.85 \cdot 10^{15}$ sec $= 27$ million years. Such an estimate of the age of the earth is, however, incompatible with the geological facts. The approximate nature of the theory being considered—that is, disregarding the earth's curvature, the variability of the thermal conductivity, and the inaccurate value of T_0—naturally cannot strongly influence the order of magnitude of the value found for the age of the earth, which according to modern investigation has been estimated at around $2 \cdot 10^9$ years.

The physical scheme of the course of the temperature in the earth can be represented in a different manner, using radioactive decay. The radioactive elements distributed in the earth's crust generate by their decay a certain amount of heat which naturally contributes to the warming of the earth. Therefore, the corresponding heat-conduction equation must have the form

$$\frac{\partial u}{\partial t} = a^2 \frac{\partial^2 u}{\partial z^2} + f , \qquad f = \frac{A}{c\rho} ,$$

where A represents the volume density of the heat source. On the basis of numerous measurements of the radioactivity of rocks and the amount of heat generated by their radioactive decay we usually choose the value

$$A = 1.3 \cdot 10^{-12} \frac{\text{cal}}{\text{cm}^3\,\text{sec}} .$$

This value is considered to be the heat developed by uranium, thorium, and potassium, including their decay products.

We shall now assume that the density of the radioactive source in the interior of the earth sphere is constant and has the value A on the upper layer of the earth's crust. Under this assumption we obtain for the amount of heat generated in the entire sphere during a unit of time

$$Q = \frac{4}{3} \pi R^3 A .$$

We assume further that the earth is not warmed by the radioactive-generated heat. In this case, for the amount of heat flowing per unit of surface area we obtain

$$q = k\frac{\partial u}{\partial z}\bigg|_{z=0} \geqq \frac{Q}{4\pi R^2},$$

where k is the coefficient of heat conductivity and $\partial u/\partial z|_{z=0}$ is the geothermal gradient at the earth's surface.

From this we find

$$\frac{\partial u}{\partial z}\bigg|_{z=0} \geqq \frac{AR}{3k} \approx 6.3 \cdot 10^{-2}\,\frac{\text{degrees}}{\text{cm}},$$

where $R = 6.\ 3 \cdot 10^3$ km is the earth's radius and $k = 0.004$ is the average heat conductivity of the soil rocks.

Accordingly, under the assumption that the distribution of the radioactive elements are constant and the earth is not warmed by the radioactive decay, the calculated geothermal coefficient exceeds the observed value

$$\gamma = 3 \cdot 10^{-4}\ \text{degree/cm}$$

by two orders of magnitude.

We now drop the hypothesis that the radioactive elements are distributed uniformly and assume instead that they lie in a layer of thickness H of the earth's crust. Without considering the curvature of the earth we then obtain for the determination of the stationary temperature the equation

$$\begin{aligned} \frac{\partial^2 u}{\partial z^2} &= -\frac{A}{k} \qquad &&\text{for } 0 \leqq z \leqq H \\ &= 0 &&\text{for } z > H \end{aligned}$$

with the conditions

$$u(0) = 0, \qquad \frac{\partial u}{\partial z}\bigg|_{z\to\infty} = 0.$$

The solution of this problem is obviously given by

$$\begin{aligned} u(z) &= \frac{A}{k}\left(Hz - \frac{z^2}{2}\right), \qquad &&0 \leqq z \leqq H \\ &= \frac{A}{k}\frac{H^2}{2}, &&z \geqq H \end{aligned}$$

since this function including its first derivative at $z = H$ is continuous and the conditions of the problem are satisfied.

If now we calculate the value of the gradient of this function at $z = 0$

$$\frac{\partial u}{\partial z}\bigg|_{z=0} = \frac{AH}{k},$$

and compare it with the observed value

$$\gamma = 3 \cdot 10^{-4}\ \text{degree/cm},$$

then we find

$$H = \frac{\gamma k}{A} \approx 10^6 \text{ cm} = 10 \text{ km}.$$

We shall now estimate how the assumption that the temperature is stationary affects the size of the geothermal coefficient. To this end we consider the solution of the heat-conduction equation

$$\frac{\partial w}{\partial t} = a^2 \frac{\partial^2 w}{\partial z^2} + f$$

$$f = \frac{A}{c\rho}, \qquad 0 \leqq z \leqq H$$

$$= 0, \qquad z > H$$

with the homogeneous initial and boundary conditions

$$w(z, 0) = 0$$

$$w(0, t) = 0.$$

As we saw in Section 3-3 the solution of this problem is represented by the integral

$$w(z, t) = \int_0^\infty \int_0^t G(z, \zeta, t - \tau) f(\zeta) d\tau d\zeta.$$

In this case G is the Green's function for the one-sided bounded straight line:

$$G(z, \zeta, t - \tau) = \frac{1}{2\sqrt{\pi}\sqrt{a^2(t-\tau)}} \{e^{-(z-\zeta)^2/4a^2(t-\tau)} - e^{-(z+\zeta)^2/4a^2(t-\tau)}\}.$$

For the value of the gradient of the function $w(z, t)$ for $z = 0$, by consideration of the value of f there results therefore

$$\left.\frac{\partial w}{\partial z}\right|_{z=0} = \frac{A}{c\rho 2\sqrt{\pi}} \int_0^H \int_0^t \frac{\zeta}{\sqrt{[a^2(t-\tau)]^3}} e^{-\zeta^2/4a^2(t-\tau)} d\zeta d\tau$$

$$= \frac{A}{c\rho\sqrt{\pi}} \int_0^t \frac{1}{\sqrt{a^2(t-\tau)}} \int_0^{H^2/4a^2(t-\tau)} e^{-\alpha} d\alpha d\tau$$

$$= \frac{A}{c\rho\sqrt{\pi}} \int_0^t \frac{1}{\sqrt{a^2\theta}} [1 - e^{-H^2/4a^2\theta}] d\theta, \qquad \theta = t - \tau.$$

Therefore

$$\left.\frac{\partial w}{\partial z}\right|_{z=0} = \frac{A}{c\rho\sqrt{\pi}} \left\{ \frac{2\sqrt{t}}{a} - \frac{H}{a^2} \int_{\sigma_0}^\infty e^{-\sigma^2} \frac{d\sigma}{\sigma^2} \right\},$$

where

$$\sigma = \frac{H}{2\sqrt{a^2\theta}}, \qquad \sigma_0 = \frac{H}{2\sqrt{a^2 t}}, \qquad \frac{d\sigma}{\sigma^2} = -\frac{a^2}{H} \frac{d\theta}{\sqrt{a^2\theta}}.$$

Now

$$\int_{\sigma_0}^{\infty} e^{-\sigma^2} \frac{d\sigma}{\sigma^2} = -\frac{e^{-\sigma^2}}{\sigma}\Big|_{\sigma_0}^{\infty} - 2\int e^{-\sigma^2} d\sigma = \frac{e^{-\sigma_0^2}}{\sigma_0} - 2\int_{\sigma_0}^{\infty} e^{-\sigma^2} d\sigma ,$$

so that

$$\frac{\partial w}{\partial z}\Big|_{z=0} = \frac{A}{c\rho a^2}\left\{\frac{2a\sqrt{t}}{\sqrt{\pi}}[1 - e^{-H^2/4a^2t}] + H\frac{2}{\sqrt{\pi}}\int_{H/2\sqrt{a^2t}}^{\infty} e^{-\sigma^2} d\sigma\right\}. \qquad (3\text{-}5.4)$$

Further,

$$\lim_{t\to\infty} \frac{\partial w}{\partial z}\Big|_{z=0} = \frac{A}{k} H ;$$

then $c\rho a^2 = k$, the limit value of the first summand in the curved brackets vanishes and the limit value of the second summand is equal to H.

We now calculate the difference between the limit value of $\partial w/\partial z$ obtained above and the value of $\partial w/\partial z$ for

$$t = 2 \cdot 10^9 \text{ years} = 6 \cdot 10^{16} \text{ sec.}$$

Then σ_0 is small:

$$\sigma_0 = \frac{H}{2\sqrt{a^2t}} = \frac{10^6}{2\sqrt{6 \cdot 10^{-3} \cdot 6 \cdot 10^{16}}} = \frac{1}{2 \cdot 19} \approx 0.025 .$$

By expanding in series the functions appearing in formula (3-5.4) we obtain

$$\frac{A}{k}H - \frac{\partial w}{\partial z}\Big|_{z=0} = \frac{A}{k}H\left\{\frac{1}{\sqrt{\pi}\,\sigma_0}(\sigma_0^2 + \cdots) + \frac{2}{\sqrt{\pi}} \cdot \sigma_0\right\} \approx \frac{A}{k}H \cdot 0.04 ,$$

i.e., $\partial w/\partial z\,|_{z=0}$ differs by about 4 per cent from its limit value as $t \to \infty$.

We can calculate the function $w(z, t)$ for $z > 0$ and prove that for $z \geqq H$, when one introduces the age of the earth for t, the function still deviates considerably from its limit value[71] (although, as we see at the surface, the gradient is practically equal to its limit value).

These considerations are all only estimates; nevertheless we must conclude from the fact that the rate of the radioactive decay does not change with the temperatures and pressures obtainable, that the concentration of the radioactive elements with increasing depth decreases rapidly when the value of A for the upper layers of the earth's crust, as it has been determined by numerous measurements, is taken as a basis. A physical theory which would allow us to derive a law for the decrease of the concentration of radioactive elements with increasing depth has not yet been developed.

3. The method of analogy in the theory of heat conduction

The method of analogy has been shown to be very useful for the solution of a series of problems of heat conduction. As an example, therefore, we shall consider the following two problems.

[71] A. N. Tychonoff, "Concerning the Influence of Radioactive Decay on the Temperature of the Earth's Crust," *Investigations of the Academy of Science of the USSR,* Division of Mathematics and Natural Sciences, pp. 431-459, 1937.

1. *The Green's function for the infinite straight line.* The heat-conduction equation obviously remains unchanged by the substitution

$$x' = kx\,, \qquad t' = k^2 t\,. \tag{3-5.5}$$

That is, when the linear scale of the rod changes k-fold, and the time scale changes k^2-fold.

We seek next the solution of the heat-conduction equation

$$u_t = a^2 u_{xx} \tag{3-5.6}$$

with the initial condition

$$u(x, 0) = \begin{cases} u_0 & \text{for } x > 0 \\ 0 & \text{for } x < 0\,. \end{cases} \tag{3-5.7}$$

Also, the initial condition (3-5.7) is not changed by the above scale changes. Therefore, for the function $u(x, t)$, the equation

$$u(x, t) = u(kx, k^2 t) \tag{3-5.8}$$

holds for all $x, t,$ and k.

Now if we set

$$k = \frac{1}{2\sqrt{t}}\,, \tag{3-5.9}$$

then we obtain

$$u(x, t) = \left(\frac{x}{2\sqrt{t}}, \frac{1}{4}\right) = u_0 f\left(\frac{x}{2\sqrt{t}}\right). \tag{3-5.10}$$

The function u therefore depends only on the argument

$$z = \frac{x}{2\sqrt{t}}\,. \tag{3-5.11}$$

For the derivatives there results from (3-5.10)

$$\frac{\partial^2 u}{\partial x^2} = u_0 \frac{d^2 f}{dz^2} \cdot \frac{1}{4t}\,, \qquad \frac{\partial u}{\partial t} = -\frac{x \cdot u_0}{4t^{3/2}} \frac{df}{dz} = -u_0 \cdot \frac{z}{2t} \frac{df}{dz}\,.$$

If we introduce this expression into Eq. (3-5.6) and divide it by $u_0/4t$, then it follows that

$$a^2 \frac{d^2 f}{dz^2} = -2z \frac{df}{dz} \tag{3-5.12}$$

with the auxiliary conditions

$$f(-\infty) = 0\,, \qquad f(\infty) = 1\,, \tag{3-5.13}$$

which correspond to the initial condition for the function $u(x, t)$.

By integration of Eq. (3-5.12) we obtain

$$a^2 \frac{f''}{f'} = -2z\,, \qquad f' = Ce^{-z^2/a^2}\,, \qquad f = C\int_{-\infty}^{z} e^{-\xi^2/a^2} d\xi = C_1 \int_{-\infty}^{z/a} e^{-\zeta^2} d\zeta\,.$$

Therefore, the lower limit is so chosen that the first condition of (3-5.13) is fulfilled. The second will similarly be fulfilled if we set

$$C_1 = \frac{1}{\sqrt{\pi}}.$$

Therefore

$$u(x, t) = \frac{u_0}{\sqrt{\pi}} \int_{-\infty}^{x/2\sqrt{a^2t}} e^{-\xi^2} d\xi = \frac{u_0}{2}\left[1 + \Phi\left(\frac{x}{2\sqrt{a^2t}}\right)\right]. \tag{3-5.14}$$

where

$$\Phi(z) = \frac{2}{\sqrt{\pi}} \int_0^z e^{-\xi^2} d\xi$$

is the error integral. If the initial value has the general form

$$u(x, 0) = \begin{cases} u_0 & \text{for } x > \bar{x} \\ 0 & \text{for } x < \bar{x} \end{cases} \tag{3-5.15}$$

then

$$u(x, t) = \frac{u_0}{2}\left[1 + \Phi\left(\frac{x - \bar{x}}{2\sqrt{a^2t}}\right)\right]. \tag{3-5.16}$$

We turn now to the solution of the second auxiliary problem for which the initial conditions have the form

$$\begin{aligned} u(x, 0) &= 0 \quad &&\text{for} \quad x_2 < x \\ &= u_0 \quad &&\text{for} \quad x_1 < x < x_2 \\ &= 0 \quad &&\text{for} \quad x < x_1 . \end{aligned} \tag{3-5.17}$$

In this case

$$u(x, t) = \frac{u_0}{2}\left[\Phi\left(\frac{x - x_1}{2\sqrt{a^2t}}\right) - \Phi\left(\frac{x - x_2}{2\sqrt{a^2t}}\right)\right].$$

The initial temperature u_0 corresponds to an amount of heat

$$Q = c\rho(x_2 - x_1)u_0 .$$

If $Q = c\rho$, then

$$u(x, t) = -\frac{1}{x_2 - x_1} \cdot \frac{1}{2}\left[\Phi\left(\frac{x - x_2}{2\sqrt{a^2t}}\right) - \Phi\left(\frac{x - x_1}{2\sqrt{a^2t}}\right)\right]. \tag{3-5.18}$$

The Green's function then obviously represents the limit value of the function $u(x, t)$ as $(x_2 - x_1) \to 0$ in the passage to a point source.

The corresponding passage to the limit in formula (3-5.18) gives

$$u(x, t) = -\frac{\partial}{\partial \xi}\left[\frac{1}{2}\Phi\left(\frac{x - \xi}{2\sqrt{a^2t}}\right)\right]_{\xi = x_1}, \tag{3-5.19}$$

since on the right side of (3-5.18) the difference quotient arises whose limit value is the derivative in (3-5.19).

Now if we perform the differentiation we find

$$u(x, t) = \frac{1}{2\sqrt{\pi}} \frac{1}{\sqrt{a^2 t}} e^{-(x-x_1)^2/4a^2 t} , \qquad (3\text{-}5.20)$$

i.e., $u(x, t) = G(x, x_1, t)$ is the Green's function.

2. *Boundary-value problems for the nonlinear heat-conduction equation.* We consider the equation

$$\frac{\partial}{\partial x}\left[k(u)\frac{\partial u}{\partial x}\right] = c\rho\frac{\partial u}{\partial t} \qquad (3\text{-}5.21)$$

and seek the solution which satisfies the boundary condition

$$u(0, t) = u_1 \qquad (3\text{-}5.22)$$

and the initial condition

$$u(x, 0) = u_2 . \qquad (3\text{-}5.23)$$

Also in this case a substitution of the form (3-5.5) changes neither the Eq. (3-5.21) nor the auxiliary conditions (3-5.22) and (3-5.23).

From this it follows that

$$u(x, t) = f\left(\frac{x}{2\sqrt{t}}\right) = f(z) , \qquad z = \frac{x}{2\sqrt{t}} . \qquad (3\text{-}5.24)$$

By using this expression we obtain for f the equation

$$\frac{d}{dz}\left[k(f)\frac{df}{dz}\right] = -2c\rho z\frac{df}{dz} \qquad (3\text{-}5.25)$$

with the auxiliary conditions

$$f(0) = u_1 , \; f(\infty) = u_2 . \qquad (3\text{-}5.26)$$

The function $f(z)$ can be calculated by numerical integration in those cases in which it cannot be found in closed form.

Equation (3-5.25), under very general assumptions on k and $c\rho$, also possesses a uniquely determined solution which satisfies the conditions (3-5.26).

As an example of (3-5.21) we consider the case in which $k(u) = k_0 + k_1 u$ is a linear function in u and $c\rho$ is a constant. By a suitable change of the time scale and a scaling of the values of u we then obtain the equation

$$\frac{\partial}{\partial x}\left[(1 + \alpha u)\frac{\partial u}{\partial x}\right] = \frac{\partial u}{\partial t} , \qquad (3\text{-}5.27)$$

with the initial and boundary conditions

$$u(x, 0) = 0 , \qquad u(0, t) = 1 . \qquad (3\text{-}5.28)$$

Now if we set

$$u(x, t) = f(z) , \qquad z = \frac{x}{2\sqrt{t}} ,$$

then $f(z)$ must satisfy the condition

$$\frac{d}{dz}\left[(1+\alpha f)\frac{df}{dz}\right] = -2z\frac{df}{dz} \tag{3-5.29}$$

$$f(0) = 1\,, \qquad f(\infty) = 0\,. \tag{3-5.30}$$

Figure 42 shows the results of the numerical integration of (3-5.29) for different values of α.

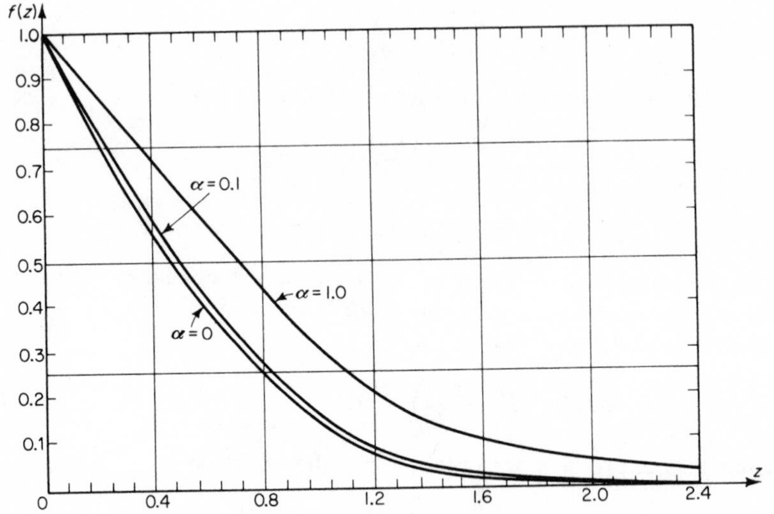

FIG. 42.

4. The solidification problem

If the temperature of a body changes, then its physical (state) condition changes. If, in particular, the temperature change includes the melting point, then the body is transformed from the fluid to the solid state (or conversely). Moreover, the temperature on the transition surface during the entire time remains constant. Owing to the motion of the transition surface, a latent heat of fusion is freed (melting). In the following we shall formulate the additional conditions which must be fulfilled by the solidifying surface.[72]

To this end we shall consider the problem in which the transition surface is described by the plane $x = \xi(t)$. During the time interval $(t, t + \Delta t)$ the boundary $x = \xi$ can be displaced from the point $\xi = x_1$ to the point $\xi = x_2 = x_1 + \Delta\xi$. In so doing, the mass $\rho\Delta\xi$ solidifies (or melts in case $\Delta\xi < 0$) and an amount of heat $\lambda\rho\Delta\xi$ is released.

To satisfy the energy conservation law, this amount of heat must be equal to the difference of the amount of heat passing through the boundaries $\xi = x_1$ and $\xi = x_2$. Therefore, the condition

$$\left[k_1\frac{\partial u_1}{\partial x}\bigg|_{x_1} - k_2\frac{\partial u_2}{\partial x}\bigg|_{x_2}\right]\Delta t = \lambda\rho\Delta\xi$$

72 Ph. Frank and R. v. Mises, *Differential and Integral Equations of Mechanics and Physics*, Braunschweig, 1930/1935; Ch. 13.

must also be fulfilled where k_1 and k_2 are the heat conductivity coefficients of the first and the second states while λ is the heat of fusion.

If now in this expression we let Δt tend to zero, then the auxiliary condition on the transition surface takes the form

$$k_1 \frac{\partial u_1}{\partial x}\bigg|_{x=\xi} - k_2 \frac{\partial u_2}{\partial x}\bigg|_{x=\xi} = \lambda\rho \frac{d\xi}{dt} . \tag{3-5.31}$$

This condition is valid for the solidification process (for $\Delta\xi > 0$ and $d\xi/dt > 0$) and also for the melting process (for $\Delta\xi < 0$ and $d\xi/dt < 0$); the direction in which the process proceeds can be determined from the signs on the left side.

Now we shall consider the freezing process of water where the melting temperature is zero. Let the half space $x \geqq 0$ be filled with water. This amount of water then is bounded on one side by the plane $x = 0$. At the initial moment $t = 0$, the water has the constant temperature $c > 0$. If the surface $x = 0$ steadily maintains the constant temperature $c_1 < 0$, then the transition surface $x = \xi$ penetrates, with time, into the fluid.

According to the above, the problem of the temperature distribution in the freezing water and the determination of the velocity of propagation of the transition surface leads to the equations

$$\begin{aligned} \frac{\partial u_1}{\partial t} &= a_1^2 \frac{\partial^2 u_1}{\partial x^2} \qquad \text{for } 0 < x < \xi \\ \frac{\partial u_2}{\partial t} &= a_2^2 \frac{\partial^2 u_2}{\partial x^2} \qquad \text{for } \xi < x < \infty \end{aligned} \tag{3.5.32}$$

with the auxiliary conditions

$$\begin{aligned} u_1 &= c_1 \qquad \text{for } x = 0 \\ u_2 &= c \qquad \text{for } t = 0 . \end{aligned} \tag{3-5.33}$$

Moreover, on the transition surface the conditions

$$u_1 = u_2 = 0 \qquad \text{for } x = \xi \tag{3-5.34}$$

$$k_1 \frac{\partial u_1}{\partial x}\bigg|_{x=\xi} - k_2 \frac{\partial u_2}{\partial x}\bigg|_{x=\xi} = \lambda\rho \frac{d\xi}{dt} \tag{3-5.31}$$

must be fulfilled where k_1, a_1^2 or k_2, a_2^2 are the coefficients of the heat and thermal conductivity of the solid and liquid states.

For the solution of the problem we make the Ansatz

$$u_1 = A_1 + B_1 \Phi\left(\frac{x}{2a_1\sqrt{t}}\right)$$

$$u_2 = A_2 + B_2 \Phi\left(\frac{x}{2a_2\sqrt{t}}\right)$$

where A_1, B_1, A_2, and B_2 are constants to be determined while Φ is the error integral

$$\Phi(x) = \frac{2}{\sqrt{\pi}} \int_0^x e^{-\xi^2}\, d\xi .$$

If we consider the conditions (3-5.33) and (3-5.34) then we obtain from (3-5.33)

$$A_1 = c_1\,, \qquad A_2 + B_2 = c$$

and from (3-5.34)

$$A_1 + B_1\Phi\left(\frac{\xi}{2a_1\sqrt{t}}\right) = 0$$

$$A_2 + B_2\Phi\left(\frac{\xi}{2a_2\sqrt{t}}\right) = 0\,.$$

These conditions must hold for arbitrary values of t. This is possible only when

$$\xi = \alpha\sqrt{t} \tag{3-5.35}$$

is valid, where α is a fixed constant. The expression (3-5.35) determines the law of motion of the transition surface between the fluid and the solid states.

For the constants A_1, B_1, A_2, B_2, and α the following expressions result:

$$\begin{aligned} A_1 &= c_1\,, & B_1 &= -\frac{c_1}{\Phi(\alpha/2a_1)} \\ A_2 &= -\frac{c\Phi(\alpha/2a_2)}{1-\Phi(\alpha/2a_2)}\,, & B_2 &= \frac{c}{1-\Phi(\alpha/2a_2)}\,. \end{aligned} \tag{3-5.36}$$

For the determination of α the requirement (3-5.31) leads to:

$$\frac{k_1c_1e^{-\alpha^2/4a_1^2}}{a_1\Phi(\alpha/2a_1)} + \frac{k_2ce^{-\alpha^2/4a_2^2}}{a_2[1-\Phi(\alpha/2a_2)]} = -\lambda\rho\alpha\frac{\sqrt{\pi}}{2}\,. \tag{3-5.37}$$

The solution of this transcendental equation gives directly the value of α. That at least one solution of $c_1 < 0$, $c > 0$ exists follows from the fact that the left side of this equation varies from $-\infty$ to $+\infty$ when α passes through all values from 0 to ∞,[73] while the right side for such α assumes only the values between 0 and $-\infty$. In the case when c is equal to the melting temperature ($c = 0$), expressions (3-5.36) and (3-5.37) for the determination of the coefficients reduce to a simpler form:

$$A_2 = B_2 = 0\,, \quad A_1 = c_1\,, \quad B_1 = -\frac{c_1}{\Phi(\alpha/2a_1)} \tag{3-5.36'}$$

and

$$\frac{k_1c_1e^{-\alpha^2/4a_1^2}}{a_1\Phi(\alpha/2a_1)} = -\lambda\rho\alpha\frac{\sqrt{\pi}}{2}\,. \tag{3-5.37'}$$

If we set $\alpha/2a_1 = \beta$, then (3-5.37′) can also be written in the form

$$\frac{1}{\sqrt{\pi}}\frac{e^{-\beta^2}}{\Phi(\beta)} = -D\beta\,,$$

where D is determined by

[73] For an asymptotic representation of the function $1 - \Phi(z)$ as $z \to \infty$ see the Appendix.

$$D = \frac{\lambda \rho a_1^2}{k_1 c_1} < 0 .$$

By use of the graphic representation of the function $\varphi(\beta) = e^{-\beta^2}/\sqrt{\pi}\,\Phi(\beta)$ given in Figure 43, the value of α can be determined.

The solution of the solidification problem can also be found with the help of the analogy method as discussed in Section 3-5 § 3. To a certain degree the solidification problem is a limiting case of a nonlinear boundary-value problem similar to that in the previous section. The coefficients of heat conductivity and heat capacity for solidification problems are piecewise constant functions. Moreover, the heat capacity for $u(x, t) = 0$ is infinite. This case can also be obtained as a limiting case as $\varepsilon \to 0$ if one assumes that the latent heat is not freed instantaneously but is released during a fixed interval $(-\varepsilon, +\varepsilon)$. Therefore, we naturally must have

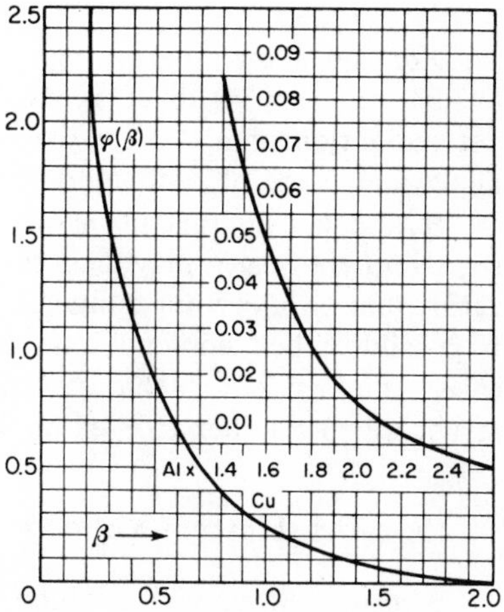

FIG. 43.

$$\int_{-\varepsilon}^{\varepsilon} c(u)du = \lambda .$$

One can easily prove that all the conditions of the problem remain unchanged when the length scale changes k-fold and the time scale k^2-fold. Therefore the solution depends only on the argument $x/\sqrt{t}$, i.e.,

$$u(x, t) = f\left(\frac{x}{\sqrt{t}}\right) .$$

Hence, in particular, it follows that the motion of the zero isotherm can be described by the equation

$$\xi = \alpha\sqrt{t} ,$$

when α is the value of the argument, for which

$$f(\alpha) = 0$$

is valid.

For the determination of the of the function f the following conditions result:

$$a_1^2 \frac{d^2 f_1}{dz^2} = -2z \frac{df_1}{dz} \qquad \text{for } 0 < z < \alpha$$

$$a_2^2 \frac{d^2 f_2}{dz^2} = -2z \frac{df_2}{dz} \qquad \text{for } \alpha < z < \infty$$

$$f_1(0) = c_1 , \qquad f_2(\infty) = c , \qquad f_1(\alpha) = f_2(\alpha) = 0$$

$$k_1 f_1'(\alpha) - k_2 f_2'(\alpha) = \lambda \rho \frac{\alpha}{2} .$$

Therefore,

$$f(z) = \begin{cases} f_1(z) = A_1 + B_1\Phi\left(\dfrac{z}{2a_1}\right) & \text{for } 0 < z < \alpha \\ f_2(z) = A_2 + B_2\Phi\left(\dfrac{z}{2a_2}\right) & \text{for } \alpha < z < \infty \,. \end{cases}$$

For the determination of the constants A_1, B_1, A_2, B_2, the requirements (3-5.33) and (3-5.34) must again be used, from which (3-5.36) results. For the determination of α the condition (3-5.37) is used. Therefore the respective analytical parts of both methods of solution coincide.

These considerations show that the solidification problem can also be solved in the cases in which the latent heat is freed not for a fixed temperature but in a certain temperature interval. In a similar manner the solution is possible when not one but many critical temperatures are given. Such cases can occur for changes of state in the transition from one crystalline structure to another (for example, for the recrystallization of steel).

5. The Einstein-Kolmogoroff equation

Microscopic particles which are free to move in a medium are in a constant, permanent state of unordered motion (Brownian molecular motion). The probability therefore that a particle found at time t_0 at the point M_0 is found at time t in a small neighborhood ΔV of the point M can be described by the function

$$W(M, t; M_0, t_0) \cdot \Delta V \,. \tag{3-5.38}$$

In this case by "probability" we mean the following:

If a sufficiently large number N of particles moves from the point M_0 (we shall disregard the opposing influences) during a small time interval $t_0 + \Delta t$, $W(N, t; M_0 t_0)$ is equal to the concentration of these particles as $\Delta t \to 0$ at the point M at the time t, if the total mass of the particles issuing from the point M_0 is chosen as the unit of mass of the particles.

A similar phenomenon occurs also in the diffusion of gases in, for example, a gaseous medium.

The function $W(M, t; M_0, t_0)$ represents the Green's function corresponding to the unit mass. Obviously, we must have the condition

$$\int W(M, t; M_0, t_0) dV_M = 1 \,, \qquad t > t_0 \,. \tag{3-5.39}$$

If the initial concentration of the particles at a fixed time t_0 is equal to $\varphi(M)$, the concentration $u(M, t)$ of these particles at time $t > t_0$ must be equal to

$$u(M, t) = \int W(M, t; P, t_0)\varphi(P) dV_P \,, \tag{3-5.40}$$

where the integral is extended throughout all space.

From this relation results the Einstein-Kolmogoroff equation:[74]

$$W(M, t; M_0, t_0) = \int W(M, t; P, \theta) W(P, \theta; M_0, t_0) dV_P, \qquad t_0 < \theta < t. \qquad (3\text{-}5.41)$$

We shall now show that, under certain conditions which the function $W(M, t; M_0, t_0)$ must satisfy, the solution of the Einstein-Kolmogoroff equation satisfies a parabolic differential equation. Therefore, we shall consider the case in which the position of the point M is described by a single coordinate x and assume that the function $W(x,t; x_0, t_0)$ satisfies the following conditions:

(*a*)
$$\lim_{\tau\to 0} \frac{\overline{x-\xi}}{\tau} = \lim \frac{1}{\tau} \int (x-\xi) W(x, t+\tau; \xi, t) d\xi = A(x, t). \qquad (3\text{-}5.42)$$

If the particles during the time τ are displaced from the position ξ to the position x, then $(\overline{x-\xi}/\tau)$ is the average velocity of the particles. Consequently, requirement (*a*) means that the ordered motion of the particles takes place with a finite velocity.

(*b*)
$$\lim_{\tau\to 0} \frac{\overline{(x-\xi)^2}}{\tau} = \lim \frac{1}{\tau} \int (x-\xi)^2 W(x, t+\tau; \xi, t) d\xi = 2B(x, t). \qquad (3\text{-}5.43)$$

The quantity $(x-\xi)^2$ does not depend on the direction of the displacement of the point x with respect to the point ξ. The average value of the square of the distance during the time τ,

$$\overline{(x-\xi)^2} = \int (x-\xi)^2 W(x, t+\tau; \xi, t) d\xi,$$

is ordinarily regarded as the measure of the unordered motion during this time interval. The requirement (*b*) says, therefore, that the average square for sufficiently small τ shall be linearly dependent on the time.

(*c*)
$$\lim_{\tau\to 0} \frac{\overline{|x-\xi|^3}}{\tau} = \lim \frac{1}{\tau} \int |x-\xi|^3 \cdot W(x, t+\tau; \xi, t) d\xi = 0. \qquad (3\text{-}5.44)$$

The Green's function $W(x, t+\tau; \xi, t)$ for small τ values shall decrease rapidly when $|x-\xi| \to \infty$ and increase when $|x-\xi|$ is small.

Now in order to derive the Einstein-Kolmogoroff differential equation we multiply both sides of Eq. (3-5.41) with an arbitrary function $\psi(x)$, which, including its derivatives, vanishes at the boundary of the region of integration, and integrate over the entire region:

$$\int W(x, t+\tau; x_0, t_0)\psi(x) dx = \int W(\xi, t; x_0, t_0) d\xi \int W(x, t+\tau; \xi, t)\psi(x) dx.$$

Then we develop $\psi(x)$ on the right side according to Taylor's formula,

$$\psi(x) = \psi(\xi) + \psi'(\xi)(x-\xi) + \frac{\psi''(\xi)}{2}(x-\xi)^2 + \frac{\psi'''(\xi^*)}{3!}(x-\xi)^3,$$

[74] M. A. Leontovich, *Statistical Physics*, Moscow, 1944, Ch. 6; A. N. Kolmogoroff, "Analytical Methods in the Calculus of Probability," *Uspechi mat. nauk*. 5, 1938.

where ξ^* is a value lying between x and ξ. After some simple transformations, division by τ gives

$$\int \psi(x) \frac{W(x, t+\tau;, x_0, t_0) - W(x, t; x_0, t_0)}{\tau} dx$$

$$= \int W(\xi, t; x_0, t_0) \left[\psi'(\xi) \frac{\overline{x-\xi}}{\tau} + \psi''(\xi) \frac{\overline{(x-\xi)^2}}{2\tau} \right] d\xi$$

$$+ \frac{1}{3!\tau} \iint \psi'''(\xi^*)(x-\xi)^3 W(\xi, t; x_0, t_0) W(x, t+\tau; \xi, t) d\xi dx .$$

If we assume $\psi'''(x)$ to be bounded, i.e.,

$$|\psi'''(x)| < A ,$$

and take into consideration

$$\int W(\xi, t; x_0, t_0) d\xi = 1 ,$$

we obtain

$$\left| \frac{1}{\tau} \iint \psi'''(\xi^*)(x-\xi)^3 W(\xi, t; x_0, t_0) W(x, t+\tau; \xi, t) d\xi dx \right|$$

$$\leqq \frac{A}{\tau} \int |x-\xi|^3 W(x, t+\tau; \xi, t) dx = \frac{\overline{A|x-\xi|^3}}{\tau} .$$

From condition (c) it follows that this expression approaches zero as $\tau \to 0$. Therefore, with the use of conditions (a) and (b) and as $\tau \to 0$, we find

$$\int \psi(x) \frac{\partial W(x, t; x_0, t_0)}{\partial t} dx$$

$$= \int W(\xi, t; x_0, t_0)[\psi'(\xi) A(\xi, t) + \psi''(\xi) B(\xi, t)] d\xi .$$

Now if we integrate the right side by parts and note that the function $\psi(x)$, including its derivatives, vanishes at the boundary of the region of integration, then we find

$$\int \psi(x) \left[\frac{\partial W}{\partial t} + \frac{\partial(AW)}{\partial x} - \frac{\partial^2(BW)}{\partial x^2} \right] dx = 0 .$$

Since this relation must hold for an arbitrary function $\psi(x)$, the Einstein-Kolmogoroff differential equation

$$\frac{\partial W}{\partial t} = -\frac{\partial(AW)}{\partial x} + \frac{\partial^2(BW)}{\partial x^2} \tag{3-5.45}$$

results for the function $W(x, t; x_0, t_0)$.

This equation, similar to the heat-conduction equation, is a parabolic differential equation and can be written in the form

$$W_t = \frac{\partial}{\partial x}(BW_x) + \alpha W_x + \beta W , \tag{3-5.46}$$

where

$$\alpha = -A + B_x$$
$$\beta = -A_x + B_{xx} = \alpha_x \, .$$

From Eq. (3-5.46) we recognize that the quantity B has the physical significance of a diffusion coefficient. If the process considered is homogeneous in time and space, i.e., the function W depends only on the difference $\xi = x - x_0$ and $\theta = t - t_0$, then the coefficients A and B are not dependent on x and t and are constant. Eq. (3-5.45) is then a differential equation with constant coefficients:

$$\frac{\partial W}{\partial t} = - A \frac{\partial W}{\partial x} + B \frac{\partial^2 W}{\partial x^2} \, . \tag{3-5.47}$$

If W depends only on $|x - \xi|$, i.e., the probability for a right- and left-sided displacement at the same distance from the point ξ, coincide, then obviously A must be equal to zero. Analytically this follows from the formula (3-5.42), since the integrand is an odd function.

In this case, Eq. (3-5.45) is transformed into the simple heat-conduction equation

$$\frac{\partial W}{\partial t} = B \frac{\partial^2 W}{\partial x^2} \, . \tag{3-5.48}$$

6. The δ function

1. *Definition of the δ function.* In addition to the continuously distributed quantities (mass, charge, heat sources, impulse, etc.), point-form quantities (point mass, point charge, point-form heat source, point-form impulse, etc.) also often occur. We emphasize that this idea represents a "limiting case," although it is used by physicists principally as an independent concept—by omission of the corresponding passage to the limit.

With regard to the physical significance of the δ function, we shall first consider the following relations. Let a unit of mass exist inside a fixed region of space T in the neighborhood of a point M_0. At some other point M of the space, the mass then produces a fixed potential (see Chapter 4, Section 5). We now select a sequence of functions $\{\rho_n\}\,(\rho_n > 0)$, each of which is equal to zero outside of a sphere S of radius ε_n about the center point M_0, whereby ε_n for $n \to \infty$ approaches zero. From a fixed n on, we always have

$$\iiint_T \rho_n(P) d\tau_P = \iiint_S \rho_n(P) d\tau_P = 1 \, . \tag{3-5.49}$$

Then we consider the sequence of functions

$$u_n = \iiint_T \frac{\rho_n}{r} d\tau \, .$$

This obviously represents the potential of the masses which are distributed with the density ρ_n. For $n \to \infty$ we obtain

$$\lim_{n\to\infty} u_n = \frac{1}{r_{M_0M}} . \tag{3-5.50}$$

These results obviously do not depend on the choice of the sequence $\{\rho_n\}$, and although the sequence $\{u_n\}$ now approaches $1/r$, the sequence $\{\rho_n\}$ possesses no limit value in the class of the considered piecewise continuous functions. The "limit form" corresponding to the sequence $\{\rho_n\}$ is called the Dirac δ function and is designated by $\delta(M, M_0)$.

The basic property which defines the δ function is the formal relation

$$\iiint_T \delta(M_0, M) f(M) d\tau_M = \begin{cases} f(M_0) & \text{for } M_0 \in T \\ 0 & \text{for } M_0 \notin T \end{cases} \tag{3-5.51}$$

where $f(M)$ is an arbitrary continuous function of the point M. From the fact that the functions ρ_n, for $n \to \infty$ in each region which does not contain the point M_0, converge uniformly to zero and become unbounded in the neighborhoods of S of the point M_0, one often defines the δ function formally by the relations

$$\begin{aligned} \delta(M, M_0) &= 0 \qquad \text{for } M \neq M_0 \\ \delta(M, M_0) &= \infty \qquad \text{for } M = M_0 \end{aligned} \tag{3-5.52}$$

and

$$\iiint_T \delta(M, M_0) d\tau_M = \begin{cases} 1 & \text{for } M_0 \in T \\ 0 & \text{for } M_0 \notin T . \end{cases} \tag{3-5.53}$$

Eq. (3-5.53) is then a trivial consequence of (3-5.51) for $f = 1$.

In order to consider a sequence of functions in different problems we must introduce some new concepts of convergence:

We say that a sequence of functions

$$\{u_n(x)\} = u_1(x) , \quad u_2(x) , \cdots , u_n(x), \cdots \tag{3-5.54}$$

converges in an interval (a, b) uniformly if an N exists for every $\varepsilon > 0$ such that the condition

$$| u_n(x) - u_m(x) | < \varepsilon \qquad \text{for} \qquad n, m > N$$

is satisfied for $n, m > N$ and an arbitrary x in (a, b).

A sequence (3-5.54) is said to be convergent in the mean in an interval (a, b) if an N exists for every $\varepsilon > 0$, such that the relation

$$\int_a^b | u_n(x) - u_m(x) |^2 dx < \varepsilon$$

holds for all $n, m > M$.

A sequence (3-5.54) is said to be weakly convergent in an interval (a, b) if the limit value

$$\lim_{n\to\infty} \int_a^b f(x) u_n(x) dx$$

exists for each continuous function f.

In the treatment of convergent sequences we usually introduce the notion of limit elements of a sequence. Let us consider the class of continuous functions in the interval (a, b). In the case of uniform convergence the limit value already belongs to the same class of functions, but this is not necessarily true for mean and weak convergence.

If the limit element does not belong to the considered class of functions, then this class can be extended by addition of the limit elements. In this case, by an extension will be understood all the original functions (perhaps by equivalent classes) and the limit element. Such an extension is already known from the theory of real numbers. There the irrational numbers are introduced as the limit elements which are defined by classes of equivalent sequences of rational numbers.

With respect to the limit element for weak convergence we shall say that two sequences $\{u_n\}$ and $\{v_n\}$ possess one and the same limit element if they are equivalent, i.e., if the sequence $\{u_n - v_n\}$ converges weakly towards zero:

$$\lim_{n\to\infty} \int_a^b f(x)[u_n(x) - v_n(x)]dx = 0 .$$

We shall now call a sequence $\{\delta_n\}$ of nonnegative functions a locally normalized sequence of a point x_0 if δ_n is equal to zero outside the interval $(x_0 - \varepsilon_n, x_0 + \varepsilon_n)$, where ε_n for $n \to \infty$ approaches zero, while

$$\int_a^b \delta_n(x)dx = 1 .$$

Obviously then, $\{\delta_n\}$ is a weakly convergent sequence. The limit element of the sequence $\{\delta_n\}$ will be called the δ function of the point x_0.

If in the case of weak convergence the limit element u is formed by a sequence $\{u_n\}$ obtained from the class of functions u_n, the integral of the product of a function $f(x)$ with the element u is defined by

$$\int_a^b f(x)u\,dx = \lim_{n\to\infty} \int_a^b f(x)u_n(x)dx .$$

Obviously, the equation

$$\int_a^b f(x)\delta(x_0, x)dx = f(x_0)$$

holds for the δ function of the point x_0.

This relation is often used also in the definition of the δ function.

2. *Development of the δ function in a Fourier series.* The δ function can also be defined as the limit element of another series when this, in the sense of a weak convergence of the above given sequence $\{\delta_n(x)\}$, is equivalent to the locally normalized functions of the point x_0.

We consider the sequence of functions defined in the interval $(-l, l)$ by

$$\begin{aligned} \bar{\delta}_n(x_0, x) &= \frac{1}{2l} + \frac{1}{l}\sum_{m=1}^{n}\left(\cos\frac{m\pi}{l}x_0 \cdot \cos\frac{m\pi}{l}x + \sin\frac{m\pi}{l}x_0 \sin\frac{m\pi}{l}x\right) \\ &= \frac{1}{2l} + \frac{1}{l}\sum_{m=1}^{n}\cos\frac{m\pi}{l}(x - x_0) \end{aligned} \qquad (3\text{-}5.55)$$

or, in complex representation

$$\bar{\delta}_n(x, x_0) = \frac{1}{2l} \sum_{-n}^{n} e^{im(\pi/l)(x-x_0)} . \tag{3-5.55'}$$

Obviously then, for each function $g(x)$ which can be developed in a Fourier series, the relation

$$\lim_{n\to\infty} \int_{-l}^{l} \bar{\delta}_n(x_0, x) g(x) dx = g(x_0) \tag{3-5.56}$$

holds, which shows that in this class of functions $\{g(x)\}$ the above-introduced sequence $\{\delta_n(x_0, x)\}$ in the sense of weak convergence is equivalent to the sequence $\{\bar{\delta}_n(x_0, x)\}$. Further,

$$\delta(x_0, x) = \frac{1}{2l} + \frac{1}{l} \sum_{m=1}^{\infty} \cos \frac{m\pi}{l}(x_0 - x) , \tag{3-5.57}$$

when this expression is understood in the sense of the above explained weak convergence; and in the same sense the relation

$$\delta(x_0, x) = \sum_{n=1}^{\infty} \varphi_n(x) \varphi_n(x_0) \tag{3-5.58}$$

holds, where $\{\varphi_n(x)\}$ is a complete orthonormal system in the interval (a, b); similarly

$$\delta(x_0, x) = \frac{1}{2\pi} \int_{-\infty}^{\infty} e^{ik(x_0-x)} dk = \frac{1}{\pi} \int_{0}^{\infty} \cos k(x_0 - x) dk . \tag{3-5.59}$$

We shall now show that for the calculation of the integrals which contain the δ function, the series (3-5.57) can be used and can be integrated term by term. To this end we consider a function $g(x)$ which can be developed in a Fourier series, and the integral

$$\int_{-l}^{l} g(x) \delta(x_0, x) dx .$$

Here if we introduce, in place of $\delta(x_0, x)$, the expression from (3-5.57) and integrate the series term by term, we obtain

$$g(x) = \frac{\bar{g}_0}{2} + \sum_{m=1}^{\infty} \left(\bar{g}_m \cos \frac{\pi m}{l} x + \bar{\bar{g}}_m \sin \frac{\pi m}{l} x \right) \tag{3-5.59'}$$

with

$$\begin{aligned} \bar{g}_0 &= \frac{1}{l} \int_{-l}^{l} g(x_0) dx_0 \\ \bar{g}_m &= \frac{1}{l} \int_{-l}^{l} g(x_0) \cos \frac{\pi m}{l} x_0 dx_0 \\ \bar{\bar{g}}_m &= \frac{1}{l} \int_{-l}^{l} g(x_0) \sin \frac{\pi m}{l} x_0 dx_0 . \end{aligned} \tag{3-5.60}$$

By comparison of (3-5.59) with

$$\int_{-l}^{l} \delta(x, x_0)g(x)dx = g(x_0) , \qquad -l < x_0 < l$$

we recognize that the above-executed term-by-term integration of the series for the δ function leads to a correct result.

Therefore, in the class of functions developable in a Fourier series, the sequence of partial sums

$$\frac{1}{2l}\sum_{n=-k}^{k} e^{i(\pi n/l)(x-x')}$$

is equivalent to the locally normalized sequence $\{\delta_n\}$.

Other representations of the δ function are based on the use of a certain sequence of functions which in the sense of weak convergence is equivalent to the sequence $\{\delta_n\}$.

3. *Use of the δ function in the construction of the Green's function.* We consider the following problem:

$$u_t = a^2 u_{xx} \tag{3-5.61}$$

$$u(x, 0) = \varphi(x) \tag{3-5.62}$$

$$u(0, t) = u(l, t) = 0 . \tag{3-5.63}$$

Here a prescribed function $\varphi(x)$ corresponds to a uniquely determined solution

$$u(x, t) = \boldsymbol{L}[\varphi(x)]$$

of the problem. We assume that the operator $\boldsymbol{L}$ can be represented in the form

$$u(x, t) = \boldsymbol{L}[\varphi(x)] = \int_0^l G(x, \xi, t)\varphi(\xi)d\xi \tag{3-5.64}$$

where $G(x, \xi, t)$ is the kernel of the operator $\boldsymbol{L}$.

For the determination of $G(x, \xi, t)$ we set

$$\varphi(x) = \delta(x - x_0) . \tag{3-5.62'}$$

If in formula (3-5.64) the initial function $\varphi(x)$ is replaced by the δ function, the result is

$$u(x, t) = G(x, x_0, t) , \tag{3-5.65}$$

i.e., $G(x, x_0, t)$ is the solution of (3-5.61) with the initial condition (3-5.62).

We now write the δ function in the form of a Fourier series:

$$\delta(x - x_0) = \sum_{n=1}^{\infty} \frac{2}{l} \sin\frac{n\pi}{l}x \sin\frac{n\pi}{l}x_0 .$$

The kernel G must then obviously be of the form

$$G(x, x_0, t) = \sum_{n=1}^{\infty} A_n(t) \sin\frac{n\pi}{l} , \tag{3-5.66}$$

where each summand must satisfy the heat-conduction equation. Hence there follows

$$A_n(t) = B_n e^{-a^2(n\pi/l)^2 t} .$$

From the initial condition there also follows

$$B_n = \frac{2}{l} \sin \frac{n\pi}{l} x_0 .$$

Therefore we arrive formally at the following expression for the kernel G,

$$G(x, x_0, t) = \frac{2}{l} \sum_{n=1}^{\infty} e^{-(\pi n/l)^2 a^2 t} \sin \frac{n\pi}{l} x \sin \frac{n\pi}{l} x_0 . \tag{3-5.67}$$

This agrees with the representation of the Green's function given in Section 5-3. The solution of the problem (3-5.61)–(3-5.63) is given by the formula (3-5.64), where $G(x, x_0, t)$ is the function defined by (3-5.67).

In a similar manner, we can arrive at an expression for the Green's function for an infinite straight line. The function G is defined here by the conditions

$$u_t - a^2 u_{xx} = 0 , \qquad -\infty < x < \infty \tag{3-5.68}$$

$$u(x, 0) = \varphi(x) = \delta(x - x_0) . \tag{3-5.69}$$

Since here the δ function should be defined by a Fourier integral

$$\delta(x - x_0) = \frac{1}{\pi} \int_0^\infty \cos \lambda(x - x_0) d\lambda ,$$

we make for $G(x, x_0, t)$ the Ansatz

$$G(x, x_0, t) = \frac{1}{\pi} \int_0^\infty A_\lambda(t) \cos \lambda(x - x_0) d\lambda . \tag{3-5.70}$$

From Eq. (3-5.68) we then find

$$A_\lambda(t) = A_\lambda^{(0)} e^{-a^2 \lambda^2 t} . \tag{3-5.71}$$

If we set $t = 0$, then we obtain

$$A_\lambda^{(0)} = 1$$

by comparison of formulas (3-5.69) and (3-5.71).
Consequently,

$$G(x, x_0, t) = \frac{1}{\pi} \int_0^\infty e^{-a^2 \lambda^2 t} \cos \lambda(x - x_0) d\lambda .$$

The calculation of these integrals as carried out in Chapter 3, Section 3, gave

$$G(x, x_0, t) = \frac{1}{2\sqrt{\pi a^2 t}} e^{-(x-x_0)^2/4a^2 t} .$$

Hence it follows that the solution of the problem of the propagation of an initial temperature on an infinite straight line must be representable by the formula

$$u(x, t) = \int_{-\infty}^{\infty} G(x, \xi, t)\varphi(\xi)d\xi \tag{3-5.72}$$

Under which conditions the formulas derived by use of the δ function are valid, is a question that must be investigated separately.

As an example, we shall now treat the inhomogeneous equation

$$u_t = a^2 u_{xx} + \frac{F(x, t)}{c\rho} . \tag{3-5.73}$$

In this case $F(x, t)$ is the density distribution of the heat sources. If at the point $x = \xi$, at time $t = t_0$, a momentary heat source of intensity G_0 exists, then

$$F(x, t) = Q_0 \delta(x - \xi)\delta(t - t_0) . \tag{3-5.74}$$

Therefore, we must find the solution of the inhomogeneous equation

$$u_t = a^2 u_{xx} + \frac{Q_0}{c\rho}\delta(x - \xi)\delta(t - t_0) , \qquad t_0 > 0 \tag{3-5.75}$$

with the homogeneous initial condition

$$u(x, 0) = 0 .$$

Thus, by consideration of the integral representation

$$\delta(x - \xi) = \frac{1}{\pi}\int_0^{\infty} \cos \lambda(x - \xi)d\lambda$$

for the function $u(x, t)$, we make the Ansatz

$$u(x, t) = \frac{1}{\pi}\int_0^{\infty} u_\lambda(t) \cos \lambda(x - \xi)d\lambda .$$

If we put this expression into Eq. (3-5.75), we obtain for $u_\lambda(t)$ the equation

$$\dot{u}_\lambda(t) + a^2\lambda^2 u_\lambda(t) = \frac{Q_0}{c\rho}\delta(t - t_0)$$

with the initial condition

$$u_\lambda(0) = 0 .$$

Now, as is known, the solution of the inhomogeneous equation

$$\dot{u} + a^2 u = f(t) , \qquad u(0) = 0$$

has the form

$$u(t) = \int_0^t e^{-a^2(t-\tau)} f(\tau) d\tau . \tag{3-5.76}$$

In our case, however,

$$u_\lambda(t) = \frac{Q_0}{c\rho}\int_0^t e^{-a^2\lambda^2(t-\tau)}\delta(\tau - t_0)d\tau = \begin{cases} 0 & \text{for } t < t_0 \\ \dfrac{Q_0}{c\rho} e^{-a^2\lambda^2(t-t_0)} & \text{for } t > t_0 . \end{cases} \tag{3-5.77}$$

Therefore,

$$u(x, t) = \frac{Q_0}{c\rho}\frac{1}{\pi}\int_0^\infty e^{-a^2\lambda^2(t-t_0)} \cos \lambda(x - \xi)d\lambda = \frac{Q_0}{c\rho}G(x, \xi, t - t_0) ,$$

where

$$G(x, \xi, t - t_0) = \frac{1}{2\sqrt{\pi a^2(t - t_0)}} e^{-(x-\xi)^2/4a^2(t-t_0)}$$

represents the Green's function. Similar methods for the construction of the Green's function have often been used in theoretical physics.[75]

[75] A detailed investigation of the theory of the δ function and a number of examples of application of the δ function are found in D. D. Ivanenko and A. A. Sokolov, *Classical Field Theory*, (trans. from Russian), Berlin, 1953, Ch. I.

4

ELLIPTIC DIFFERENTIAL EQUATIONS

The investigation of different stationary physical processes (vibrations, heat conduction, diffusion, etc.) usually leads to elliptic equations. Very often Laplace's differential equation occurs:

$$\Delta u = 0 .$$

A function u is said to be harmonic in a region T if in this region the function and its derivatives up to the second order are continuous and satisfy Laplace's equation.

For the investigation of the properties of harmonic functions, different mathematical methods have been constructed which can be successfully applied to hyperbolic and parabolic differential equations.

4-1. PROBLEMS WHICH LEAD TO LAPLACE'S DIFFERENTIAL EQUATION

1. Formulation of the boundary-value problem for stationary heat fields

It was shown in Chapter 3 that the temperature of a nonstationary heat field satisfies the differential equation

$$u_t = a^2 \Delta u , \qquad a^2 = \frac{k}{c\rho} .$$

If a stationary process occurs, then a stationary heat field also occurs, so that the temperature distribution is constant in time; thus it is only a function of position $u(x, y, z)$. Consequently, in this case it satisfies Laplace's equation

$$\Delta u = 0 . \tag{4-1.1}$$

If heat sources are present, however, the equation

$$\Delta u = - f , \qquad f = \frac{F}{k} \tag{4-1.2}$$

results, where F is the density of the heat sources and k is the coefficient of heat conductivity. The inhomogeneous Laplace Eq. (4-1.2) is usually called the Poisson differential equation.

We consider now a region T of space which is bounded by a surface Σ. The problem of the stationary temperature distribution $u(x, y, z)$ in the interior of the body T reads as follows:

Determine a function $u(x, y, z)$ which in the interior of T satisfies the differential equation

$$\Delta u = -f(x, y, z) \tag{4-1.2}$$

and one of the following boundary conditions:

first boundary-value problem: $u = f_1$ on Σ

second boundary-value problem: $\dfrac{\partial u}{\partial n} = f_2$ on Σ

third boundary-value problem: $\dfrac{\partial u}{\partial n} + h(u - f_3) = 0$ on Σ.

Here f_1, f_2, f_3, h are given functions and $\partial u/\partial n$ is the derivative in the direction of the exterior normal to the surface Σ.[76]

The physical significance of these boundary conditions is clear (see Section 3–1). The first boundary-value problem for Laplace's equation is usually called the Dirichlet problem; the second is called the Neumann problem. If we are dealing with the solution of a problem in a region T_0 which lies outside of the surface Σ, then one speaks of an exterior boundary-value problem.

2. Irrotational fluid motion (potential flow); the potential of a stationary flow and of an electrostatic field

As a second example, we now treat the potential flow of a source-free fluid. In the interior of a region of space T with the boundary Σ a stationary flow of an incompressible fluid (with density $\rho =$ const.) moves with the velocity $\boldsymbol{v}(x, y, z)$. If the fluid motion is irrotational then the velocity $\boldsymbol{v}$ has a potential, i.e., a scalar function φ exists such that

$$\boldsymbol{v} = -\operatorname{grad} \varphi \tag{4-1.3}$$

or in terms of components

$$v_x = \frac{\partial \varphi}{\partial x}, \quad v_y = \frac{\partial \varphi}{\partial y}, \quad v_z = \frac{\partial \varphi}{\partial z}.$$

In a curl-free fluid motion, therefore, the three velocity components can be derived from a single function $\varphi(x, y, z)$, which is called the velocity potential of the motion in question. If the flow is source-free throughout, then

$$\operatorname{div} \boldsymbol{v} = 0. \tag{4-1.4}$$

[76] Obviously a stationary temperature distribution can occur only when the total heat flow through the boundary of the region is equal to zero. Consequently, the function f_2 must still satisfy the auxiliary requirement

$$\iint_\Sigma f_2 \, d\sigma = 0.$$

If we introduce the expression (4-1.3) for $\boldsymbol{v}$ then we obtain

$$\operatorname{div} \operatorname{grad} \varphi = 0$$

or

$$\Delta\varphi = 0 , \tag{4-1.5}$$

i.e., the velocity potential satisfies Laplace's differential equation.

In a homogeneous conducting medium, let a stationary electrical current flow whose spatial density is $\boldsymbol{j}(x, y, z)$. If there are no spatial current sources in the medium, then

$$\operatorname{div} \boldsymbol{j} = 0 . \tag{4-1.6}$$

The electrical field strength $\boldsymbol{E}$ is determined by the current density, that is, according to Ohm's law

$$\boldsymbol{E} = \frac{\boldsymbol{j}}{\lambda} , \tag{4-1.7}$$

where λ is the conductivity of the medium. Since now the process is stationary, the curl-free electrical field must be a potential field,[77] i.e., a scalar function $\varphi(x, y, z)$ exists such that

$$\boldsymbol{E} = - \operatorname{grad} \varphi . \tag{4-1.8}$$

From this we obtain by consideration of (4-1.6) and (4-1.7) the relation

$$\Delta\varphi = 0 , \tag{4-1.9}$$

i.e., the potential of the electric field of a stationary flow satisfies Laplace's differential equation.

We consider further an electrical field generated by stationary charges. Because of the time independence,

$$\operatorname{rot} \boldsymbol{E} = 0 \tag{4-1.10}$$

also follows here, i.e., the field is a potential field, hence

$$\boldsymbol{E} = - \operatorname{grad} \varphi . \tag{4-1.8}$$

Now let $\rho(x, y, z)$ be a spatial charge density in a medium whose dielectric constant ε is equal to one. Then, according to a known law of electrodynamics,

$$\int_S\!\!\int E_n \, dS = 4\pi \sum e_i = 4\pi \int\!\!\int_T\!\!\int \rho \, d\tau , \tag{4-1.11}$$

where T is the region of space considered, S is the boundary and $\sum e_i$ is the sum of all the charges in the interior of T. By Green's theorem

$$\int_S\!\!\int E_n \, dS = \int\!\!\int_T\!\!\int \operatorname{div} \boldsymbol{E} \, d\tau \tag{4-1.12}$$

we obtain

[77] From the second Maxwell equation $(\mu/c)\boldsymbol{H} = - \operatorname{rot} \boldsymbol{E}$, it follows that $\operatorname{rot} \boldsymbol{E} = 0$.

$$\operatorname{div} \boldsymbol{E} = 4\pi\rho \, .$$

If we substitute the expression (4-1.8) for $\boldsymbol{E}$, it follows that

$$\Delta\varphi = -\,4\pi\rho \, , \tag{4-1.13}$$

i.e., the electrostatic potential φ satisfies the Poisson differential equation. If, however, no spatial charges exist ($\rho = 0$), then φ satisfies the Laplace equation

$$\Delta\varphi = 0 \, .$$

The basic boundary-value problems for the processes considered correspond to the three types given above. We shall not consider here other boundary-value problems which also are important for the description of definite physical processes. One of these problems is discussed in Section 4–7.

3. Orthogonal transformation of the Laplace differential expression in curvilinear coordinates

In our further investigations, we shall consider a new orthogonal curvilinear coordinate system defined by the unique reversible and continuous differentiable transformation

$$x = \varphi_1(q_1, q_2, q_3), \quad y = \varphi_2(q_1, q_2, q_3), \quad z = \varphi_3(q_1, q_2, q_3) \, , \tag{4-1.14}$$

rather than use the rectilinear coordinates x, y, z. The new orthogonal curvilinear coordinate system is denoted by

$$q_1 = f_1(x, y, z), \quad q_2 = f_2(x, y, z), \quad q_3 = f_3(x, y, z) \, . \tag{4-1.15}$$

If we set $q_1 = C_1$, $q_2 = C_2$, $q_3 = C_3$, where C_1, C_2, C_3 are constants, we obtain the three families of coordinate surfaces

$$f_1(x, y, z) = C_1 \, , \qquad f_2(x, y, z) = C_2$$

and

$$f_3(x, y, z) = C_3 \, . \tag{4-1.16}$$

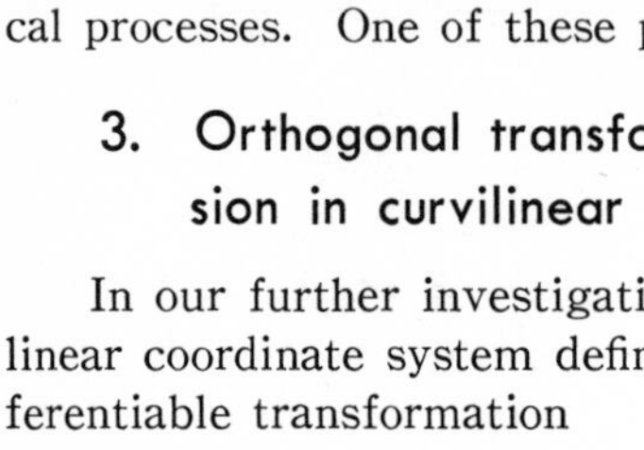

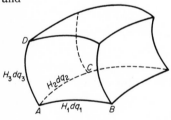

FIG. 44.

Now we consider an element of volume in the new coordinates q_1, q_2, q_3, which are bounded by three pairs of these coordinate surfaces (Figure 44). Hence $q_2 =$ const., $q_3 =$ const. along AB, $q_1 =$ const., $q_2 =$ const. along AD, and $q_1 =$ const., $q_3 =$ const. along AC. The direction cosines of the tangents at the edges AB,· AD, and AC are then proportional to

$$\frac{\partial\varphi_1}{\partial q_1}, \quad \frac{\partial\varphi_2}{\partial q_1}, \quad \frac{\partial\varphi_3}{\partial q_1},$$

$$\frac{\partial\varphi_1}{\partial q_2}, \quad \frac{\partial\varphi_2}{\partial q_2}, \quad \frac{\partial\varphi_3}{\partial q_2},$$

$$\frac{\partial\varphi_1}{\partial q_3}, \quad \frac{\partial\varphi_2}{\partial q_3}, \quad \frac{\partial\varphi_3}{\partial q_3}.$$

Therefore, the orthogonality conditions for the edges of the elements of the volume can be written in the form

$$\frac{\partial \varphi_1}{\partial q_i}\frac{\partial \varphi_1}{\partial q_k} + \frac{\partial \varphi_2}{\partial q_i}\frac{\partial \varphi_2}{\partial q_k} + \frac{\partial \varphi_3}{\partial q_i}\frac{\partial \varphi_3}{\partial q_k} = 0\,, \qquad i \neq k\,. \tag{4-1.17}$$

The line element of a curve in the new coordinates is given by

$$\begin{aligned} ds^2 = dx^2 + dy^2 + dz^2 &= \left(\frac{\partial \varphi_1}{\partial q_1}dq_1 + \frac{\partial \varphi_1}{\partial q_2}dq_2 + \frac{\partial \varphi_1}{\partial q_3}dq_3\right)^2 \\ &+ \left(\frac{\partial \varphi_2}{\partial q_1}dq_1 + \frac{\partial \varphi_2}{\partial q_2}dq_2 + \frac{\partial \varphi_2}{\partial q_3}dq_3\right)^2 \\ &+ \left(\frac{\partial \varphi_3}{\partial q_1}dq_1 + \frac{\partial \varphi_3}{\partial q_2}dq_2 + \frac{\partial \varphi_3}{\partial q_3}dq_3\right)^2. \end{aligned} \tag{4-1.18}$$

If we expand the parentheses and use the orthogonality conditions (4-1.17), we obtain

$$ds^2 = H_1^2 dq_1^2 + H_2^2 dq_2^2 + H_3^2 dq_3^2\,, \tag{4-1.19}$$

where

$$\left.\begin{aligned} H_1^2 &= \left(\frac{\partial \varphi_1}{\partial q_1}\right)^2 + \left(\frac{\partial \varphi_2}{\partial q_1}\right)^2 + \left(\frac{\partial \varphi_3}{\partial q_1}\right)^2 \\ H_2^2 &= \left(\frac{\partial \varphi_1}{\partial q_2}\right)^2 + \left(\frac{\partial \varphi_2}{\partial q_2}\right)^2 + \left(\frac{\partial \varphi_3}{\partial q_2}\right)^2 \\ H_3^2 &= \left(\frac{\partial \varphi_1}{\partial q_3}\right)^2 + \left(\frac{\partial \varphi_2}{\partial q_3}\right)^2 + \left(\frac{\partial \varphi_3}{\partial q_3}\right)^2. \end{aligned}\right\} \tag{4-1.20}$$

Only one coordinate changes along each edge of the element of volume. The lengths of these edges are therefore given according to (4-1.19)

$$ds_1 = H_1 dq_1\,, \qquad ds_2 = H_2 dq_2\,, \qquad ds_3 = H_3 dq_3\,. \tag{4-1.21}$$

so that a volume element equals

$$dv = ds_1 ds_2 ds_3 = H_1 H_2 H_3 \qquad dq_1 dq_2 dq_3\,. \tag{4-1.22}$$

Given a vector field $\boldsymbol{A}(x, y, z)$, then by a known formula of vector analysis

$$\operatorname{div} \boldsymbol{A} = \lim_{v_M \to 0} \frac{\iint_S A_n dS}{v_M}\,, \tag{4-1.23}$$

where S is the boundary of a spatial region v_M which contains the point M, and A_n is the component of the vector $\boldsymbol{A}$ in the direction of the exterior normal. When we apply this formula to the element of volume dv represented in Figure 44, we can calculate the divergence of the field vector $\boldsymbol{A}$.

Next, the difference of the flux through two opposite boundary surfaces, for example, through the left and right, by use of the mean-value theorem, can be written in the form

$$Q_1 = A_1 ds_2 ds_3 |_{q_1+dq_1} - A_1 ds_2 ds_3 |_{q_1}\,.$$

Now from (4-1.21) we obtain

$$Q_1 = [H_2H_3A_1|_{q_1+dq_1} - H_2H_3A_1|_{q_1}]dq_2dq_3 = \frac{\partial}{\partial q_1}(H_2H_3A_1)dq_1dq_2dq_3 \,. \tag{4-1.24}$$

In a similar way, we find for the other pairs of bounding surfaces the net flux:

$$Q_2 = \frac{\partial}{\partial q_2}(H_3H_1A_2)dq_1dq_2dq_3 \tag{4-1.25}$$

$$Q_3 = \frac{\partial}{\partial q_3}(H_1H_2A_3)dq_1dq_2dq_3 \,. \tag{4-1.26}$$

Now if we substitute in formula (4-1.23) the value

$$\int_S\!\!\int A_n dS = Q_1 + Q_2 + Q_3$$

and use (4-1.22), we obtain for the divergence, in the orthogonal curvilinear coordinates, the expression

$$\operatorname{div} \boldsymbol{A} = \frac{1}{H_1H_2H_3}\left[\frac{\partial}{\partial q_1}(H_2H_3A_1) + \frac{\partial}{\partial q_2}(H_3H_1A_2) + \frac{\partial}{\partial q_3}(H_1H_2A_3)\right]. \tag{4-1.27}$$

If we assume that $\boldsymbol{A}$ has a potential, i.e.,

$$\boldsymbol{A} = \operatorname{grad} u \,, \tag{4-1.28}$$

then

$$A_1 = \frac{\partial u}{\partial s_1} = \frac{1}{H_1}\frac{\partial u}{\partial q_1}, \qquad A_2 = \frac{1}{H_2}\frac{\partial u}{\partial q_2}, \qquad A_3 = \frac{1}{H_3}\frac{\partial u}{\partial q_3}. \tag{4-1.29}$$

If these expressions for A_1, A_2, and A_3 are substituted in (4-1.27), then Laplace's differential equation becomes

$$\begin{aligned} \Delta u &= \operatorname{div} \operatorname{grad} u \\ &= \frac{1}{H_1H_2H_3}\left[\frac{\partial}{\partial q_1}\left(\frac{H_2H_3}{H_1}\frac{\partial u}{\partial q_1}\right) + \frac{\partial}{\partial q_2}\left(\frac{H_3H_1}{H_2}\frac{\partial u}{\partial q_2}\right) + \frac{\partial}{\partial q_3}\left(\frac{H_1H_2}{H_3}\frac{\partial u}{\partial q_3}\right)\right]. \end{aligned} \tag{4-1.30}$$

Laplace's differential equation $\Delta u = 0$ therefore has the form

$$\Delta u = \frac{1}{H_1H_2H_3}\left\{\frac{\partial}{\partial q_1}\left(\frac{H_2H_3}{H_1}\frac{\partial u}{\partial q_1}\right) + \frac{\partial}{\partial q_2}\left(\frac{H_3H_1}{H_2}\frac{\partial u}{\partial q_2}\right) + \frac{\partial}{\partial q_3}\left(\frac{H_1H_2}{H_3}\frac{\partial u}{\partial q_3}\right)\right\} = 0 \tag{4-1.31}$$

in the orthogonal curvilinear coordinates q_1, q_2, q_3.

We shall now consider two special cases.

1. *Spherical coordinates.* In this case $q_1 = r$, $q_2 = \theta$, and $q_3 = \varphi$. The transformation formula (4-1.15) therefore assumes the form

$$x = r\sin\theta\cos\varphi\,, \qquad y = r\sin\theta\sin\varphi\,, \qquad z = r\cos\theta\,.$$

The line element is defined by

$$ds^2 = (\sin\theta\cos\varphi\, dr + r\cos\theta\cos\varphi\, d\theta - r\sin\theta\sin\varphi\, d\varphi)^2$$
$$+ (\sin\theta\sin\varphi\, dr + r\cos\theta\sin\varphi\, d\theta + r\sin\theta\cos\varphi\, d\varphi)^2 + (\cos\theta\, dr - r\sin\theta\, d\theta)^2$$

where, after simplification

$$ds^2 = dr^2 + r^2 d\theta^2 + r^2\sin^2\theta\, d\varphi^2 ,$$

i.e.,

$$H_1 = 1 , \qquad H_2 = r , \qquad H_3 = r\sin\theta .$$

By substituting these values for H_1, H_2, H_3 in (4-1.31) we arrive at Laplace's differential equation in spherical coordinates:

$$\frac{1}{r^2\sin\theta}\left[\frac{\partial}{\partial r}\left(r^2\sin\theta\frac{\partial u}{\partial r}\right) + \frac{\partial}{\partial\theta}\left(\sin\theta\frac{\partial u}{\partial\theta}\right) + \frac{\partial u}{\partial\varphi}\left(\frac{1}{\sin\theta}\frac{\partial u}{\partial\varphi}\right)\right] = 0$$

or finally

$$\frac{1}{r^2}\frac{\partial}{\partial r}\left(r^2\frac{\partial u}{\partial r}\right) + \frac{1}{r^2\sin\theta}\frac{\partial}{\partial\theta}\left(\sin\theta\frac{\partial u}{\partial\theta}\right) + \frac{1}{r^2\sin^2\theta}\frac{\partial^2 u}{\partial\varphi^2} = 0 . \qquad (4\text{-}1.32)$$

2. *Cylindrical coordinates.* Here $q_1 = \rho$, $q_2 = \varphi$, $q_3 = z$;

$$x = \rho\cos\varphi , \qquad y = \rho\sin\varphi , \qquad z = z ;$$

thus

$$H_1 = 1 , \qquad H_2 = \rho , \qquad H_3 = 1 .$$

Therefore Laplace's differential equation in cylindrical coordinates has the form

$$\frac{1}{\rho}\frac{\partial}{\partial\rho}\left(\rho\frac{\partial u}{\partial\rho}\right) + \frac{1}{\rho^2}\frac{\partial^2 u}{\partial\varphi^2} + \frac{\partial^2 u}{\partial z^2} = 0 . \qquad (4\text{-}1.33)$$

In particular, if the sought function u does not depend on z as in plane potential flow, then Eq. (4-1.33) simplifies to

$$\frac{1}{\rho}\frac{\partial}{\partial\rho}\left(\rho\frac{\partial u}{\partial\rho}\right) + \frac{1}{\rho^2}\frac{\partial^2 u}{\partial\varphi^2} = 0 . \qquad (4\text{-}1.34)$$

4. Some particular solutions of Laplace's differential equation

Of great interest are the spherically and cylindrically symmetric solutions of Laplace's differential equation, that is, those which depend only on the variables r and ρ, respectively.

The spherically symmetric solutions $u = U(r)$ of Laplace's equation are defined by the ordinary differential equation

$$\frac{d}{dr}\left(r^2\frac{dU}{dr}\right) = 0 ,$$

whose general integral is given by

$$U = \frac{C_1}{r} + C_2 ,$$

where C_1 and C_2 are arbitrary constants. For example, if we set $C_1 = 1$, $C_2 = 0$, then we find the function

$$U_0 = \frac{1}{r}, \tag{4-1.35}$$

which is often denoted as the fundamental solution of the three-dimensional Laplace differential equation.

In a similar way, by setting

$$u = U(\rho)$$

and by use of (4-1.33) or (4-1.34), we find the general form of the cylindrically or circularly symmetric solutions (in the case of two-dimensional problems):

$$U(\rho) = C_1 \ln \rho + C_2 .$$

For $C_1 = -1$ and $C_2 = 0$ we obtain the function

$$U_0 = \ln \frac{1}{\rho}, \tag{4-1.36}$$

which is also often called the fundamental solution of the two-dimensional Laplace differential equation.

The function $U_0 = 1/r$ satisfies the equation $\Delta u = 0$ throughout with the exception of the point $r = 0$, where it becomes infinite. To within a constant factor it coincides with the potential due to a charge e placed at the origin of the coordinates; the potential of this field is actually

$$u = \frac{e}{r}.$$

The function $\ln 1/\rho$ satisfies Laplace's differential equation throughout with the exception of the point $\rho = 0$, at which it becomes logarithmically infinite. To within a factor it agrees with the potential of an infinitely long wire (see Section 4-5 § 2), whose potential is given by

$$u = 2e_1 \ln \frac{1}{\rho}$$

where e_1 is the charge density per unit of length. This function plays an important role in the theory of harmonic functions.

5. Harmonic and analytic functions of a complex variable

A very general method for the solution of two-dimensional problems for Laplace's differential equation results if one employs the theory of functions of a complex variable.

Let

$$w = f(z) = u(x, y) + iv(x, y)$$

be a function of the complex variable $z = x + iy$; let u and v be real functions of the variables x and y. Of particular interest are the so-called analytic functions for which the derivative

$$\frac{dw}{dz} = \lim_{\Delta z \to 0} \frac{\Delta w}{\Delta z} = \lim_{\Delta z \to 0} \frac{f(z + \Delta z) - f(z)}{\Delta z}$$

exists. The increments $\Delta z = \Delta x + i\Delta y$ can approach zero in an arbitrary manner. In general, each of the paths by which Δz approaches zero corresponds to a definite limit value. If $w = f(z)$ is an analytic function, the limit value $\lim_{\Delta z \to 0} \Delta f / \Delta z = f'(z)$ is independent of the choice of path. In this case, the limit value is unique.

A function $w = f(z)$ is analytic if the partial derivatives u_x, u_y, v_x, v_y exist and are continuous, and provided, moreover, that the real part $u(x, y)$ and the imaginary part $v(x, y)$ satisfy the Cauchy-Riemann differential equations

$$\begin{aligned} u_x &= v_y \\ u_y &= -v_x . \end{aligned} \tag{4-1.37}$$

These conditions are necessary and sufficient. We can derive them as follows:

Let $w = u + iv = f(z)$ be an analytic function. If we calculate the derivatives

$$\begin{aligned} w_x &= u_x + iv_x = \frac{\partial w(z)}{\partial z} z_x = \frac{dw}{dz} \\ w_y &= u_y + iv_y = \frac{\partial w(z)}{\partial z} z_y = i \frac{dw}{dz} \end{aligned}$$

and require that the value of dw/dz coincide with both expressions, then it follows that

$$u_x + iv_x = v_y - iu_y = \frac{dw}{dz} ,$$

from which the Cauchy-Riemann differential equations result directly. We shall not prove here that this is also sufficient.

In the theory of functions it is shown that every analytic function defined in a region G of the z plane has derivatives of all orders and can be developed in a power series. In particular, for each such function, the real part $u(x, y)$ and the imaginary part $v(x, y)$ are twice continuously differentiable with respect to x and y.

By differentiation of the first expression of (4-1.37) with respect to x and the second with respect to y we obtain

$$u_{xx} + u_{yy} = 0 \qquad \text{or} \qquad \Delta_2 u = 0 .$$

Correspondingly, by reversing the scheme of differentiation we obtain

$$v_{xx} + v_{yy} = 0 \qquad \text{or} \qquad \Delta_2 v = 0 .$$

The real and imaginary parts of an analytic function therefore satisfy Laplace's differential equation. Two functions u and v which satisfy the

Cauchy-Riemann differential equations are said to be harmonic conjugate functions of each other.

We consider now the transformation

$$\left.\begin{array}{ll} x = x(u, v) & u = u(x, y) \\ y = y(u, v) & v = v(x, y) . \end{array}\right\} \tag{4-1.38}$$

This maps a region G of the x, y plane onto a region G' of the u, v plane such that each point of G uniquely corresponds to a point of G', and conversely.

Now let

$$U = U(x, y)$$

be a real, twice continuously differentiable function which is defined in the interior of the region G.

We shall investigate how the Laplace operator behaves under the transformation $U = U[x(u, v), y(u, v)] = \tilde{U}(u, v)$. To this end we first calculate the derivatives

$$U_x = \tilde{U}_u u_x + \tilde{U}_v v_x , \qquad U_y = \tilde{U}_u u_y + \tilde{U}_v v_y$$
$$U_{xx} = \tilde{U}_{uu} u_x^2 + \tilde{U}_{vv} v_x^2 + 2\tilde{U}_{uv} u_x v_x + \tilde{U}_u u_{xx} + \tilde{U}_v v_{xx}$$
$$U_{yy} = \tilde{U}_{uu} u_y^2 + \tilde{U}_{vv} v_y^2 + 2\tilde{U}_{uv} u_y v_y + \tilde{U}_u u_{yy} + \tilde{U}_v v_{yy}$$

from which we obtain

$$\begin{aligned} U_{xx} + U_{yy} = \tilde{U}_{uu}(u_x^2 + u_y^2) + \tilde{U}_{vv}(v_x^2 + v_y^2) \\ + 2\tilde{U}_{uv}(u_x v_x + u_y v_y) + \tilde{U}_u(u_{xx} + u_{yy}) + \tilde{U}_v(v_{xx} + v_{yy}) . \end{aligned} \tag{4-1.39}$$

Now if u and v are harmonic functions conjugate to each other, then the transformation (4-1.38) is equivalent to those transformations which are brought about by the analytic function

$$w = f(z) = u + iv , \qquad z = x + iy . \tag{4-1.40}$$

In this case, then, because of the Cauchy-Riemann differential equations for u and v, the expression

$$u_x^2 + u_y^2 = u_x^2 + v_x^2 = v_y^2 + v_x^2 = |f'(z)|^2$$
$$u_x v_x + u_y v_y = 0$$

must be satisfied. Therefore from (4-1.39) we obtain

$$U_{xx} + U_{yy} = (U_{uu} + U_{vv}) |f'(z)|^2 \tag{4-1.41}$$

or

$$\Delta_{u,v} \tilde{U} = \frac{1}{|f'(z)|^2} \Delta_{x,y} U . \tag{4-1.41$'$}$$

By the transformation (4-1.40), the harmonic function $U(x, y)$ in the region G is transformed into the harmonic function $U = U(u, v)$ in the region G' provided $|f'(z)|^2 \neq 0$.

6. Transformation by reciprocal radii

In the investigation of the properties of harmonic functions one often uses the transformation of reciprocal radii. By a transformation of reciprocal radii of a sphere of radius a we mean a transformation with the following properties:

1. To each point M there corresponds a point M' which lies on the same straight line drawn from the origin of the coordinates through the point M.
2. The radius vector r' of the point M' is related to the radius vector r of the point M by the expression

$$r'r = a^2 \qquad \text{or} \qquad r' = \frac{a^2}{r}\,. \tag{4-1.42}$$

In the following, we shall assume $a = 1$, which is always possible by a suitable choice of the unit of length.

We shall now show that a harmonic function $u(\rho, \varphi)$ of two independent variables is transformed by a transformation of reciprocal radii into a harmonic function

$$v(\rho', \varphi) = u(\rho, \varphi) \qquad \text{with} \qquad \rho = \frac{1}{\rho'}\,. \tag{4-1.43}$$

The function $u(\rho, \varphi)$ and, therefore, the function $v(1/\rho, \varphi)$, considered as functions of the variables ρ and φ, satisfy the differential equation

$$\rho^2 \Delta_{\rho,\varphi} u = \rho \frac{\partial}{\partial \rho}\left(\rho \frac{\partial u}{\partial \rho}\right) + \frac{\partial^2 u}{\partial \varphi^2} = 0$$

and

$$\rho^2 \Delta_{\rho,\varphi} v = \rho \frac{\partial}{\partial \rho}\left(\rho \frac{\partial v}{\partial \rho}\right) + \frac{\partial^2 v}{\partial \varphi^2} = 0\,.$$

From this, by passage to the variables ρ' and φ, it follows that

$$\rho \frac{\partial v}{\partial \rho} = \rho \frac{\partial v}{\partial \rho'} \cdot \frac{\partial \rho'}{\partial \rho} = -\rho' \frac{\partial v}{\partial \rho'}\,,$$

i.e., $v(\rho', \varphi)$ satisfies the equation $\Delta_{\rho',\varphi} v = 0$, since

$$\rho'^2 \Delta_{\rho',\varphi} v = \rho' \frac{\partial}{\partial \rho'}\left(\rho' \frac{\partial v}{\partial \rho'}\right) + \frac{\partial^2 v}{\partial \varphi^2} = 0\,.$$

We proceed now to functions of three variables and show that

$$v(r', \theta, \varphi) = r u(r, \theta, \varphi)\left(r = \frac{1}{r'}\right) \tag{4-1.44}$$

satisfies Laplace's differential equation $\Delta_{r',\theta,\varphi} v = 0$. If $u(r, \theta, \varphi)$ is a harmonic function of the variables r, θ, φ, then $\Delta_{r,\theta,\varphi} u = 0$ is valid.

The transformation (4-1.44) is called the Kelvin transformation.

Next, we can show by differentiation that the first summand of Laplace's differential expression assumes the form

$$\frac{1}{r^2}\frac{\partial}{\partial r}\left(r^2\frac{\partial u}{\partial r}\right) = \frac{\partial^2 u}{\partial r^2} + \frac{2}{r}\frac{\partial u}{\partial r} = \frac{1}{r}\frac{\partial^2(ru)}{\partial r^2}. \tag{4-1.45}$$

Consequently,

$$r\Delta_{r,\theta,\varphi}u = \frac{\partial^2(ru)}{\partial r^2} + \frac{1}{r}\left[\frac{1}{\sin\theta}\frac{\partial}{\partial\theta}\left(\sin\theta\frac{\partial u}{\partial\theta}\right) + \frac{1}{\sin^2\theta}\frac{\partial^2 u}{\partial\varphi^2}\right] = 0$$

or

$$\frac{\partial^2 v}{\partial r^2} + \frac{1}{r^2}\left[\frac{1}{\sin\theta}\frac{\partial}{\partial\theta}\left(\sin\theta\frac{\partial v}{\partial\theta}\right) + \frac{1}{\sin^2\theta}\frac{\partial^2 v}{\partial\varphi^2}\right] = 0\,.$$

Now, however,

$$\frac{\partial v}{\partial r} = \frac{\partial v}{\partial r'}\cdot\frac{\partial r'}{\partial r} = -r'^2\frac{\partial v}{\partial r'},$$

so that v satisfies Laplace's differential equation $\Delta_{r',\theta,\varphi}v = 0$ since

$$r'^2\frac{\partial}{\partial r'}\left(r'^2\frac{\partial v}{\partial r'}\right) + r'^2\left[\frac{1}{\sin\theta}\frac{\partial}{\partial\theta}\left(\sin\theta\frac{\partial v}{\partial\theta}\right) + \frac{1}{\sin^2\theta}\frac{\partial^2 v}{\partial\varphi^2}\right] = 0$$

or

$$r'^4\Delta_{r',\theta,\varphi}v = 0\,.$$

4-2. GENERAL PROPERTIES OF HARMONIC FUNCTIONS

In the present discussion we give a description of the integral of harmonic functions which will prove to be an important aid in the investigation of its general properties. One of the important consequences of this integral representation is the principle of the maximum which we shall use many times—for example, for the proof of uniqueness, as well as for the solution of boundary-value problems. Further in the subsequent paragraphs the interior and exterior boundary-value problems for Laplace's differential equation will be formulated. Finally we shall prove the uniqueness theorem and the continuous dependence of the solutions on the auxiliary conditions (the stability).

1. Green's integral formulas; integral representation of the solution

In the treatment of elliptic differential equations we shall often use Green's formula, which can be shown to be a direct consequence of the formula of Ostrogradski.

In the simplest case this formula has the form

$$\iiint_T \frac{\partial R}{\partial z}dx\,dy\,dz = \iint_\Sigma R\cos\gamma\,d\sigma\,, \tag{4-2.1}$$

where T is a definite region of space bounded by a sufficiently smooth surface Σ; furthermore, $R(x, y, z)$ is an arbitrary function which is continuous in $T + \Sigma$ and which in T possesses continuous partial derivatives; γ is the angle between the z axis and the exterior normal to the surface Σ. The correctness of this formula is obtained by integration with respect to z. Ordinarily we write the Ostrogradski formula† in the form

$$\iint_T\int\left(\frac{\partial P}{\partial x}+\frac{\partial Q}{\partial y}+\frac{\partial R}{\partial z}\right)d\tau=\int_\Sigma\int\{P\cos\alpha+Q\cos\beta+R\cos\gamma\}\,d\sigma\,, \tag{4-2.2}$$

where $d\tau = dx\,dy\,dz$ is the element of volume, and $\alpha = (\widehat{nx})$, $\beta = (\widehat{ny})$, $\gamma = (\widehat{nz})$ are the angles between the exterior normal n to the surface Σ and the coordinate axes; P, Q, and R are arbitrary differentiable functions.[78]

If we denote P, Q, R as components of a vector $\boldsymbol{A} = P\boldsymbol{i} + Q\boldsymbol{j} + R\boldsymbol{k}$, then the Ostrogradski formula can also be written as follows

$$\iint_T\int \operatorname{div}\boldsymbol{A}\,d\tau=\int_\Sigma\int A_n\,d\sigma\,, \tag{4-2.2'}$$

where

$$\operatorname{div}\boldsymbol{A}=\frac{\partial P}{\partial x}+\frac{\partial Q}{\partial y}+\frac{\partial R}{\partial z}\,,$$

and

$$A_n = P\cos\alpha + Q\cos\beta + R\cos\gamma$$

denotes the component of the vector $\boldsymbol{A}$ in the direction of the exterior normal.

We proceed now to the derivation of Green's formulas.

Let $u = u(x, y, z)$ and $v = v(x, y, z)$ be two functions which including their first derivatives are continuous in $T + \Sigma$ and which in T possess continuous second derivatives.

If we set

$$P=u\frac{\partial v}{\partial x}\,,\qquad Q=u\frac{\partial v}{\partial y}\,,\qquad R=u\frac{\partial v}{\partial z}\,,$$

then by the use of the Ostrogradski formula we obtain the so-called first Green's formula

$$\iint_T\int u\Delta v\,d\tau=\int_\Sigma\int u\frac{\partial v}{\partial n}\,d\sigma-\iint_T\int\left(\frac{\partial u}{\partial x}\frac{\partial v}{\partial x}+\frac{\partial u}{\partial y}\frac{\partial v}{\partial y}+\frac{\partial u}{\partial z}\frac{\partial v}{\partial z}\right)d\tau\,, \tag{4-2.3}$$

where $\Delta = \partial^2/\partial x^2 + \partial^2/\partial y^2 + \partial^2/\partial z^2$ is the Laplace operator, and

$$\frac{\partial}{\partial n}=\cos\alpha\frac{\partial}{\partial x}+\cos\beta\frac{\partial}{\partial y}+\cos\gamma\frac{\partial}{\partial z}$$

is the derivative in the direction of the exterior normal.

By use of the relation

78 In the following, it is always assumed that the Ostrogradski formula is applicable in the region considered.

† Editor's note: In the English literature the formulas of Ostrogradski and Green are identical.

$$\operatorname{grad} u \operatorname{grad} v = \nabla u \cdot \nabla v = \frac{\partial u}{\partial x}\frac{\partial v}{\partial x} + \frac{\partial u}{\partial y}\frac{\partial v}{\partial y} + \frac{\partial u}{\partial z}\frac{\partial v}{\partial z},$$

Green's formula can also be represented in the form

$$\iiint_T u\Delta v\, d\tau = -\iiint_T \nabla u \cdot \nabla v\, d\tau + \iint_\Sigma u\frac{\partial v}{\partial n}\, d\sigma. \tag{4-2.3'}$$

By interchanging the roles of u and v there follows

$$\iiint_T v\Delta u\, d\tau = -\iiint_T \nabla v \cdot \nabla u\, d\tau + \iint_\Sigma v\frac{\partial u}{\partial n}\, d\sigma. \tag{4-2.4}$$

If now we subtract the identity (4-2.4) from (4-2.3′), we obtain the second Green's formula

$$\iiint_T (u\Delta v - v\Delta u)\, d\tau = \iint_\Sigma \left(u\frac{\partial v}{\partial n} - v\frac{\partial u}{\partial n}\right) d\sigma. \tag{4-2.5}$$

The region T can be bounded by several surfaces. Green's formulas also remain applicable in this case in which the surface integral is extended over all surfaces which bound the region T.

As we have already seen (Section 4-1 § 4), the function $U_0(M) = 1/r$, where $r = \sqrt{(x-x_0)^2 + (y-y_0)^2 + (z-z_0)^2}$ is the distance between the points $M(x, y, z)$ and $M_0(x_0, y_0, z_0)$, satisfies Laplace's differential equation.

Now let $u(M)$ be a harmonic function which including its first derivatives is continuous in $T + \Sigma$ and which in T possesses a second derivative. Further, let us consider the function $v = 1/r_{MM_0}$, where M_0 is any interior point of T. Since this function in T possesses a point of discontinuity at $M_0(x_0, y_0, z_0)$ the second Green's formula in T cannot be applied directly to the functions u and v. However, $v = 1/r_{MM_0}$ is bounded in $T - K_\varepsilon$ with the boundary $\Sigma + \Sigma_\varepsilon$, where K_ε is a sphere of radius ε, with center at M_0 and surface Σ_ε (Figure 45).

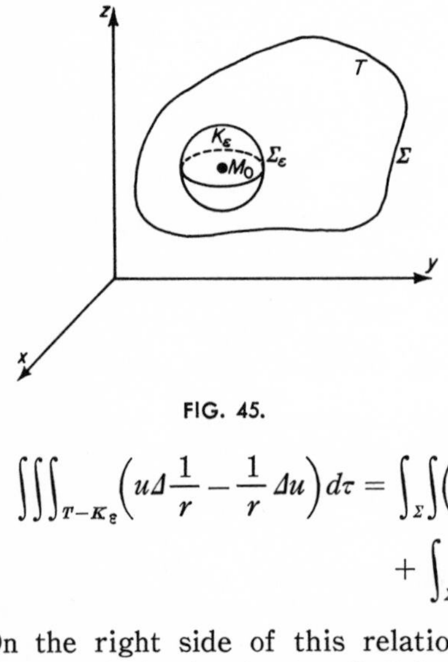

FIG. 45.

Now if we apply the second Green's formula (4-2.5) to the functions u and v in $T - K_\varepsilon$ then we obtain

$$\begin{aligned}\iiint_{T-K_\varepsilon}\left(u\Delta\frac{1}{r} - \frac{1}{r}\Delta u\right) d\tau &= \iint_\Sigma \left(u\frac{\partial}{\partial n}\left(\frac{1}{r}\right) - \frac{1}{r}\frac{\partial u}{\partial n}\right) d\sigma \\ &+ \iint_{\Sigma_\varepsilon} u\frac{\partial}{\partial n}\left(\frac{1}{r}\right) d\sigma - \iint_{\Sigma_\varepsilon} \frac{1}{r}\frac{\partial u}{\partial n}\, d\sigma.\end{aligned} \tag{4-2.6}$$

On the right side of this relation the last two integrals depend only on ε. For the derivative in the direction of the exterior normal to Σ_ε we find

$$\left.\frac{\partial}{\partial n}\left(\frac{1}{r}\right)\right|_{\Sigma_\varepsilon} = -\left.\frac{\partial}{\partial r}\left(\frac{1}{r}\right)\right|_{r=\varepsilon} = \frac{1}{\varepsilon^2}.$$

Therefore,

$$\iint_{\Sigma_\varepsilon} u\frac{\partial}{\partial n}\left(\frac{1}{r}\right)d\sigma = \frac{1}{\varepsilon^2}\iint_{\Sigma_\varepsilon} u\,d\sigma = \frac{1}{\varepsilon^2}\,4\pi\varepsilon^2 u^* = 4\pi u^*\,, \tag{4-2.7}$$

where u^* is a suitable average value of $u(M)$ on Σ_ε. Further, the third integral can be transformed as follows

$$\iint_{\Sigma_\varepsilon}\frac{1}{r}\frac{\partial u}{\partial n}d\sigma = \frac{1}{\varepsilon}\iint_{\Sigma_\varepsilon}\frac{\partial u}{\partial n}d\sigma = \frac{1}{\varepsilon}\,4\pi\varepsilon^2\left(\frac{\partial u}{\partial n}\right)^* = 4\pi\varepsilon\left(\frac{\partial u}{\partial n}\right)^*, \tag{4-2.8}$$

where $(\partial u/\partial n)^*$ is a suitable average value of the normal derivative $\partial u/\partial n$ on Σ_ε. If we substitute the expression (4-2.7) and (4-2.8) into (4-2.6) and note that $\Delta(1/r) = 0$ in $T - K_\varepsilon$, then

$$\iiint_{T-K_\varepsilon}\left(-\frac{1}{r}\right)\Delta u\,d\tau = \iint_{\Sigma}\left[u\frac{\partial}{\partial n}\left(\frac{1}{r}\right) - \frac{1}{r}\frac{\partial u}{\partial n}\right]d\sigma + 4\pi u^* - 4\pi\varepsilon\left(\frac{\partial u}{\partial n}\right)^*. \tag{4-2.9}$$

Now if we let the radius ε approach zero, we obtain:

1. $\lim_{\varepsilon\to 0} u^* = u(M_0)$, since $u(M)$ is a continuous function and u^* is an average value on the sphere of radius ε with center point M_0;

2. $\lim_{\varepsilon\to 0} 4\pi\varepsilon(\partial u/\partial n)^* = 0$, since from the continuity of the first derivatives of $u(M)$ in T, the boundedness of the normal derivative

$$\frac{\partial u}{\partial n} = \frac{\partial u}{\partial x}\cos\alpha + \frac{\partial u}{\partial y}\cos\beta + \frac{\partial u}{\partial z}\cos\gamma$$

in the neighborhood of M_0 follows;

3. according to the definition of an improper integral,

$$\lim_{\varepsilon\to 0}\iiint_{T-K_\varepsilon}\left(-\frac{1}{r}\Delta u\right)d\tau = \iiint_{T}\left(-\frac{1}{r}\Delta u\right)d\tau\,.$$

The passage to the limit $\varepsilon\to 0$ therefore yields the fundamental formula of the theory of harmonic functions:

$$4\pi u(M_0) = -\iint_{\Sigma}\left[u(P)\frac{\partial}{\partial n}\left(\frac{1}{r_{M_0P}}\right) - \frac{1}{r_{M_0P}}\frac{\partial u}{\partial n}\right]d\sigma_P - \iiint_{T}\frac{\Delta u}{r}d\tau\,. \tag{4-2.10}$$

If we apply formula (4-2.10) to a harmonic function $u(M)$, ($\Delta u = 0$), then we obtain

$$u(M) = \frac{1}{4\pi}\iint_{\Sigma}\left[\frac{1}{r_{MP}}\frac{\partial u}{\partial n} - u(P)\frac{\partial}{\partial n}\left(\frac{1}{r_{MP}}\right)\right]d\sigma_P\,. \tag{4-2.11}$$

Therefore, the value of a harmonic function at an arbitrary interior point M can be expressed in terms of its values and its normal derivative on the boundary of the region. Here we assume the continuity of the function u and its first derivatives in the closed region. We shall prove directly that each of the integrals

$$\iint_{\Sigma}\mu(P)\frac{1}{r_{MP}}d\sigma_P \quad\text{and}\quad \iint_{\Sigma}\frac{\partial}{\partial n_P}\left(\frac{1}{r_{MP}}\right)\nu(P)\,d\sigma_P\,, \tag{4-2.12}$$

where μ and ν are continuous functions, represents a harmonic function. That is, since the integrands including their derivatives are continuous throughout with the exception of the boundary Σ, the derivatives of arbitrary order of (4-2.12) can be formed by differentiation under the integral signs. Moreover, since the functions

$$\frac{1}{r_{MP}} \quad \text{and} \quad \frac{\partial}{\partial n_P}\left(\frac{1}{r_{MP}}\right) = \frac{\partial}{\partial \xi}\left(\frac{1}{r}\right)\cos\alpha_P + \frac{\partial}{\partial \eta}\left(\frac{1}{r}\right)\cos\beta_P + \frac{\partial}{\partial \zeta}\left(\frac{1}{r}\right)\cos\gamma_P$$

satisfy Laplace's differential equation with respect to the variable points $M(x, y, z)$, the functions (4-2.12) by the generalized superposition principle (see the lemma on page 63) similarly satisfy Laplace's differential equation with respect to x, y, z.

Hence we arrive at an important conclusion: Every harmonic function, in the interior of the region in which it is harmonic, possesses derivatives of all orders.[79] Further we note that a harmonic function in a region T at each point M_0 in T is analytic (i.e., it can be developed in a power series). This assertion also results from the integral representation (4-2.11).

Corresponding formulas hold also for harmonic functions of two independent variables. Let S be any region in the x, y plane and C its boundary curve. Further let n be the direction of the exterior normal (with respect to S) to this curve. Then if $v = \ln(1/r_{M_0P})$ is introduced where $r_{M_0P} = \sqrt{(x-x_0)^2+(y-y_0)^2}$ is the distance from a point M_0 in the interior of S, then, by similar considerations as above, instead of (4-2.10) we arrive at the expression

$$2\pi u(M_0) = -\int_C\left[u\frac{\partial}{\partial n}\left(\ln\frac{1}{r_{M_0P}}\right) - \ln\frac{1}{r_{M_0P}}\frac{\partial u}{\partial n}\right]ds_P - \int\!\!\int_S \ln\frac{1}{r}\,\Delta u\,dS\,, \qquad (4\text{-}2.12')$$

where M_0 is an arbitrary fixed point in the region S.

For a harmonic function $u(M)$ it follows that

$$u(M_0) = \frac{1}{2\pi}\int_C\left[\ln\frac{1}{r}\frac{\partial u}{\partial n} - u\frac{\partial}{\partial n}\left(\ln\frac{1}{r}\right)\right]ds\,. \qquad (4\text{-}2.12'')$$

2. Some fundamental properties of harmonic functions

Harmonic functions possess the following important properties:

1. If $v(M)$ is a harmonic function in a region T which is bounded by the surface Σ, then

$$\int\!\!\int_S \frac{\partial v}{\partial n}\,d\sigma = 0\,, \qquad (4\text{-}2.13)$$

where S is an arbitrary closed surface which lies entirely in the region T.

If in the first Green's formula (4-2.3) an arbitrary harmonic function v ($\Delta v = 0$) is introduced and $u \equiv 1$ then formula (4-2.13) follows. From (4-2.13) we con-

[79] If for a function u which is harmonic in T the condition that it and its first derivatives are continuous on the boundary Σ is not fulfilled, the theorem still remains valid. By this we mean that each point M is enclosed by a region, including its boundary, lying in the interior of T.

clude that the second boundary-value problem ($\Delta u = 0$ in T, $\partial u/\partial n = f|_\Sigma$) possesses a solution only if

$$\iint_\Sigma f\, d\sigma = 0 .$$

This property of a harmonic function can be interpreted as a condition that no sources exist in the region T.

2. If $u(M)$ is a harmonic function in a region T, and M_0 is a point lying in the interior of T, then

$$u(M_0) = \frac{1}{4\pi a^2}\iint_{\Sigma_a} u\, d\sigma , \tag{4-2.14}$$

where Σ_a is a spherical surface with radius a and center point M_0 which lies entirely in the region T. This property is stated by the average-value theorem, which reads:

Theorem. The value of a harmonic function at any point M_0 is equal to the average value of the function on an arbitrary spherical surface Σ_a with center at M_0, provided Σ_a lies entirely in the region in which $u(M)$ is harmonic.

For the proof of this proposition we apply formula (4-2.11) to a sphere K_a with center M_0 and surface Σ_a:

$$4\pi u(M_0) = -\iint_{\Sigma_a}\left[u\frac{\partial}{\partial n}\left(\frac{1}{r}\right) - \frac{1}{r}\frac{\partial u}{\partial n}\right] d\sigma .$$

If we bear in mind that

$$\frac{1}{r} = \frac{1}{a} \quad \text{on } \Sigma_a \qquad \text{and} \qquad \iint_{\Sigma_a}\frac{\partial u}{\partial n}\, d\sigma = 0$$

as well as

$$\frac{\partial}{\partial n}\left(\frac{1}{r}\right)\Big|_{\Sigma_a} = \frac{\partial}{\partial r}\left(\frac{1}{r}\right)\Big|_{r=a} = -\frac{1}{a^2}$$

(the direction of the exterior normal to Σ_a coincides with the direction of increasing radius) then we obtain

$$u(M_0) = \frac{1}{4\pi a^2}\iint_{\Sigma_a} u\, d\sigma ,$$

which was to be proved.[80]

For two independent variables the analogous theorem is valid:

[80] For the proof of this theorem we have used Eq. (4-2.13). This, however, assumes that the derivatives also exist on the spherical surface. If a function $u(M)$, which is continuous in the closed region $T + \Sigma$, satisfies the equation $\Delta u = 0$ only for interior points of T, then this conclusion would not be correct for a sphere Σ_{a_0}, which borders the boundary Σ. However, if the theorem for each $a < a_0$ is true, then as $a \to a_0$ we obtain

$$u(M_0) = \frac{1}{4\pi a_0^2}\iint_{\Sigma_{a_0}} u(M)\, d\sigma .$$

$$u(M_0) = \frac{1}{2\pi a} \int_{C_a} u\, ds\,, \tag{4-2.15}$$

where C_a is a circle of radius a about the center M_0.

3. If a function $u(M)$ is continuous and defined in a closed region $T + \Sigma$ and satisfies Laplace's differential equation $\Delta u = 0$ in the interior of T, then it assumes its maximum and its minimum on the boundary Σ (principle of the maximum).

If the function $u(M)$ were to assume its maximum at an interior point M_0 in T, then $u_0 = u(M_0) \geqq u(M)$ for each M in T.

Now enclose the point M_0 with a sphere of radius ρ whose surface Σ_ρ lies entirely within T. Since by hypothesis $u(M_0)$ is the maximum of the function $u(M)$ in $T + \Sigma$, then $u\,|_\Sigma \leqq u(M_0)$. Therefore, by use of the average-value formula (4-2.14), provided that everywhere under the integral signs we replace $u(M)$ by $u(M_0)$, we obtain

$$u(M_0) = \frac{1}{4\pi\rho^2} \int_{\Sigma_\rho}\!\!\int u(M)\, d\sigma_M \leqq \frac{1}{4\pi\rho^2} \int_{\Sigma_\rho}\!\!\int u(M_0)\, d\sigma = u(M_0)\,. \tag{4-2.16}$$

Now if we assume that at least one point M exists on Σ_ρ such that the inequality $u(M) < u(M_0)$ is valid, then obviously in the last formula the inequality sign must hold, which in turn implies a contradiction; consequently on the entire surface Σ_ρ we must have $u(M) \equiv u(M_0)$.

If ρ_0^m is the minimal distance of the point M_0 from the boundary Σ_ρ, then $u(M) \equiv u(M_0)$ is also valid for points belonging to $\Sigma_{\rho_0^m}$. Hence, because of continuity, it also follows that at those points M^* which belong to the intersection of $\Sigma_{\rho_0^m}$ and Σ the relation $u(M^*) = u(M_0)$ is valid. Therefore our theorem is proved; and the last conclusion shows that the maximum $u(M_0)$ is assumed at least at one point on the boundary.

It is easily seen that $u(M) \equiv u(M_0)$ must be valid in the entire region when the region T is connected and if at least at one interior point M_0 the maximum is assumed.

To demonstrate the above, we select another arbitrary point $M^{(0)}$ in T and connect it with M_0 by the polygonal line L (Figure 46), whose length is designated by l. Let M_1 be the last current point of L through the spherical surface $\Sigma_{\rho_0^m}$. At this point, then, $u(M_1) = u(M_0)$ is still valid. Now we enclose this point by the spherical surface $\Sigma_{\rho_1^m}$, where ρ_1^m is the minimal distance of the point M_1 from the boundary. We obtain another such point M_2 as the last current point of L through the spherical surface $\Sigma_{\rho_1^m}$. By this procedure, we arrive after a finite number of steps (the number p of necessary steps is certainly not larger than $1/\rho^{(m)}$ if $\rho^{(m)}$ denotes the minimum distance between L and Σ) at a

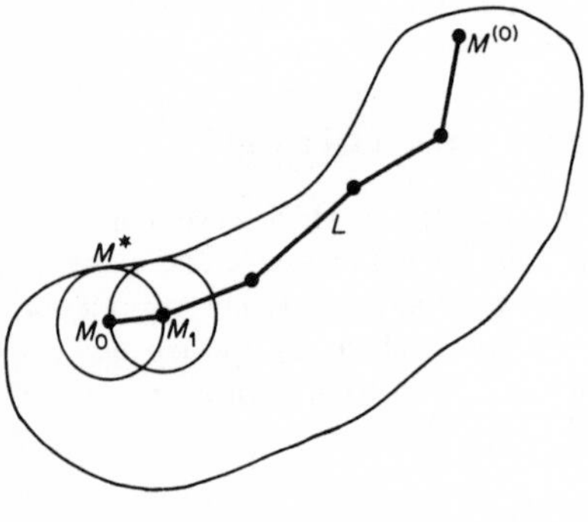

FIG. 46.

spherical surface which contains the point $M^{(0)}$. From this it follows that $u(M^{(0)}) = u(M_0)$. Because of the arbitrary choice of the point $M^{(0)}$ and the continuity of $u(M)$ in the closed region $T + \Sigma$ we conclude that $u(M) \equiv u(M_0)$ holds everywhere (including the boundary). Of all harmonic functions, therefore, only the constant functions can assume their maximum at an interior point.

The corresponding statement is also true for the minimum.

Conclusion 1:

If u and U are continuous in $T + \Sigma$ and are harmonic functions in T for which

$$u \leqq U \qquad \text{on } \Sigma$$

then also $u \leqq U$ holds at all points in the interior of T.

The function $U - u$ is therefore continuous in $T - \Sigma$, harmonic in T; hence

$$U - u \geqq 0 \qquad \text{on } \Sigma .$$

Consequently, according to the principle of the maximum we must have

$$U - u \geqq 0$$

at all points in the interior of T—precisely our assertion.

Conclusion 2:

If u and U are continuous in the region $T + \Sigma$ and are harmonic functions in T for which

$$| u | \leqq U \qquad \text{on } \Sigma$$

then also

$$| u | \leqq U$$

at all points in the interior of T.

From the above assumptions it follows that the three harmonic functions $-U$, u, and U satisfy the relation

$$- U \leqq u \leqq U \qquad \text{on } \Sigma .$$

However, it follows by a twice-repeated application of Conclusion 1 that

$$- U \leqq u \leqq U$$

at all points in the interior of T, or

$$| u | \leqq U$$

in the interior of T.

3. Uniqueness and stability of the solution of the first boundary-value problem

Let us consider a region T which is bounded by the surface Σ. Then the first boundary-value problem for Laplace's differential equation in the region T reads as follows:

Determine a function u which

(1) satisfies the equation $\Delta u = 0$ in the interior of the region T;

(2) is defined and continuous in the closed region $T + \Sigma$, i.e., both in the interior as well as on the boundary.

(3) on the boundary Σ assumes a prescribed value.

Condition (1) requires that the sought function is harmonic in the interior of T. To require that the function also be harmonic on the boundary would result in additional limitations for the boundary values. This requirement is superfluous. On the other hand, continuity in the closed region (or any other corresponding condition) for the uniqueness of the solution is necessary. If we waive this requirement, then each such function, which in T is equal to a constant C and coincides on Σ with the prescribed function f, could be considered as a solution of the problem, since the conditions (1) and (2) would also be fulfilled.

We now prove the uniqueness theorem:

Theorem. The first interior boundary-value problem for Laplace's differential equation is uniquely solvable.

We assume that two different solutions u_1 and u_2 exist which are continuous in the closed region $T + \Sigma$, satisfy Laplace's differential equation in the interior of T, and on the boundary Σ assume one and the same value f.

Then the difference $u = u_1 - u_2$ has the following properties:

1. $\Delta u = 0$ in the interior of T.
2. u is continuous in the closed region $T + \Sigma$.
3. $u \mid_\Sigma = 0$.

Consequently, $u(M)$ represents a continuous and harmonic function in the interior of T which on the boundary is equal to zero. As is known, a continuous function assumes its maximum in a closed region. Therefore we must have $u \equiv 0$. That is, if $u \neq 0$ and for at least one point $u > 0$, then u must assume its maximum at an interior point of the region, which is impossible. In exactly the same way we show that u is never negative in T. Consequently,

$$u \equiv 0 .$$

We turn now to the proof of the continuous dependence of the solution of the first boundary-value problem on the boundary conditions. As stated previously, a problem is said to be determined physically if a small change in the conditions which determine the solution of the problem—in our case the boundary conditions—implies a small change in the solution itself, that is, "the solution is stable."

Let u_1 and u_2 be two functions which are continuous in $T + \Sigma$ and harmonic in the interior of T, for which the magnitude of the difference of the boundary values does not exceed $\varepsilon > 0$. Then throughout the region under consideration,

$$| u_1 - u_2 | \leqq \varepsilon .$$

This assertion follows directly from Conclusion 2 in the previous section, since $U \equiv \varepsilon$ is a harmonic function.

Therefore we have proved the continuous dependence of the solution on the boundary conditions and the unique solvability of the first interior boundary-value problem.

4. Problems with discontinuous boundary conditions

Often one has to deal with a first boundary-value problem with discontinuous boundary conditions. Naturally, a continuous function in the closed region cannot be a solution to this problem, and we must therefore modify the formulation of the first boundary-value problem accordingly.

Let a piecewise continuous function $f(P)$ be defined on a curve C which bounds a bounded region S. We seek a function $u(M)$ with the following properties:

1. $u(M)$ is harmonic in the interior of S.
2. $u(M)$ continuously approaches the boundary values at all points where these are continuous.
3. $u(M)$ is bounded in the closed region $S + C$.

We note that the additional requirement of boundedness is essential only in the neighborhood of the points of discontinuity of $f(P)$. Therefore, the following theorem holds:

Theorem. The solution of the first boundary-value problem with piecewise continuous boundary conditions is uniquely determined.

Let u_1 and u_2 be two solutions of the stated problem. Then we have for the difference $v = u_1 - u_2$:

1. v is a harmonic function in the interior of S;
2. v continuously approaches the value zero on the boundary with the exception of the points of discontinuity of $f(P)$ at which v can be discontinuous;
3. v is bounded in $S + C$; $|v| < A$.

We now construct the harmonic function

$$U(M) = \varepsilon \sum_{i=1}^{n} \ln \frac{D}{r_i}.$$

Here ε denotes any positive number, D is the set theoretic diameter of the region S, and r_i is the distance of the ith point of discontinuity P_i under consideration. The function $U(M)$ is positive since all the summands are positive.

Further we enclose each point of discontinuity P_i with a circle K_i of radius δ and let δ be sufficiently small so that each summand

$$\varepsilon \ln \frac{D}{r_i}$$

of the corresponding circle C_i is larger than A, i.e., let $\varepsilon \ln D/\delta > A$. Then, in the closed region $S = \bigcup_{i=1}^{n} K_i$, v is continuous.

According to the principle of the maximum, U in this region is a majorant of v:

$$| v(M) | \leqq U(M) .$$

For a fixed point M in S, as $\varepsilon \to 0$ we obtain

$$\lim_{\varepsilon \to 0} U(M) = 0 .$$

Therefore,

$$v(M) = 0 ,$$

since v is independent of ε; or

$$u_1 \equiv u_2 ,$$

which was to be proved.

5. Isolated singularities

We shall now investigate the singularities of a harmonic function. If P is an isolated singular point in a region in which the function u is harmonic then two cases are possible:

1. The harmonic function is bounded in the neighborhood of the point P.
2. The harmonic function is unbounded in the neighborhood of the point P.

We have already dealt with singularities of the second type (for example $\ln 1/r$). The following theorem shows that singularities of the first type cannot occur:

Theorem. If a bounded function $u(M)$ is harmonic in the interior of a region S with the exception of a point P, then $u(M)$ at the point P can be defined such that the function $u(M)$ is harmonic throughout S.

For the proof of this theorem we choose a circle K_α of radius α about the center point P, which lies entirely in S, and consider a harmonic function v in the circle which coincides with the function u on the circumference C_α of the circle K_α.[81]

The difference

$$w = u - v$$

then has the following properties:

1. With the exception of the point P, at which w is not defined at all, it is harmonic everywhere in K_α.
2. It continuously approaches the boundary value zero on C_α.
3. It is bounded in the closed region $K_\alpha + C_\alpha$, ($| v | < A$).

As in the proof of the previous theorems (Section 4–2 § 4), we again construct the non-negative harmonic function

$$U(M) = \varepsilon \ln \frac{\alpha}{r} .$$

Here ε denotes a positive number, α is the radius of the circle K_α, and r is

[81] The existence of such a function will be shown in Section 4–3. Its construction therefore does not depend on the theorem proved here.

the distance of the point M from the singularity P. Further we choose a circle K_δ with center point P, whose radius δ is such that on its circumference the value of U is larger than A. Then we consider the region $K_\alpha - K_\delta$. The function w in the closed region $\delta \leqq r \leqq \alpha$ is continuous and on its boundary $|w| \leqq U$. On the basis of the principle of the maximum, therefore, the positive function U is a majorant of w:

$$|w| \leqq U(M) \qquad \text{for} \qquad \delta \leqq r \leqq \alpha .$$

Now if we fix any point M on K_α, which does not coincide with P, and let ε approach zero, we obtain

$$\lim_{\varepsilon \to 0} U(M) = 0 ,$$

thus

$$w = 0 .$$

Therefore, the function u, with the exception of the point P, coincides with the function v everywhere in the region S. Now if we set $u(P) = v(P)$ then we arrive at the function $u \equiv v$, which is harmonic everywhere in S. Therefore our theorem is proved.

Similarly, we proceed to the proof of the theorem for the three-dimensional case in which the function $U(M) = 2(1/r - 1/\alpha)$ can be used as the majorant function.

For the proof of this theorem we should assume that the function u remains bounded in the neighborhood of the point P. The proof also remains valid if instead of assuming the boundedness we assume only that the function u, in the neighborhood of the point P, satisfies the inequality

$$|u(M)| < \varepsilon(r) \log \frac{1}{r_{PM}} , \tag{4-2.17}$$

where $\varepsilon(r)$ is an arbitrary function which as $r \to 0$ also approaches zero. This requirement indicates that $u(M)$ in the neighborhood of P increases slower than $\log 1/r_{PM}$.

Therefore if the function $u(M)$ is harmonic with the exception of a point P in a region S, where as $M \to P$ it increases slower than $\log 1/r_{PM}$, then in the neighborhood of P, $u(M)$ is bounded, and the value $u(P)$ can be defined so that u is harmonic in the entire region S.

This is also the case for three independent variables. If a harmonic function $u(M)$ in the neighborhood of an isolated singular point P increases slower than $1/r$:

$$|u(M)| < \varepsilon(r) \frac{1}{r_{MP}} , \qquad \varepsilon(r) \to 0 , \qquad r \to 0 , \tag{4-2.18}$$

then it is bounded in the neighborhood of this point, and the value $u(P)$ can be so defined that $u(M)$ is also harmonic at the point P.

6. Regularity of a harmonic function at infinity

A harmonic function $u(x, y, z)$ is said to be regular at infinity if for $r \geqq r_0$

the following conditions are fulfilled:

$$|u| < \frac{A}{r}, \qquad \left|\frac{\partial u}{\partial x}\right| < \frac{A}{r^2}, \qquad \left|\frac{\partial u}{\partial y}\right| < \frac{A}{r^2}, \qquad \left|\frac{\partial u}{\partial z}\right| < \frac{A}{r^2}. \tag{4-2.19}$$

The following theorem is valid: If a function u, outside of a closed surface Σ, is harmonic and as $r \to \infty$ tends uniformly towards zero, then it is regular at infinity.

The assertion that u tends uniformly towards zero as $r \to \infty$ requires also that a function $\varepsilon^*(r)$ exist such that

$$|u(M)| < \varepsilon^*(r), \qquad \varepsilon^*(r) \to 0, \qquad r \to \infty, \tag{4-2.20}$$

where r denotes the radius vector of M.

For the proof we use the Kelvin transformation

$$v(r', \theta, \varphi) = ru(r, \theta, \varphi) \qquad \text{with} \qquad r' = \frac{1}{r}.$$

The function v so obtained is then harmonic everywhere in the interior of the surface Σ', which arises by the transformation of reciprocal radii from Σ. An exception is the origin of coordinates at which v has an isolated singularity.

From the condition (4-2.20) it follows that in the neighborhood of the origin of coordinates the function v satisfies the inequality

$$|v(r', \theta, \varphi)| \leqq \varepsilon^*\left(\frac{1}{r'}\right)\frac{1}{r'} = \varepsilon(r')\frac{1}{r'}$$

with

$$\varepsilon(r') = \varepsilon^*\left(\frac{1}{r'}\right) \to 0 \qquad \text{for} \qquad r' \to 0.$$

Therefore, $v(r', \theta, \varphi)$, on the basis of the last theorem in Section 4–2 § 5, is bounded and harmonic for $r' = r_0'$:

$$|v(r', \theta, \varphi)| \leqq A \qquad \text{for} \qquad r' \leqq r_0', \tag{4-2.21}$$

from which it follows that

$$|u(r, \theta, \varphi)| = \frac{|v(r', \theta, \varphi)|}{r} \leqq \frac{A}{r} \qquad \text{for} \qquad r \geqq r_0 = \frac{1}{r_0'}.$$

Since now for $r' = 0$, v is harmonic, we can write:

$$\frac{\partial u(x, y, z)}{\partial x} = \frac{\partial}{\partial x}\left(\frac{1}{r} \cdot v(x', y', z')\right)$$

$$= -\frac{x}{r^3} \cdot v + \frac{1}{r}\left[\frac{\partial v}{\partial x'} \cdot \frac{\partial x'}{\partial x} + \frac{\partial v}{\partial y'} \cdot \frac{\partial y'}{\partial x} + \frac{\partial v}{\partial z'} \cdot \frac{\partial z'}{\partial x}\right], \tag{4-2.22}$$

where

$$x' = \frac{x}{r} r', \qquad y' = \frac{y}{r} r', \qquad z' = \frac{z}{r} r'.$$

If we now calculate the derivatives $\partial x'/\partial x$, $\partial y'/\partial x$, $\partial z'/\partial x$ and consider the boundedness of the first derivatives of v in the neighborhood of the point $r' = 0$, we find

$$\left|\frac{\partial u}{\partial x}\right| \leqq \frac{A}{r^2} \quad \text{for } r \to \infty .$$

Corresponding estimates are obtained for $\partial u/\partial y$ and $\partial u/\partial z$.

7. Exterior boundary-value problems; the uniqueness of the solution for two- and three- dimensional problems

In the formulation of the exterior boundary-value problems we have to distinguish between two and three independent variables.

We consider first the three-dimensional case. Let T be an unbounded region which can be bounded by a closed bounded surface Σ. The exterior first boundary-value problem then reads as follows:

Determine a function $u(x, y, z)$ which satisfies the following conditions:

1. $\Delta u = 0$ in the unbounded region T.
2. u is everywhere continuous, including on the surface Σ.
3. $u|_\Sigma = f(x, y, z)$, where f is a prescribed function on Σ.
4. $u(M)$ tends uniformly to zero as $M \to \infty$.

A simple example will show that the last condition is essential for the uniqueness of the solution. To this end we consider the following problem: Determine a solution of the exterior boundary-value problem for a sphere S_R of radius R with a constant boundary condition

$$u|_{S_R} = \text{const.} = f_0 .$$

If Condition 4 is dropped, then both the functions $u_1 = f_0$ and $u_2 = f_0 R/r$ as well as the functions

$$u = \alpha u_1 + \beta u_2 \quad \text{with} \quad \alpha + \beta = 1$$

are admissible solutions of the problem. On the other hand we have the following theorem:

Theorem. The exterior first boundary-value problem for the three-dimensional Laplace differential equation has a uniquely determined solution.

If u_1 and u_2 are two solutions which satisfy Conditions 1 to 4, then their difference $u = u_1 - u_2$ represents a solution which satisfies the corresponding homogeneous boundary condition. Since Condition 4 for the function u is also fulfilled then for every $\varepsilon > 0$, an R^* can be found such that

$$|u(M)| < \varepsilon \quad \text{for } r \geqq R^* .$$

If the point $\bar{M}$ lies in a region T' (Figure 47), which lies between the surface Σ and a sphere S_{Σ} $(r \geqq R^*)$, then obviously $u(\bar{M}) < \varepsilon$. This follows from the principle of the maximum applied to the region T'. Since ε can be chosen arbitrarily we conclude that u, in T' as well as in the entire region T, vanishes identically. Therefore we have demonstrated the unique solvability of the exterior first boundary-value problem in the three-dimensional case.

The exterior first boundary-value problem in the two-dimensional case reads as follows:

Determine a function $u(x, y)$ which satisfies the following conditions:

1. $\Delta u = 0$ in the unbounded region Σ under consideration whose boundary forms a closed curve C.
2. u is continuous everywhere and also on C.
3. $u|_C = f(x, y)$, where f is a prescribed function on C.
4. $u(M)$ is bounded at infinity, i.e., a number N exists such that $|u(M)| \leqq N$.

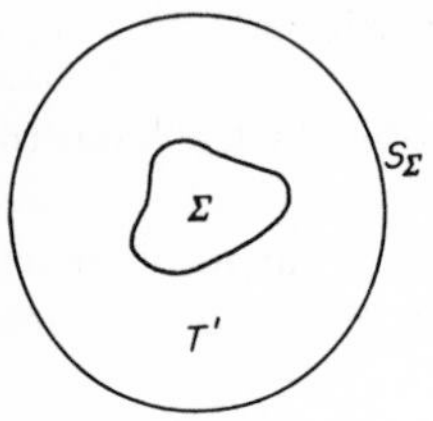

FIG. 47.

Here the requirement that the solution is equal to zero at infinity would also be sufficient to prove that there could not be two distinct solutions. However, this would be too strong a requirement and in general the problem would not be solvable.

The following theorem is valid:

Theorem. The exterior first boundary-value problem for the two-dimensional Laplace differential equation has a uniquely determined solution.

From the existence of two distinct solutions u_1 and u_2 it follows that their difference $u = u_1 - u_2$ represents a solution of the first boundary-value problem with homogeneous boundary conditions. Further, because of Condition 4 we have

$$|u| \leqq N = N_1 + N_2,$$

where N_1 and N_2 are such that $|u_1| \leqq N_1$, $|u_2| \leqq N_2$. We denote by Σ_1 the complement of Σ, so that $\Sigma + \Sigma_1$ represents the entire plane. Further we select a point M_0 on Σ_1, and also a circle of radius R with center point M_0, which lies entirely in Σ_1 (Figure 48). Then the harmonic function $\ln 1/r_{MM_0}$ has no singularity in the region Σ; the function $\ln r_{MM_0}/R$ is positive in all of Σ and on C.

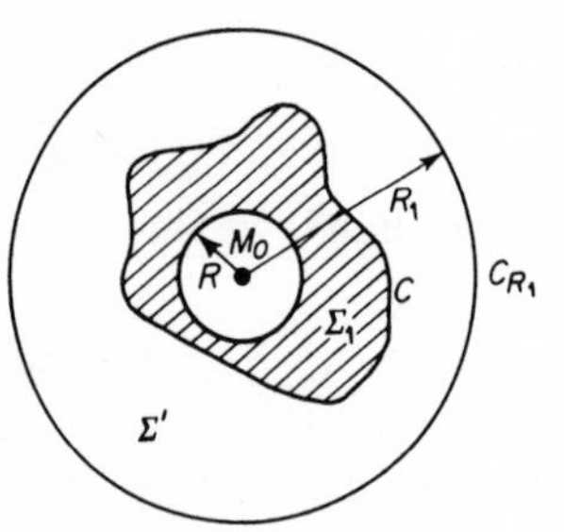

FIG. 48.

Further, let C_{R_1} be a circumference with radius R_1 and center point M_0 which entirely contains the curve C, and let Σ' be the region bounded by C and C_{R_1}. The function u_{R_1} defined by

$$u_{R_1} = N \frac{\ln r/R}{\ln R_1/R} \tag{4-2.23}$$

is then a harmonic function which is equal to N on the circumference C_{R_1} and is positive on C. From the principle of the maximum it follows that u_{R_1} is a majorant of the absolute value of $u(M)$ in the region Σ:

$$|u(M)| < u_{R_1}(M).$$

We fix M and let R_1 increase unboundedly. Obviously, then, as $R_1 \to \infty$, $u_{R_1}(M)$ approaches zero, so that $u(M) = 0$. However, since M can be chosen arbitrarily, the unique solvability of the problem considered is demonstrated.

We can also prove the unique solvability of this problem by using the transformation of reciprocal radii. With this transformation the curve C in this case is transformed into the curve C', so that the region lying in the exterior of C is transformed into the region lying in the interior of C'. Thus, the point at infinity transforms into an isolated singular point in whose neighborhood the function v remains bounded. From the theorem of the harmonic functions in Section 4–2 § 5, it then follows that v is harmonic at the origin of coordinates and the solution is unique.

From these considerations it follows that a harmonic function which is bounded at infinity tends towards a definite limit value as $M \to \infty$.

The difference in the formulation of the exterior first boundary-value problem for two and three variables can be clarified by the following physical example. Given a sphere of radius R whose surface is held at a constant temperature u_0, find the stationary temperature distribution of the surrounding space. The function $u = u_0 R/r$ represents the solution of this problem which vanishes at infinity.

We consider now the corresponding two-dimensional problem. Thus, let a circle of radius R be given, on whose circumference a constant temperature

$$u\,|_\Sigma = f_0 = \text{const.}$$

prevails. In this case $u \equiv f_0$ is the uniquely determined bounded solution of the problem and no further solution exists which would be equal to zero at infinity. Earlier we emphasized the essential difference in the relation of harmonic functions at infinity for two and three independent variables (for example, the relation of $1/r$ and $\ln 1/r$ at infinity).

Also, for spatial and plane unbounded regions the principle of the maximum remains valid. This we know from the considerations which parallel the arguments in the proof of the uniqueness theorem. From this follows again the continuous dependence of the solution on the boundary conditions.

8. The second boundary-value problem, regularity at infinity, and the uniqueness theorem

A function u is said to be the solution of the second boundary-value problem if it and $\partial u/\partial n$ are continuous in a region $T + \Sigma$, and if u satisfies Laplace's differential equation in T and on the boundary Σ satisfies the prescribed condition

$$\left.\frac{\partial u}{\partial n}\right|_\Sigma = f(M)\,.$$

The solution of the second boundary-value problem is uniquely determined to within an arbitrary constant.

We proceed to the proof with the additional assumption that the function $u(M)$ has continuous first derivatives in the region $T + \Sigma$.[82]

[82] In order to simplify the proof, we assume the continuity of the first derivatives in $T + \Sigma$. Under more general assumptions, the uniqueness theorem was proved by M. V. Keldysh and M. A. Lavrentev (Doklady A. N. SSSR **16**, 1937). See also V. I. Smirnov, *op. cit.* footnote 15, Part IV.

Let us assume that u_1 and u_2 are two distinct continuously differentiable functions in $T+\Sigma$, each of which satisfies the equation $\Delta u = 0$ in T and the condition $\partial u/\partial n|_\Sigma = f(x, y, z)$ on Σ. The difference $u = u_1 - u_2$ then satisfies

$$\left.\frac{\partial u}{\partial n}\right|_\Sigma = 0 .$$

Now if we set $v = u$ into the first Green's formula (4-2.3) and take into consideration that $\Delta u = 0$ and $\partial u/\partial n|_\Sigma = 0$, we obtain

$$\iiint_T \left[\left(\frac{\partial u}{\partial x}\right)^2 + \left(\frac{\partial u}{\partial y}\right)^2 + \left(\frac{\partial u}{\partial z}\right)^2\right] d\tau = 0 .$$

However, because of the continuity of the function u and its first derivatives, it follows that

$$\frac{\partial u}{\partial x} = \frac{\partial u}{\partial y} = \frac{\partial u}{\partial z} \equiv 0 ,$$

i.e.,

$$u \equiv \text{const.} ,$$

which was to be proved.

The method of proof used here can also be applied to the case of an unbounded region when the function under consideration is regular at infinity. First of all, we prove the following theorem:

Theorem. In the case of an unbounded region, Green's formula (4-2.3) is applicable to functions which are regular at infinity.

Therefore, we consider an unbounded region T whose boundary we denote by Σ. Further we choose a sphere of radius R and denote by T_R that part of our region which lies entirely in this sphere. The region T_R is then bounded by that part of the spherical surface Σ_R which belongs to T and by the surface Σ_1 which forms a portion of the surface Σ (Figure 49). Now if we apply Green's formula in the region T_R to the two functions u and v which are regular at infinity, we obtain

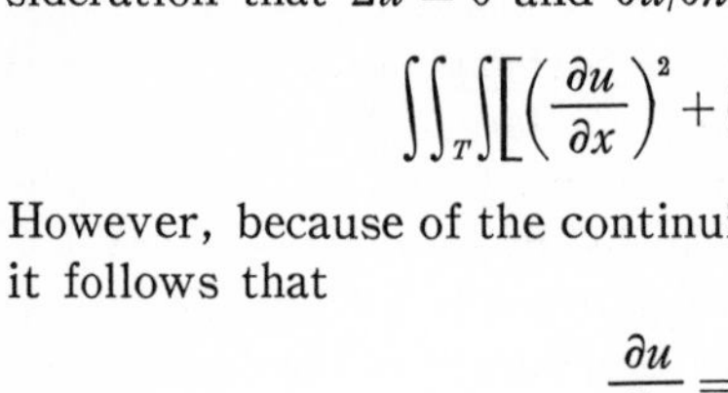

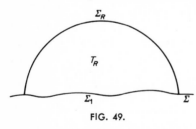

FIG. 49.

$$\iiint_{T_R} u\Delta v\, d\tau = -\iiint_{T_R}\left[\frac{\partial u}{\partial x}\frac{\partial v}{\partial x} + \frac{\partial u}{\partial y}\frac{\partial v}{\partial y} + \frac{\partial u}{\partial z}\frac{\partial v}{\partial z}\right] d\tau + \iint_{\Sigma_1} u\frac{\partial v}{\partial n} d\sigma + \iint_{\Sigma_R} u\frac{\partial v}{\partial n} d\sigma . \tag{4-2.23'}$$

By using the regularity of the functions u and v we estimate the integral over Σ_R:

$$\left|\iint_{\Sigma_R} u\frac{\partial v}{\partial n} d\sigma\right| = \left|\iint_{\Sigma_R} u(v_x\cos\alpha + v_y\cos\beta + v_z\cos\gamma)\, d\sigma\right|$$
$$\leqq \left|\iint_{\Sigma_R}\frac{A}{R}\cdot\frac{3A}{R^2} d\sigma\right| \leqq \frac{3A^2}{R^3}4\pi R^2 = \frac{12\pi A^2}{R} .$$

Hence, there follows

$$\lim_{R\to\infty}\int_{\Sigma_R}\!\!\int u\frac{\partial v}{\partial n}\,d\sigma = 0\,.$$

The integral over T_R on the right side as $R\to\infty$ tends toward the integral extended throughout the entire region T. This integral exists since the integrand, because of the regularity of u and v at infinity, approaches zero as $1/R^4$. If, however, the limit value of the integral over Σ_1, which is equal to the integral over Σ, exists, then the limit value of the right side of (4-2.23′) also exists and is given by

$$\lim_{R\to\infty}\iint_{T_R}\!\!\int u\Delta v\,d\tau = \iint_{T}\!\!\int u\Delta v\,d\tau\,.$$

Therefore we arrive at the formula

$$\iint_{T}\!\!\int u\Delta v\,d\tau = -\iint_{T}\!\!\int\left[\frac{\partial u}{\partial x}\frac{\partial v}{\partial x}+\frac{\partial u}{\partial y}\frac{\partial v}{\partial y}+\frac{\partial u}{\partial z}\frac{\partial v}{\partial z}\right]d\tau + \int_{\Sigma}\!\!\int u\frac{\partial v}{\partial n}\,d\sigma\,. \tag{4-2.24}$$

Hence, the applicability of the first and consequently also of the second Green's formula in the unbounded region, under the assumption that the functions which occur are regular at infinity, is proved.

We are now in a position to prove the following uniqueness theorem:

Theorem. The second boundary-value problem for an unbounded region possesses a uniquely determined solution which is regular at infinity.

If in formula (4-2.24) we set $v = u = u_1 - u_2$ and bear in mind that $\Delta u = 0$ and $\partial u/\partial n\,|_\Sigma = 0$, then we obtain

$$\iint_{T}\!\!\int (u_x^2 + u_y^2 + u_z^2)\,d\tau = 0\,.$$

Hence, because of the continuity of the derivatives of u, it follows that

$$u_x = 0\,,\qquad u_y = 0\,,\qquad u_z = 0\,,\qquad \text{and}\qquad u \equiv \text{const}\,.$$

Now, however, at infinity $u = 0$, so that

$$u \equiv 0\,,$$

i.e.,

$$u_1 \equiv u_2\,,$$

which was to be proved.

There now remains the question of whether or not the uniqueness of the solution of the first boundary-value problem can also be proved by this method.

Let u_1 and u_2 be distinct solutions of the first (interior) boundary-value problem. We then apply formula (4-2.3) to the function $u = u_1 - u_2$ and $v = u$ in the region T. Let Σ be the bounded boundary surface of T. Then we obtain

$$\iint_{T}\!\!\int u\Delta u\,d\tau = -\iint_{T}\!\!\int (u_x^2 + u_y^2 + u_z^2)\,d\tau + \int_{\Sigma}\!\!\int u\frac{\partial u}{\partial n}\,d\sigma\,,$$

where by consideration of the expression

$$\Delta u = 0\,, \qquad u\,|_{\Sigma} = 0$$

the equation

$$\iiint_T (u_x^2 + u_y^2 + u_z^2)\,d\tau = 0$$

results. Consequently we find

$$u_x = u_y = u_z = 0 \qquad \text{and} \qquad u = \text{const}\,.$$

The function u on the surface Σ is equal to zero. We can therefore conclude that

$$u \equiv 0 \qquad \text{and} \qquad u_1 \equiv u_2\,.$$

This proof is incorrect, however, since in the method of proof the existence of the derivatives of the sought function on the surface Σ was assumed. The proof of uniqueness which is based on the principle of the maximum does not contain this weakness.

4-3. SOLUTION OF THE BOUNDARY-VALUE PROBLEMS FOR SIMPLE REGIONS BY SEPARATION OF VARIABLES

For simple regions, the solution of the corresponding boundary-value problem can be treated by separation of variables. Accordingly, certain auxiliary equations occur which make it necessary to use special classes of functions. This discussion will be limited, however, to those problems which can be solved by means of trigonometric functions alone. Later, in the investigation of certain special functions, we shall consider the solution of other problems.

1. The first boundary-value problem for the circle

We begin with the solution of the first boundary-value problem for the circle.

Determine the function u which satisfies the equation

$$\Delta u = 0 \tag{4-3.1}$$

inside a circle and the boundary condition

$$u = f \tag{4-3.2}$$

on the periphery, where f is a prescribed function.

Let us first assume f to be continuous and differentiable; later we shall drop the differentiability requirement and also the continuity of f (see Section 4–2 § 4). We shall consider both the interior and the exterior boundary-value problems.

We first introduce the polar coordinates ρ, φ whose origin lies at the center point of the considered circle of the radius a. Eq. (4-3.1), as is known, has the form

$$\Delta u \equiv \frac{1}{\rho}\frac{\partial}{\partial\rho}\left(\rho\frac{\partial u}{\partial\rho}\right) + \frac{1}{\rho^2}\frac{\partial^2 u}{\partial\varphi^2} = 0 \tag{4-2.3}$$

in polar coordinates (see formula (4-1.34)). We now investigate the separation of variables, i.e., we seek the solution in the form

$$u(\rho, \varphi) = R(\rho)\Phi(\varphi) .$$

By substitution into Eq. (4-3.3), we obtain

$$\frac{d/d\rho\cdot(\rho(dR/d\rho))}{R/\rho} = -\frac{\Phi''}{\Phi} = \lambda ,$$

where $\lambda = \text{const}$. Hence, we obtain for Φ and R the two differential equations

$$\Phi'' + \lambda\Phi = 0 \tag{4-3.4}$$

and

$$\rho\frac{d}{d\rho}\left(\rho\frac{dR}{d\rho}\right) - \lambda R = 0 . \tag{4-3.5}$$

From Eq. (4-3.4) there results

$$\Phi(\varphi) = A\cos\sqrt{\lambda}\varphi + B\sin\sqrt{\lambda}\varphi .$$

Moreover, we note that the single-valued function $u(\rho, \varphi)$ under a change of the angle φ by an amount of 2π is assumed to equal its original value

$$u(\rho, \varphi + 2\pi) = u(\rho, \varphi) .$$

Consequently,

$$\Phi(\varphi + 2\pi) = \Phi(\varphi) ,$$

i.e., $\Phi(\varphi)$ is a periodic function of the angle φ with the period 2π. This, however, is possible only when $\sqrt{\lambda} = n$ is an integer and

$$\Phi_n(\varphi) = A_n\cos n\varphi + B_n\sin n\varphi .$$

We assume the function $R(\rho)$ to be of the form

$$R(\rho) = \rho^\mu .$$

With this and (4-3.5),

$$n^2 = \mu^2 \qquad \text{or} \qquad \mu = \pm n , \qquad n > 0$$

results after replacing $R(\rho)$ by ρ^μ. Consequently,

$$R(\rho) = C\rho^n + D\rho^{-n} ,$$

where C and D are arbitrary constants.

For the solution of the interior problem we have $R(\rho) = C\rho^n$ $(\mu = +n)$, i.e., $D = 0$. For, if $D \neq 0$, then $u(\rho, \varphi) = R(\rho)\Phi(\varphi)$ for $\rho = 0$ would increase unboundedly and would not represent a harmonic function in the circle. By contrast, $R(\rho) = D\rho^{-n}$ $(\mu = -n)$ must be assumed for the solution of the exterior problem, since this solution must be bounded at infinity.

Therefore we have found the following particular solutions of our problem:[83]

$$u_n(\rho, \varphi) = \rho^n(A_n \cos n\varphi + B_n \sin n\varphi) \qquad \text{for } \rho \leqq a\,,$$

$$u_n(\rho, \varphi) = \frac{1}{\rho^n}(A_n \cos n\varphi + B_n \sin n\varphi) \qquad \text{for } \rho \geqq a\,.$$

The sums of these solutions,

$$u(\rho, \varphi) = \sum_{n=0}^{\infty} \rho^n(A_n \cos n\varphi + B_n \sin n\varphi) \qquad \text{for the interior problem}$$

and

$$u(\rho, \varphi) = \sum_{n=0}^{\infty} \frac{1}{\rho^n}(A_n \cos n\varphi + B_n \sin n\varphi) \qquad \text{for the exterior problem,}$$

are also harmonic functions, provided they converge.

Now in order to determine the coefficients A_n and B_n we use the boundary condition

$$u(a, \varphi) = \sum_{n=0}^{\infty} a^n(A_n \cos n\varphi + B_n \sin n\varphi) = f\,. \tag{4-3.6}$$

We assume that f can be written as a function of the angle φ. Then the Fourier series for f has the form

$$f(\varphi) = \frac{\alpha_0}{2} + \sum_{n=1}^{\infty} (\alpha_n \cos n\varphi + \beta_n \sin n\varphi) \tag{4-3.7}$$

with

$$\alpha_0 = \frac{1}{\pi}\int_{-\pi}^{\pi} f(\psi)\,d\psi\,, \qquad \alpha_n = \frac{1}{\pi}\int_{-\pi}^{\pi} f(\psi)\cos n\psi\,d\psi$$

$$\beta_n = \frac{1}{\pi}\int_{-\pi}^{\pi} f(\psi)\sin n\psi\,d\psi\,.$$

By comparison of series (4-3.6) and (4-3.7) we then obtain

[83] The Laplace differential expression in polar coordinates (4-3.3) loses its meaning for $\rho = 0$. Therefore, we still have to prove that $\Delta u_n = 0$ also for $\rho = 0$. For this proof we shall use not polar but rectangular coordinates; the particular solutions

$$\rho^n \cos n\varphi \quad \text{and} \quad \rho^n \sin n\varphi$$

are then the real or imaginary parts of the function

$$\rho^n e^{in\varphi} = (\rho e^{i\varphi})^n = (x + iy)^n\,;$$

it is a polynomial in x and y. Now, however, it is clear that a polynomial which satisfies the equation $\Delta u = 0$ for $\rho > 0$ also is satisfied for $\rho = 0$, because of the continuity of the second derivatives of this equation.

$$A_0 = \frac{\alpha_0}{2}, \qquad A_n = \frac{\alpha_n}{a^n}, \qquad B_n = \frac{\beta_n}{a^n}$$

for the interior problem and

$$A_0 = \frac{\alpha_0}{2}, \qquad A_n = \alpha_n a^n, \qquad B_n = \beta_n a^n$$

for the exterior problem. In this manner, we have found a solution of the interior first boundary-value problem for the circle in the form

$$u(\rho, \varphi) = \frac{\alpha_0}{2} + \sum_{n=1}^{\infty} \left(\frac{\rho}{a}\right)^n (\alpha_n \cos n\varphi + \beta_n \sin n\varphi) \tag{4-3.8}$$

and the solution of the exterior problem in the form

$$u(\rho, \varphi) = \frac{\alpha_0}{2} + \sum_{n=1}^{\infty} \left(\frac{a}{\rho}\right)^n (\alpha_n \cos n\varphi + \beta_n \sin n\varphi) . \tag{4-3.9}$$

In order to prove that these functions represent the sought solutions, we also have to prove the applicability of the superposition principle. For this purpose we show the convergence of the series, the termwise differentiability, and finally the continuity of the functions represented by it on the circumference of the circle. Both series can be subsumed in the homogeneous formula

$$u(\rho, \varphi) = \sum_{n=1}^{\infty} t^n(\alpha_n \cos n\varphi + \beta_n \sin n\varphi) + \frac{\alpha_0}{2},$$

where

$$t = \begin{cases} \dfrac{\rho}{a} \leqq 1 & \text{for} \quad \rho \leqq a \quad \text{(interior problem)} \\[2ex] \dfrac{a}{\rho} \leqq 1 & \text{for} \quad \rho \geqq a \quad \text{(exterior problem)} \end{cases}$$

and α_n, β_n are the Fourier coefficients of $f(\varphi)$.

To prove that series (4-3.8) and (4-3.9) for $t < 1$ are arbitrarily often termwise differentiable, we set

$$u_n = t^n(\alpha_n \cos n\varphi + \beta_n \sin n\varphi)$$

and calculate the kth derivative of the function u_n with respect to φ:

$$\frac{\partial^k u_n}{\partial \varphi^k} = t^n n^k \left[\alpha_n \cos\left(n\varphi + k\frac{\pi}{2}\right) + \beta_n \sin\left(n\varphi + k\frac{\pi}{2}\right)\right].$$

Hence we obtain the estimate

$$\left|\frac{\partial^k u_n}{\partial \varphi^k}\right| \leqq t^n n^k 2M,$$

where M is the maximum of the absolute values of the Fourier coefficients α_n and β_n, i.e.,

$$|\alpha_n| < M, \qquad |\beta_n| < M. \tag{4-3.10}$$

Now we choose a fixed value $\rho_0 < a$ (for the interior problem) or $\rho_1 = a^2/\rho_0 > a$ (for the exterior problem) where $t_0 = \rho_0/a < 1$. Then,

$$\sum_{n=1}^{\infty} t^n n^k(|\alpha_n| + |\beta_n|) \leqq 2M \sum_{n=1}^{\infty} t_0^n n^k , \qquad t \leqq t_0 ,$$

from which because of the convergence of the series on the right we infer the uniform convergence on the left for $t \leqq t_0 < 1$ and arbitrary k. Therefore series (4-3.8) and (4-3.9) at each point lying inside (outside) the circle can be differentiated arbitrarily often with respect to φ. Correspondingly, we show that series (4-3.8) and (4-3.9) inside (outside) a circle of radius $\rho_0 < a$ can be differentiated arbitrarily often with respect to ρ.

Now ρ_0 was chosen arbitrarily under the given restrictions. Therefore, series (4-3.8) and (4-3.9) at each interior (exterior) point of the circle are termwise differentiable. Consequently, the superposition principle is applicable and the functions (4-3.8) and (4-3.9) satisfy the equation $\Delta u = 0$.[84]

For the proof we only used the fact that the Fourier coefficients of $f(\varphi)$ were bounded (formula (4-3.10)). However, this is valid for every bounded function (indeed for every absolutely integrable function). Therefore, provided $f(\varphi)$ is a bounded function, the series (4-3.8) and (4-3.9) define functions which satisfy the equation

$$\Delta u = 0 \qquad \text{for} \quad t < 1 .$$

We shall use this fact later for the generalization of the results found in this section.

We turn now to the proof of the continuity of the solutions in the closed region $t \leqq 1$. It is easy to see that we must go into the properties of the function $f(\varphi)$ more precisely.

Because of the assumed continuity and differentiability of $f(\rho)$, it follows that $f(\varphi)$ can be developed in a Fourier series and that the series

$$\sum_{n=1}^{\infty} (|\alpha_n| + |\beta_n|) \tag{4-3.11}$$

converges. On the other hand, we have

$$|t^n \alpha_n \cos n\varphi| \leqq |\alpha_n|$$
$$|t^n \beta_n \sin n\varphi| \leqq |\beta_n|$$

so that series (4-3.8) and (4-3.9) converge uniformly for $t \leqq 1$. The functions represented by them are therefore continuous on the circumference of the circle. Finally, formula (4-3.11) shows that the function (4-3.9), as the solution of the exterior problem, is bounded at infinity. Therefore, we have proved

[84] The Laplace differential equation is also satisfied for $\rho = 0$; if, therefore, the derivatives with respect to the polar coordinates are expressed through the derivatives in terms of the cartesian coordinates, we can easily see that the functions (4-3.8) and (4-3.9) are differentiable for $t \leqq t_0$ arbitrarily often with respect to x and y. On the basis of footnote 83, it follows that

$$\Delta u = 0 \qquad \text{for} \quad \rho = 0 .$$

that series (4-3.8) and (4-3.9) completely satisfy the conditions of the problem.

2. Poisson's integral

We shall first transform formulas (4-3.8) and (4-3.9) to a simpler form. For this purpose we consider, for example, the interior problem. Corresponding results hold also for the exterior problem.

By introduction of the expression for the Fourier coefficients into (4-3.8) and by an interchange of the order of summation and integration we obtain first of all

$$\begin{aligned} u(\rho, \varphi) &= \frac{1}{\pi}\int_{-\pi}^{\pi} f(\psi)\left\{\frac{1}{2} + \sum_{n=1}^{\infty}\left(\frac{\rho}{a}\right)^n(\cos n\psi \cos n\varphi + \sin n\psi \sin n\varphi)\right\}d\psi \\ &= \frac{1}{\pi}\int_{-\pi}^{\pi} f(\psi)\left\{\frac{1}{2} + \sum_{n=1}^{\infty}\left(\frac{\rho}{a}\right)^n \cos n(\varphi - \psi)\right\}d\psi \, . \end{aligned} \tag{4-3.12}$$

Now we use the following identity:

$$\begin{aligned} \frac{1}{2} + \sum_{n=1}^{\infty} t^n \cos n(\varphi - \psi) &= \frac{1}{2} + \frac{1}{2}\sum_{n=1}^{\infty} t^n[e^{in(\varphi-\psi)} + e^{-in(\varphi-\psi)}] \\ &= \frac{1}{2}\left\{1 + \sum_{n=1}^{\infty}[(te^{i(\varphi-\psi)})^n + (te^{-i(\varphi-\psi)})^n]\right\} \\ &= \frac{1}{2}\left\{1 + \frac{te^{i(\varphi-\psi)}}{1 - te^{i(\varphi-\psi)}} + \frac{te^{-i(\varphi-\psi)}}{1 - te^{-i(\varphi-\psi)}}\right\} \\ &= \frac{1}{2}\,\frac{1 - t^2}{1 - 2t\cos(\varphi - \psi) + t^2}\, , \qquad t = \frac{\rho}{a} < 1\, . \end{aligned}$$

If we introduce this result into (4-3.12) we obtain

$$u(\rho, \varphi) = \frac{1}{2\pi}\int_{-\pi}^{\pi} f(\psi)\frac{1 - \rho^2/a^2}{(\rho^2/a^2) - 2(\rho/a)\cos(\varphi - \psi) + 1}d\psi$$

or

$$u(\rho, \varphi) = \frac{1}{2\pi}\int_{-\pi}^{\pi} f(\psi)\frac{a^2 - \rho^2}{\rho^2 - 2a\rho\cos(\varphi - \psi) + a^2}d\psi \, . \tag{4-3.13}$$

This formula for the solution of the first boundary-value problem for the interior of a circle is the Poisson integral, and the expression under the integral sign

$$K(\rho, \varphi, a, \psi) = \frac{a^2 - \rho^2}{\rho^2 - 2a\rho\cos(\varphi - \psi) + a^2}$$

is called the Poisson kernel. For $\rho < a$, we have $K(\rho, \varphi, a, \psi) > 0$, since $2a\rho < a^2 + \rho^2$ for $\rho \neq a$.

The Poisson integral was derived under the assumption that $\rho > a$; for $\rho = a$, expression (4-3.8) loses its meaning. However,

$$\lim_{\substack{\rho \to a \\ \varphi \to \varphi_0}} u(\rho, \varphi) = f(\varphi_0)\, ,$$

because the series from which we obtained the Poisson integral is a continuous function in a closed region.

Consequently the function defined by

$$u(\rho, \varphi) = \begin{cases} \dfrac{1}{2\pi} \displaystyle\int_{-\pi}^{\pi} f(\psi) \frac{a^2 - \rho^2}{\rho^2 - 2a\rho\cos(\varphi - \psi) + a^2} d\psi & \text{for } \rho < a \,, \\ f(\varphi) & \text{for } \rho = a \end{cases} \tag{4-3.13'}$$

is a solution of the equation $\Delta u = 0$ for $\rho < a$, and in the closed region, including the boundary $\rho = a$, it is continuous.

The solution of the exterior problem has the form

$$u(\rho, \varphi) = \begin{cases} \dfrac{1}{2\pi} \displaystyle\int_{-\pi}^{\pi} f(\psi) \frac{\rho^2 - a^2}{\rho^2 - 2a\rho\cos(\varphi - \psi) + a^2} d\psi & \text{for } \rho > a \,, \\ f(\varphi) & \text{for } \rho = a \,. \end{cases} \tag{4-3.14}$$

Under our initial assumption that the function $f(\varphi)$ is continuous and differentiable, we proved that the solution can be represented by a series. Finally, by means of the above-cited identity, we arrive at the Poisson integral.

Now we shall prove that the Poisson integral represents the solution of the first boundary-value problem when the function $f(\varphi)$ is continuous only.

The Poisson integral represents the solution of the Laplace differential equation in the region $\rho < a$ $(t < 1)$ for an arbitrary bounded function $f(\varphi)$. Therefore for $\rho < a$ $(t < 1)$ the Poisson integral is identical with the series (4-3.8) and the equation $\Delta u = 0$ is satisfied for every bounded function $f(\varphi)$.

It still remains to be proved that the function $u(\rho, \varphi)$ in our case continuously approaches the boundary values. For this purpose we choose any sequence of continuous and differentiable functions

$$f_1(\varphi), f_2(\varphi), \ldots, f_k(\varphi), \ldots,$$

which converges uniformly towards the function $f(\varphi)$:[85]

$$\lim_{k \to \infty} f_k(\varphi) = f(\varphi) \,.$$

The sequence of boundary functions then corresponds to a sequence of harmonic functions $u_k(\rho, \varphi)$, which are defined by (4-3.13) or (4-3.8).

From the uniform convergence of the sequence $\{f_k(\varphi)\}$ it follows that for every $\varepsilon > 0$, a $k_0(\varepsilon) > 0$ exists such that

$$| f_k(\varphi) - f_{k+l}(\varphi) | < \varepsilon \qquad \text{for} \quad k > k_0(\varepsilon) \,, \qquad l > 0 \,.$$

For the functions $u_k(r, \varphi)$ which are solutions of the first boundary-value problem it follows from the principle of the maximum that

$$| u_k(\rho, \varphi) - u_{k+l}(\rho, \varphi) | < \varepsilon \qquad \text{for} \quad \rho \leqq \rho_0 \,, \qquad k > k_0(\varepsilon) \,, \qquad \varepsilon > 0 \,.$$

Consequently the sequence $\{u_k\}$ converges uniformly towards a definite

85 We shall not concern ourselves how it arises; such a sequence can be chosen in many ways.

function $u = \lim_{k\to\infty} u_k(\rho, \varphi)$. The limit function $u(\rho, \varphi)$ is continuous in the closed region, since all functions $u_k(\rho, \varphi)$ which are represented by the integral

$$u_k(\rho, \varphi) = \frac{1}{2\pi}\int_{-\pi}^{\pi} \frac{a^2 - \rho^2}{\rho^2 - 2a\rho\cos(\varphi - \psi) + a^2} f_k(\psi)\, d\psi$$

are continuous in the closed region. Finally we have

$$u(\rho, \varphi) = \lim_{k\to\infty} u_k(\rho, \varphi) = \begin{cases} \dfrac{1}{2\pi}\displaystyle\int_{-\pi}^{\pi} \frac{a^2 - \rho^2}{a^2 - 2a\rho\cos(\varphi - \psi) + \rho^2} f(\varphi)\, d\psi & \text{for } \rho < a \\ f(\varphi) & \text{for } \rho = a \end{cases}$$

since the sequence $\{f_k(\varphi)\}$ converges uniformly towards $f(\varphi)$ and therefore the passage to the limit can be carried out under the integral sign.

The function

$$u(\rho, \varphi) = \frac{1}{2\pi}\int_{-\pi}^{\pi} \frac{a^2 - \rho^2}{\rho^2 - 2a\rho\cos(\varphi - \psi) + a^2} f(\psi)\, d\psi$$

is thus, for every continuous function $f(\varphi)$, a solution of the Laplace differential equation which can assume the continuous boundary values given on the circumference of a circle.

3. Discontinuous boundary values

We now show that formulas (4-3.13′) and (4-3.14) for every piecewise continuous function $f(\varphi)$ represent the solution of the boundary-value problem, i.e., that this solution in the entire region is bounded and tends continuously to the boundary value at the points of continuity of the function $f(\varphi)$. Therefore also it is a unique solution (see Section 4-2 § 4). If φ_0 denotes any point of continuity of the function $f(\varphi)$, we have to prove that a δ exists for every $\varepsilon > 0$ such that

$$|u(\rho, \varphi) - f(\varphi_0)| < \varepsilon\,,$$

provided

$$|\rho - a| < \delta(\varepsilon) \qquad \text{and} \qquad |\varphi - \varphi_0| < \delta(\varepsilon)\,.$$

Because of the continuity of $f(\varphi)$, a $\delta_0(\varepsilon)$ can be found such that

$$|f(\varphi) - f(\varphi_0)| < \frac{\varepsilon}{2}$$

holds when

$$|\varphi - \varphi_0| < \delta_0(\varepsilon)\,.$$

We consider now two continuous differentiable auxiliary functions $\bar{f}(\varphi)$ and $\underline{f}(\varphi)$ which satisfy the conditions

$$\bar{f}(\varphi) = f(\varphi_0) + \frac{\varepsilon}{2} \qquad \text{for} \qquad |\varphi - \varphi_0| < \delta_0(\varepsilon)$$

$$\bar{f}(\varphi) \geqq f(\varphi) \qquad \text{for} \qquad |\varphi - \varphi_0| > \delta_0(\varepsilon)$$

and

$$\underline{f}(\varphi) = f(\varphi_0) - \frac{\varepsilon}{2} \qquad \text{for} \qquad |\varphi - \varphi_0| < \delta_0(\varepsilon)$$

$$\underline{f}(\varphi) \leqq f(\varphi) \qquad \text{for} \qquad |\varphi - \varphi_0| > \delta_0(\varepsilon)$$

but are otherwise arbitrary and for which formula (4-3.13) is applicable. Then if we define the functions $\bar{u}(\rho, \varphi)$ and $\underline{u}(\rho, \varphi)$ by the formula (4-3.13) for $\bar{f}$ and $\underline{f}$, then these are harmonic functions which have the functions $\bar{f}(\varphi)$ and $\underline{f}(\varphi)$ as boundary values.

Since the Poisson kernel is positive, then

$$\underline{u}(\rho, \varphi) \leqq u(\rho, \varphi) \leqq \bar{u}(\rho, \varphi)$$

because

$$\underline{f}(\varphi) \leqq f(\varphi) \leqq \bar{f}(\varphi) .$$

Further, from the continuity of $\bar{u}(\rho, \varphi)$ and $\underline{u}(\rho, \varphi)$ on the boundary for $\varphi = \varphi_0$, it follows that a $\delta_1(\varepsilon)$ exists such that

$$|\bar{u}(\rho, \varphi) - \bar{f}(\varphi_0)| \leqq \frac{\varepsilon}{2}$$

for

$$|\rho - a| < \delta_1(\varepsilon) , \qquad |\varphi - \varphi_0| < \delta_1(\varepsilon) ,$$

and

$$|\underline{u}(\rho, \varphi) - \underline{f}(\varphi_0)| \leqq \frac{\varepsilon}{2}$$

for

$$|\rho - a| < \delta_1(\varepsilon) , \qquad |\varphi - \varphi_0| < \delta_1(\varepsilon) .$$

From these inequalities we find

$$\bar{u}(\rho, \varphi) \leqq \bar{f}(\varphi_0) + \frac{\varepsilon}{2} = f(\varphi_0) + \varepsilon$$

$$f(\varphi_0) - \varepsilon = \underline{f}(\varphi_0) - \frac{\varepsilon}{2} \leqq \underline{u}(\rho, \varphi)$$

for

$$|\rho - a| < \delta(\varepsilon), \ |\varphi - \varphi_0| < \delta(\varepsilon) \qquad \delta = \min(\delta_0 , \delta_1) .$$

If now we collect these inequalities, we obtain

$$f(\varphi_0) - \varepsilon \leqq \underline{u}(\rho, \varphi) \leqq u(\rho, \varphi) \leqq \bar{u}(\rho, \varphi) \leqq f(\varphi) + \varepsilon$$

or

$$|u(\rho, \varphi) - f(\varphi_0)| < \varepsilon \qquad \text{for} \qquad |a - \rho| < \delta(\varepsilon), \ |\varphi - \varphi_0| < \delta(\varepsilon)$$

and hence the continuity of $u(\rho, \varphi)$ at the point (a, φ_0).

We shall now show the boundedness of $u(\rho, \varphi)$. Since the Poisson kernel is positive, then

$$u(\rho, \varphi) < M\frac{1}{2\pi}\int_0^{2\pi} \frac{a^2 - \rho^2}{a^2 + \rho^2 - 2a\rho\cos(\varphi - \psi)} d\psi = M ,$$

provided $|f(\varphi)| < M$. Now, however, we have

$$\frac{1}{2\pi}\int_0^{2\pi} \frac{(a^2 - \rho^2)d\psi}{\rho^2 - 2a\rho\cos(\varphi - \psi) + a^2} \equiv 1 ,$$

since the left side, as was proved earlier, represents a harmonic function which tends continuously toward the boundary value $f \equiv 1$. Such a function, however, is identically equal to 1. Correspondingly, we [could] show that $u(\rho, \varphi) > M_1$ for $f > M_1$ and therefore prove the boundedness of the absolute value of $u(\rho, \varphi)$.

4-4. GREEN'S FUNCTION (SOURCE FUNCTION)

The use of Green's function is a convenient aid in the analytical treatment of boundary-value problems. In this section we give the definition and basic properties of the Green's function for the Laplace differential equation as well as the construction of the Green's function for a class of simple regions (circle, sphere, semi-infinite body). The construction follows by using the method of images in electrostatics.

1. Green's function for the equation $\Delta u = 0$ and its basic properties

Let $u(M)$ be a function which with its first derivatives in a closed region T bounded by a sufficiently smooth finite surface Σ, is continuous; further, let $u(M)$ in the interior of T possess continuous second derivatives. Then, as was proved in Section 4-2 § 1, the integral representation

$$u(M_0) = \frac{1}{4\pi}\int_\Sigma\int\left[\frac{1}{r_{PM_0}}\frac{\partial u}{\partial n} - u(P)\frac{\partial}{\partial n}\left(\frac{1}{r_{PM_0}}\right)\right]d\sigma_P - \frac{1}{4\pi}\int\int_T\int\frac{\Delta u}{r_{MM_0}}d\tau_M \tag{4-4.1}$$

is valid. If $u(M)$ is a harmonic function, the volume integral equals zero; if $u(M)$ satisfies the Poisson equation, the volume integral represents a known function.

Further let $v(M)$ be a harmonic function which nowhere possesses singularities. The second Green's formula

$$\int\int_T\int(u\Delta v - v\Delta u)d\tau = \int_\Sigma\int\left(u\frac{\partial v}{\partial n} - v\frac{\partial u}{\partial n}\right)d\sigma$$

then yields

$$0 = \int_\Sigma\int\left(v\frac{\partial u}{\partial n} - u\frac{\partial v}{\partial n}\right)d\sigma - \int\int_T\int v\Delta u d\tau . \tag{4-4.2}$$

By addition of (4-4.2) and (4-4.1) we obtain

$$u(M_0) = \int_\Sigma\int\left(G\frac{\partial u}{\partial n} - u\frac{\partial G}{\partial n}\right)d\sigma - \int\int_T\int\Delta u \cdot G d\tau , \tag{4-4.3}$$

where

$$G(M, M_0) = \frac{1}{4\pi r_{MM_0}} + v \qquad (4\text{-}4.3')$$

is a function of two points $M_0(x, y, z)$ and $M(\xi, \eta, \zeta)$. The point M_0 is held fixed so that the variables x, y, z play the role of parameters.

In the interior of the region T the function $G(M, M_0)$, except at point $M = M_0$ where it possesses a singularity of the form $1/4\pi r$, everywhere satisfies the equation

$$\Delta G = 0 .$$

We now choose $v(M)$ so that

$$G \,|_{\Sigma} = 0 ,$$

i.e.

$$v \,|_{\Sigma} = -\frac{1}{4\pi r} .$$

The function G defined in this manner is called the Green's function of the first boundary-value problem for the Laplace differential equation $\Delta u = 0$ (or also, the function of an instantaneous point source of the first boundary-value problem for the differential equation $\Delta u = 0$). It permits us to give a direct representation of the solution of the first boundary-value problem for the equation $\Delta u = 0$. From (4-4.3) follows

$$u(M_0) = -\int_{\Sigma}\!\!\int u\frac{\partial G}{\partial n}d\sigma = -\int_{\Sigma}\!\!\int f\frac{\partial G}{\partial n}d\sigma , \qquad f = u \,|_{\Sigma} . \qquad (4\text{-}4.4)$$

It must also be noted that formula (4-4.4) was derived by the use of Green's formula, where certain conditions concerning the functions $u(M)$ and $G(M, M_0)$ as well as the boundary Σ were assumed. Moreover, the expression $\partial G/\partial n$ occurs, whose existence on Σ is not immediately seen from the definition of G.

In the derivation of (4-4.4) we proceed from the existence of a harmonic function $u(M)$ which assumes the value f on Σ. For the region in which the Green's function exists and for which the Green's formula is applicable, formula (4-4.4) thus yields an explicit representation of only such solutions $u(M)$ of the first boundary-value problem as satisfy the conditions for the applicability of the Green's formula. (This formula also proves the uniqueness of this class of solutions of the first boundary-value problem.)

A detailed investigation by A. M. Liapunov showed that under very general assumptions formula (4-4.4) represents the solution of the first boundary-value problem for a wide class of boundaries—the so-called Liapunov surfaces (see Section 4-5).

We turn now once more to the definition of the Green's function $G(M, M_0)$ which was introduced by means of the function $v(M)$—itself a solution of the first boundary-value problem for the equation $\Delta v = 0$ with the boundary-values

$v|_\Sigma = -1/4\pi r$. This gives the impression that here this one problem (the determination of the solution u of the first boundary-value problem) would lead back to another of equal difficulty (the determination of v as the solution of the same problem). This is not the case, however, since the knowledge of the Green's function allows the boundary-value problem to be solved for an arbitrary boundary condition ($u|_\Sigma = f$), while for the determination of the function G itself only the boundary-value problem with the particular boundary condition ($v|_\Sigma = -1/4\pi r$) is to be solved. This problem is considerably simpler, as we shall see from a series of examples.

In electrostatics, the Green's function

$$G(M, M_0) = \frac{1}{4\pi r} + v$$

represents the potential[86] at a point M of a point charge which is found inside of a grounded conducting surface Σ at the point M_0.

The first summand $1/4\pi r$ is obviously the potential of the point charge in free space whereas the second summand v represents the potential of the fields which arises from the charges induced on the conducting surface Σ. The construction of the Green's function therefore follows from the determination of the induced fields.

In the following, we shall investigate several properties of the Green's function. We shall assume that the region considered is such that the Green's function $G(M, M_0)$ exists for it and possesses a continuous normal derivative $\partial G/\partial n$. Moreover, we assume that Green's formula is applicable on Σ.

1. The Green's function is positive everywhere in the interior of T. G is equal to zero on the boundary Σ of the region and is positive on the surface of a sufficiently small sphere about the pole. Therefore G must be positive according to the principle of the maximum in the entire region. Further we note that $(dG/dn)|_\Sigma \leqq 0$, which follows directly from the positivity and the condition $G|_\Sigma = 0$.

2. The Green's function is symmetric with respect to its arguments $M_0(x, y, z)$ and $M(\xi, \eta, \zeta)$:

$$G(M, M_0) = G(M_0, M)\,.$$

[86] It is well known that the potential v of a point charge of magnitude e in a medium with dielectric constant ε in the cgs system is given by $v = e/\varepsilon r$. Hence the Green's function corresponds to a charge of $\varepsilon/4\pi$ in absolute electrostatic units. If, on the other hand, we use the so-called Giorgi system, in which Coulomb's law has the form $f = ee'/4\pi\varepsilon r$, then in vacuum ($\varepsilon = 1$) the Green's function $G(M, M_0)$ corresponds to a unit charge.

In heat-conduction theory, the stationary temperature of a point-forming heat source of intensity q is determined by the expression $q/4\pi kr$, where k is the coefficient of thermal conductivity. Therefore, $G(M, M_0)$ is the temperature at the point M, provided the temperature of the surface of the body is equal to zero and at the point M_0 a heat source exists of intensity $q = k$.

If the units of length are so chosen that $k = 1$, then the function $G(M, M_0)$ corresponds to a source of unit intensity.

For the proof, we consider two spheres Σ_1 and Σ_2 of radius ε with M_0' and M_0'' as center points; thus let M_0' and M_0'' be two arbitrary fixed points in T (Figure 50). By T_ε we shall designate the region which results from T by the removal of the regions enclosed by Σ_1 and Σ_2. Now if we set

$$u = G(M, M_0'), \qquad v = G(M, M_0'')$$

and apply the Green's formula

$$\iiint_{T_\varepsilon} (u\Delta v - v\Delta u)d\tau = \iint_{\Sigma_1+\Sigma_2+\Sigma}\left(u\frac{\partial v}{\partial n} - v\frac{\partial u}{\partial n}\right)d\sigma \tag{4-4.5}$$

to T_ε, we obtain

$$\iint_{\Sigma_1}\left[G(M, M_0')\frac{\partial G(M, M_0'')}{\partial n} - G(M, M_0'')\frac{\partial G(M, M_0')}{\partial n}\right]d\sigma_M$$
$$+\iint_{\Sigma_2}\left[G(M, M_0')\frac{\partial G(M, M_0'')}{\partial n} - G(M, M_0'')\frac{\partial G(M, M_0')}{\partial n}\right]d\sigma_M = 0$$

since because $\Delta G = 0$, the left side of (4-4.5) is equal to 0, while the integral over Σ vanishes because of the boundary conditions.

Now, if we let ε approach zero and consider the singularity of the Green's function, we obtain the expression:[87]

$$G(M_0', M_0'') = G(M_0'', M_0')$$

or

$$G(M, M_0) = G(M_0, M).$$

The above-proven symmetry of the Green's function is a mathematical expression of the principle of reciprocity in physics: A source situated at the point M_0 has the same effect at a point M as the same source situated at point M has at point M_0. The principle of reciprocity is of a very general character and arises in different physical fields (electromagnetics, elastic, etc.).

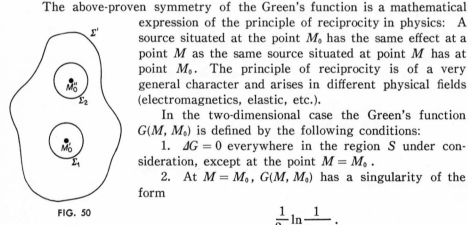

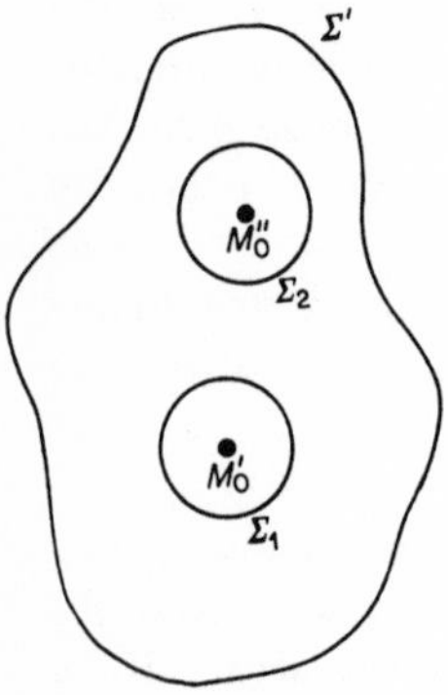

FIG. 50

In the two-dimensional case the Green's function $G(M, M_0)$ is defined by the following conditions:

1. $\Delta G = 0$ everywhere in the region S under consideration, except at the point $M = M_0$.

2. At $M = M_0$, $G(M, M_0)$ has a singularity of the form

$$\frac{1}{2\pi}\ln\frac{1}{r_{MM_0}}.$$

3. $G|_C = 0$ if C is the boundary of S. In this case the Green's function has the form

$$G(M, M_0) = \frac{1}{2\pi}\ln\frac{1}{r_{MM_0}} + v(M, M_0),$$

[87] Liapunov derived this theorem in the application to the class of so-called Liapunov surfaces.

where v is any harmonic function everywhere continuous and on the boundary satisfies the condition

$$v|_\sigma = -\frac{1}{2\pi}\ln\frac{1}{r_{MM_0}} .$$

The solution of the first boundary-value problem for $\Delta u = 0$ is then given by

$$u(M_0) = -\int_\sigma f\frac{\partial G}{\partial n}ds , \qquad f = u|_\sigma .$$

2. The method of images in electrostatics (the electrostatic image) and the Green's function for the sphere

A method often used for the construction of the Green's function is the method of images in electrostatics. Its fundamental idea in the construction of the Green's function

$$G(M, M_0) = \frac{1}{4\pi r_{MM_0}} + v$$

arises from the fact that the induced field v can be represented by the field of the charges which are distributed on the exterior of the surface Σ and are so chosen that the condition

$$v|_\Sigma = -\frac{1}{4\pi r}$$

is satisfied. These charges are called the electrostatic image points of the unit charge found at the point M_0, which, if Σ were not present, would produce the potential $1/4\pi r$. In many cases the choice of such charges causes no difficulty. We shall give three examples for the construction of the Green's function by means of the method of electrostatic images. From the representations of the Green's function, which will be given for the three examples, the continuity of the first derivatives of G on Σ will be obvious.

As the first example we consider the Green's function for the sphere: Given a sphere with radius R whose center lies at the origin of coordinates O, find the corresponding Green's function.

For the determination of this function we place a unit charge at the point M_0 and choose the segment OM_1 on the radial line passing through M_0 such that

$$\rho_0\rho_1 = R^2 , \tag{4-4.6}$$

where $\rho_0 = OM_0$ and $\rho_1 = OM_1$ (Figure 51).

Figure 51 shows the correspondence of the point M_0 with a definite point M_1, by a transformation of reciprocal radii. The point M_1 is called the point conjugate to M_0. This construction is reversible, that is, the point M_0 can be regarded as the point conjugate to M_1.

We prove now that the distances of all the points P lying on the spherical surface are proportional to M_0 and M_1 respectively. Therefore we consider the triangles OPM_0 and OPM_1 (Figure 51); they are similar since the angle at O is the same for both triangles and the adjacent sides are proportional:

$$\frac{\rho_0}{R}=\frac{R}{\rho_1} \quad \text{or} \quad \frac{OM_0}{R}=\frac{R}{OM_1}\,.$$

However, from the similarity of the triangles

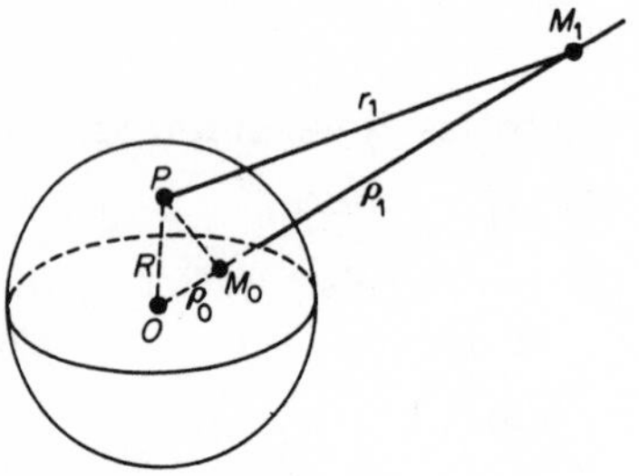

FIG. 51.

$$\frac{r_0}{r_1}=\frac{\rho_0}{R}=\frac{R}{\rho_1} \tag{4-4.7}$$

follows, where $r_0=|\overrightarrow{M_0P}|$, $r_1=|\overrightarrow{M_1P}|$. From (4-4.7) we obtain

$$r_0=\frac{\rho_0}{R}r_1$$

for all points of the spherical surface. Therefore, the harmonic function $v=-(R/\rho_0)(1/r_1)$ on the spherical surface assumes the same values as the function $1/r_0$. It obviously represents the potential of the charge found at M_1 of magnitude $-R/\rho_0$.

Therefore the function

$$G(P, M_0)=\frac{1}{4\pi}\left(\frac{1}{r_0}-\frac{R}{\rho_0}\frac{1}{r_1}\right) \tag{4-4.8}$$

is the sought Green's function for the sphere; thus it is a harmonic function which at M_0 has the singularity $(1/4\pi)(1/r_0)$ and is equal to zero on the spherical surface.

The solution of the first boundary-value problem can then be obtained from formula (4-4.4).

We now calculate the normal derivative

$$\frac{\partial G}{\partial n}=\frac{1}{4\pi}\left[\frac{\partial}{\partial n}\left(\frac{1}{r_0}\right)-\frac{R}{\rho_0}\frac{\partial}{\partial n}\left(\frac{1}{r_1}\right)\right] \tag{4-4.9}$$

where n is the exterior normal and $r_1=\overrightarrow{M_1M}$ (in general, M does not lie on the spherical surface).

For the derivatives of $1/r_0$ and $1/r_1$ along the normal $\boldsymbol{n}$ we have

$$\left.\begin{aligned}\frac{\partial}{\partial n}\left(\frac{1}{r_0}\right)&=\frac{\partial}{\partial r_0}\left(\frac{1}{r_0}\right)\frac{\partial r_0}{\partial n}=-\frac{1}{r_0^2}\cos(\boldsymbol{r}_0,\boldsymbol{n})\,,\\ \frac{\partial}{\partial n}\left(\frac{1}{r_1}\right)&=\frac{\partial}{\partial r_1}\left(\frac{1}{r_1}\right)\frac{\partial r_1}{\partial n}=-\frac{1}{r_1^2}\cos(\boldsymbol{r}_1,\boldsymbol{n})\,,\end{aligned}\right\} \tag{4-4.10}$$

since

$$\frac{\partial r_0}{\partial n}=\cos(\boldsymbol{r}_0,\boldsymbol{n})\,,\qquad \frac{\partial r_1}{\partial n}=\cos(\boldsymbol{r}_1,\boldsymbol{n})\,. \tag{4-4.11}$$

For $\cos(\boldsymbol{r}_0,\boldsymbol{n})$ and $\cos(\boldsymbol{r}_1,\boldsymbol{n})$ we easily find

$$\cos(\boldsymbol{r}_0, \boldsymbol{n}) = \frac{R^2 + r_0^2 - \rho_0^2}{2Rr_0}, \tag{4-4.11'}$$

$$\cos(\boldsymbol{r}_1, \boldsymbol{n}) = \frac{R^2 + r_1^2 - \rho_1^2}{2Rr_1}. \tag{4-4.11''}$$

With the help of (4-4.7) we obtain

$$\cos(\boldsymbol{r}_1, \boldsymbol{n})|_\Sigma = \frac{R^2 + \dfrac{R^2}{\rho_0^2} r_0^2 - \dfrac{R^4}{\rho_0^2}}{2R\dfrac{R}{\rho_0}r} = \frac{\rho_0^2 + r_0^2 - R^2}{2\rho_0 r_0},$$

since according to the definition of the points M_1 the relation

$$\rho_1 = \frac{R^2}{\rho_0}$$

holds, and

$$r_1 = \frac{R}{\rho_0} r_0 \qquad \text{on } \Sigma .$$

By using (4-4.10), (4-4.9), (4-4.11'), and (4-4.11''), we find

$$\left.\frac{\partial G}{\partial n}\right|_\Sigma = \frac{1}{4\pi}\left[-\frac{1}{r_0^2}\frac{R^2 + r_0^2 - \rho_0^2}{2Rr_0} + \frac{\rho_0^2}{R^2 r_0^2}\frac{R}{\rho_0}\frac{\rho_0^2 + r_0^2 - R^2}{2\rho_0 r_0}\right] = -\frac{1}{4\pi R}\frac{R^2 - \rho_0^2}{r_0^3}.$$

Consequently $u(M_0)$, with the use of (4-4.4), equals

$$u(M_0) = \frac{1}{4\pi R}\iint_\Sigma f(P)\frac{R^2 - \rho_0^2}{r_0^3}\,d\sigma_P . \tag{4-4.12}$$

We now introduce a spherical coordinate system whose origin lies at the center of the sphere. Now let R, θ, φ be the coordinates of the point P and ρ_0, θ_0, φ_0 the coordinates of the point M_0; let γ be the angle between the radius vectors $\overrightarrow{OP}$ and $\overrightarrow{OM_0}$. Formula (4-4.12) can then be written in the form

$$u(\rho_0, \theta_0, \varphi_0) = \frac{R}{4\pi}\int_0^{2\pi}\int_0^{\pi} f(\theta, \varphi)\frac{R^2 - \rho_0^2}{(R^2 - 2R\rho_0\cos\gamma + \rho_0^2)^{3/2}}\sin\theta\, d\theta\, d\varphi \tag{4-4.12'}$$

where[88]

$$\cos\gamma = \cos\theta\cos\theta_0 + \sin\theta\sin\theta_0\cos(\varphi - \varphi_0) . \tag{4-4.13}$$

This formula is called the Poisson integral for the spherical surface.

By the same method the Green's function can also be constructed for the region lying exterior to the sphere:

88 The direction cosines of the vectors $\overrightarrow{OP}$ and $\overrightarrow{OM_0}$ are therefore equal to

$$(\sin\theta\cos\varphi, \sin\theta\sin\varphi, \cos\theta) \qquad \text{or} \qquad (\sin\theta_0\cos\varphi_0, \sin\theta_0\sin\varphi_0, \cos\theta_0) .$$

Thus

$$\begin{aligned}\cos\gamma &= \cos\theta\cdot\cos\theta_0 + \sin\theta\sin\theta_0(\cos\varphi\cos\varphi_0 + \sin\varphi\sin\varphi_0)\\ &= \cos\theta\cos\theta_0 + \sin\theta\sin\theta_0\cos(\varphi - \varphi_0) .\end{aligned}$$

$$G(M, M_1) = \frac{1}{4\pi}\left(\frac{1}{r_1} - \frac{R}{\rho_1}\frac{1}{r_0}\right). \tag{4-4.14}$$

$= MM_1$ is the distance of a fixed point M_1 lying outside of the sphere, M_0 is the distance of the point M_0 conjugate to M_1, ρ_2 is the distance point M_1 from the origin of coordinates, and R is the radius of the sphere.

If we bear in mind the distinction between the direction of the normals for the interior and the exterior problem, then we obtain

$$u(\rho_1, \theta_1, \varphi_1) = \frac{R}{4\pi}\int_0^{2\pi}\int_0^{\pi}\frac{\rho_1^2 - R^2}{[R^2 - 2\rho_1 R\cos\gamma + \rho_1^2]^{3/2}} f(\theta, \varphi)\sin\theta\, d\theta\, d\varphi\,,$$

where $\cos\gamma$ is given by formula (4-4.13) (the subscript zero is there replaced by 1).

3. The Green's function for the circle

The Green's function for the circle can be obtained in the same manner as the Green's function for the sphere. In this case the Green's function assumes the form

$$G = \frac{1}{2\pi}\ln\frac{1}{r} + v\,. \tag{4-4.15}$$

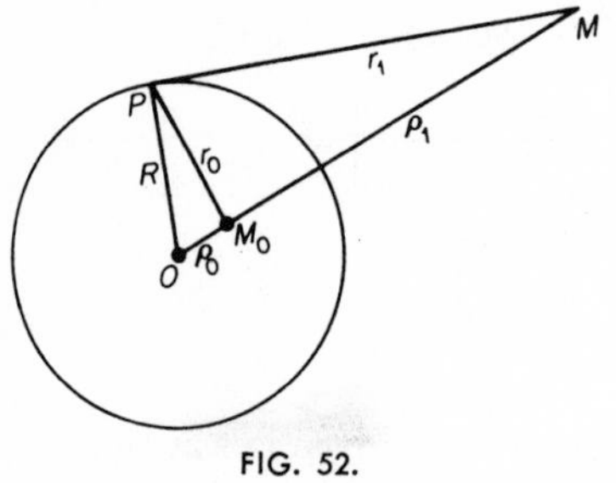

FIG. 52.

If we repeat the arguments of the previous section from formula (4-4.6) to formula (4-4.8), we obtain for $G(P, M_0)$ the representation

$$G(P, M_0) = \frac{1}{2\pi}\left[\ln\frac{1}{r_0} - \ln\frac{R}{\rho_0}\frac{1}{r_1}\right], \tag{4-4.16}$$

where $\rho_0 = OM_0$, $r_0 = M_0P$, $r_1 = M_1P$, and $R = OP$ is the radius of the circle (Figure 52). We see immediately that the harmonic function so defined on the boundary C is equal to zero,

$$G|_C = 0\,.$$

For the solution of the first boundary-value problem the normal derivative $\partial G/\partial n$ on the circumference C must be calculated. The calculation proceeds as for the sphere and yields

$$\left.\frac{\partial G}{\partial n}\right|_C = -\frac{1}{2\pi R}\frac{R^2 - \rho_0^2}{r_0^2}\,.$$

Now let ρ, θ be the polar coordinates of the points P lying on the circumference and ρ_0, θ_0 the coordinates of M_0. Then, first of all, we have

$$r_0^2 = R^2 + \rho_0^2 - 2R\rho_0\cos(\theta - \theta_0)\,.$$

If we substitute this expression for r_0 into the formula

$$u(\rho_0, \theta_0) = \frac{1}{2\pi}\int_C u(P)\frac{R^2 - \rho_0^2}{r_0^2}\frac{ds}{R}$$

and note that

$$u(P)\,|_C = f(\theta) \qquad \text{and} \qquad ds = Rd\theta$$

then we obtain for the function $u(M_0)$ the expression

$$u(\rho_0, \theta_0) = \frac{1}{2\pi}\int_0^{2\pi} \frac{R^2 - \rho_0^2}{R^2 + \rho_0^2 - 2R\rho_0 \cos(\theta - \theta_0)} f(\theta)\, d\theta \,, \qquad (4\text{-}4.17)$$

the so-called Poisson integral for the interior of a circle. Except for the signs this formula also gives the solution of the exterior problem.

4. The Green's function for the half space

The notion of the Green's function and formula (4) are also valid for an unbounded region of space, provided the functions considered are regular at infinity (see Section 4-2 § 6).

To determine the Green's function for the half space $z > 0$, we place at the point $M_0(x_0, y_0, z_0)$ a unit charge which produces in the unbounded region of space a field whose potential is defined by the function

$$\frac{1}{4\pi}\frac{1}{r_{M_0M}}, \qquad \left(r_{M_0M} = \sqrt{(x - x_0)^2 + (y - y_0)^2 + (z - z_0)^2}\right).$$

We easily see that the induced field v is the field of a negative unit charge placed at the point $M_1(x_0, y_0, -z_0)$, which is the mirror image of the point M_0 in the plane $z = 0$ (Figure 53). The function $G(M, M_0)$ is equal to

$$G(M, M_0) = \frac{1}{4\pi r_0} - \frac{1}{4\pi r_1},$$

where

$$r_0 = \overrightarrow{M_0M} = \sqrt{(x - x_0)^2 + (y - y_0)^2 + (z - z_0)^2}$$

$$r_1 = \overrightarrow{M_1M} = \sqrt{(x - x_0)^2 + (y - y_0)^2 + (z + z_0)^2}\,.$$

$G(M, M_0)$ is equal to zero for $z = 0$ and has the required singularity at the point M_0.

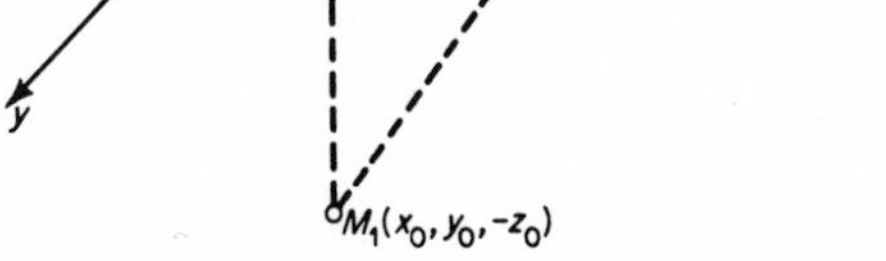

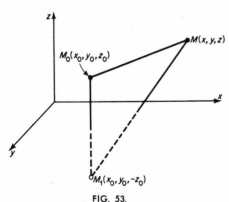

FIG. 53.

We now calculate

$$\left.\frac{\partial G}{\partial n}\right|_{z=0} = -\left.\frac{\partial G}{\partial z}\right|_{z=0}.$$

Obviously,

$$\frac{\partial G}{\partial z} = \frac{1}{4\pi}\left[-\frac{z - z_0}{r_0^3} + \frac{z + z_0}{r_1^3}\right].$$

For $z = 0$, we thus find

$$\left.\frac{\partial G}{\partial n}\right|_{z=0} = -\left.\frac{\partial G}{\partial z}\right|_{z=0} = -\frac{z_0}{2\pi r_0^3}.$$

The solution of the first boundary-value problem is therefore given by

$$u(M_0) = \frac{1}{2\pi}\int_{\Sigma_0}\int \frac{z_0}{r^3_{M_0P}} f(P) d\sigma_P ,$$

where Σ_0 is the surface $z = 0$ and $f(P) = u|_{z=0}$. Thus we can also write

$$u(x_0, y_0, z_0) = \frac{1}{2\pi}\int_{-\infty}^{\infty}\int_{-\infty}^{\infty} \frac{z_0}{[(x-x_0)^2 + (y-y_0)^2 + z_0^2]^{3/2}} f(x, y) dx dy . \quad (4\text{-}4.18)$$

4-5. POTENTIAL THEORY

The function

$$\frac{1}{r} = \frac{1}{\sqrt{(x-\xi)^2 + (y-\eta)^2 + (z-\zeta)^2}} ,$$

which represents the potential of the field of a unit mass (charge) placed at the point $M_0(\xi, \eta, \zeta)$, is a solution of Laplace's equation. Here ξ, η, and ζ are interpreted as parameters. The integral of this function with respect to the parameters is called the potential. It has a significant meaning both in physics and also in the development of the methods of solution for boundary value problems.

1. Spatial potential (Newtonian potential)

Let a mass m_0 exist at $M_0(\xi, \eta, \zeta)$. According to the law of gravitation, the attracting force on a mass m placed at the point $M(x, y, z)$ is

$$\boldsymbol{F} = -\gamma \frac{m m_0}{r^3} \boldsymbol{r} . \quad (4\text{-}5.1)$$

Here $\boldsymbol{r} = \overrightarrow{M_0M}$ and γ is the gravitational constant. By a suitable choice of units we can make $\gamma = 1$. Further, if we set $m = 1$, we obtain

$$\boldsymbol{F} = -\frac{m_0}{r^3} \boldsymbol{r} .$$

The projections of this force on the coordinate axes are

$$\begin{aligned} X &= F \cos \alpha = -\frac{m_0}{r^3}(x-\xi) \\ Y &= F \cos \beta = -\frac{m_0}{r^3}(y-\eta) \\ Z &= F \cos \gamma = -\frac{m_0}{r^3}(z-\zeta) \end{aligned} \quad (4\text{-}5.2)$$

where α, β, and γ are the angles between the vector $\boldsymbol{F}$ and the coordinate axes.

Through

$$\boldsymbol{F} = \text{grad}\, u$$

or

$$X = \frac{\partial u}{\partial x}, \qquad Y = \frac{\partial u}{\partial y}, \qquad Z = \frac{\partial u}{\partial z}$$

we introduce the so-called potential $u(x, y, z)$ of the force field.[89] In our case we have

$$u = \frac{m_0}{r}.$$

By superposition of the force fields, the potential field of n mass points can be expressed by the formula

$$u = \sum_{i=1}^{n} u_i = \sum_{i=1}^{n} \frac{m_i}{r}.$$

We treat now the case of a continuous distribution of mass and consider a bounded region of space T with a density distribution $\rho(\xi, \eta, \zeta)$. In order to determine the potential of this spatial region at a point $M(x, y, z)$, we divide T into sufficiently small volume elements $\Delta\tau$ and assume that the influence of a spatial element $\Delta\tau$ is equivalent to the influence of a mass concentrated at an interior point (ξ, η, ζ) of $\Delta\tau$.[90]

For the X component of the force acting on the point M we then obtain

$$\Delta X = -\frac{\rho \Delta\tau}{r^3}(x - \xi),$$

with

$$r^2 = (x - \xi)^2 + (y - \eta)^2 + (z - \zeta)^2.$$

The X component of the potential of the total region T at M is obtained by summation of the individual potentials over all spatial elements, i.e., by integration over T:

$$X = -\iiint_T \rho \frac{x - \xi}{r^3} d\tau. \qquad (4\text{-}5.3)$$

Therefore we obtain for the potential of a spatial region T at the point M the so-called Newtonian potential

$$u(M) = \iiint_T \rho \frac{1}{r} d\tau. \qquad (4\text{-}5.4)$$

If M lies outside of T, then this follows directly by differentiation under the

[89] The potential introduced here should not be confused with the energy potential of a force field. Potential here is understood in the sense of the force function in mechanics.

[90] More precisely stated, it is assumed that the influence of a body T of mass m on a point lying outside a convex region T containing this body can be replaced by the influence of a certain concentrated force with the same mass m which lies in the interior of T.

integral sign.[91] We calculate the higher derivatives in a similar way. For each point M lying in the exterior of T, $u(M)$ satisfies the Laplace differential equation.

In the following we shall use the above-mentioned properties of the potential and formulate a series of theorems under the condition that $\rho(\xi, \eta, \zeta)$ is a bounded (and also integrable) function. We do not intend to develop the theory under the most possible general assumptions.

If the point M lies in the interior of T, then we cannot directly conclude that $X = \partial u / \partial x$. We shall go into the necessary additional investigation later.

2. The planar problem (logarithmic potential)

We now investigate a special mass distribution which depends only on the two coordinates x and y. Obviously then the potentials on each of the planes $v =$ const. assume one and the same value. Therefore it is sufficient to consider the potential at the points (x, y) which lie in the plane $z = 0$.

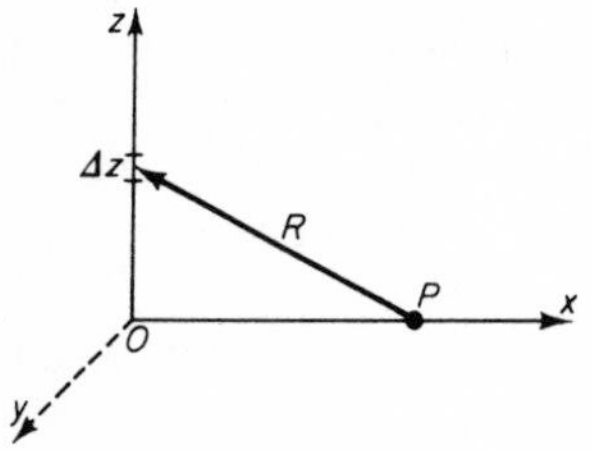

FIG. 54.

First we shall determine the potential of a homogeneous infinite straight line L. For this we choose the z axis in the direction of this straight line. Let the linear density (i.e. the mass per unit of length) be equal to μ. For an element Δz on a point $P(x, 0)$ (Figure 54), we obtain the attracting force whose component with respect to the x axis is

$$\Delta F = -\frac{\mu \Delta z}{R^2} = -\frac{\mu \Delta z}{(x^2 + z^2)}$$

$$\Delta X = \Delta F \cos \alpha = -\mu \Delta z \cdot \frac{x}{\sqrt{(x^2 + z^2)^3}} .$$

Hence it follows that

$$X = -\int_{-\infty}^{\infty} \mu x \frac{dz}{(x^2 + z^2)^{3/2}} = -\mu x^2 \frac{1}{x^3} \int_{-\pi/2}^{\pi/2} \cos \alpha \, d\alpha = -\frac{2\mu}{x} ,$$

$$\frac{z}{r} = \operatorname{tg} \alpha .$$

If $P(x, y)$ is an arbitrary point, then the attracting force acting on a point at O obviously is in the direction of $\overrightarrow{OP}$ and its magnitude is equal to

[91] A sufficient condition for differentiation under the integral sign, with respect to a parameter, for an integral of the form

$$f(M) = \int_T F(M, P) \varphi(P) d\tau_P$$

is the continuity of the derivative of $F(M, P)$ with respect to the parameter and the absolute integrability of $\varphi(P)$. Ordinarily this theorem is formulated only for $\varphi(P) = 1$, although the proof for this and the general case are not different.

$$F = -\frac{2\mu}{\rho},$$

where

$$\rho = \sqrt{x^2 + y^2}.$$

The potential of this force is called the logarithmic potential; it is equal to

$$V = 2\mu \ln \frac{1}{\rho}, \tag{4-5.5}$$

which we recognize directly by differentiation.

The logarithmic potential represents a solution of the two-dimensional Laplace differential equation which is circularly symmetric with respect to the point $\rho = 0$ and at this point becomes logarithmically infinite. Thus the potential of a homogeneous straight line represented by formula (4-5.5) produces a planar field. The representation of the potential in the form of an integral was derived only for a bounded region.[92]

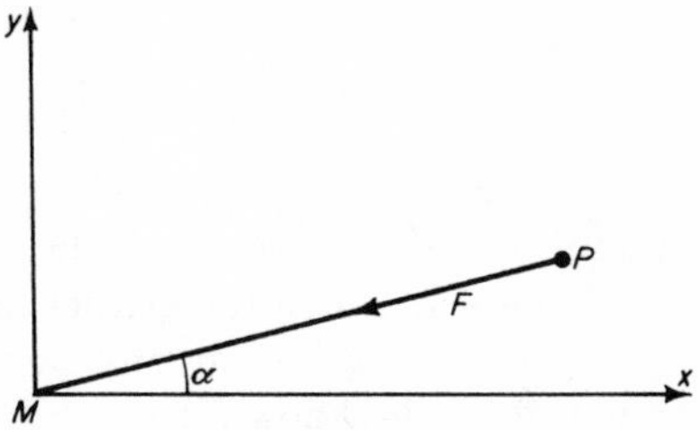

FIG. 55.

We note that in contrast to the spatial potential, the logarithmic potential at infinity does not equal zero but has a logarithmic singularity there.

For the components of the attracting force at point P (Figure 55) we find

$$X = F\cos\alpha = -2\mu\frac{x}{\rho^2}, \qquad \cos\alpha = \frac{x}{\rho}$$

$$Y = F\sin\alpha = -2\mu\frac{y}{\rho^2}, \qquad \sin\alpha = \frac{y}{\rho}.$$

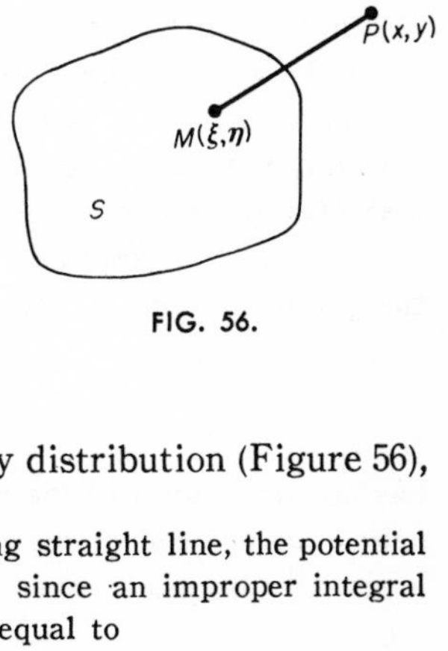

FIG. 56.

If several points (an infinite straight line with distributed mass) exist, then because of the superposition of the force fields the potentials at the point P can be added (straight line).

In the case of a region S with continuous density distribution (Figure 56),

[92] In the calculation of the potential of an infinitely long straight line, the potential of the individual elements cannot be integrated directly since an improper integral would result. The potential of an element Δz is therefore equal to

$$\Delta u = \mu \frac{\Delta z}{\sqrt{\rho^2 + z^2}},$$

so that formal integration would yield the improper integral

$$u = \int_{-\infty}^{\infty} \mu \frac{dz}{\sqrt{\rho^2 + z^2}}.$$

the components of the attractive force on the point P can be expressed by the double integrals

$$X = -2\int_S\int \mu(\xi, \eta)\frac{x-\xi}{(x-\xi)^2+(y-\eta)^2}d\xi\, d\eta$$
$$Y = -2\int_S\int \mu(\xi, \eta)\frac{y-\eta}{(y-\eta)^2+(x-\xi)^2}d\xi\, d\eta \tag{4-5.6}$$

and for the potential we find

$$u(x, y) = 2\int_S\int \mu(\xi, \eta)\ln\frac{1}{\sqrt{(x-\xi)^2+(y-\eta)^2}}d\xi\, d\eta\ , \tag{4-5.7}$$

which we can prove by differentiation if the point lies outside the region S. If P lies inside of S, then an additional investigation is necessary in the proof.

3. Improper integrals

Potentials and components of gravitational forces can be represented by integrals whose integrands become infinite when we consider their value at the points at which the attracting masses are placed.

If the integrand at any point of the region of integration is infinite, the integral as is known cannot be defined as the limit value of the integral sum. In this case, therefore, the integral sum has no limit value, since the summand corresponding to the element of volume containing the singularity can arbitrarily change the magnitude of the sum, depending on how one selects the corresponding intermediate points. The integrals of such functions are defined as improper integrals.

Let $F(x, y, z)$ be a function which becomes infinite at an arbitrary point $M_0(x_0, y_0, z_0)$ in a region T. We then consider the integral over a region $T - K_\varepsilon$, where K_ε denotes an arbitrary neighborhood of the point M_0 whose diameter does not exceed ε.

If now the sequence of regions K_ε shrinks in an arbitrary manner about the point M_0 and if the sequence of integrals

$$I_n = \iint_{T-K_{\varepsilon_n}}\int F\, d\tau \qquad \varepsilon_n \to 0$$

has a limit value independent of the choice of K_{ε_n}, then the limit value is called an improper integral of the function $F(x, y, z)$ over the region T and is usually denoted by

$$\iint_T\int F\, d\tau\ .$$

If at least one sequence of neighborhoods $\bar{K}_{\varepsilon_n}$ exists such that as $\varepsilon_n \to 0$ a limit value $\bar{I}$ exists, whereas for another sequence $\{K_{\varepsilon_n}\}$ this limit value has another value or does not exist, then the limit value $\bar{I}$ is called a conditionally convergent improper integral. Naturally, for the consideration of a conditionally convergent integral, a sequence of neighborhoods $\{\bar{K}_{\varepsilon_n}\}$ must exist through which it is defined.

We limit ourselves here to the consideration of those cases in which the integrand has an isolated singularity, such as integrals of the form

$$\iiint_T \frac{C}{r^\alpha} d\tau_M , \tag{4-5.8}$$

where C and $\alpha > 0$ are constants and

$$r = r_{MM_0} = \sqrt{(x_0 - \xi)^2 + (y_0 - \eta)^2 + (z_0 - \zeta)^2}$$

and M_0 denotes a point in T. Without loss of generality we can assume T to be a sphere of radius R about M_0. Further, we choose as neighborhoods K_{ε_n} spheres of radii ε_n about M_0. For the calculation of the sought limit value of the corresponding sequence of integrals we first obtain

$$\iiint_{T-K_{\varepsilon_n}} \frac{C}{r^\alpha} d\tau = \int_0^{2\pi} d\varphi \int_0^\pi \sin\theta \, d\theta \int_{\varepsilon_n}^R \frac{C}{r^{\alpha-2}} dr = 2\pi \cdot 2C \int_{\varepsilon_n}^R \frac{dr}{r^{\alpha-2}}$$

$$= \begin{cases} 4\pi C \left[\dfrac{1}{3-\alpha} r^{3-\alpha}\right]_{\varepsilon_n}^R & \text{for} \quad \alpha \neq 3 \\ 4\pi C \, [\ln r]_{\varepsilon_n}^R , & \text{for} \quad \alpha = 3 . \end{cases}$$

Now if we let $\varepsilon_n \to 0$, then it can be shown that the limit value exists for $\alpha < 3$ but not for $\alpha \geqq 3$.

Now let $F(x, y, z)$ be a nonnegative function and let the following limit value exist

$$I = \lim_{\varepsilon_n \to 0} \iiint_{T-\bar{K}_{\varepsilon_n}} F \, d\tau ,$$

where $\bar{K}_{\varepsilon_n}$ represents spheres of radii ε_n about M. Further let $\{K_{\varepsilon_n}\}$ be an arbitrary sequence of regions, which shrink to the point M. Then, also, for this sequence of neighborhoods the limit value of the corresponding sequence of integrals exists and the value of this limit value is independent of the form of the K_{ε_n}. For the proof we proceed from the fact that each of the regions K_{ε_n} can be enclosed by two spheres $\bar{K}_{\varepsilon_{n_1}}$ and $\bar{K}_{\varepsilon_{n_2}}$, whose radii ε_{n_1} and ε_{n_2} together with ε_n approach zero (Figure 57). Since the integrand is always nonnegative, we obtain

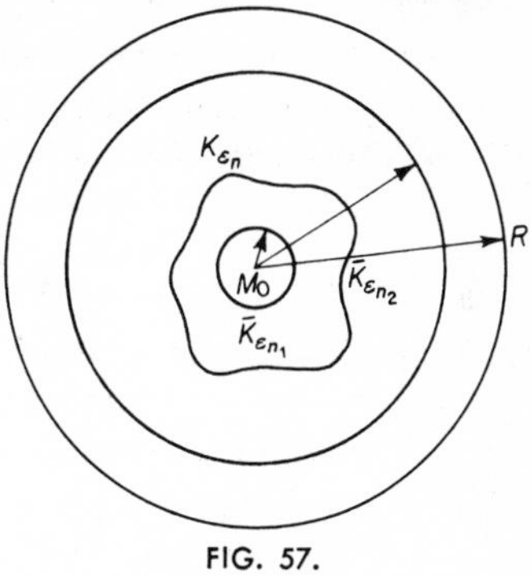

FIG. 57.

$$\iiint_{T-\bar{K}_{\varepsilon_{n_1}}} F \, d\tau \geqq \iiint_{T-K_{\varepsilon_n}} F \, d\tau \geqq \iiint_{T-\bar{K}_{\varepsilon_{n_2}}} F \, d\tau .$$

It follows, however, that

$$\lim_{n\to\infty} \iiint_{T-K_{\varepsilon_n}} F \, d\tau = \lim_{n\to\infty} \iiint_{T-\bar{K}_{\varepsilon_n}} F \, d\tau = I ,$$

since the limit value of the outer integral exists and coincides with it.

Thus we have the following results:

In the case of three independent variables, the improper integral

$$\iiint_T \frac{C}{r^\alpha} d\tau \tag{4-5.8}$$

exists, provided $\alpha < 3$, and does not exist if $\alpha \geqq 3$.

In general, if the critical value α which determines the convergence of the integral of the form (4-5.8) is equal to the number of independent variables, then in the two-dimensional case the integral

$$\iint_\Sigma \frac{C}{\rho^\alpha} d\sigma$$

converges for $\alpha < 2$ and is divergent for $\alpha \geqq 2$.

We shall now establish the following criterion for the convergence of improper integrals:

To guarantee the convergence of an improper integral

$$\iiint_T F(x, y, z) dx\, dy\, dz \tag{4-5.9}$$

it is sufficient that a nonnegative function $\bar{F}(x, y, z)$ exist for which the improper integral over the region T converges and such that the inequality

$$|F(x, y, z)| \leqq \bar{F}(x, y, z) \tag{4-5.10}$$

is valid.

For the proof, we consider any sequence of regions K_{ε_n} which entirely contains the singular point M_0. Because of the convergence of the sequence $\{\bar{I}_n\}$ of the integrals of $\bar{F}(x, y, z)$, an $N(\varepsilon)$ exists for each $\varepsilon > 0$ such that

$$|\bar{I}_{n_1} - \bar{I}_{n_2}| = \left| \iiint_{K_{\varepsilon_{n_1}} - K_{\varepsilon_{n_2}}} \bar{F}\, d\tau \right| < \varepsilon$$

is valid when $n_1, n_2 > N(\varepsilon)$. Since $\bar{F}(x, y, z)$ is a majorant of $|F(x, y, z)|$, we can write

$$|I_{n_1} - I_{n_2}| = \left| \iiint_{K_{\varepsilon_{n_1}} - K_{\varepsilon_{n_2}}} F\, d\tau \right| \leqq \iiint_{K_{\varepsilon_{n_1}} - K_{\varepsilon_{n_2}}} |F|\, d\tau \leqq \iiint_{K_{\varepsilon_{n_1}} - K_{\varepsilon_{n_2}}} \bar{F}\, d\tau < \varepsilon \tag{4-5.10'}$$

when $n_1, n_2 > N(\varepsilon)$ holds. On the basis of the Cauchy convergence criterion, the condition (4-5.10′) is, however, sufficient for the convergence of the sequence

$$I_n = \iiint_{T - K_{\varepsilon_n}} F\, d\tau$$

toward a limit value

$$I = \lim_{n \to \infty} I_n = \iiint_T F\, d\tau .$$

We easily see that this limit value is not dependent on the choice of the K_{ε_n}. Therefore, the existence of the improper integral (4-5.9) is completely proved.

If, on the other hand, a nonnegative function $\bar{F}(x, y, z)$ can be found such that $F(x, y, z) \geqq \bar{F}(x, y, z)$, and if the improper integral of $\bar{F}$ diverges over the region T, then the integral of F also diverges.

Conclusion:

If for a function $F(M, P)$ which becomes unbounded at $P = M$ the inequality

$$|F(M, P)| < \frac{C}{r_{MP}^{\alpha}}, \qquad \alpha < 3,$$

is satisfied, then the improper integral

$$\iiint_T F(M, P) d\tau_P$$

converges over the region T which contains the point M.

As is known from the theory of integrals containing a parameter, the continuity of the integrand with respect to the parameter and the independent variables is sufficient for the continuity of the integral with respect to the parameter. For the improper integrals considered here, however, the integrands are not continuous functions and therefore the above criterion is not applicable.

To find a criterion for the continuity of improper integrals which depend on a parameter, we shall consider the improper integral

$$V(M) = \int_T F(P, M) f(P) d\tau_P, \tag{4.5-11}$$

for which $F(P, M)$ at $P = M$ is unbounded but with respect to M is a continuous function, whereas $f(P)$ is a bounded function.

An integral (4-5.11) is said to be uniformly convergent at the point M_0 if for every $\varepsilon > 0$ a $\delta(\varepsilon)$ exists such that the inequality

$$|V_{\delta(\varepsilon)}(M)| = \left|\int_{T_{\delta(\varepsilon)}} F(P, M) f(P) d\tau_P\right| \leqq \varepsilon$$

is valid for each point M whose distance from M_0 is less than $\delta(\varepsilon)$, and for every region $T_{\delta(\varepsilon)}$ which contains the point M_0 and whose diameter $d \leqq \delta(\varepsilon)$.

We prove now that at the point M_0 a uniformly convergent integral

$$V(M) = \int_T F(P, M) f(P)\, d\tau_P$$

represents a continuous function. Thus we have to show that for every $\varepsilon > 0$, a $\delta(\varepsilon)$ can be found such that

$$|V(M_0) - V(M)| < \varepsilon$$

is valid when

$$|\overrightarrow{MM_0}| < \delta(\varepsilon).$$

First, inside the region T we select a subregion T_1 which contains the point M_0 (Figure 58), and split the integral into two summands

$$V = V_1 + V_2,$$

where the integral V_1 is taken over T_1 and the integral V_2 over $T_2 = G - T_1$. We shall consider later the magnitude over T_1. The following estimate is valid:

$$|V(M_0) - V(M)| \leqq |V_2(M_0) - V_2(M)| + |V_1(M_0)| + |V_1(M)|.$$

Each summand standing on the right can be made smaller than $\varepsilon/3$ for sufficiently small $|\overrightarrow{M_0M}|$. Now if we choose T_1 in the interior of a sphere of radius $\delta(\varepsilon/3)$, we obtain

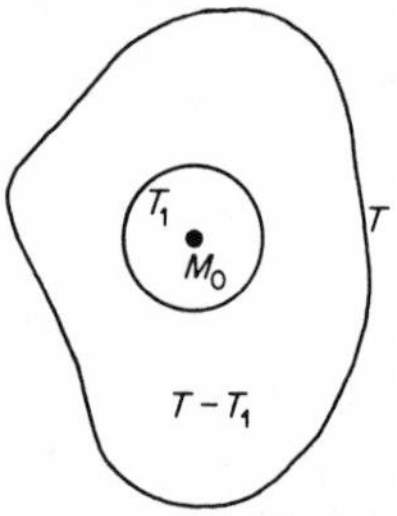

FIG. 58.

$$|V_1(M_0)| \leqq \frac{\varepsilon}{3} \quad \text{and} \quad |V_1(M)| \leqq \frac{\varepsilon}{3},$$

when

$$|\overrightarrow{M_0M}| \leqq \delta'\left(\frac{\varepsilon}{3}\right).$$

The existence of such a δ' follows from the uniform convergence of the integrals (4.5.11) at the point M_0. By the selection T_1, T_2 also is determined.

Since M_1 lies in the exterior of T_2, V_2 is a continuous function at this point. From this follows the existence of a $\delta''(\varepsilon/3)$ such that

$$|V_2(M_0) - V_2(M)| \leqq \frac{\varepsilon}{3},$$

provided

$$|\overrightarrow{M_0M}| \leqq \delta''\left(\frac{\varepsilon}{3}\right).$$

Now if we set

$$\delta(\varepsilon) = \min\,[\delta'(\varepsilon), \delta''(\varepsilon)],$$

then we obtain

$$|V(M) - V(M_0)| \leqq \varepsilon \quad \text{for} \quad |\overrightarrow{M_0M}| \leqq \delta,$$

whereby the continuity of a uniformly convergent integral is proved.

These results are valid not only for spatial integrals but for surface and line integrals as well, a fact that we shall utilize in the following calculations.

We consider now a potential

$$V(M) = \iiint_T \frac{\rho(P)}{r_{MP}}\, d\tau_P \tag{4-5.12}$$

and the components of the corresponding attracting force

$$\left.\begin{aligned} X(M) &= -\iiint_T \frac{\rho(P)}{r_{MP}^3}(x-\xi)d\tau_P \\ Y(M) &= -\iiint_T \frac{\rho(P)}{r_{MP}^3}(y-\eta)d\tau_P \\ Z(M) &= -\iiint_T \frac{\rho(P)}{r_{MP}^3}(z-\zeta)d\tau_P \end{aligned}\right\} \qquad (4\text{-}5.13)$$

at the points which lie in the interior of the attracting body. The improper integrals (4-5.12) and (4-5.13) converge when the density $\rho(M)$ is bounded, $\rho|(M)| < C$. For the potential $V(M)$ this is obvious since

$$\frac{|\rho|}{r} < \frac{C}{r^\alpha}, \qquad \alpha = 1 < 3 .$$

For the components of the attractive force the assertion follows from the inequality

$$\frac{|\rho|}{r^2}\frac{|x-\xi|}{r} < \frac{C}{r^\alpha}, \qquad \alpha = 2 < 3$$

since $|x-\xi| < r$.

As an illustration of the uniform convergence of an improper integral we show that the integrals (4-5.12) and (4-5.13) are continuous functions.

Therefore, we have to prove that the integrals (4-5.12) and (4-5.13) converge uniformly at each point M_0.

First,

$$\left|\iiint_{T_\delta} \frac{\rho(P)}{r_{MP}} d\tau_P\right| \leqq C\iiint_{K_\delta^{M_0}} \frac{d\tau_P}{r_{MP}}$$

is valid,[93] where $K_\delta^{M_0}$ is a sphere of radius δ about M_0 which contains the region T_δ. For the calculation of the integral on the right over the sphere $K_\delta^{M_0}$ we introduce suitable spherical coordinates whose origin is at the point M. Then obviously

$$C\left|\iiint_{K_\delta^{M_0}} \frac{d\tau_P}{r_{MP}}\right| \leqq C\left|\iiint_{K_{2\delta}^{M_0}} \frac{d\tau_P}{r_{MP}}\right| = 8C\pi\delta^2 ,$$

where $K_{2\delta}^M$ is the sphere of radius 2δ about M. Now if $\varepsilon > 0$ is prescribed, then we have only to choose

$$\delta \leqq \delta(\varepsilon) = \sqrt{\frac{\varepsilon}{8\pi C}} .$$

Thus the condition for the uniform convergence of the integral V is satisfied.

By a corresponding consideration for the integral

$$X(M) = \iiint_T \rho(P)\frac{x-\xi}{r_{MP}^3} d\tau_P ,$$

[93] The integral (4-5.12) results from integral (4-5.11) for $F(M, P) = 1/r_{MP}$, $f(P) = \rho(P)$.

we obtain

$$\left|\iiint_{T_\delta} \rho(P) \frac{x-\xi}{r_{MP}^3} d\tau_P \right| \leqq C \left|\iiint_{K_\delta^{M_0}} \frac{d\tau_P}{r_{MP}^2}\right| \leqq C \left|\iiint_{K_{2\delta}^{M}} \frac{d\tau_P}{r_{MP}^2}\right| = 8\pi\delta C \leqq \varepsilon ,$$

when

$$\delta \leqq \delta(\varepsilon) = \frac{\varepsilon}{8\pi C} .$$

Therefore the potential V and the components $X(M)$, $Y(M)$, and $Z(M)$ of the attracting force in the entire space are shown to be continuous functions.[94]

4. The first derivatives of spatial potentials

The integrands of the integral

$$X(M) = -\iiint_T \rho(P) \frac{x-\xi}{r_{MP}^3} d\tau_P , \qquad Y(M) , \qquad Z(M)$$

are the derivatives of the integrands of

$$V(M) = \iiint_T \frac{\rho(P)}{r_{MP}} d\tau_P .$$

If the differentiation under the integral signs is carried out for the function $V(M)$, then

$$X = \frac{\partial V}{\partial x} , \qquad Y = \frac{\partial V}{\partial y} , \qquad Z = \frac{\partial V}{\partial z} , \tag{4-5.14}$$

i.e., V is the potential of a field with components X, Y, and Z.

If the point M lies outside the region T, then

$$-\frac{x-\xi}{r_{MP}^3} = \frac{-(x-\xi)}{[(x-\xi)^2 + (y-\eta)^2 + (z-\zeta)^2]^{3/2}} = \frac{\partial}{\partial x} \frac{1}{r_{MP}}$$

is a continuous function with respect to the two arguments $M(x, y, z)$ and $P(\xi, \eta, \zeta)$. Consequently, in this case differentiation under the integral sign can be easily carried out.

The higher derivatives can be calculated by differentiation under the integral sign at all points exterior to T. Hence it follows on the basis of the lemma from Chapter 3, Section 2 that the potential outside the attracting mass satisfies the Laplace differential equation

$$\Delta V = 0 .$$

We shall now show that the derivatives of the first order of the potential V also can be obtained by differentiation under the integral sign when the point M considered lies inside of the region T.

[94] The uniform convergence of the integrals $V(M)$ and $X(M)$ was shown under the assumption that the density ρ is bounded ($|\rho| < C$). Consequently, these integrals also are continuous at the points of discontinuity of the function ρ, in particular on the boundary of the region covered with a continuous distribution of mass.

For the proof we use the boundedness but not the continuity of the function $\rho(x, y, z)$ ($|\rho(x, y, z)| < C$). It follows that $V(x, y, z)$ also is continuous at the boundary points of T. These points can be considered as points of discontinuity of the function $\rho(P)$ which vanishes outside of T.

We shall now prove that for every $\varepsilon > 0$ a $\delta(\varepsilon)$ exists such that

$$\left|\frac{V(x + \Delta x, y, z) - V(x, y, z)}{\Delta x} - X\right| < \varepsilon$$

when

$$|\Delta x| < \delta(\varepsilon) .$$

To this end we enclose the point $M_0(x, y, z)$ by a sufficiently small sphere $K_{\delta'}^{M_0}$, whose magnitude will be fixed later, and split V into two summands

$$V = V_1 + V_2 ,$$

where V_1 corresponds to integration over $T_1 = K_{\delta'}^{M_0}$, and V_2 to integration over $T_2 = T - K_{\delta'}^{M_0}$. Then

$$\frac{V(x + \Delta x, y, z) - V(x, y, z)}{\Delta x} = \frac{V_1(x + \Delta x, y, z) - V_1(x, y, z)}{\Delta x} + \frac{V_2(x + \Delta x, y, z) - V_2(x, y, z)}{\Delta x} .$$

For an arbitrarily fixed T_1, we have

$$\lim_{\Delta x \to 0} \frac{V_2(x + \Delta x, y, z) - V_2(x, y, z)}{\Delta x} = X_2 = \iiint_{T_2} \rho(\xi, \eta, \zeta) \frac{\partial}{\partial x}\left(\frac{1}{r}\right) d\tau ,$$

since M_0 lies outside of T_2.

Now the following estimate is valid:

$$\left|X - \frac{V(x + \Delta x, y, z) - V(x, y, z)}{\Delta x}\right| \leqq \left|X_2 - \frac{V_2(x + \Delta x, y, z) - V_2(x, y, z)}{\Delta x}\right| + |X_1| + \left|\frac{V_1(x + \Delta x, y, z) - V_1(x, y, z)}{\Delta x}\right| .$$

Each of the summands occurring here can be made smaller than $\varepsilon/3$. First we find

$$|X_1| = \left|\iiint_{T_1} \rho \frac{x - \xi}{r^3} d\tau\right| < C \int_0^{\delta'} \int_0^{2\pi} \int_0^{\pi} \frac{r^2 \sin \vartheta d\vartheta d\varphi dr}{r^2} = 4\pi C \delta' < \frac{\varepsilon}{3} , \quad (4\text{-}5.15)$$

since $|(x - \xi)/r| \leqq 1$ and $|\rho| < C$. Further, we have for the third summand

$$|S| = \left|\frac{V_1(x + \Delta x, y, z) - V_1(x, y, z)}{\Delta x}\right|$$
$$= \left|\frac{1}{\Delta x} \iiint_{T_1} \rho\left(\frac{1}{r_1} - \frac{1}{r}\right) d\tau\right| = \left|\frac{1}{\Delta x} \iiint_{T_1} \rho \frac{r - r_1}{r r_1} d\tau\right|$$

with

$$r_1 = \sqrt{[(x + \Delta x) - \xi]^2 + (y - \eta)^2 + (z - \zeta)^2}$$
$$r = \sqrt{(x - \xi)^2 + (y - \eta)^2 + (z - \zeta)^2} .$$

The sides of the triangle M_0MM_1 are equal to r, r_1, and $|\Delta x|$. Hence it follows that

$$|r - r_1| \leqq |\Delta x|,$$

so that

$$|S| \leqq C\iint_{T_1}\int \frac{d\tau}{rr_1} \leqq C\frac{1}{2}\left\{\iint_{T_1}\int \frac{d\tau}{r_1^2} + \iint_{T_1}\int \frac{d\tau}{r^2}\right\},$$

since for arbitrary numbers a and b

$$ab \leqq \frac{1}{2}(a^2 + b^2).$$

Therefore,

$$\iint_{T_1}\int \frac{d\tau}{r^2} = 4\pi\delta',$$

and

$$\iint_{T_1}\int \frac{d\tau}{r_1^2} \leqq \iint_{K_{2\delta'}^{M_1}}\int \frac{d\tau}{r_1^2} = 8\pi\delta',$$

where $K_{2\delta'}^{M_1}$ is a sphere of radius $2\delta'$ about M_1.

By a suitable choice of δ' the inequality

$$|S| < \frac{C}{2}12\pi\delta' = 6\pi C\delta' < \frac{\varepsilon}{3} \tag{4-5.16}$$

can be satisfied. If we choose δ' according to the condition (4-5.16), then the inequality (4-5.15) also is satisfied. Now we set $T_1 = K_{\delta'}^{M_0}$ and therefore also $T_2 = T - T_1$.

The first equation of (4-5.14) applied to the region T_2 so selected means that for every $\varepsilon > 0$, a δ'' exists such that

$$\left|\frac{V_2(x + \Delta x, y, z) - V_2(x, y, z)}{\Delta x} - X_2\right| < \frac{\varepsilon}{3}$$

when $|\Delta x| < \delta''$.

Finally, if we choose $\delta = \min[\delta', \delta'']$, we obtain

$$\left|\frac{V(x + \Delta x, y, z) - V(x, y, z)}{\Delta x} - X\right| < \varepsilon \qquad \text{for} \qquad |\Delta x| < \delta.$$

Therefore, it is proved that

$$\frac{\partial V}{\partial x} = X. \tag{4-5.17}$$

The expressions

$$\frac{\partial V}{\partial y} = Y \qquad \text{and} \qquad \frac{\partial V}{\partial z} = Z$$

can be proved similarly.

Therefore we have proved that by differentiation under the integral sign the components X, Y, Z of the force field are the components of grad V.

5. The second derivatives of spatial potentials

The improper integral

$$\iint_T\int \rho(P)\frac{\partial^2}{\partial x^2}\left(\frac{1}{r_{MP}}\right)d\tau_P = -\iint_T\int \rho\left(\frac{1}{r^3} - 3\frac{(x-\xi)^2}{r^5}\right)d\tau \qquad (4\text{-}5.18)$$

does not converge absolutely at an interior point P of the bounded region T. Here the majorant of the magnitude of the integrands has the form

$$\frac{C}{r^\alpha} \quad \text{with} \quad \alpha = 3\,.$$

In the following, a formula will be given which permits the calculation of the second derivatives of the potential $V(M)$ in the region T when the continuity and the continuous differentiability of the density $\rho(x, y, z)$ are assumed in the neighborhood of point P. Above all, the investigation is not applicable at a boundary point at which the density as a rule has a point of discontinuity.

We again write the potential $V(M)$ in the form

$$V = V_1 + V_2\,,$$

where as before the summands refer to the two regions T_1 and T_2. Here $T_1 = K_\delta^{M_0}$ denotes a sphere of radius δ about M_0 in which the density $\rho(x, y, z)$ is differentiable.

The second derivatives of V_2 can be obtained by differentiation under the integral sign since the point M_0 lies outside of T_2, e.g.,

$$\frac{\partial^2 V_2}{\partial x^2} = \frac{\partial}{\partial x}\left(\frac{\partial V_2}{\partial x}\right) = \iint_{T_2}\int \rho(\xi, \eta, \zeta)\frac{\partial^2}{\partial x^2}\left(\frac{1}{r}\right)d\tau\,.$$

For the first derivative of V_1 with respect to x we find

$$\frac{\partial V_1}{\partial x} = \iint_{T_1}\int \rho\frac{\partial}{\partial x}\left(\frac{1}{r}\right)d\tau = -\iint_{T_1}\int \rho\frac{\partial}{\partial \xi}\left(\frac{1}{r}\right)d\tau\,, \qquad (4\text{-}5.19)$$

since

$$\frac{\partial}{\partial x}\left(\frac{1}{r}\right) = -\frac{\partial}{\partial \xi}\left(\frac{1}{r}\right).$$

By applying the Green's formula, the integral (4-5.19) is transformed into

$$\frac{\partial V_1}{\partial x} = -\iint_{T_1}\int \rho\frac{\partial}{\partial \xi}\left(\frac{1}{r}\right)d\tau = -\iint_{T_1}\int\left[\frac{\partial}{\partial \xi}\left(\rho\frac{1}{r}\right) - \frac{1}{r}\frac{\partial \rho}{\partial \xi}\right]d\tau$$

$$= -\int_{\Sigma_\delta^{M_0}}\int \frac{\rho}{r}\cos\alpha\, d\sigma + \iint_{T_1}\int \frac{1}{r}\frac{\partial \rho}{\partial \xi}\, d\tau$$

where $\Sigma_\delta^{M_0}$ is the spherical surface bounding T_1 and α denotes the angle between the exterior normal to the surface $\Sigma_\delta^{M_0}$ and the x axis. The first summand is a differentiable function at the point M_0, since M_0 lies outside of $\Sigma_\delta^{M_0}$. Similarly, if the second summand is differentiable in the neighborhood of the point M_0, then ρ is differentiable in T_1. From this it follows that at the point M_0 the second derivative of the function V_1 exists. Consequently,

$$\frac{\partial}{\partial x}\left(\frac{\partial V_1}{\partial x}\right) = -\int_{\Sigma_\delta^{M_0}}\!\!\int \rho \frac{\partial}{\partial x}\left(\frac{1}{r}\right) \cos\alpha \, d\sigma + \iint_{T_1}\!\!\int \frac{\partial}{\partial x}\left(\frac{1}{r}\right)\frac{\partial \rho}{\partial \xi} d\tau \, .$$

For the second summand at M_0 the following estimate holds:

$$\left|\iint_{T_1}\!\!\int \frac{\partial}{\partial x}\left(\frac{1}{r}\right)\frac{\partial\rho}{\partial\xi} d\tau\right| < C_1 \iint_{T_1}\!\!\int \frac{d\tau}{r^2} = C_1 4\pi\delta \, , \tag{4.5-20}$$

provided

$$\left|\frac{\partial\rho}{\partial\xi}\right| < C_1 \, .$$

If we apply the mean-value theorem to the surface integral, we obtain

$$-\int_{\Sigma_\delta^{M_0}}\!\!\int \rho \frac{\partial}{\partial x}\left(\frac{1}{r}\right)\cos\alpha\, d\sigma = -\int_{\Sigma_\delta^{M_0}}\!\!\int \rho \frac{\cos^2\alpha}{r^2} d\sigma = -\rho^* \frac{4\pi}{3} \, .$$

Here ρ^* is a suitable intermediate value of the density at a point of $\Sigma_\delta^{M_0}$. Further,

$$-\frac{\partial}{\partial x}\left(\frac{1}{r}\right) = \frac{x-\xi}{r^3} = -\frac{1}{r^2}\cos\alpha$$

and

$$\int_{\Sigma_\delta^{M_0}}\!\!\int \frac{\cos^2\alpha}{r^2} d\tau = \frac{1}{3}\int_{\Sigma_\delta^{M_0}}\!\!\int \frac{1}{r^2}(\cos^2\alpha + \cos^2\beta + \cos^2\gamma) d\sigma = \frac{4}{3}\pi \, .$$

By passage to the limit as $\delta \to 0$, we obtain

$$\lim_{\delta\to 0} \frac{\partial^2 V_1}{\partial x^2} = \lim_{\delta \to 0}\left[-\int_{\Sigma_\delta^{M_0}}\!\!\int \rho \frac{\partial}{\partial x}\left(\frac{1}{r}\right)\cos\alpha\, d\sigma\right] = -\frac{4\pi}{3}\rho(M_0) \, . \tag{4-5.21}$$

The equation

$$\frac{\partial^2 V}{\partial x^2} = \frac{\partial^2 V_1}{\partial x^2} + \frac{\partial^2 V_2}{\partial x^2}$$

is true for every δ. Since, moreover, its left side does not depend on δ, then

$$\frac{\partial^2 V}{\partial x^2} = \lim_{\delta\to 0}\left(\frac{\partial^2 V_1}{\partial x^2} + \frac{\partial^2 V_2}{\partial x^2}\right) = -\frac{4\pi}{3}\rho(M) + \lim_{\delta\to 0}\iint_{T_2}\!\!\int \rho \frac{\partial^2}{\partial x^2}\left(\frac{1}{r}\right) d\tau \, . \tag{4-5.22}$$

The existence of the limit value

$$\lim_{\delta\to 0}\iint_{T_2}\!\!\int \rho\frac{\partial^2}{\partial x^2}\left(\frac{1}{r}\right) d\tau = \overline{\iint_{T}\!\!\int} \rho \frac{\partial^2}{\partial x^2}\left(\frac{1}{r}\right) d\tau \tag{4-5.23}$$

follows from the existence of the second derivative $\partial^2 V/\partial x^2$ proved above.

This integral was obtained by a special choice of passage to the limit, and indeed the sphere was shrunk to the point M_0.[95] This is indicated in formula (4-5.23) by the bar above the integral sign. In general, a change in the shape of this region implies a change of the limit value; the integral (4-5.23) is conditionally convergent (in the sense of the above definition). Accordingly,

$$\frac{\partial^2 V}{\partial x^2}(M_0) = \overline{\iiint_T} \rho \frac{\partial^2}{\partial x^2}\left(\frac{1}{r}\right) d\tau - \frac{4\pi}{3}\rho(M_0) \,. \tag{4-5.24}$$

From this we see that the calculation of the second derivatives of the potential by formal differentiation under the integral sign would lead to an incorrect result.

Analogous expressions hold for the derivatives $\partial^2 V/\partial y^2$ and $\partial^2 V/\partial z^2$. By substitution of the three derivatives into the expression for the Laplace operator we find

$$\begin{aligned} \Delta V &= \frac{\partial^2 V}{\partial x^2} + \frac{\partial^2 V}{\partial y^2} + \frac{\partial^2 V}{\partial z^2} \\ &= \overline{\iiint_T} \rho\left[\frac{\partial^2}{\partial x^2}\left(\frac{1}{r}\right) + \frac{\partial^2}{\partial y^2}\left(\frac{1}{r}\right) + \frac{\partial^2}{\partial z^2}\left(\frac{1}{r}\right)\right] d\tau - 4\pi\rho(M_0) \\ &= -4\pi\rho(M_0) \end{aligned} \tag{4-5.25}$$

since $1/r$ is a harmonic function.[96]

Therefore the spatial potential satisfies Poisson's equation

$$\Delta V = -4\pi\rho$$

inside the body, and the Laplace equation

$$\Delta V = 0$$

outside the body.

The inhomogeneous equation

$$\Delta u = -f \tag{4-5.25'}$$

possesses the particular solution

$$u_0 = \frac{1}{4\pi}\iiint_T \frac{f d\tau}{r} ,$$

provided f is differentiable in a fixed region T.

From this it is evident that the solution of a boundary-value problem for the inhomogeneous Eq. (4-5.25′) can lead back to the solution of the corresponding boundary-value problem for the Laplace equation $\Delta v = 0$, in which the sought function is put in the form $u = u_0 + v$.

[95] The limit value (4-5.23) can be regarded as the principal value of the integral.

[96] Formula (4-5.25) was derived under the assumption that the function $\rho(M)$ was differentiable. This condition can be replaced by weaker conditions. However, the continuity of $\rho(M)$ would be insufficient for the validity of (4-5.25), since continuous functions $\rho(M)$ exist for which the spatial potential possesses no second derivatives.

6. Surface potentials

As the Green's formula shows:

$$U(M) = \frac{1}{4\pi}\int_{\Sigma}\!\!\int\left[\frac{1}{r_{MP}}\frac{\partial u}{\partial n} - u\frac{\partial}{\partial n}\left(\frac{1}{r}\right)\right]d\sigma_P$$

(see Section 4-2), every harmonic function can be represented by integrals which are surface potentials.

We will now determine the potential of the field of a surface Σ loaded with a mass. For the definition of the surface density $\mu(P)$ at the point P of Σ, we proceed in the following manner. Let $\{\Sigma_\nu\}$ be a sequence of surface elements which shrink down to a fixed point P on Σ, i.e., the relation

$$\lim_{\nu\to\infty} \sigma_\nu = 0$$

holds provided we understand σ_ν to be its surface area. Each Σ_ν corresponds to a mass layer m, which is considered as a function of σ_ν, i.e., it can be written in the form $m = m(\sigma_\nu)$. Thus we denote the limit value

$$\mu(P) = \lim_{\sigma_\nu\to 0}\frac{m(\sigma_\nu)}{\sigma_\nu} = \frac{dm}{d\sigma_P}$$

as the surface density of the surface Σ at the point P.[97] The potential of this mass load can then be represented by the surface integral

$$V(M) = \int_{\Sigma}\!\!\int\frac{\mu(P)}{r_{MP}}d\sigma_P\,, \tag{4-5.26}$$

the so-called potential of a single layer.

Another type of a surface potential represents the potential layer whose definition we shall now develop.

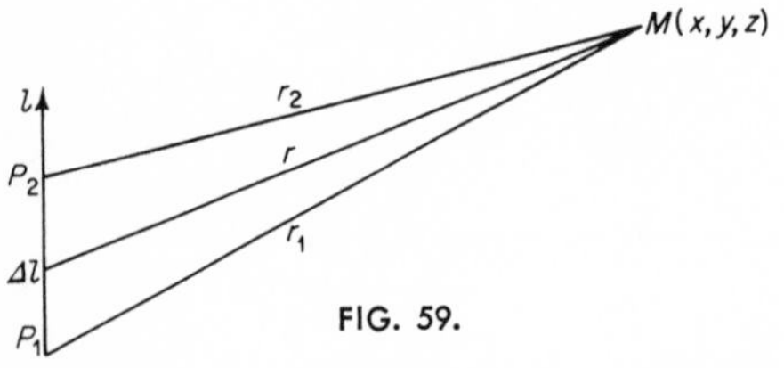

FIG. 59.

We consider a dipole which is formed by two masses $-m$ and m situated at the points P_1 and P_2 and at a distance Δl (Figure 59) from each other. The product $m\Delta l = N$ is called the moment of the dipole. For the potential at an arbitrary point $M(x, y, z)$ we then have

$$V = \frac{m}{r_2} - \frac{m}{r_1} = m\left(\frac{1}{r_2} - \frac{1}{r_1}\right) = N\frac{1}{\Delta l}\left(\frac{1}{r_2} - \frac{1}{r_1}\right),$$

where r_1 and r_2 are the distances of the points M from T_1 and T_2, respectively.

[97] If the mass with spatial density ρ is distributed into layers of thickness h on the surface Σ and the field is considered at the points whose distances from the surface are large in comparison with h, $(h/r \ll 1)$, then the consideration of the thickness of the layer in general is unimportant. It is suitable however to consider, instead of the spatial potential with density ρ, the corresponding surface potential with a surface density $\mu = \rho h$.

If Δl is small in comparison with the distance to the point M ($\Delta l/r_1 \ll 1$), then by use of the mean-value theorem we can write

$$V = N\frac{d}{dl}\left(\frac{1}{r}\right), \qquad r = \sqrt{(x-\xi)^2 + (y-\eta)^2 + (z-\zeta)^2}.$$

Here the vector $\boldsymbol{l}$ is along the direction from the repelling mass to the attracting mass, and r is the distance of the point $M(x, y, z)$ from a fixed intermediate point $P(\xi, \eta, \zeta)$ of the interval Δl.

For the derivative in the $\boldsymbol{l}$ direction we obtain

$$\frac{d}{dl}\left(\frac{1}{r}\right) = \frac{1}{r^2}\cos(\boldsymbol{r}, \boldsymbol{l}) = \frac{\cos\varphi}{r^2},$$

where the vector $\boldsymbol{r}$ is directed along the dipole to a fixed point M, whereas φ is the angle between the vectors $\boldsymbol{l}$ and $\boldsymbol{r}$. Hence, the potential of the dipole is

$$V(M) = N\frac{\cos\varphi}{r^2}, \tag{4-5.27}$$

where N is the moment of the dipole.

Now let two surfaces Σ and Σ' (Figure 60) which are parallel and at a distance δ from each other be loaded with a mass in such a way that the mass of each of the elements of Σ' accordingly is equal and opposite to the magnitude and the signs of the corresponding element of Σ. By $\boldsymbol{n}$, we denote the normal common to the surfaces Σ and Σ', which are directed from the repelling to the attracting masses. Now if we let δ approach zero, then we obtain the double layer as the totality of two infinitesimally close layers whose densities have opposite signs. If ν is the surface density of the moment, then the moment of the surface element $d\sigma_P$ equals

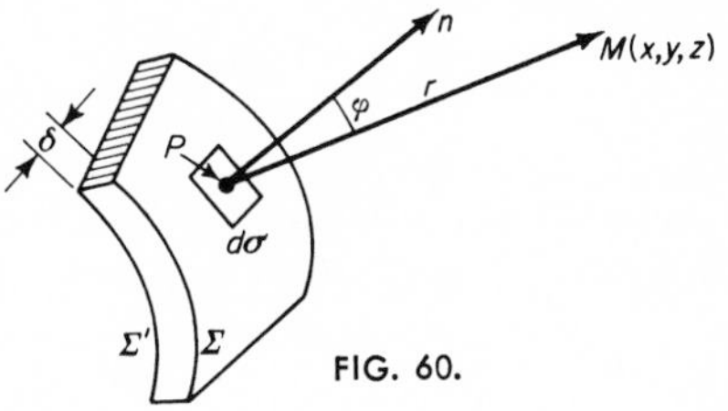

FIG. 60.

$$dN = \nu d\sigma_P.$$

For the potential of the element $d\sigma$ at the point $M(x, y, z)$ we then have

$$\nu\frac{d}{dn_P}\left(\frac{1}{r_{MP}}\right)d\sigma_P = \nu(P)\frac{\cos\varphi}{r_{MP}}d\sigma_P,$$

where φ is the angle between $\boldsymbol{n}$ and $\overrightarrow{PM}$.

The integral

$$W(M) = -\int\!\!\int_\Sigma \frac{d}{dn_P}\left(\frac{1}{r_{MP}}\right)\nu(P)d\sigma_P \tag{4-5.28}$$

is called the potential of a double layer. This definition obviously corresponds to the case in which the outer side of the surface acts so as to repel and the inner side acts so as to attract.

If φ_1 is the angle between the interior normal and the direction $\overrightarrow{PM}$, then

$$W = \int_\Sigma\int \frac{\cos\varphi_1}{r^2_{MP}} \nu(P) d\sigma_P .$$

If the surface is not closed then we have to regard it as two-sided, since the potential of the double layer is defined only for such surfaces.

The potential of the single and double layers assumes, in the two-dimensional case, the form

$$V = \int_\sigma \mu(P) \ln \frac{1}{r_{MP}} ds , \tag{4-5.29}$$

$$W = -\int_\sigma \nu(P) \frac{d}{dn_P}\left(\ln \frac{1}{r_{MP}}\right) ds = \int_\sigma \frac{\cos\varphi_1}{r_{MP}} \nu(P) ds \tag{4-5.30}$$

where C is an arbitrary curve, μ is the linear density of the single layer, ν is the moment density of the double layer on the curve, and φ_1 is the angle between the interior normal to the curve and the direction to the test point.

If the test point $M(x, y, z)$ lies exterior to the surface (i.e., outside of the attracting mass), then the integrands in the equations

$$V(M) = \int_\Sigma\int \mu(P) \frac{1}{r_{MP}} d\sigma_P$$

$$W(M) = -\int_\Sigma\int \nu(P) \frac{d}{dn_P}\left(\frac{1}{r_{MP}}\right) d\sigma_P$$

including their derivatives of arbitrary order are continuous functions of x, y, z. Therefore the derivatives of the surface potential at the points which lie outside of the surface Σ can be calculated by differentiation under the integral sign. Hence it follows on the basis of the superposition principle that the surface potential everywhere outside the attracting mass satisfies the Laplace differential equation. The functions (4-5.29) and (4-5.30) obviously satisfy the two-dimensional Laplace differential equation.

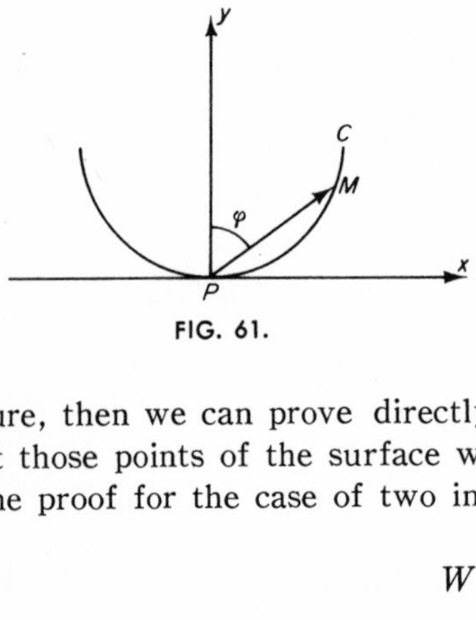

FIG. 61.

At the points on Σ, the surface potential can be represented by an improper integral. If the surface possesses a continuous curvature, then we can prove directly that the potential of a double layer exists at those points of the surface where the curvature is continuous. To give the proof for the case of two independent variables

$$W = \int_\sigma \frac{\cos\varphi}{r} \nu ds ,$$

we consider the curve C in the x, y plane and select as the origin of coordinates the point P. The x axis coincides with the tangent to the curve, the y axis with the normals at this point (Figure 61). In a fixed neighborhood of the point P, the equation of the curve can be written in the form

$$y = y(x) .$$

Now C, by assumption, has a continuous curvature, i.e., $y(x)$ possesses a continuous second derivative. Consequently,

$$y(x) = y(0) + xy'(0) + \frac{x^2}{2}y''(\vartheta x) , \qquad 0 < \vartheta < 1 ,$$

where, because of the special choice of the coordinate axes, it follows that

$$y(x) = \frac{1}{2}x^2 y''(\vartheta x) .$$

Therefore, we have

$$r = \sqrt{x^2 + y^2} = \sqrt{x^2 + x^4\left[\frac{y''(\vartheta x)}{2}\right]^2} = x\sqrt{1 + x^2\left[\frac{y''(\vartheta x)}{2}\right]^2} ,$$

$$\cos\varphi = \frac{y}{r} = \frac{xy''(\vartheta x)}{2\sqrt{1 + x^2\left[\frac{y''(\vartheta x)}{2}\right]^2}}$$

and

$$\frac{\cos\varphi}{r} = \frac{y''(\vartheta z)}{2\left\{1 + x^2\left[\frac{y''(\vartheta x)}{2}\right]^2\right\}} .$$

Further, for the curvature,

$$y''(0) = K(P)$$

results from the expression

$$K = \frac{y''}{(1 + y'^2)^{3/2}} .$$

Therefore,

$$\lim_{MP \to 0} \frac{\cos\varphi}{r} = \frac{1}{2}K(P) .$$

This expression shows the continuity of $(\cos\varphi)/r$ along the segments of the curve and therefore also the existence of the potentials of the double layer at the points of the curve C, provided ν is bounded.

In the three-dimensional case, the potential of the double layer also exists at the points of the surface considered, since the function

$$\frac{\cos\varphi}{r^2}$$

has an integrable singularity of order $1/r$. The existence of the potential of a single layer presents no difficulties.

7. Liapunov surfaces and curves

The requirement that the surface Σ considered possess a finite curvature, is considered superfluous for the existence of the corresponding surface potential.

As is known, the potential of the single and the double layer are improper integrals at the points of Σ. We shall show that these integrals for a definite class of surfaces, the so-called Liapunov surfaces, converge, if the density of the layer is bounded, that is, if $|\nu(P)| < C, C = \text{const.}$

A surface Σ is called a Liapunov surface if the following conditions are satisfied:

1. At each point of Σ a well-defined normal (tangent plane) exists.
2. A number $d > 0$ exists such that the elements Σ'_P of the surface Σ parallel to the normals at any point P of Σ which lie within a sphere of radius d about P do not intersect Σ more than once. These surface elements Σ'_P are called a Liapunov neighborhood.
3. The angle $\gamma(P, P') = (\boldsymbol{n}_P, \boldsymbol{n}_{P'})$ formed by the normals at two points P and P' satisfies the condition

$$\gamma(P, P') < Ar^{\delta}, \tag{4-5.31}$$

where r is the distance between the points P and P', A is a fixed constant, and $0 < \delta \leqq 1$.

Now let P_0 be an arbitrary point of Σ. We then choose a rectangular coordinate system whose origin is at P_0 and whose z axis is in the direction of the exterior normal. The x, y plane then coincides with the tangent plane at this point. Because of condition (4-5.2), a ρ_0 exists such that the equation of the surface Σ can be written in the form[98]

$$z = f(x, y), \tag{4-5.32}$$

provided

$$\rho = \sqrt{x^2 + y^2} < \rho_0 . \tag{4-5.33}$$

Now let Σ'_{P_0} be a neighborhood of the point P_0 on the surface Σ determined by the conditions (4-5.32) and (4-5.33).

From the existence of the normals at each point on the surface (Condition 1) the differentiability of $f(x, y)$ follows. The direction cosines of the exterior normals, therefore, are given by the formula

$$\cos\alpha = \frac{z_x}{\sqrt{1 + z_x^2 + z_y^2}} \qquad \cos\beta = \frac{z_y}{\sqrt{1 + z_x^2 + z_y^2}} \qquad \cos\gamma = \frac{1}{\sqrt{1 + z_x^2 + z_y^2}} .$$

Because of the special choice of our coordinate system, however, $z_x(P_0) = 0$, and $z_y(P_0) = 0$. We assume the surface Σ'_{P_0} to be so small (i.e., ρ_0 is sufficiently small), that

[98] If the function $f(x, y)$ in the neighborhood of the point P_0 has a continuous second derivative, then the surface satisfies the Liapunov conditions. Consequently, surfaces with continuous curvature belong to the class of Liapunov surfaces.

$$1 \geqq \cos\gamma = \frac{1}{\sqrt{1 + z_x^2 + z_y^2}} > \frac{1}{2}\,. \qquad (4\text{-}5.34)$$

Further, we denote by $\boldsymbol{n}'_P$ the projection of the vectors $\boldsymbol{n}_P$ on the x, y plane and by α', β' the angles formed by the vectors $\boldsymbol{n}'_P$ with the x axis and the y axis, respectively. Obviously then,

$$\cos\alpha = \sin\gamma\cos\alpha' \qquad \cos\beta = \sin\gamma\sin\alpha'\,.$$

Condition (3) now asserts that

$$\sin\gamma < \gamma < Ar_{PP_0}^{\delta}\,,$$

hence

$$|\cos\alpha| < Ar_{PP_0}^{\delta}\,, \qquad |\cos\beta| < Ar_{PP_0}^{\delta}\,, \qquad (4\text{-}5.35)$$

and since

$$z_x = \frac{\cos\alpha}{\cos\gamma}\,, \quad z_y = \frac{\cos\beta}{\cos\gamma} \qquad \text{with} \qquad \frac{1}{\cos\gamma} < 2$$

then

$$|z_x| < 2Ar_{PP_0}^{\delta}\,, \qquad |z_y| < 2Ar_{PP_0}^{\delta}\,.$$

If we now apply Taylor's formula to $z = f(x, y)$ in the neighborhood of the point $P_0(0, 0)$, we obtain

$$z(x, y) = z(0, 0) + xz_x(\bar{x}, \bar{y}) + yz_y(\bar{x}, \bar{y})\,,$$

where

$$0 \leqq \bar{x} \leqq x\,, \qquad 0 \leqq \bar{y} \leqq y\,.$$

From this follows the estimate

$$|z(x, y)| < 4Ar_{PP_0}^{1+\delta}\,. \qquad (4\text{-}5.36)$$

The estimates (4-5.34) and (4-5.36) now permit the proof of the proposition that the potential of the double layer

$$W(M) = \iint_{\Sigma} \frac{\cos\varphi}{r_{MP}^2}\nu(P)d\sigma_P \qquad (4\text{-}5.28)$$

at points of the surface Σ represents a convergent improper integral, provided Σ is a Liapunov surface. Now let $M = P_0$ be a point on the surface Σ. If we choose our coordinate system again in the above-described manner, we can write the equation of the surface Σ in the neighborhood of the point P_0 in the form

$$z = f(x, y)\,,$$

where the function $f(x, y)$ satisfies the inequalities (4-5.34) and (4-5.36).

Now if φ is the angle between the direction of the interior normal at the point $P(\xi, \eta, \zeta)$ and the direction $\overrightarrow{PP_0}$, then we can easily obtain the relation

$$|\cos\varphi| = \left|\frac{\xi}{r}\cos\alpha + \frac{\eta}{r}\cos\beta + \frac{\zeta}{r}\cos\gamma\right| \leqq |\cos\alpha| + |\cos\beta| + \frac{|\zeta|}{r}$$
$$\leqq Ar^{\delta}_{PP_0} + Ar^{\delta}_{PP_0} + 4Ar^{\delta}_{PP_0} = 6Ar^{\delta}_{PP_0}$$

and

$$\left|\frac{\cos\varphi}{r^2}\right| \leqq 6A\frac{1}{r^{2-\delta}}, \qquad 0 < \delta \leqq 1 . \tag{4-5.37}$$

Further, we can write the integral $W(M)$ as the sum of two integrals:

$$W = W_1 + W_2 .$$

Here W_1 denotes the integral over the surface Σ'_{P_0} containing the singular point P_0, and W_2 is the integral over the remaining part of the surface, that is, it is extended over $\Sigma - \Sigma'_{P_0}$. For proof of the convergence of W it is sufficient to show the convergence of W_1, since the integrand of W_2 remains finite everywhere. In polar coordinates $\rho = \sqrt{\xi^2 + \eta^2}$ and θ in the x, y plane,

$$d\sigma = \frac{d\xi\, d\eta}{\cos\gamma} = \frac{\rho d\rho\, d\theta}{\cos\gamma},$$

holds, so that by a transformation of the variables we obtain

$$W_1 = \int_{\Sigma'_{P_0}}\!\!\int \frac{\cos\varphi}{r^2_{PP_0}}\nu(P)d\sigma_P = \int_0^{\rho_0}\!\!\int_0^{2\pi} \frac{\cos\varphi}{r^2_{PP_0}}\nu(P)\frac{1}{\cos\gamma}\rho d\rho d\theta .$$

On the basis of the estimates (4-5.34), (4-5.36), and (4-5.37) and because $\rho < r$ we have for the integrands

$$\left|\nu(P)\frac{\cos\varphi}{r^2}\frac{1}{\cos\gamma}\right| \leqq \bar{F} = \frac{12AC}{\rho^{2-\delta}} .$$

This form of the majorant function $\bar{F}$, however, guarantees, in the case of two independent variables, the convergence of the improper integrals (see Section 4-3).

It can easily be shown that for a Liapunov surface the potential of a single layer

$$V(M) = \int_{\Sigma}\!\!\int \frac{1}{r_{MP}}\mu(P)d\sigma_P \tag{4-5.26}$$

also converges at points of this surface. Let it also be noted that the potential for a more comprehensive class of surfaces converges.

In the two-dimensional case the potential of the single and double layers converges at points of the curve considered [see formulas (4-5.29) and (4-5.30)], provided this potential exists on a Liapunov curve. The conditions for these curves are analogous to Conditions 1–3 for the Liapunov surfaces.

8. Discontinuities of the potential of a double layer

We shall now prove that the potential of a double layer at a point P_0

on the surface Σ is a discontinuous function, for which the relations

$$\begin{aligned} W_I(P_0) &= W(P_0) + 2\pi\nu(P_0) \\ W_A(P_0) &= W(P_0) - 2\pi\nu(P_0) \end{aligned} \tag{4-5.38}$$

are valid. Here $W_I(P_0)$ denotes the limit value of the potential of the double layer for an approach to the point P_0 from the inner side, and $W_A(P_0)$ the limit value for an approach from the exterior side of the surface.[99]

In the case of two independent variables, the corresponding formulas have the form

$$\begin{aligned} W_I(P_0) &= W(P_0) + \pi\nu(P_0) \\ W_A(P_0) &= W(P_0) - \pi\nu(P_0) . \end{aligned} \tag{4-5.39}$$

For simplicity, we shall limit ourselves to the proof of these formulas for two independent variables.

The potential of a double layer is represented in this case by the integral

$$W(M) = \int_C \frac{\cos\varphi}{r_{MP}} \nu(P) ds_P .$$

We begin with an arbitrary element of arc ds, whose end points are P and P_1. Through the point P we construct a circular arc of radius MP about M. This cuts the ray MP_1 at the point Q. Then we can write to within terms of higher order

$$ds \cos\varphi = d\sigma , \qquad \frac{d\sigma}{r} = d\omega \tag{4-5.40}$$

(Figure 62), where $ds = \widehat{PP_1}$ and $d\sigma = \widehat{PQ}$, while $d\omega$ denotes the angle by which one observes the arc ds from M. The sign of $d\omega$ coincides with the sign of $\cos\varphi$. Consequently, $d\omega > 0$, provided φ (the angle between the interior normal at the point P and the vector $\overrightarrow{PM}$) is less than $\pi/2$, and $d\omega < 0$, provided $\varphi > \pi/2$. If $d\omega > 0$, i.e., $\varphi < \pi/2$, then the point M is seen from the "interior" side, and if $d\omega < 0$ ($\varphi > \pi/2$), by contrast, it is seen from the "exterior" side of the curve C. From this it follows that the angle by which one sees an arc $\widehat{P_1P_2}$, from the point M equals the angle P_1MP_2, which describes the ray MP, when the point traverses the arc $\widehat{P_1P_2}$.

We now consider the potential W^0 of a double layer with constant density $\nu = \nu_0 = \text{const}$. The ray MP describes the angle

$$\Omega = \begin{cases} 2\pi & \text{providing the point } M \text{ lies in the interior of curve } C \\ \pi & \text{providing the point } M \text{ lies on the curve } C \\ 0 & \text{providing the point } M \text{ lies in the exterior of curve } C \end{cases}$$

when the point P traverses the entire curve C. From this we find for the potential W^0:

[99] If Σ is an unclosed surface, we have to decide which normal shall be designated at the point P_0 as "interior" and which as "exterior"; this choice is completely arbitrary. We have only to observe that for unclosed surfaces the potential of the double layer is defined only for two-sided surfaces.

$$W^0 = \Omega\nu_0 = \begin{cases} 2\pi\nu_0 & \text{providing the point } M \text{ lies in the interior of curve } C \\ \pi\nu_0 & \text{providing the point } M \text{ lies on the curve } C \\ 0 & \text{providing the point } M \text{ lies in the exterior of } C. \end{cases}$$

Therefore, the potential with constant density is a piecewise constant function and is given by

$$\begin{aligned} W_I^0 &= W_O^0 + \pi\nu_0 \\ W_A^0 &= W_O^0 - \pi\nu_0 \end{aligned} \tag{4-5.41}$$

when W_I^0, W_O^0, W_A^0 are the values of potentials in the interior, on the curve, and on the exterior of the curve C, respectively.

Correspondingly, for three independent variables:

$$\frac{d\sigma \cos\varphi}{r^2} = d\omega\,, \tag{4-5.42}$$

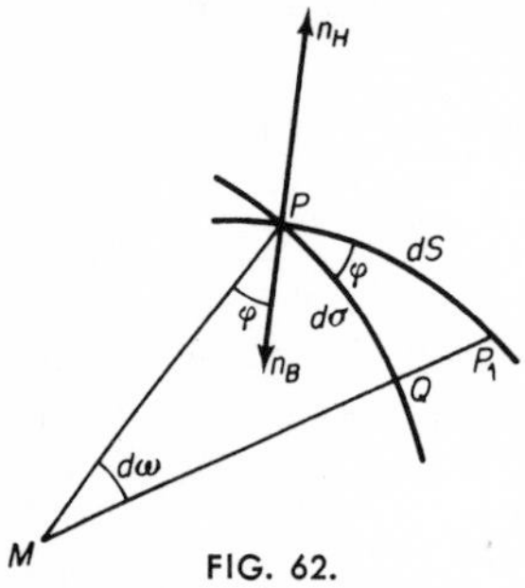

FIG. 62.

where $d\omega$ is the solid angle subtended by the element $d\sigma$ of the surface Σ. Now let $d\sigma'$ be an element of the spherical surface which we obtain when we let a cone whose vertex is at point M and whose base is the surface element $d\sigma$ intersect the sphere of radius MP about M. We then obtain for the spherical surface element

$$d\sigma' = d\sigma \cos\varphi\,.$$

From this formula (4-5.42) also follows. The above observations with regard to the signs of $d\omega$ also remain valid here. This leads to the relations.

$$W^0 = \nu_0\Omega = \begin{cases} 4\pi\nu_0 & \text{provided } M \text{ lies inside of } \Sigma \\ 2\pi\nu_0 & \text{provided } M \text{ lies on } \Sigma \\ 0 & \text{provided } M \text{ lies outside of } \Sigma \end{cases}$$

by which the piecewise constant function W^0 is determined. Further, we arrive at the formulas

$$W_I^0 = W_\Sigma^0 + 2\pi\nu_0 \quad \text{and} \quad W_A^0 = W_\Sigma^0 - 2\pi\nu_0 \tag{4-5.41'}$$

in which W_I^0, W_A^0 denote the values of the potential W^0 in the interior and in the exterior of the surface Σ, while W_Σ^0 is the value of the potential on Σ.

We proceed now to the consideration of the potential of a double layer with a variable density and show that at the points of continuity of the density, relations exist which correspond to formulas (4-5.41) and (4-5.41′).

Let P_0 be a point of the surface Σ at which the function $\nu(P)$ is continuous. Further, let W^0 be the potential of the double layer with constant density $\nu_0 = \nu(P_0)$. Then the function

$$I(M) = W(M) - W^0(M) = \int_\Sigma\!\!\int [\nu(P) - \nu_0]\frac{\cos\varphi}{r^2_{MP}}\,d\sigma_P\,,$$

as we can prove immediately, is continuous at the point P_0. Therefore, it is sufficient to prove the uniform convergence of the integrals $I(M)$ at the point P_0. Let us prescribe an arbitrary number $\varepsilon > 0$. From the continuity of $\nu(P)$ at the point P_0 it follows that for an arbitrary prescribed $\eta > 0$ a neighborhood Σ_1 exists of P_0 on the surface Σ, such that

$$|\nu(P) - \nu(P_0)| < \eta$$

when P is in Σ_1. Now we write the integral $I(M)$ in the form

$$I = I_1 + I_2 ,$$

where I_1 is extended over Σ_1 and I_2 over $\Sigma_2 = \Sigma - \Sigma_1$. From the definition of Σ_1 it then follows that

$$|I_1| < \eta B_\Sigma ,$$

where B_Σ is a constant which for all M satisfies the inequality

$$\iint_\Sigma \frac{|\cos\varphi|}{r^2_{MP}} d\sigma_P \leqq B_\Sigma \tag{4-5.43}$$

but which does not depend on the choice of the surface Σ_1. More details will be given later about this constant.

If we now select $\eta = \varepsilon / B_\Sigma$, we know that for every $\varepsilon > 0$ there actually exists a Σ_1 containing a P_0 such that for each point M we have

$$|I_1(M)| < \varepsilon .$$

From this, however, follows the uniform convergence of the integral $I(M)$ at the point P_0 and therefore also the continuity at this point.

If $W_I(P_0)$ and $W_A(P_0)$ are the limit values of the potentials W_N as $M \to P$ on Σ^+ and Σ^-, respectively (Σ^+ and Σ^- denote the interior and the exterior sides of Σ), then

$$W_I(P_0) = W_I^0(P_0) + I(P_0) = W^0(P_0) + I(P_0) + 2\pi\nu_0 = W(P_0) + 2\pi\nu(P_0)$$

and analogously

$$W_A(P_0) = W(P_0) - 2\pi\nu(P_0) .$$

Therefore, the validity of (4-5.43) is proved.

The above proof holds for surfaces which satisfy the boundedness condition (4-5.43). For convex surfaces in which each ray from the point M cuts the surface twice at most, we find $B_\Sigma \leqq 8\pi$; for surfaces composed of a finite number of convex pieces, B_Σ likewise is bounded. Therefore the proof given here holds for a very wide class of surfaces.

These calculations also remain valid for functions of two independent variables, except that here formula (4-5.41) has the form

$$W_I(P_0) = W(P_0) + \pi\nu(P_0)$$
$$W_A(P_0) = W(P_0) - \pi\nu(P_0) .$$

9. Properties of the potential of a single layer

In contrast to the potential of the double layer, the potential of a single layer

$$V(M) = \iint_{\Sigma} \frac{1}{r_{MP}} \mu(P) d\sigma_P \tag{4-5.26}$$

is continuous at points of the surface Σ. For the proof it is sufficient to show the uniform convergence of the integrals $V(M)$ at points of the surface Σ.

If P_0 is an arbitrary point of the surface Σ, we can write the potential $V(M)$ in the form

$$V = \iint_{\Sigma_1} \frac{1}{r_{MP}} \mu(P) d\sigma_P + \iint_{\Sigma_2} \frac{1}{r_{MP}} \mu(P) d\sigma_P = V_1 + V_2 ,$$

where Σ_1 is a sufficiently small part of Σ which is contained in a sphere of radius δ about the point P. We shall consider the magnitude of δ later.

We consider now a coordinate system whose origin is at the point P_0 and whose z axis is in the direction of the exterior normal at P_0. Let $M(x, y, z)$ be an arbitrary point whose distance from $P_0(0, 0, 0)$ is equal to $MP_0 < \delta$. Further, let Σ_1' be the projection of Σ_1 on the x, y plane and $K_{2\delta}^{M'}$ a circle of radius 2δ about $M'(x, y, z)$ which lies entirely in Σ_1'. If we assume the boundedness of the density $\mu(P)$

$$|\mu(P)| < A$$

and note that

$$d\sigma = \frac{d\sigma'}{\cos\gamma} = \frac{d\xi d\eta}{\cos\gamma}$$

and

$$r = \sqrt{(x-\xi)^2 + (y-\eta)^2 + (z-\zeta)^2} \geqq \sqrt{(x-\xi)^2 + (y-\eta)^2} = \rho ,$$

we obtain the estimate

$$\begin{aligned} V_1(M) &< A \iint_{\Sigma_1} \frac{d\sigma}{r_{MP}} = A \iint_{\Sigma_1'} \frac{1}{\sqrt{(x-\xi)^2 + (y-\eta)^2 + (z-\zeta)^2}} \frac{d\sigma'}{\cos\gamma} \\ &\leqq 2A \iint_{\Sigma_1'} \frac{d\xi\, d\eta}{\sqrt{(x-\xi)^2 + (y-\eta)^2}} \leqq 2A \iint_{K_{2\delta}^{M'}} \frac{d\xi\, d\eta}{\sqrt{(x-\xi)^2 + (y-\eta)^2}} \end{aligned}$$

when δ is so small that $\cos\gamma > 1/2$.

Now we introduce the polar coordinates ρ and φ in the x, y plane with origin at M'. Then we can write

$$V_1(M) < 2A \iint_{K_{2\delta}^{M'}} \frac{d\xi\, d\eta}{\sqrt{(x-\xi)^2 + (y-\eta)^2}} = 2A \int_0^{2\delta} \int_0^{2\pi} \frac{\rho d\rho d\varphi}{\rho} 8A\pi\delta .$$

For $\delta = \varepsilon/8\pi A$,

$$V_1(M) < \varepsilon ,$$

when $MP_0 < \delta$. Consequently, at each point P_0 on Σ, $V(M)$ converges uniformly and therefore is a continuous function.

On the other hand, however, the normal derivatives of a single layer have discontinuities on Σ of the same kind as the potential of a double layer.

The exterior and interior normal derivatives of V, that is, dV/dn_A and dV/dn_I, are defined as follows. Let P_0 be an arbitrary point on Σ. Through P_0 we draw the z axis, which then can have the direction of either the exterior or interior normal.

We now consider the derivative dV/dz at a point on the z axis. We denote by $(dV/dz)_I$ and $(dV/dz)_A$ the limit values of the derivative dV/dz as the point M approaches the point P_0 from Σ^+ or Σ^-, respectively. If the z axis has the direction of the exterior (interior) normal, then this value is called the inner (outer) limit value of the derivative with respect to the exterior (interior) normal at the point P_0.[100]

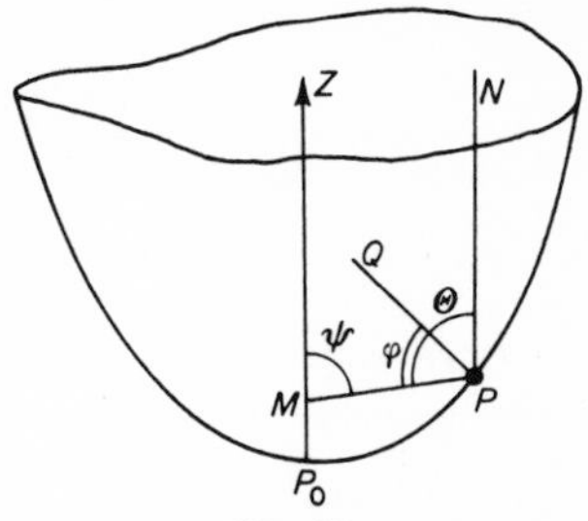

FIG. 63.

Now we investigate the discontinuity of the inner normal derivative of the potential of the single layer on Σ. The derivative dV/dz at a point M of the z axis directed along the interior normal is equal to

$$\frac{dV(M)}{dz} = \int_\Sigma\int \mu(P)\frac{\partial}{\partial n}\left(\frac{1}{r_{MP}}\right)d\sigma_P = \int_\Sigma\int \frac{\cos\psi}{r^2_{MP}}\mu(P)d\sigma_P\,, \tag{4-5.44}$$

where ψ is the angle between the z axis and the vector MP. Now we draw through P (Figure 63) the normal PQ and the straight line PN parallel to the z axis (the normals at P_0). We denote by θ the angle NPQ. This coincides with the angle between the normals at the points P and P_0.[101]

The expression for the potential of the double layer $W(M)$ contains the factor $\cos\varphi/r^2$ where $\varphi = \sphericalangle MPQ$. Since the angle MPN equals $\pi - \psi$,

$$\cos(\pi - \psi) = \cos\varphi\cos\theta + \sin\varphi\sin\theta\cos\Omega = -\cos\psi\,,$$

where Ω is an angle defined by the surface and PQ.[102] From this it follows that

$$\frac{\partial V(M)}{\partial z} = -\int_\Sigma\int(\mu\cos\theta)\frac{\cos\varphi}{r^2}d\sigma - \int_\Sigma\int \mu\sin\theta\cos\Omega\frac{\sin\varphi}{r^2}d\sigma$$
$$= - W_1 - I(M) \tag{4-5.45}$$

where $W_1(M)$ is the potential of the double layer with density $\mu_1 = \mu\cos\theta$.

[100] The limit value of the difference quotient $(V(M) - V(P_0))/MP_0$ as $M \to P_0$ is equal to the existing limit value of the derivative with respect to the exterior normal approached along the exterior normal, or equal to the limit value of the derivative with respect to the interior normal approached along the interior normal, according to the manner in which M approaches the point P, when these derivatives are continuous along the normal and on Σ.

[101] Obviously, as $P \to P_0$, θ and $\sin\theta$ approach 0. If the surface in the neighborhood of P_0 has finite curvature, i.e., if its equation can be written in the form $z = f(x, y)$, where $f(x, y)$ is twice differentiable, then $\sin\theta$ is a function differentiable with respect to x and y; consequently, $\sin\theta < Ar$ (for Liapunov surfaces $\sin\theta < Ar^\delta$).

[102] If the PQ direction is chosen as the axis of a new polar coordinate system, then this formula coincides with formula (4-5.13). For the geometrical significance of this angle, see footnote 88.

$W_1(M)$ has discontinuities on Σ. If the integral $I(M)$ is a continuous function at P_0, then $I(M)$ converges uniformly at this point (see footnote 101).

By consideration of formula (4-5.45) we obtain at the points of discontinuity of μ

$$\left(\frac{\partial V}{\partial z}\right)_I = -W_1(P_0) - 2\pi\mu_1(P_0) - I(P_0)$$

$$\left(\frac{\partial V}{\partial z}\right)_A = -W_1(P_0) + 2\pi\mu_1(P_0) - I(P_0)\,. \tag{4-5.46}$$

Now we set

$$\left(\frac{\partial V}{\partial z}\right)_0 = -W_1(P_0) - I(P_0)$$

$$= \left[-\iint_\Sigma (\mu\cos\theta)\frac{\cos\varphi}{r^2}d\sigma - \iint_\Sigma \mu\sin\theta\cos\Omega\frac{\sin\varphi}{r^2}d\sigma\right]_{M=P_0}$$

$$= \iint_\Sigma \mu\frac{\cos\psi_0}{r^2_{P_0P}}d\sigma$$

where ψ_0 is the angle between the z axis and the vector $\overrightarrow{P_0P}$. If we note that $\mu_1(P_0) = \mu(P_0)$, then

$$\left(\frac{\partial V}{\partial n_I}\right)_I = \left(\frac{\partial V}{\partial n_I}\right)_0 - 2\pi\mu(P_0)$$

$$\left(\frac{\partial V}{\partial n_I}\right)_A = \left(\frac{\partial V}{\partial n_I}\right)_0 + 2\pi\mu(P_0) \tag{4-5.47}$$

results, since by convention the z axis has the direction of the interior normal. If the z axis is in the direction of the exterior normal, the sign of $\cos\psi$ changes and we obtain

$$\left(\frac{\partial V}{\partial n_A}\right)_I = \left(\frac{\partial V}{\partial n_A}\right)_0 + 2\pi\mu(P_0)$$

$$\left(\frac{\partial V}{\partial n_A}\right)_A = \left(\frac{\partial V}{\partial n_A}\right)_0 - 2\pi\mu(P_0)\,. \tag{4-5.48}$$

In the two-dimensional cases there are corresponding formulas; we have only to replace 2π by π.

10. Application of the surface potential to the solution of boundary-value problems

The surface potential is a convenient analytical tool in the solution of boundary-value problems. We consider the interior boundary-value problem for a curve C.

Determine the function u, which is harmonic in the region T, bounded by the curve C, and on C satisfies one of the boundary conditions

first boundary-value problem: $\quad u|_C = f$

second boundary-value problem: $\quad \left.\dfrac{\partial u}{\partial n}\right|_C = f$

The exterior boundary-value problem reads correspondingly.[103]

We write the solution of the first interior boundary-value problem as the potential of a double layer

$$W(M) = \int_C \frac{\cos\varphi}{r_{MP}} \nu(P) ds_P = -\int_C \frac{d}{dn_P}\left(\ln\frac{1}{r_{MP}}\right)\nu(P) ds_P .$$

For an arbitrary choice of $\nu(P)$ the function $W(M)$ satisfies the Laplace differential equation interior to C. On C, $W(M)$ is discontinuous. Therefore if the boundary condition is to be fulfilled, we obviously must have

$$W_I(P_0) = f(P_0) .$$

By using formula (4-5.41) we obtain the equation

$$\pi\nu(P_0) + \int_C \frac{\cos\varphi}{r_{P_0P}} \nu(P) ds_P = f(P_0) \tag{4-5.49}$$

for the determination of $\nu(P)$. If s_0 and s are the values of the length of the arcs on C corresponding to the points P_0 and P, then Eq. (4-5.49) can also be written in the form

$$\pi\nu(s_0) + \int_0^L K(s_0, s)\nu(s) ds = f(s_0) , \tag{4-5.50}$$

where L is the length of the curve C and

$$K(s_0, s) = -\frac{d}{dn_P}\left(\ln\frac{1}{r_{PP_0}}\right) = \frac{\cos\varphi}{r_{PP_0}} \tag{4-5.51}$$

is the kernel of the integral equation. Here we are dealing with a Fredholm integral equation of the second kind.[104] For the exterior problem we obtain the corresponding equation

$$-\pi\nu(s_0) + \int_0^L K(s_0, s)\nu(s) ds = f(s_0) . \tag{4-5.52}$$

For the second boundary-value problem we find the equations

interior boundary-value problem: $$-\pi\mu(s_0) + \int_0^L K_1(s_0, s)\mu(s) ds = f(s_0) \tag{4-5.53}$$

exterior boundary-value problem: $$\pi\mu(s_0) + \int_0^L K_1(s_0, s)\mu(s) ds = f(s_0) \tag{4-5.54}$$

[103] For the formulation of the second boundary-value problem, it makes no difference whether in treating the interior or the exterior problem, the inner normal is always selected as the normal in the boundary condition.

[104] Linear integral equations with fixed limits of integration are called Fredholm equations:

first type: $$\int_a^b K(x, s)\varphi(s) ds = f(x)$$

second type: $$\varphi(x) + \int_a^b K(x, s)\varphi(s) ds = f(x) .$$

where

$$K_1(s_0\,,\,s) = \frac{\partial}{\partial n_{P_0}}\left(\ln\frac{1}{r_{PP_0}}\right) = \frac{\cos\psi_0}{r_{PP_0}} \tag{4-5.55}$$

when its solution is written as the potential of a simple layer[105]

$$u(M) = \int_C \ln\frac{1}{r_{MP}}\mu(P)ds_P\,.$$

The questions which relate to the solvability of these equations will be discussed in Section 4-5 § 11.

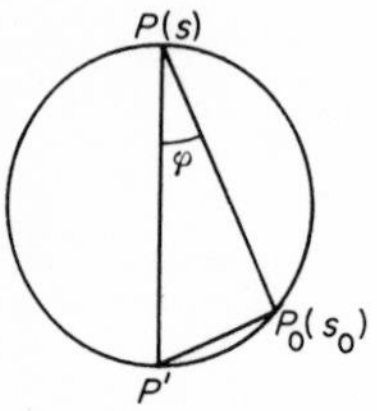

FIG. 64.

In the following we shall treat the boundary-value problem for a simply connected region for which the corresponding integral equations are easily solvable.

1. *The first boundary-value problem for the circle.* If the curve C is a circle of radius R, then the interior normal at the point P is in the direction of the diameter and is

$$\frac{\cos\varphi}{r} = \frac{1}{2R}\,,$$

since φ is the angle of P_0PP' (Figure 64). The integral equation for the function $\nu(s)$ therefore assumes the form

$$\nu(s_0) + \frac{1}{\pi}\int_C \frac{1}{2R}\nu(s)ds = \frac{1}{\pi}f(s_0)\,. \tag{4-5.56}$$

The solution of this equation is the function

$$\nu(s) = \frac{1}{\pi}f(s) + A, \tag{4-5.57}$$

where A is a constant yet to be determined. If we put this expression for the solution in (4-5.56), then

$$\frac{1}{\pi}f(s_0) + A + \frac{1}{\pi}\int_C \frac{1}{2R}\left(\frac{1}{\pi}f(s) + A\right)ds = \frac{1}{\pi}f(s_0)\,,$$

from which we obtain for A the expression

$$A = -\frac{1}{4\pi^2 R}\int_C f(s)ds\,.$$

Therefore

$$\nu(s) = \frac{1}{\pi}f(s) - \frac{1}{4\pi^2 R}\int_C f(s)ds \tag{4-5.58}$$

is the solution of the integral equation.

For the corresponding potential of the double layer we obtain

105 We easily see that $K(s_0, s) = K_1(s, s_0)$. Such kernels are called adjoint and the corresponding equations, adjoint integral equations.

$$W(M) = \int_C \frac{\cos\varphi}{r_{MP}} \nu(P) ds_P = \int_C \frac{\cos\varphi}{r}\left[\frac{1}{\pi} f(s) - \frac{1}{4\pi^2 R}\int_C f(s)ds\right]ds .$$

If M lies interior to the curve C, then the right side of the last formula is transformed as follows

$$\begin{aligned} W &= \frac{1}{\pi}\int_C \frac{\cos\varphi}{r} f(s)ds = \left(\frac{1}{4\pi^2 R}\int_C f(s)ds\right)\int_C \frac{\cos\varphi}{r} ds \\ &= \frac{1}{\pi}\int_C \frac{\cos\varphi}{r} f(s)ds - \left(\frac{1}{4\pi^2 R}\int_C f(s)ds\right)\cdot 2\pi \\ &= \frac{1}{\pi}\int_C \left(\frac{\cos\varphi}{r} - \frac{1}{2R}\right) f(s)ds . \end{aligned} \tag{4-5.59}$$

Now we see from ΔOPM (Figure 65) that

$$\begin{aligned} K &= \frac{\cos\varphi}{r} - \frac{1}{2R} = \frac{2R\cos\varphi - r}{2Rr} = \frac{2Rr\cos\varphi - r^2}{2Rr^2} \\ &= \frac{R^2 - \rho_0^2}{2R[R^2 + \rho_0^2 - 2R\rho_0\cos(\theta - \theta_0)]} . \end{aligned} \tag{4-5.60}$$

Then

$$\rho_0^2 = R^2 + r^2 - 2Rr\cos\varphi .$$

Finally, if we substitute expression (4-5.60) for K into (4-5.59), we obtain Poisson's integral

$$u = W(\rho_0, \theta_0) = \frac{1}{2\pi}\int_0^{2\pi} \frac{(R^2 - \rho_0^2) f(\theta)d\theta}{R^2 + \rho_0^2 - 2R\rho_0\cos(\theta - \theta_0)} \tag{4-5.61}$$

as the solution of the first boundary-value problem for the circle.

These considerations show that for every continuous function $f(\theta)$, a harmonic function is defined by formula (4-5.61) which continuously approaches the boundary value $f(\theta)$.

If f is only piecewise continuous, then the function W, because of the properties of the potentials of the double layer, also is everywhere continuous where f is continuous. Further, from the boundedness of f,

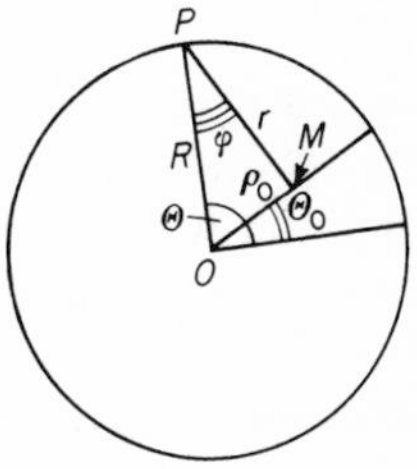

FIG. 65.

$$|f| < C ,$$

follows the boundedness of the function W from (4-5.61):

$$| W(\rho_0, \theta_0) | < C\frac{1}{2\pi}\int_0^{2\pi} \frac{R^2 - \rho_0^2}{R^2 + \rho_0^2 - 2R\rho_0\cos(\theta - \theta_0)} d\theta = C ;$$

then[106]

$$\frac{1}{2\pi}\int_0^{2\pi} \frac{R^2 - \rho_0^2}{R^2 + \rho_0^2 - 2R\rho_0\cos(\theta - \theta_0)} d\theta = 1 . \tag{4-5.62}$$

106 Equation (4-5.62) results from the fact that the left side represents the solution of the first boundary-value problem for $f = 1$ (see page 281).

2. *The first boundary-value problem for the half space.* Let us determine a harmonic function which is everywhere continuous in the half space $z \geqq 0$, assumes a prescribed value $f(x, y)$ on the boundary $z = 0$, and at infinity is equal to zero.

We write the solution of this boundary-value problem as the potential of a double layer:

$$W(x, y, z) = \int_{-\infty}^{+\infty}\int \frac{\cos\varphi}{r^2}\nu(\xi, \eta)d\xi\, d\eta\,, \qquad r^2 = (x - \xi)^2 + (y - \eta)^2 + z^2\,.$$

In the present case,

$$\frac{\cos\varphi}{r^2} = \frac{z}{r^3} = \frac{z}{[(x-\xi)^2 + (y-\eta)^2 + z^2]^{3/2}}\,,$$

and for the kernel of the integral equation we find

$$\frac{1}{2\pi}\left(\frac{\cos\varphi}{r^2}\right)_{z=0} = 0\,.$$

Therefore, the density of the potential of the double layer is given by

$$\nu(P) = \frac{1}{2\pi}f(P)\,,$$

and the function sought is equal to

$$u(x, y, z) = \frac{1}{2\pi}\int_{-\infty}^{+\infty}\int \frac{z}{[(x-\xi)^2 + (y-\eta)^2 + z^2]^{3/2}} f(\xi, \eta)d\xi\, d\eta\,.$$

It can now easily be shown that $u(x, y, z)$ tends to zero uniformly as $r = \sqrt{x^2 + y^2 + z^2} \to 0$ when f has this property also.

11. Boundary-value problems and their equivalent integral equations

In the solution of boundary-value problems for the Laplace differential equation with the help of the potentials of the single and double layer we arrived at Fredholm integral equations of the second type (4-5.50).

The conditions for solvability of the Fredholm integral equation of the second kind with continuous kernel and bounded (integrable) right side are similar to the solvability conditions for systems of linear algebraic equations (to which the integral equation leads if the integral is replaced by a corresponding integral sum).

The first Fredholm theorem reads as follows:

Theorem. An inhomogeneous Fredholm integral equation of the second kind has one and only one solution if the corresponding homogeneous equation has only the zero solution.

The Fredholm theorem is directly applicable to curves of bounded curvature, since here the kernel of the integral Eq. (4-5.50) is continuous.

The Fredholm theory, however, is also applicable if one of the iterated kernels

$$K^{(n+1)}(P_1, P_2) = \iint_\Sigma K^{(1)}(P_1, M)\, K^{(n)}(M, P_2)\, d\sigma_M$$
$$K^{(1)}(P, M) = K(P, M)$$

is continuous.

Theorem. We now prove the theorem: If Σ is a Liapunov surface, then the iterated kernels of the corresponding integral equation are continuous from a certain index on. As we have seen earlier, for a Liapunov surface we have

$$\left|\frac{\cos\varphi}{r^2}\right| < \frac{C}{r^{2-\delta}} .$$

The iterated kernels can be written in the form

$$K_{1,2}(P_1, P_2) = \iint_\Sigma K_1(P_1 M) K_2(M, P_2) d\sigma_M .$$

If

$$|K_i| < \frac{C_i}{r_i^{2-\alpha_i}} \qquad (r_i = P_i M , \quad \alpha_i > 0 , \quad i = 1, 2) ,$$

then

$$|K_{1,2}| < \frac{C}{r^{2-\alpha_1-\alpha_2}} \quad \text{for} \quad \alpha_1 + \alpha_2 < 2 , \quad r = P_1 P_2 .$$

Obviously, it is sufficient to prove this estimate for the case in which the point P_2 lies in the Liapunov neighborhood Σ_0 of the point P_1. Therefore, instead of the integrals over Σ_0, we can consider the integral over the projection S_0 of this neighborhood on the tangent plane at the point P_1, since

$$1 \geqq \frac{\rho(P, M)}{r(P,M)} \geqq B > 0 ,$$

(where $\rho(P, M)$ is the distance between the projections of P and M on the tangent plane, B is a certain constant), and since the relation $d\sigma = dS/\cos\gamma$ exists between the surface element $d\sigma$ and its projection dS; then according to formula (4-5.34), $\cos\gamma > 1/2$.

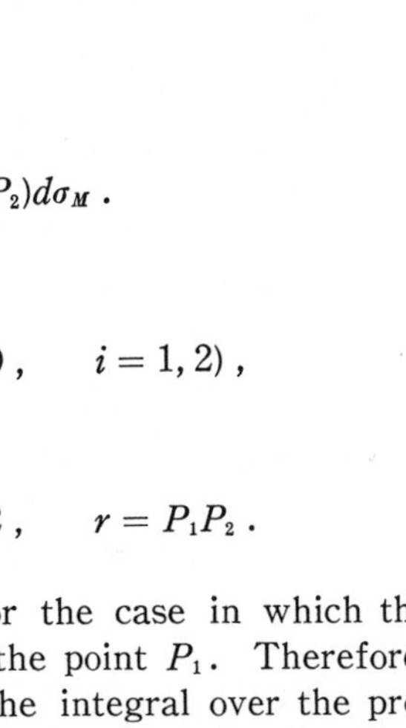

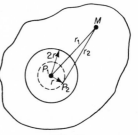

FIG. 66.

The following lemma holds for a plane region: If

$$|K_i| < \frac{C_i}{r_i^{2-\alpha_i}} ,$$

then

$$|I| = \left|\iint_{S_0} K_1(P_1, M) K_2(M, P_2) dx\, dy\right| < \frac{C}{r^{2-\alpha_1-\alpha_2}} .$$

Let R be the diameter of the region S_0. Then we split the integral I into the integral I_1, over a circle G_1 of radius $2r$ about P_1, and I_2, over the remaining region G_2 (Figure 66). Now for a point M lying in G_2 we find

$$2 \geqq \frac{r_1}{r_2} \geqq \frac{2}{3} \qquad \left(r_1 \leqq r_2 + r \leqq 2r_2 \,, \quad r_2 \leqq r_1 + r \leqq r_1 + \frac{r_1}{2} = \frac{3r_1}{2} \right) .$$

There results for I_2 the estimate

$$|I_2| < 4C_1C_2 \left| \int_0^{2\pi} \int_{2r}^{R} \frac{1}{r_1^{4-\alpha_1-\alpha_2}} r_1 dr_1 d\varphi \right| < \begin{cases} \dfrac{C_3}{r^{2-\alpha_1-\alpha_2}} \,, & \alpha_1 + \alpha_2 < 2 \\ C_3 R^{\alpha_1+\alpha_2-2} \,, & \alpha_1 + \alpha_2 > 2 \,. \end{cases}$$

Further, if we introduce in I_1 the substitution

$$x = rx'$$
$$y = ry'$$

then we obtain

$$|I_1| < \left| \frac{1}{r^{2-\alpha_1-\alpha_2}} \int_{G_1'}\!\!\int \frac{C_1C_2}{r_1'^{2-\alpha_1} r_2'^{2-\alpha_2}} dx'dy' \right| .$$

In the last integral, extended over the circle G_1' of radius $2r$, r_1' is the distance from the center and r_2' is the distance from the bisection point of the radius. Consequently, this integral converges, i.e., it does not depend on r.

From this it follows that

$$|I_1| < \frac{C_4}{r^{2-\alpha_1-\alpha_2}} .$$

Now if we set $C_3 + C_4 = C$, then we obtain the sought inequalities:

$$|I| < \begin{cases} \dfrac{C}{r^{2-\alpha_1-\alpha_2}} \,, & \alpha_1 + \alpha_2 < 2 \\ CR^{\alpha_1+\alpha_2-2} \,, & \alpha_1 + \alpha_2 > 2 \,. \end{cases}$$

Accordingly, from a certain index on, the integral, which can be represented by the iterated kernel, is bounded and converges uniformly, i.e., they are continuous functions of their arguments.

With the use of the first Fredholm theorem we shall now prove that the integral Eq. (4-5.50) has exactly one solution.

We limit ourselves here to the consideration of convex curves which contain no straight line elements. In this case, the kernel of Eq. (4-5.50) is not negative, since

$$K(P_0, P) ds_P = d\omega \,,$$

where $d\omega$ is the angle formed by the arc ds_P as seen from the point P_0.

We consider the first interior boundary-value problem. The homogeneous integral equation corresponding to Eq. (4-5.50) has the form

$$\pi\nu(s_0) + \int_0^L K(s_0, s)\, \nu(s) ds = 0 \,. \tag{4-5.63}$$

As we have already seen (Section 4-5 §8), we have the relation

$$\int_0^L K(s_0, s)\, ds = \pi .$$

With the help of this expression we can write the homogeneous Eq. (4-5.63) in the form

$$\int_0^L [\nu(s_0) + \nu(s)]\, K(s_0, s)\, ds = 0 . \tag{4-5.64}$$

Now let $P_0^*(s_0^*)$ be a point of the curve C at which the function $|\nu(s)|$ assumes its maximum. Then the sum $\nu(s_0^*) + \nu(s)$ has a constant sign. If now in (4-5.64) we set $s_0 = s_0^*$ and note that $K(s_0, s) = 0$, we obtain

$$\nu(s_0^*) + \nu(s) = 0 \qquad \text{or} \qquad \nu(s) = -\nu(s_0^*) .$$

This result, however, contradicts the continuity at the point s_0^*, if only $\nu(s_0^*) \neq 0$.

Consequently, the homogeneous Eq. (4-5.63) possesses only the zero solution so that the inhomogeneous equation for an arbitrary $f(s)$ has exactly one solution.[107]

The exterior second boundary-value problem leads, as we have already seen (Section 4-5 § 10), to the integral equation

$$\pi\mu(s_0) + \int_0^L K_1(s_0, s)\, \mu(s)\, ds = f(s_0) , \tag{4-5.54}$$

whose kernel $K_1(s_0, s)$ is adjoint to the kernel $K(s_0, s)$, i.e., $K_1(s_0, s) = K(s, s_0)$ now holds.

We shall now consider the second Fredholm theorem, which reads:

Theorem. The number of linearly independent solutions of a homogeneous Fredholm integral equation is equal to the number of linearly independent solutions of the adjoint equation.

According to this theorem, the solution of Eq. (4-5.54) is uniquely defined. The exterior first boundary-value problem corresponds to the integral equation

$$-\pi\nu(s_0) + \int_0^L K(s_0, s)\, \nu(s)\, ds = f(s_0) . \tag{4-5.52}$$

The homogeneous equation ($f = 0$) can, on the basis of the above considerations, be reduced to the form

$$\int_0^L [\nu(s_0) - \nu(s)]\, K(s_0, s)\, ds = 0 . \tag{4-5.65}$$

If s_0^* is a point at which $|\nu(s)|$ assumes its maximum, then

$$\nu(s_0^*) = \nu(s)$$

results from (4-5.61). Therefore

[107] If straight line boundary elements are present, then the considerations are somewhat complicated but present no special difficulties.

$$\nu(s) = \text{const.} = \nu_0$$

is the single solution of the homogeneous equation. On the basis of the second Fredholm theorem, therefore, the adjoint homogeneous equation has exactly one solution.

The third Fredholm theorem reads:

Theorem. If a homogeneous integral equation

$$\varphi(x) = \int_a^b K(x, s)\varphi(s)ds$$

possesses k linearly independent solutions, $\varphi_i(x)$ $(i = 1, 2, \cdots, k)$, then the inhomogeneous adjoint equation

$$\psi(x) = \int_a^b K(s, x)\psi(s)ds + f(x)$$

has solutions when

$$\int_a^b f(x)\varphi_i(x)\,dx = 0 .$$

If we apply the third Fredholm theorem to Eq. (4-5.53), which corresponds to the interior second boundary-value problem, then we obtain

$$\int_0^L f(s)ds = 0 \tag{4-5.66}$$

as a solvability condition for this problem. We have already encountered this condition in Section 4-5 § 1.

The solvability condition for the exterior first boundary-value problem has the form

$$\int_0^L f(s)h(s)ds = 0 , \tag{4-5.67}$$

where $h(s)$ is the solution of the homogeneous problem corresponding to (4-5.53). We shall discuss briefly the physical significance of this function.

Let a cylindrical conductor, with cross section S, be charged up to a fixed potential V_0. The total charge on the conductor is found on its surface; $\bar{h}(s)$ is the density of the surface charges. The potential produced by the surface charges is then the potential of a simple layer with the density $\bar{h}(s)$ and can be represented by formula (4-5.29). The normal derivative for an approach from inside the conductor is equal to 0, since there $V = \text{const.}$ Therefore $\bar{h}(s)$ satisfies the homogeneous Eq. (4-5.53) and is proportional to the above-introduced function $h(s)$, whereby the physical significance of this function is made clear.

In conclusion, we can state that the integral equations to which the boundary-value problems considered here lead are always solvable for the interior first and exterior second boundary-value problems, whereas the interior second and exterior first boundary-value problems must satisfy the conditions (4-5.66) and

(4-5.67). We shall not investigate the questions regarding the solvability of the remaining boundary-value problems.[108]

4-6. THE DIFFERENCE METHOD

1. The difference method for the Laplace differential equation

In cases in which no analytical expression for the solution can be given, then besides considering the numerical methods for the solution of the corresponding integral equations, we can also go back to difference equations which arise from the differential equation.

For a function of a single variable $y = f(x)$, instead of the second derivative we can use the difference quotient

$$\frac{\Delta^2 f}{h^2} = \frac{1}{h}\left[\frac{\Delta^+ f}{h} - \frac{\Delta^- f}{h}\right] = \frac{[f(x+h) - f(x)] - [f(x) - f(x-h)]}{h^2}$$

$$= \frac{f(x+h) + f(x-h) - 2f(x)}{h^2} \,. \qquad (4\text{-}6.1)$$

Here $\Delta^+ f = f(x+h) - f(x)$ is the first right-sided and $\Delta^- f = f(x) - f(x-h)$ is the first left-sided difference. In the case of two independent variables, the second differences read

$$\Delta^2_{xx} u = u(x+h\,,\, y) + u(x-h\,,\, y) - 2u(x\,,\, y)$$

$$\Delta^2_{yy} u = u(x\,,\, y+h) + u(x\,,\, y-h) - 2u(x\,,\, y)\,.$$

The difference quotient for the Laplace differential expression obviously then has the form

$$\frac{\bar{\Delta}_h u}{h^2} = \frac{u(x+h\,,\, y) + u(x, y+h) + u(x-h\,,\, y) + u(x\,,\, y-h) - 4u(x\,,\, y)}{h^2} \,. \qquad (4\text{-}6.2)$$

The transition from a differential equation to a difference equation corresponds to the transition from a continuous argument to a discrete argument.

We take now an arbitrary positive number h and construct a network in the x, y plane consisting of two systems of straight lines at right angles to each other, the lines of which are at a distance h from each other (Figure 67), and consider only the values of the function at the net points.

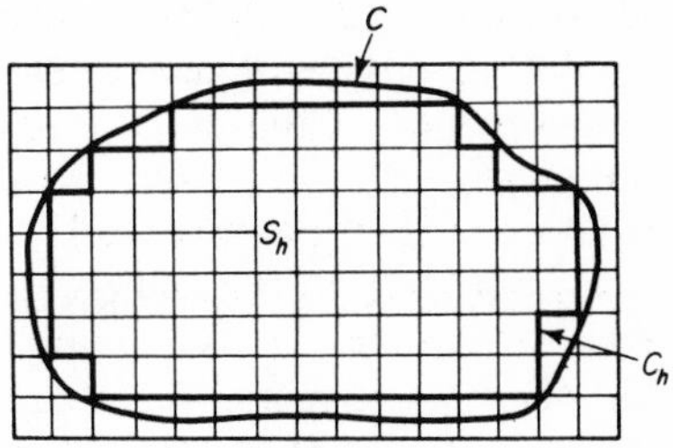

FIG. 67.

In the following we shall treat the first boundary-value problem for the Laplace differential equation in a region S, which is bounded by the curve C. On C let a bounded continuous function f be prescribed.

[108] For further details, see, for example, I. G. Petrovski, *Lectures on Partial Differential Equations*, Interscience, 1954.

For the difference method, the given region S is replaced by a network region S_h which approximates S. We assume that the region S_h consists of those squares of our network which lie entirely in S (one could also have chosen as the approximating region S_h the totality of all the squares of the network which have at least one point in common with S). Let C_h be the straight line segments bounding the region S_h. Obviously the distance of each corner point of C_h from the curve C does not exceed $h\sqrt{2}$.

Now at the corner points of C_h we define a boundary function f_h, which we take at each of these corner points to be equal to the value of the function f at the nearest point of the boundary C (or at one or more of the closest neighboring points if there are several).[109]

The first boundary-value problem for the difference equation corresponding to the Laplace differential equation can then be formulated as follows:

Determine a function which at the net points $M_{ik}(x_i, y_k)$ interior to the region S_h satisfies the Laplace difference equation

$$u^{(h)}_{i+1,k} + u^{(h)}_{i,k+1} + u^{(h)}_{i-1,k} + u^{(h)}_{i,k-1} - 4u^{(h)}_{i,k} = 0\,, \tag{4-6.3}$$

where

$$u^{(h)}_{i,k} = u(x_i, y_k)$$

and assumes the value f_h on C_h.

For the solution of this problem we must determine the value of the net function $u^{(h)}_{i,k}$ at the interior net points M_{ik} of the region S_h, and at each interior net point M_{ik} the difference Eq. (4-6.3) must be satisfied. Thus we obtain for the determination of the net function a system of algebraic equations of the first order whose number equals the number of the unknowns.

The system of difference equations possesses exactly one solution.

To prove this proposition it is sufficient to show that the corresponding homogeneous system possesses only the trivial solution.

The system of difference equations is a system of inhomogeneous equations, since the values $u_{i,k}$ at the corner points of C_h are prescribed and are equal to the values of f_h. The transition to the homogeneous system is therefore equivalent to the boundary function being everywhere equal to zero, $f_h = 0$. We shall show that in this case the solution of the difference system at all the net points of the region S_h is equal to zero.

Suppose a value $u_{i,k} \neq 0$ exists; without loss of generality we can assume

$$u_{i_1,k_1} > 0\,.$$

Further, let u_{i_0,k_0} be the maximum of our net function, so that

$$u_{i,k} \leqq u_{i_0,k_0}$$

at all points of M_{ik} in S_h. However, the equation

$$u_{i_0,k_0} = \frac{u_{i_0-1,k_0} + u_{i_0,k_0-1} + u_{i_0+1,k_0} + u_{i_0,k_0+1}}{4}$$

[109] The degree of arbitrariness in the selection can, because of the continuity of f, be made arbitrary small, when h is chosen sufficiently small.

can hold only when

$$u_{i_0-1,\,k_0} = u_{i_0,\,k_0-1} = u_{i_0+1,\,k_0} = u_{i_0,\,k_0+1} = u_{i_0,\,k_0}\,.$$

Proceding in this way for u_{i_0+1,k_0}, u_{i_0+2,k_0}, respectively, we finally arrive at a boundary point and thus obtain a contradiction since, by assumption, the boundary values are equal to zero. Also, the assumption $u_{i_0,\,k_0} < 0$ leads to a contradiction.

From this it follows that

$$u_{i,\,k} \equiv 0$$

at all interior points of the region S, i.e., the homogeneous difference system has only the trivial solution. Simultaneously, the uniqueness of the solution of the first boundary-value problem for the difference equations corresponding to the Laplace differential equation is proved.

If we solve the difference equation, the net function results as an approximate solution of the original problem for the Laplace differential equation.

2. The method of successive approximation for the solution of difference equations

The difference method in the present case consists of finding, instead of the solution of a boundary-value problem for the Laplace differential equation $\Delta u = 0$, the solution of the boundary-value problem for the corresponding difference equation. For the basis of this method one has to prove that for sufficiently small h, the function u_h differs arbitrarily little from u, the exact solution of the equation $\Delta u = 0$. We will not go into the proof of this here.[110]

Instead, we shall consider in more detail the methods for the solution of difference equations. The solution of the boundary-value problem by means of the difference method leads to the solution of a system of algebraic equations with many unknowns, of which there can be hundreds and even thousands. The solution of such systems using the methods of determinant theory gives rise to severe technical computational difficulties. On the other hand, the method of successive approximations is essentially more suitable.

For systems of linear algebraic equations the method of successive approximations proceeds as follows.

We write the existing system of equations in the form

$$\begin{aligned} u_1 &= f_1 - (a_{12}u_2 + \cdots + a_{1n}u_n) \\ u_2 &= f_2 - (a_{21}u_1 + \cdots + a_{2n}u_n) \\ &\cdots \quad \cdots \quad \cdots \\ u_n &= f_n - (a_{n1}u_1 + \cdots + a_{n,n-1}u_{n-1})\,. \end{aligned} \tag{4-6.4}$$

First we choose numbers $u_1^0, u_2^0, \cdots, u_n^0$ as the zero-th approximation and substitute these in the right side of the Eq. (4-6.4); then we obtain the first approximation $u_1^{(1)}, u_2^{(1)}, \cdots, u_n^{(1)}$. We continue this process. The $(k+1)$-th approxi-

[110] See I. G. Petrovski, *op. cit.*, fn. 109.

mation then can be calculated from the formulas

$$u_1^{(k+1)} = f_1 - (a_{12}u_2^{(k)} + \cdots + a_{1n}u_n^{(k)})$$
$$u_2^{(k+1)} = f_2 - (a_{22}u_1^{(k)} + \cdots + a_{2n}u_n^{(k)})$$
$$\cdots \quad \cdots \quad \cdots \quad \cdots$$
$$u_n^{(k+1)} = f_n - (a_{n1}u_1^{(k)} + \cdots + a_{n,\,n-1}u_{n-1}^{(k)}) \,.$$

Now if the successive approximations $\{u_n^{(k)}\}$ always converge towards a limit value

$$\lim_{k\to\infty} u_n^{(k)} = u_n \,,$$

then these limit values are the sought solutions of the systems (4-6.4).

The method of successive approximations is not applicable to every system of equations. However, it can be used to solve the first boundary-value problem for the system of difference equations $\bar{\varDelta}_h u = 0$. The system of algebraic equations which correspond to the equations $\bar{\varDelta}_h u = 0$, has the form

$$u_{i,k}^{(h)} = \frac{u_{i+1,\,k}^{(h)} + u_{i\ \,k+1}^{(h)} + u_{i-1,\,k}^{(h)} + u_{i,\,k-1}^{(h)}}{4} \,,$$

where each equation is solved for the corresponding unknowns.

We begin the successive approximation on the boundary on which the boundary values are prescribed. By $C_h^{(1)}$ we denote the totality of the net points of the region S_h, which are at a distance h from the corner points of the boundary C_h. To carry out the successive approximations at the points on $C_h^{(1)}$, the values of f_h given on C_h will be used directly. Further, we denote by $C_h^{(2)}$ the totality of the net points of S_h which are at a distance h from $C_h^{(1)}$. The successive approximations of $C_h^{(2)}$ are carried out using the values $u_{i\ k}^{(h)}$ on $C_h^{(1)}$. Correspondingly, we define the "zones" $C_h^{(3)}$, $C_h^{(4)}, \cdots$. Then the last of each of the net points in S_h belongs to one of the zones $C_h^{(i)}$, $(i = 1, 2, \cdots, N)$. N is the number of the last zone $C_h^{(N)}$.

Now let $u_{i,\,k}$ be the exact solution of the system of difference equations and $u_{i,k}^{(n)}$ the nth approximation of this system. Then the difference

$$v_{i,k}^{(n)} = u_{i,\,k} - u_{i,\,k}^{(n)}$$

on C_h is equal to zero, whereas in the interior of S_h the equations

$$v_{i,\,k}^{(n)} = \frac{v_{i+1,k}^{(n-1)} + v_{i,\,k+1}^{(n-1)} + v_{i-1,\,k}^{(n-1)} + v_{i,\,k-1}^{(n-1)}}{4} \qquad (4\text{-}6.5)$$

hold.

We prove that the difference sequence $\{v_{i,\,k}^{(n)}\}$ approaches zero:

$$\lim_{n\to\infty} v_{i,\,k}^{(n)} = 0 \,.$$

Thus, we set max $v_{i,k}^{(n)} = A_n$ and estimate the $(n+1)$-th approximation. Obviously,

$$v_{i,k}^{(n+1)} \leqq \frac{3}{4} A_n \qquad \text{on} \qquad C_h^{(1)}$$

holds, since in this case at least one of the summands in (4-6.5) is equal to zero. From this it follows that

$$v_{i,k}^{(n+1)} \leqq \left(1 - \frac{1}{4^2}\right) A_n \quad \text{on} \quad C_h^{(2)},$$

and, in general,

$$v_{i,k}^{(n+1)} \leqq \left(1 - \frac{1}{4^s}\right) A_n \quad \text{on} \quad C_h^{(s)}.$$

For the last zone $C_h^{(N)}$ we thus obtain

$$v_{i,k}^{(n+1)} \leqq \left(1 - \frac{1}{4^N}\right) A_n \quad \text{on} \quad C_h^{(N)}.$$

Therefore,

$$A_{n+1} \leqq \alpha A_n, \qquad \alpha = 1 - \frac{1}{4^N},$$

i.e., $\lim_{n \to \infty} A_n = 0$.

If now we set $\min v_{i,k}^{(n)} = B_n$, we can similarly obtain

$$\lim_{n \to \infty} B_n = 0.$$

Consequently,

$$\lim_{n \to \infty} v_{i,k}^{(n)} = 0 \quad \text{or} \quad \lim_{n \to \infty} u_{i,k}^{(n)} = u_{i,k}$$

for all points $M_{i,k}(x_i, y_k)$ in S_h.

The convergence proved here is valid for an arbitrary choice of the zero-th approximation. However, the degree of convergence (speed of convergence, etc.) depends strongly on the choice of the zero-th approximation.

3. Electronic integrators

In recent times several mathematical machines have been used for the solution of systems of difference equations. The construction of these machines is based on the analogies that exist between different physical processes which are described by one and the same differential equation.

For the solution of the Laplace differential equation (and also certain complicated equations) electronic integrators are often used. To investigate one of the simplest electrical systems for the solution of the Laplace differential equation (which was considered by Gerschgorin), we consider a network of equal ohmic resistances. One of its components is shown in Figure 68. Let V_i be the potential at the point M_i, and j_i the current in M_0M_i.

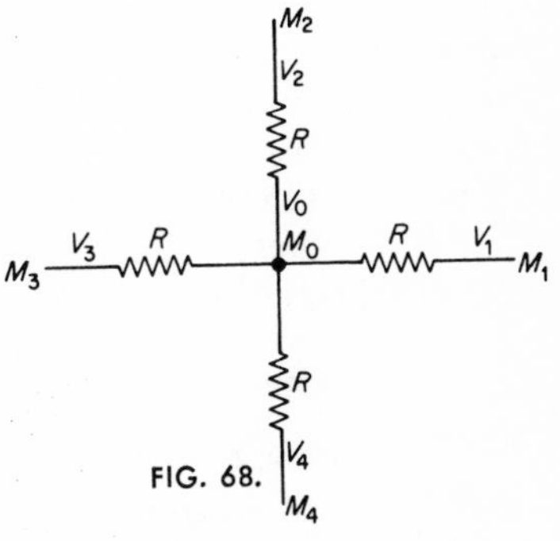

FIG. 68.

From Ohm's law

$$j_i = \frac{V_i - V_0}{R}, \qquad i = 1, 2, 3, 4$$

and Kirchhoff's law

$$j_1 + j_2 + j_3 + j_4 = 0$$

there results

$$V_0 = \frac{V_1 + V_2 + V_3 + V_4}{4}.$$

Therefore the potential at an arbitrary net point of a compound electrical system of resistances is equal to the arithmetic mean of the potential at the four neighboring points. This relation, which corresponds to Eq. (4-6.5) of the difference method described above, is of fundamental significance for the electronic integration of the Laplace differential equation.

The simplest electronic integrator consists of a sheet in which the elements are suitably arranged. Between the elements are found equal resistances. For example, let us consider the first boundary value problem for a region S of the x, y plane. Let C be the boundary of S.

We then choose, in the x, y plane, a network with distance h and construct in the above-described manner the region S_h with boundary C_h. At the net points of the boundary C_h, by means of a special voltage distribution we apply voltages which correspond to the boundary conditions of the first boundary-value problem. The voltage distribution then obtained yields an approximate solution of the problem.

In certain integrators the resistance between the individual net points can be varied. In this manner we find that equations with variable coefficients of the form

$$\frac{\partial}{\partial x}\left(k_1 \frac{\partial u}{\partial x}\right) + \frac{\partial}{\partial y}\left(k_2 \frac{\partial u}{\partial y}\right) = 0$$

with

$$k_1 = k_1(x, y), \qquad k_2 = k_2(x, y)$$

can be solved. Such electronic integrators were constructed by L. Ya. Gutenmacher. Also, for complicated regions of the x, y plane these integrators make it possible to obtain a rapid solution of boundary-value problems.

Still other methods exist for the machine integration of the Laplace differential equation—for example, the method of electrolytic tanks.

Problems

1. Find the function u which is harmonic in a circle of radius a and on the circumference C assumes the value

(a) $u|_C = A \cos \varphi$

(b) $u|_C = A + B \sin \varphi$.

2. Solve the Laplace differential equation $\Delta u = 0$ in a rectangle $0 \leqq x \leqq a$, $0 \leqq y \leqq b$ with the boundary conditions

$$u|_{x=0} = f_1(y) , \qquad u|_{y=0} = f_2(x) , \qquad u|_{x=a} = 0 , \qquad u|_{y=b} = 0 .$$

Show that the formulas derived here define the solution of the problem for every piecewise continuous function which is prescribed on the boundary. Further, solve the problem for the special case

$$f_1(y) = Ay(b-y) , \qquad f_2(x) = B\cos\frac{\pi}{2a}x , \qquad f_3 = f_4 = 0 .$$

3. Solve the equation $\Delta u = 1$ for a circle of radius a with the boundary condition $u|_{\rho=a} = 0$.

4. Solve the equation $\Delta u = Axy$ for a circle of radius a with center at $(0, 0)$ for the boundary condition $u|_{\rho=a} = 0$.

5. Determine the solution of the differential equation $\Delta u = A + B(x^2 - y^2)$ in a circular ring $a \leqq \rho \leqq b$ if

$$u\Big|_{\rho=a} = A_1 , \qquad \frac{\partial u}{\partial \rho}\Big|_{\rho=b} = 0 .$$

The origin of coordinates is at the center of the ring.

6. Construct the Green's function of the Laplace differential equation (first boundary-value problem) for (a) a half circle; (b) a ring; (c) a layer $(0 \leqq z \leqq l)$.

7. Determine a harmonic function in a ring where $a \leqq \rho \leqq b$, which satisfies the boundary conditions

$$u|_{\rho=a} = f_1(\varphi) , \qquad u|_{\rho=b} = f_2(\varphi) .$$

8. Determine the solution of the Laplace differential equation $\Delta u = 0$ in the half plane $y \geqq 0$ with the boundary conditions

$$u(x, 0) = \begin{cases} 0 & \text{for} \quad x < 0 \\ u_0 & \text{for} \quad x > 0 \end{cases} .$$

9. Find a function $u(\rho, \varphi)$ which is harmonic in a spherical sector $\rho \leqq a$, $0 \leqq \varphi \leqq \varphi_0$, and satisfies the boundary conditions

(a) $u|_{\varphi=0} = q_1$, $\quad u|_{\varphi=\varphi_0} = q_1$, $\quad u|_{\rho=a} = q_2$ $\quad$ (q_1 and q_2 are constants)

(b) $u|_{\varphi=0} = u|_{\varphi=\varphi_0} = 0$, $\quad u|_{\rho=a} = f(\varphi)$.

10. By the difference method solve the first boundary-value problem for $\Delta u = 0$ in a rectangle $0 \leqq x \leqq a$, $0 \leqq y \leqq b$, with each side of the rectangle divided into eight equal parts. The boundary conditions read:

$$u|_{x=0} = \frac{y}{b}\left(1 - \frac{y}{b}\right), \qquad u|_{y=b} = \frac{x}{a}\sin\frac{\pi}{a}x , \qquad u|_{x=a} = u|_{y=0} = 0 .$$

Compare the results with the analytical solution.

11. Calculate the spatial potential of a sphere of constant density $\rho = \rho_0$. *Hint*: Solve $\Delta u = 0$ in the exterior of the sphere and $\Delta u = 4\pi\rho_0$ in the interior of the sphere and match the solutions on the sphere.

12. Determine the potential of a simple layer distributed on a sphere with density $\nu = \nu_0$. *Hint*: Solve $\Delta u = 0$ in the exterior and in the interior of a sphere, and for the matching of the solutions on the spherical surface use the condition that the potential of a simple layer is discontinuous across the surface.

13. Solve the first boundary-value problem for a bounded circular cylinder ($\rho \leqq a, 0 \leqq z \leqq l$):

(*a*) On the end surfaces of the cylinder let the boundary value (first or second type) be equal to zero, while on the lateral surface it must satisfy

$$u\,|_{\rho=a} = f(z)\ .$$

(*b*) On the lateral surface and on one of the end surfaces let the boundary value (first or second type) be equal to zero, while on the other end surface of the cylinder the condition is

$$u = f(\rho)\ ,$$

for example, $f(\rho) = A\rho(1-(\rho/a))$.

14. Solve the inhomogeneous equation

$$\Delta u = -f$$

in an unbounded cylindrical region with homogeneous boundary conditions (first or second type) and construct the Green's function.

15. Find a harmonic function in the interior of a sphere which is equal to u_1 on one half of the spherical surface and u_2 on the other half.

16. Calculate for the density the series development using spherical functions for the charges induced on the surface of a conducting sphere due to a point charge.

17. Solve the problem of the polarization of a dielectric sphere in a field due to a point charge.

18. Determine the gravitation potential of a plane disc. Compare the solution with the asymptotic representation of the gravitation potential at large distances.

19. Find the magnetic potential of a circular current.

20. Solve the problem of the excitation of a plane-parallel electrical field for an ideal conducting sphere. Solve the same problem for a completely nonconducting sphere.

4-7. APPLICATIONS TO CHAPTER 4

1. Asymptotic representation of the spatial potentials

For the investigation of the spatial potential

$$V(M) = \iiint_T \frac{\rho(P)d\tau_P}{d}\ , \qquad d = r_{MP} \tag{4-7.1}$$

at large distances from a body T, we usually take the value of the potential as equal to m/R, where m is the total mass of T and R is the distance of the center of gravity from the exterior point M. We shall now derive an exact asymptotic representation for V.[111]

Let Σ be a sphere about the origin which entirely contains the body P. Its center is at the origin of the coordinates. Outside this sphere the potential is a harmonic function.

The distance of the test point $M(x, y, z)$ from the variable source points $M_1(x_1, y_1, z_1)$ in T (Figure 69), over which we integrate, is given by

$$d = \sqrt{r^2 + r_1^2 - 2rr_1 \cos\theta}\,, \qquad r = OM\,, \qquad r_1 = OM_1\,, \tag{4-7.2}$$

from which

$$\frac{1}{d} = \frac{1}{r}\frac{1}{\sqrt{1+\alpha^2 - 2\alpha\mu}}\,, \qquad \alpha = \frac{r_1}{r}, \qquad \mu = \cos\theta\,. \tag{4-7.3}$$

$r_1 < r$ means $\alpha < 1$; we therefore have the development

$$\frac{1}{d} = \frac{1}{r}\sum_{n=0}^{\infty} \alpha^n P_n(\mu)\,, \tag{4-7.4}$$

where $P_n(\mu)$ is the Legendre polynomial of nth order.* If we substitute this expression into formula (4-7.1) and note that $1/r$ does not depend on the variables of integration, we obtain

$$V(M) = \frac{1}{r}\iiint_T \rho \sum_{n=0}^{\infty} \alpha^n P_n(\mu) d\tau = V_1 + V_2 + V_3 + \cdots$$
$$= \frac{1}{r}\iiint_T \rho d\tau + \frac{1}{r^2}\iiint_T \rho r_1 P_1(\mu) d\tau + \frac{1}{r^3}\iiint_T \rho r_1^2 P_2(\mu) d\tau + \cdots \tag{4-7.5}$$

The first member here is equal to m/r, where m is the total mass of the body. This yields a first approximation for the calculation of the potential for large r.

We now calculate the following terms in (4-7.5). The integrand of the second member is

$$\rho P_1(\mu) r_1 = \rho\mu r_1 = \rho r_1 \cos\theta = \frac{\rho x x_1 + \rho y y_1 + \rho z z_1}{r}\,.$$

The quantities x, y, z, and r do not depend on the variables of integration and can therefore be placed in front of the integral sign. Then the second term takes the form

$$\frac{1}{r^2}\iiint_T \rho r_1 P_1(\mu) d\tau = \frac{1}{r^3}(M_1 x + M_2 y + M_3 z) = \frac{M}{r^3}(x\bar{x} + y\bar{y} + z\bar{z})\,,$$

where

$$M_1 = \iiint_T \rho x_1 d\tau = M\bar{x}\,, \qquad M_2 = \iiint_T \rho y_1 d\tau = M\bar{y}$$
$$M_3 = \iiint_T \rho z_1 d\tau = M\bar{z}$$

111 V. I. Smirnov, Part III$_2$, *op. cit.* fn. 15.

* See Whitaker and Watson, also Bateman in List of References

is the moment of the first order and $\bar{x}$, $\bar{y}$, $\bar{z}$ are the coordinates of the center of gravity. Therefore, the second term is as small as $1/r^2$. If the origin of the coordinates is at the center of gravity ($\bar{x}=0$, $\bar{y}=0$, $\bar{z}=0$), then $V_2=0$.

We consider now the third term of the development. For the integrand, we have

$$\rho r_1^2 P_2(\mu) = \rho r_1^2 \frac{3\mu^2-1}{2} = \rho r_1^2 \frac{3(xx_1+yy_1+zz_1)^2 - r_1^2 r^2}{2r_1^2 r^2}$$

$$= \frac{\rho}{2r^2}[3(x_1x+y_1y+z_1z)^2 - r_1^2 r^2].$$

With the notations

$$M_{ik} = \iiint_T \rho x_i x_k d\tau \qquad (x=x_1, \qquad y=x_2, \qquad z=x_3)$$

we obtain for V_3 the expression

$$V_3 = \frac{1}{r^3}\iiint_T \rho r_1^2 P_2(\mu) d\tau$$

$$= \frac{1}{2r^5}\{x^2[3M_{11} - (M_{11}+M_{22}+M_{33})] + y^2[3M_{22} - (M_{11}+M_{22}+M_{33})]$$

$$+ z^2[3M_{33} - (M_{11}+M_{22}+M_{33})] + 2\cdot 3xyM_{12} + 2\cdot 3xzM_{13} + 2\cdot 3yzM_{23}\}.$$

The polynomial inside the braces is harmonic, since it can be written in the form

$$V_3 = \frac{1}{2r^5}\{(x^2-y^2)[M_{11}-M_{22}] + (z^2-x^2)[M_{11}-M_{33}]$$

$$+ (y^2-z^2)[M_{22}-M_{33}] + 6[xyM_{12} + xzM_{13} + yzM_{23}]\}$$

in which each summand satisfies the Laplace differential equation. The coefficients standing in the square brackets can be expressed in terms of the moment of inertia with respect to the coordinate axes. The moment of inertia of a body T with respect to the x axis, as is known, is given by

$$A = \iiint_T \rho(y_1^2 + z_1^2) d\tau = M_{22} + M_{33}.$$

Correspondingly, the moments of inertia with respect to the y and z axes are, respectively,

$$B = M_{33} + M_{11}, \qquad C = M_{11} + M_{22}.$$

From this it follows, however, that

$$M_{11} - M_{22} = B - A, \qquad M_{11} - M_{33} = C - A, \qquad M_{22} - M_{33} = C - B.$$

Therefore we arrive at the following asymptotic representation of the spatial potential:

$$V \approx \frac{m}{r} + \frac{m}{r^3}(x\bar{x} + y\bar{y} + z\bar{z}) + \frac{1}{2r^5}\{(x^2-y^2)(B-A) + (y^2-z^2)(C-B)$$

$$+ (z^2-x^2)(A-C) + 6(xyM_{12} + yzM_{23} + zxM_{31})\} \tag{4-7.6}$$

which is exact up to terms of the order of $1/r^6$.

The representation (4-7.6) can be simplified to

$$V \approx \frac{m}{r} + \frac{1}{2r^5}\{(x^2 - y^2)(B - A) + (y^2 - z^2)(C - B) + (z^2 - x^2)(A - C)\}\,, \quad (4\text{-}7.7)$$

provided the origin of the coordinates coincides with the center of gravity and the coordinate axes have the direction of the principal axes of inertia.

This asymptotic representation of the spatial potential permits us to give the answers to a series of questions on the inverse problem of potential theory. This consists of determining the characteristic quantities of a body from its potential (or from any of the derivatives of its potentials). That is, from the coefficients of the development (4-7.6), we can calculate the mass, the coordinates of the center of gravity, and the moment of inertia.

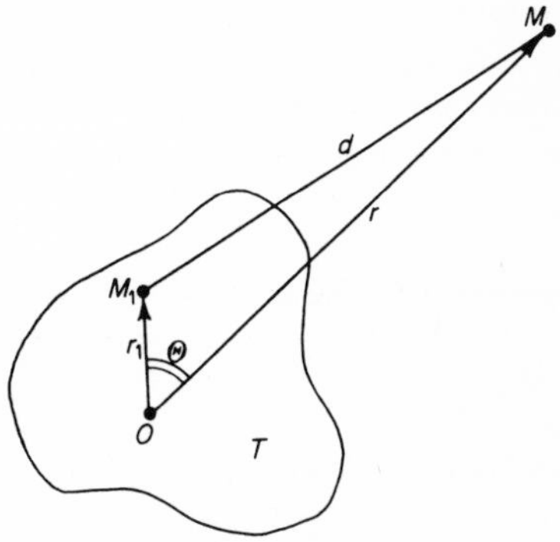

FIG. 69.

2. Problems of electrostatics

In electrostatics the solution of Maxwell's equations leads to the determination of a scalar function, the potential φ. Between φ and the electrical field strength $\boldsymbol{E}$ there exists the relation

$$\boldsymbol{E} = -\text{grad}\,\varphi\,.$$

By using Maxwell's equation

$$\text{div}\,\boldsymbol{E} = 4\pi\rho$$

we obtain

$$\Delta\varphi = -4\pi\rho\,.$$

Therefore, the potential at points of space at which electrical charges are found satisfies the Poisson differential equation, and at points where no charges are found it satisfies the Laplace differential equation.

1. The basic problem of electrostatics is to determine the field which is produced by a system of charges on a given conductor. Two different formulations of this problem are possible.

(*a*) Given the potential of the conductor, determine the field exterior to the conductor and the charge density on the conductor. The mathematical formulation here reads as follows:

Determine the function φ which satisfies the Laplace differential equation $\Delta\varphi = 0$ everywhere exterior to the given conducting system, vanishes at infinity, and on the conducting surface assumes the prescribed value φ_i:

$$\varphi\,|_{S_i} = \varphi_i\,.$$

In this case, therefore, we arrive at the first boundary-value problem for the Laplace differential equation. Its unique solvability results from the general theory discussed above.

(*b*) The inverse statement of the problem is also possible, i.e., given the total charges on the conductor, determine its potential, the charge distribution on its surface, and the field in the interior of the conductor. The solution of this problem leads to the following problem:

Determine a function φ which satisfies the Laplace differential equation

$$\Delta\varphi = 0$$

exterior to the given conducting system, vanishes at infinity, and on the surface of the conductor assumes a certain constant value

$$\varphi \,|_{S_i} = \text{const.}$$

and also satisfies the condition

$$\oint_{S_i} \frac{\partial\varphi}{\partial n} d\sigma = -4\pi e_i .$$

Here e_i is the total charge on the ith conductor.

2. The unique solvability of the secondary-value problem does not result from the general theory; however, it can easily be proved.

Let us assume that there are two distinct solutions φ_1 and φ_2 of Problem (*b*) above. Then their difference

$$\varphi' = \varphi_1 - \varphi_2$$

satisfies the equation

$$\Delta\varphi' = 0$$

and the conditions

$$\varphi' \,|_{S_i} = \text{const.} , \qquad \oint_{S_i} \frac{\partial\varphi'}{\partial n} d\sigma = 0 , \qquad \varphi' \,|_{\infty} = 0 .$$

We imagine the given conductor to be completely enclosed by a sphere Σ_R of sufficiently large radius R and apply to φ' the first Green's formula in the region T_R bounded by the surface of the sphere Σ_R and the conducting surfaces S_i;

$$\int_{T_R} (\nabla\varphi')^2 d\tau = \int_{\Sigma_R} \varphi' \frac{\partial\varphi'}{\partial n} d\sigma + \sum_{i=1}^{n} \int_{S_i} \varphi' \frac{\partial\varphi'}{\partial n} d\sigma .$$

From this, because of the above conditions,[112] we obtain

$$\lim_{R\to\infty} \int_{T_R} (\nabla\varphi')^2 d\tau = 0 .$$

[112] As a consequence of the condition $\varphi' \,|_{\infty} = 0$, the function φ' is regular at infinity (see page 270); then

$$\int_{\Sigma_R} \varphi' \frac{\partial\varphi'}{\partial n} d\sigma \to 0 \quad \text{for} \quad R \to \infty .$$

Since the integrand is positive it follows that

$$\nabla\varphi' = 0$$

or

$$\varphi' = \text{const.}$$

everywhere in the region under consideration. By considering the condition

$$\varphi'\,|_\infty = 0$$

we finally obtain

$$\varphi' \equiv 0\,,$$

and hence the uniqueness is proved.

3. From the uniqueness of the solution of the boundary-value problem for the Laplace differential equation it follows that the potential φ of an individual conductor is directly proportional to its total charge e, i.e.,

$$e/\varphi = C\,.$$

Therefore, if the charges e and $e' = me$ lie entirely on a single conductor, then the corresponding potentials φ and φ' must satisfy the equations

$$\Delta\varphi = 0\,, \qquad \Delta\varphi' = 0$$

and the boundary conditions

$$-\frac{1}{4\pi}\oint_S \frac{\partial\varphi}{\partial n}d\sigma = e\,, \qquad -\frac{1}{4\pi}\oint_S \frac{\partial\varphi'}{\partial n}d\sigma = me\,.$$

Consequently, $\varphi' - m\varphi = 0$, i.e., $\varphi'/\varphi = e'/e$.

On the surface of a single conductor we therefore have

$$e'/\varphi' = e/\varphi = C = \text{const.}$$

The constant C is called the capacity of the single conductor. It does not depend on the charge on the conductor but is determined by its shape and size. Therefore, the relation

$$e = C\varphi$$

exists for a single conductor. The capacity of an individual conductor is numerically equal to the charge when the potential of the conductor is equal to unity. If, in addition to the given conductor, still another conductor is present, its potential depends essentially on the shape and distribution of charges on the other conductor; indeed, for a system of conductors we have

$$\begin{aligned}
e_1 &= C_{11}\varphi_1 + C_{12}(\varphi_2 - \varphi_1) + \cdots + C_{1n}(\varphi_n - \varphi_1)\\
e_2 &= C_{21}(\varphi_1 - \varphi_2) + C_{22}\varphi_2 + \cdots + C_{2n}(\varphi_n - \varphi_2)\\
&\cdots \qquad\qquad\qquad\qquad\qquad \cdots\\
e_n &= C_{n1}(\varphi_1 - \varphi_n) + C_{n2}(\varphi_2 - \varphi_n) + \cdots + C_{nn}\varphi_n
\end{aligned}$$

where e_i and φ_i are the charge and the potential, respectively, of the ith conductor. The coefficient C_{ik} is the "partial capacity" of the ith conductor with respect to the kth conductor. C_{ik} can be defined numerically as the charge which must reside on the ith conductor in order for the kth conductor to maintain the potential when all the remaining potentials become zero.

4. The matrix of coefficients C_{ik} is symmetric:

$$C_{ik} = C_{ki}.$$

For simplicity we shall consider the case of two conductors; for a larger number of conductors the proof proceeds analogously.

Given two conductors a and b, the determination of the coefficients C_{ab} and C_{ba} leads to the determination of the solutions $u^{(1)}$ and $u^{(2)}$ of the equations $\Delta u^{(1)} = 0$ and $\Delta u^{(2)} = 0$, which satisfy the boundary conditions

$$u^{(1)}|_{S_a} = 0\,, \qquad u^{(1)}|_{S_b} = 1\,, \qquad u^{(1)}|_\infty = 0$$

$$-\frac{1}{4\pi}\oint_{S_a} \frac{\partial u^{(1)}}{\partial n} d\sigma = e_a^{(1)} = C_{ab}$$

$$u^{(2)}|_{S_a} = 1\,, \qquad u^{(2)}|_{S_b} = 0\,, \qquad u^{(2)}|_\infty = 0$$

$$-\frac{1}{4\pi}\oint_{S_b} \frac{\partial u^{(2)}}{\partial n} d\sigma = e_b^{(2)} = C_{ba}\,.$$

Now let Σ_R be a sphere of sufficiently large radius R which encloses both conductors a and b. Then we apply the Green's formula to the functions $u^{(1)}$ and $u^{(2)}$ in the region T_R lying between the surface of sphere Σ_R and the conductor surfaces S_a and S_b:

$$\int_{T_R} (u^{(1)}\Delta u^{(2)} - u^{(2)}\Delta u^{(1)}) d\tau = \int_{\Sigma_R + S_a + S_b} \left(u^{(1)} \frac{\partial u^{(2)}}{\partial n} - u^{(2)} \frac{\partial u^{(1)}}{\partial n} \right) d\sigma\,.$$

The integral on the left side of this equation vanishes. By using the boundary conditions and the conditions at infinity we therefore obtain

$$\int_{S_b} \frac{\partial u^{(2)}}{\partial n} d\sigma - \int_{S_a} \frac{\partial u^{(1)}}{\partial n} d\sigma = 0$$

or

$$C_{ab} = C_{ba}\,,$$

which was to be proved.

5. As a concrete example we shall consider the field of a charged sphere. On the surface of a charged sphere of radius a let the potential φ_0 be given. The field and the charge density (see Problem 1 above) on the sphere can be represented by

$$\varphi = \frac{\varphi_0}{r} a \qquad \text{and} \qquad \sigma = \frac{\varphi_0}{4\pi a}\,.$$

If the total charge e_0 on the sphere is given instead of the potential φ_0, then

$$\varphi_0 = \frac{e_0}{a}\,, \qquad \sigma = \frac{e_0}{4\pi a^2}\,, \qquad \varphi = \frac{e_0}{r} \qquad (r > a)\,.$$

Here the sphere has the capacity

$$C = a\,,$$

i.e., in absolute units the capacity of a sphere is numerically equal to its radius.

As another example, we shall investigate the spherical condenser (a system of two concentric conducting spherical surfaces).

The inner sphere has the radius r_1 and the potential V_0; the outer sphere has a radius r_2 and is grounded. Then the determination of the field inside of the condenser amounts to the determination of the function φ which satisfies the equation

$$\Delta\varphi = 0$$

and the conditions

$$\varphi\,|_{r_1} = V_0\,, \qquad \varphi\,|_{r_2} = 0\,.$$

As one can easily see, in this case

$$\varphi = \frac{r_1 r_2}{r_2 - r_1}\, V_0\left(\frac{1}{r} - \frac{1}{r_2}\right),$$

so that the spherical condenser has the capacity

$$C = \frac{r_1 r_2}{r_2 - r_1}\,.$$

A complicated problem is represented by the calculation of the potential of a sphere when the second sphere is not concentric to the first. This problem is solved with the help of the method of images. Since the analytical solution is quite extensive, we shall not go into it here.[113]

The first sphere can be mapped onto a plane by means of an inversion.[114] We shall now show that by means of a second inversion the determination of the potential of a plane surface and of a sphere leads to the calculation of the potential of a system of two concentric conducting spheres.

For our purposes it is sufficient to consider, instead of a plane surface and a sphere, a straight line E and a circle K with the center 0 and radius

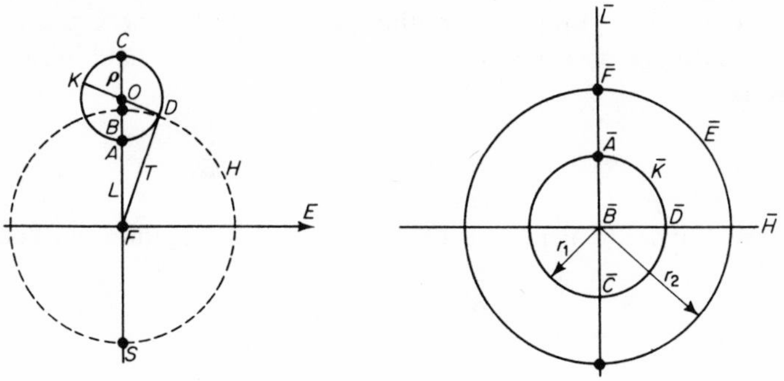

FIG. 70

[113] See Ph. Frank and R. v. Mises, *Differential and Integral Equations of Mechanics and Physics*, Vol. II, Braunschweig, 1937, p. 713.

[114] *Ibid.*

ρ (Figure 70). From the point 0 we drop the perpendicular OF on the straight line E (let l be the length of OF) and from the point F draw the tangent FD to the circle K. With FD as a radius we let the point F trace a circle H, which cuts the extension of the perpendicular line OF at a point S. We choose the point S as the center of the inversion.

By this inversion, the straight line $L = SO$, which cuts the circle K at the point A, and the circle H are transformed into the straight line $\bar{L}$ and $\bar{H}$ perpendicular to each other, while the straight line E and the circle K are transformed into the circles $\bar{E}$ and $\bar{K}$.

Since orthogonality is preserved under an inversion, the circles $\bar{E}$ and $\bar{K}$ must be orthogonal to the straight lines $\bar{L}$ and $\bar{H}$. This is possible, however, only when the centers of the circles $\bar{E}$ and $\bar{K}$ coincide with the intersection point $\bar{B}$ of the straight lines $\bar{L}$ and $\bar{H}$.

Consequently, the given inversion transforms the straight line and the circle into a pair of concentric circles.

By some simple calculations we find the radii of the circles $\bar{K}$ and $\bar{E}$:

$$r_1 = \frac{\sqrt{l^2-\rho^2} - (l-\rho)}{2\sqrt{l^2-\rho^2}\,[(l-\rho) + \sqrt{l^2-\rho^2}]}, \qquad r_2 = \frac{1}{2\sqrt{l^2-\rho^2}}.$$

Thus

$$C = \frac{1}{2\ln\dfrac{\sqrt{l^2-\rho^2} + (l-\rho)}{\sqrt{l^2-\rho^2} - (l-\rho)}}.$$

6. As an example of another two-dimensional problem, we shall investigate a cylindrical condenser which is formed of two infinitely long coaxial cylinders. Let a uniform electrical charge be distributed on one of these cylinders. Obviously, the potentials in all planes which are parallel to the normal cross sections of the cylinders are equal. The problem can therefore be treated as a plane problem and, instead of using the total charge, only the charge κ per unit length need be given.

If the exterior cylinder of radius r_2 is grounded, whereas on the inner cylinder of radius r_1 the charge κ is given, then the field potential in the condenser is

$$\varphi = 2\kappa \ln \frac{r_2}{r_1},$$

and for the capacity per unit of length for the cylindrical condenser we obtain

$$C = \frac{1}{2\ln(r_2/r_1)}.$$

The above-considered example allows us to solve a somewhat difficult problem, namely, to determine the capacity of a wire which lies above a conducting surface. An infinitely long wire of radius ρ is placed above an infinite plane and at a distance l from it. Let a charge with density κ (charge per unit length) be distributed on this wire. This problem can also be solved as a two-dimensional problem.

3. The basic problem of electrical exploration

Several electrical methods are used in the investigation of the inhomogeneities of the earth's crust for the purpose of assaying the soil. The basic idea of electrical exploration using direct current consists of the following: By means of grounded electrodes a current is passed through the earth from a battery. On the surface of the earth we measure the strength of the field so produced. From the results of the surface observations conclusions can be drawn about the structure of the interior of the earth. The methods used here are based on the mathematical solution of the corresponding problem.

The potential of the field of a direct current in a homogeneous medium satisfies the Laplace differential equation

$$\Delta V = 0 , \qquad z > 0 \tag{4-7.8}$$

with the auxiliary condition

$$\left.\frac{\partial V}{\partial z}\right|_{z=0} = 0 , \tag{4-7.9}$$

which asserts that the vertical component of the current density on the surface $z = 0$ is equal to zero. This is the case since the half space $z < 0$ is nonconducting (air).

We now consider a point-forming electrode on the boundary of the half space at the point A. Obviously, the field potential satisfies

$$V = \frac{I\rho}{2\pi R} , \tag{4-7.10}$$

where R is the distance from the source, ρ is the specific resistance of the medium, and I is the current strength.

This function differs from the Green's function in an unbounded space on the basis of condition (4-7.9) by a factor of 2.

Now if we measure, by means of a resistance bridge, the potential difference between two points M and N which lie on a straight line through A, we obtain

$$V(M) - V(N) = \frac{\partial V}{\partial r} \Delta r ,$$

where Δr is the distance between M and N.

Under the assumption that the points M and N lie sufficiently close to each other, we can write

$$\frac{V(M) - V(N)}{\Delta r} \approx \left| \frac{\partial V}{\partial r} \right| \approx \frac{I\rho}{2\pi r^2} .$$

Here r is the distance of the point 0 (the center point of the segment MN)

from the current-conducting electrode. The current strength I, as is known, must be considered since it can be measured during the observation. From this we obtain, for the resistance of the homogeneous half space,

$$\rho = \frac{2\pi r^2}{I} \cdot \left| \frac{\partial V}{\partial r} \right| . \tag{4-7.11}$$

If the medium is inhomogeneous then we call the quantity ρ determined by (4-7.11) the apparent resistance. We denote it by ρ_k; ρ_k is not constant.

We shall now consider the problem of vertical electrical probing. Let the layers of the earth's crust be horizontal, and let their resistance depend only on the depth: $\rho = \rho(z)$.

In this case, the apparent resistance is a function of the distance $r = AO$. The problem raised by the vertical electrical probing thus consists of determining the function $\rho(z)$, which yields the "electric layer" of the medium with respect to a known value $\rho_k(r)$.

We turn next to the problem of a two-layered medium. A homogeneous layer of density l and resistance ρ_0 is in contact with a homogeneous medium of resistance ρ_1.

$$\rho(z) = \begin{cases} \rho_0 & \text{for} \quad 0 \leqq z < l \\ \rho_1 & \text{for} \quad l < z . \end{cases}$$

Obviously for distances $r \ll l$ the apparent resistance ρ_k is equal to ρ_0, since the influence of the lower medium here is very weak. For large distances ($R \gg l$), by contrast, ρ_k becomes equal to ρ_1.

Our problem therefore leads to the determination of the solution of the Laplace differential equation which in the layer $0 < z < l$ is equal to V_0 and in the half space $z > l$ is equal to V_1. At $z = l$ the potential must satisfy the continuity condition

$$V_0 |_{z=l} = V_1 |_{z=l} . \tag{4-7.12}$$

Also the normal components of the current density must be continuous:

$$\frac{1}{\rho_0} \frac{\partial V_0}{\partial z}\bigg|_{z=l} = \frac{1}{\rho_1} \frac{\partial V_1}{\partial z}\bigg|_{z=l} . \tag{4-7.13}$$

At $z = 0$ the potential V_0 must satisfy the condition (4-7.9), while at the point A, which we chose as the origin of a cylindrical coordinate system (φ, r, z), it must possess a singularity of the form (4-7.10):

$$V_0 = \frac{\rho_0 I}{2\pi} \frac{1}{\sqrt{z^2 + r^2}} + v_0 , \tag{4-7.14}$$

where v_0 is a bounded function.

The potential V_1 must be bounded at infinity. The functions V_0 and V_1 satisfy Eq. (4-7.8), which, because of the cylindrical symmetry of the problem, assumes the form

$$\frac{\partial^2 V}{\partial r^2} + \frac{1}{r} \frac{\partial V}{\partial r} + \frac{\partial^2 V}{\partial z^2} = 0 .$$

By separation of variables two types of solutions for V can result, which are bounded at $r = 0$:

$$e^{\pm\lambda z} J_0(\lambda r) .$$

Here J_0 is the Bessel function of the zero-th order (see Appendix) and λ is the separation parameter. We write the solution in the form

$$V_0(r, z) = \frac{\rho_0 I}{2\pi} \cdot \frac{1}{\sqrt{r^2 + z^2}} + \int_0^\infty (A_0 e^{-\lambda z} + B_0 e^{\lambda z}) J_0(\lambda r) d\lambda$$

$$V_1(r, z) = \int_0^\infty (A_1 e^{-\lambda z} + B_1 e^{\lambda z}) J_0(\lambda r) d\lambda$$

where A_0, B_0, A_1, B_1 are constants. The condition (4-7.9) relates A_0 and B_0. We calculate the derivative

$$\frac{\partial V_0}{\partial z} = -\frac{\rho_0 I}{2\pi} \cdot \frac{z}{(z^2 + r^2)^{3/2}} + \int_0^\infty (-\lambda A_0 e^{-\lambda z} + \lambda B_0 e^{\lambda z}) J_0(\lambda r) d\lambda .$$

Condition (4-7.9) then assumes the form

$$\int_0^\infty (B_0 - A_0) J_0(\lambda r) \lambda d\lambda = 0 .$$

This relation must hold for arbitrary r; therefore,

$$B_0 = A_0 .$$

From the boundedness of V_1 as $z \to \infty$ there follows

$$B_1 = 0 .$$

Therefore,

$$V_1(r, z) = \int_0^\infty A_1 e^{-\lambda z} J_0(\lambda r) d\lambda ,$$

and

$$V_0(r, z) = \int_0^\infty [q e^{-\lambda z} + A_0 (e^{-\lambda z} + e^{\lambda z})] J_0(\lambda r) d\lambda .$$

Here we have used the formula

$$\frac{1}{\sqrt{r^2 + z^2}} = \int_0^\infty J_0(\lambda r) e^{-\lambda z} d\lambda \tag{4-7.15}$$

(see Appendix) and $\rho_0 I/2\pi = q$.

We have yet to determine the constants A_0 and A_1 from the conditions (4-7.12) and (4-7.13) at $z = l$, which leads to the system of algebraic equations

$$A_0(e^{-2\lambda l} + 1) - A_1 e^{-2\lambda l} = - q e^{-2\lambda l}$$

$$\frac{1}{\rho_0} A_0 (e^{-2\lambda l} - 1) - \frac{1}{\rho_1} A_1 e^{-2\lambda l} = - \frac{q}{\rho_0} e^{-2\lambda l} .$$

From this we find

$$A_0 = q\frac{(\rho_1 - \rho_0)e^{-2\lambda l}}{(\rho_1 + \rho_0) - (\rho_1 - \rho_0)e^{-2\lambda l}},$$

so the solution V_0 for the upper layer is given by

$$V_0(r, z) = \frac{I\rho_0}{2\pi}\int_0^\infty\left[e^{-\lambda z} + \frac{ke^{-2\lambda l}}{1 - ke^{-2\lambda l}}(e^{-\lambda z} + e^{\lambda z})\right]J_0(\lambda r)d\lambda . \tag{4-7.16}$$

Here we have set

$$\frac{\rho_1 - \rho_0}{\rho_1 + \rho_0} = k .$$

We shall now transform expression (4-7.16). Since $|k| < 1$, we can write

$$\frac{ke^{-2\lambda l}}{1 - ke^{-2\lambda l}} = \sum_{n=1}^\infty k^n \cdot e^{-2\lambda l n}$$

and

$$V_0(r, z) = \frac{I\rho_0}{2\pi}\sum_{n=0}^\infty \int_0^\infty k^n e^{-\lambda(2nl+z)} J_0(\lambda r)d\lambda + \frac{I\rho_0}{2\pi}\sum_{n=1}^\infty \int_0^\infty k^n e^{-\lambda(2nl-z)} J_0(\lambda r)d\lambda . \tag{4-7.16'}$$

Thus, by use of formula (4-7.15) we obtain

$$V_0(r, z) = \frac{I\rho_0}{2\pi}\left(\sum_{n=1}^\infty k^n \frac{1}{\sqrt{r^2 + (z - 2nl)^2}} + \sum_{n=0}^\infty k^n \frac{1}{\sqrt{r^2 + (z + 2nl)^2}}\right). \tag{4-7.17}$$

This expression for solution (4-7.16) can be written immediately when the problem is solved by the method of images. If $z = 0$, then for the potential on the earth's surface we obtain

$$V_0(r, 0) = \frac{I\rho_0}{2\pi}\left[\frac{1}{r} + 2\sum_{n=0}^\infty \frac{k^n}{\sqrt{r^2 + (2nl)^2}}\right], \tag{4-7.18}$$

from which follows

$$\frac{\partial V_0}{\partial r} = -\frac{I\rho_0}{2\pi}\left[\frac{1}{r^2} + 2\sum_{n=1}^\infty \frac{k^n r}{[r^2 + (2nl)^2]^{3/2}}\right],$$

whereas for ρ_k, according to formula (4-7.11), we find

$$\begin{aligned}\rho_k &= \rho_0\left[1 + 2\sum_{n=1}^\infty \frac{k^n r^3}{[r^2 + (2nl)^2]^{3/2}}\right] \\ &= \rho_0\left[1 + 2\sum_{n=1}^\infty \frac{k^n(\xi/2)^3}{[(\xi/2)^2 + n^2]^{3/2}}\right] = \rho_0 f(\xi)\end{aligned} \tag{4-7.19}$$

where $\xi = r/l$ and $f(\xi)$ are the expressions in the square brackets. For $r \ll l$,

$$\rho_k \approx \rho_0 .$$

In order to estimate the behavior of ρ_k for large r, use formula (4-7.19) and let $r \to \infty$ $(\xi \to \infty)$. The limit value of this nth term of the sum equals k^n; hence

$$\begin{aligned}\lim_{r\to\infty} \rho_k &= \rho_0\left(1 + 2\sum_{n=1}^\infty k^n\right) = \rho_0\left(1 + \frac{2k}{1 - k}\right) \\ &= \rho_0\frac{1 + k}{1 - k} = \rho_0\frac{\rho_1 + \rho_0 + (\rho_1 - \rho_0)}{\rho_1 + \rho_0 - (\rho_1 - \rho_0)} = \rho_1 .\end{aligned}$$

By a comparison of the experimentally determined data with the curve determined by formula (4-7.19), we can determine ρ_0 from the values of ρ_k for small r and ρ_1 from the values of ρ_k for large r. The thickness l of the upper conducting layer is determined according to the selection principle. It is equal to that value of l for which the empirical curve as a function of $\rho(\xi) = \rho(r/l)$ coincides best with the curve calculated by formula (4-7.19). Here we shall not dwell on the technicalities of the selection which can be carried out by means of bilogarithmic measurements.[115]

In the case of multiple layers, the curves for ρ_k can be calculated analogously. The character of the electric layers of the medium under consideration is determined by the selection of those theoretical curves that coincide best with the empirical curves. By increasing the number of layers, the technicalities of interpretation become complicated, since the number of theoretical curves entering into consideration is greatly increased.

We have proved, therefore, that for different electrical layers $\rho_1(z) \neq \rho_2(z)$ the corresponding apparent resistances also are different:

$$\rho_k^{(1)}(r) \neq \rho_k^{(2)}(r)\,.$$

Consequently, the problem—to determine the electric layer from the apparent resistances—appears from the mathematical side to have a uniquely determined solution.[116]

Problems analogous to those of electrical exploration considered above occur in different areas of physics and technology. Electrostatic problems of this type arise in the construction of electronic equipment, whereas heat-theory and hydrodynamic problems arise in different areas of technology (heat loss of buildings, filtration of water under a retaining dam, etc.).[117] The problem of the determination of a magnetic field in an inhomogeneous medium occurs, for example, in magnetic testing of materials. To determine an ultimate failure in a sample—for example, an air bubble below the surface—the metallic sample is placed between the poles of a magnet, and the magnetic field on the surface is measured. From the perturbations of the magnetic field, the presence of the defects is observed, and if possible their extent, the depth at which they occurred, etc., are also determined.

For the solution of such problems several methods of analogy can be applied. Therefore the analogy between the potential fields of different physical processes is used.[118]

We consider now the potential field in an inhomogeneous medium (for example, a stationary temperature field, a magnetic field in an inhomogeneous

115 See, for example, the excellent book by A. I. Zaborovskii, *Electrical Exploration*, 1943.

116 A. N. Tychonoff, "On the uniqueness of solutions of problems of electrical exploration," *Doklady*, **69**, (6): 797 (1949).

117 N. N. Pavlovskii, *Theory of Motion of Ground Waters for Hydro-technical Installations and its Fundamental Applications*, 1922, Ch. XIV.

118 A. V. Lukyanov, "On the electrolytic simulation of spatial problems," *Doklady*, **75** (5): (1950).

medium, an electrostatic field, the velocity field of a liquid during filtering). The potential functions $u(x, y, z)$ of these fields in each homogeneous subregion satisfy the Laplace differential equation $\Delta u = 0$. At the boundary between two regions G_1 and G_2 with different heat-conduction coefficients, magnetic permeabilities, etc., the condition

$$k_1 \frac{\partial u^{(1)}}{\partial n} = k^2 \frac{\partial u^{(2)}}{\partial n}$$

holds in which k_1 and k_2 are the corresponding physical constants.

On the boundaries of similar geometric regions the corresponding numerical values of the potential or the normal derivatives of different physical fields are prescribed. We shall assume that the physical inhomogeneities of this region are not different geometrically and are distributed similarly. The ratios of the physical constants (heat conductivity, magnetic permeability, etc.) of an arbitrary pair of corresponding inhomogeneities are also equal. Then the values of the potential of this field at the corresponding points coincide numerically, since the potential solutions are one and the same mathematical problem and this problem permits only a single solution.

The direct measurement of a temperature, in magnetic or other fields, is significantly more difficult than the measurement of a current field in an electrolytic tank. We replace it therefore in a suitable manner by measurements in such a tank. We can also choose the units in a suitable way.

4. The determination of vector fields

In addition to scalar problems, the problem often arises in electrodynamics and hydrodynamics of determining a vector field from the given rotation and divergence of these fields.

We shall prove that a vector field $\boldsymbol{A}$ interior to a region G, whose boundary S is bounded, is uniquely defined when the rotation and the divergence of $\boldsymbol{A}$ are known in G, that is,

$$\operatorname{rot} \boldsymbol{A} = \boldsymbol{B} \tag{4-7.20}$$

$$\operatorname{div} \boldsymbol{A} = C \tag{4-7.21}$$

and on the boundary S the normal component of $\boldsymbol{A}$ is prescribed:

$$A_n |_S = f(\mathrm{M}) . \tag{4-7.22}$$

The functions $\boldsymbol{B}, C,$ and f are not arbitrarily prescribed. Often the relations

$$\operatorname{div} \boldsymbol{B} = 0 \tag{4-7.23}$$

$$\iint_S f(M) dS = \iiint_G C d\tau \tag{4-7.24}$$

must be satisfied. Now we assume f to be continuous on the surface S and the functions $\boldsymbol{B}$ and C, including their derivatives, to be continuous in G; further, let the surface S be so constituted that the second interior boundary-value problem with continuous boundary values is solvable for it. We shall solve our problem in three steps. First, we shall seek a vector $\boldsymbol{A}_1$ which satisfies the conditions

$$\operatorname{rot} \boldsymbol{A}_1 = 0 \tag{4-7.25}$$

$$\operatorname{div} \boldsymbol{A}_1 = C\,. \tag{4-7.26}$$

From (4-7.25) there follows

$$\boldsymbol{A}_1 = \operatorname{grad} \varphi\,. \tag{4-7.27}$$

If we assume φ in the form

$$\varphi(P) = -\frac{1}{4\pi}\iiint_G \frac{C(Q)}{r_{PQ}}\,d\tau_Q \tag{4-7.28}$$

then we satisfy (4-7.26). Now we define a vector $\boldsymbol{A}_2$ such that

$$\operatorname{rot} \boldsymbol{A}_2 = \boldsymbol{B} \tag{4-7.29}$$

$$\operatorname{div} \boldsymbol{A}_2 = 0\,. \tag{4-7.30}$$

If we set

$$\boldsymbol{A}_2 = \operatorname{rot} \vec{\psi}\,, \tag{4-7.31}$$

then the condition (4-7.30) is satisfied.

If we substitute (4-7.31) into (4-7.29), we obtain

$$\operatorname{grad}\operatorname{div} \vec{\psi} - \Delta\vec{\psi} = \boldsymbol{B}\,. \tag{4-7.32}$$

Now we require

$$\operatorname{div} \vec{\psi} = 0\,. \tag{4-7.33}$$

Then Eq. (4-7.32) for $\vec{\psi}$ assumes the form

$$\Delta\vec{\psi} = -\boldsymbol{B}\,. \tag{4-7.34}$$

We consider a region G_1 which entirely contains G and is bounded by a surface S_1. We continue $\boldsymbol{B}$ into the region $G_1 - G$, where the following conditions are to be fulfilled:

(*a*) The normal component B_n of $\boldsymbol{B}$ on S is continuous ($\boldsymbol{B}$ itself in general is discontinuous), $B_{n_i} = B_{n_a}$.

(*b*) $B_n = 0$ on S_1. (4-7.35)

(*c*) In $G_1 - G$, $\operatorname{div} \boldsymbol{B} = 0$. (4-7.23′)

We show how this continuation of $\boldsymbol{B}$ into $G_1 - G$ can be realized and therefore set

$$\boldsymbol{B} = \operatorname{grad} \chi \quad \text{in} \quad G_1 - G\,.$$

The condition $\operatorname{div} \boldsymbol{B} = 0$ yields

$$\Delta\chi = 0 \quad \text{in} \quad G_1 - G\,. \tag{4-7.36}$$

The boundary condition, according to (*a*) and (*b*), has the form

$$\frac{\partial \chi}{\partial n} = B_{n_i} \quad \text{on} \quad S \tag{4-7.36'}$$

$$\frac{\partial \chi}{\partial n} = 0 \quad \text{on} \quad S_1 \tag{4-7.36''}$$

where B_{n_i} is the limit value of B_n from the interior side of S. For the function χ, we obtain the second boundary-value problem (4-7.36)—(4-7.36″).

The necessary and sufficient condition for the solvability of this problem is that

$$\iint_{S+S_1} \frac{\partial \chi}{\partial n} dS = \iint_S B_n dS = 0$$

be satisfied, because the relation

$$\iint_S B_n dS = \iiint_G \operatorname{div} \boldsymbol{B} d\tau = 0$$

is satisfied.

If we set

$$\vec{\psi}(P) = \frac{1}{4\pi} \iiint_{G_1} \frac{\boldsymbol{B}(Q)}{r_{PQ}} d\tau_Q \tag{4-7.34}$$

with $P = P(x, y, z)$, $Q = Q\ (\xi, \eta, \zeta)$, then (4-7.34) is obviously satisfied; the condition (4-7.33) also is satisfied.

Therefore, we calculate the derivatives

$$\frac{\partial \psi_x}{\partial x}, \quad \frac{\partial \psi_y}{\partial y}, \quad \frac{\partial \psi_z}{\partial z}.$$

If we represent the integral over G_1 as the sum of integrals over G and $G_1 - G$ and bear in mind the relation

$$\frac{\partial}{\partial x} \iiint \frac{B_x}{r} d\tau = \iiint B_x \frac{\partial}{\partial x}\left(\frac{1}{r}\right) d\tau = - \iiint B_x \frac{\partial}{\partial \xi}\left(\frac{1}{r}\right) d\tau,$$

then by partial integration

$$\frac{\partial}{\partial x} \iiint_G \frac{B_x}{r} d\tau = \iiint_G \frac{\partial B_x}{\partial \xi} \frac{1}{r} d\tau - \iint_S (B_x)_i \frac{\cos \alpha}{r} dS$$

$$\frac{\partial}{\partial x} \iiint_{G_1 - G} \frac{B_x}{r} d\tau = \iiint_{G_1 - G} \frac{\partial B_x}{\partial \xi} \frac{1}{r} d\tau + \iint_S (B_x)_a \frac{\cos \alpha}{r} dS - \iint_{S_1} B_x \frac{\cos \alpha_1}{r} dS$$

follows, where $\cos \alpha = \cos (n, x)\,|_S$, $\cos \alpha_1 = \cos (n, x)\,|_{S_1}$, and n is the direction of the exterior normal to the surface.

For $\partial \psi_x / \partial x$ we find

$$\frac{\partial \psi_r}{\partial x} = \frac{1}{4\pi} \iiint_{G_1} \frac{\partial B_x}{\partial \xi} \frac{1}{r} d\tau + \frac{1}{4\pi} \iint \frac{[B_{xa} - B_{xi}] \cos \alpha}{r} dS - \frac{1}{4\pi} \iint_{S_1} B_x \frac{\cos \alpha_1}{r} dS.$$

Analogous expressions result for $\partial \psi_y / \partial y$ and $\partial \psi_z / \partial z$. Hence, on the basis of

(4-7.23) and the continuity of the normal components of $\boldsymbol{B}$ on S ($B_{n_a} = B_{n_i}$), it follows that

$$\operatorname{div} \vec{\psi} = \frac{1}{4\pi}\iiint_{G_1} \frac{\operatorname{div} \boldsymbol{B}}{r} d\tau - \frac{1}{4\pi}\iint_{S_1} \frac{B_n}{r} dS + \frac{1}{4\pi}\iint_{S} \frac{(B_{n_a} - B_{n_i})}{r} dS = 0 .$$

The vector $\boldsymbol{A}_2$ defined by (4-7.31) satisfies (4-7.29) when the vector $\vec{\psi}$ satisfies conditions (4-7.33) and (4-7.34).

Therefore, the sought vector $\boldsymbol{A}$ satisfies the boundary condition (4-7.22). Now a vector $\boldsymbol{A}_3$ is to be determined which satisfies the following conditions:

$$\left.\begin{aligned} \operatorname{rot} \boldsymbol{A}_3 &= 0 \\ \operatorname{div} \boldsymbol{A}_3 &= 0 \end{aligned}\right\} \text{ inside of } G \qquad \begin{aligned} &(4\text{-}7.37) \\ &(4\text{-}7.38) \end{aligned}$$

$$A_n|_S = f(M) - A_{1n}|_S - A_{2n}|_S = f^*(M) \quad \text{on } S . \tag{4-7.39}$$

It is clear that the function $f^*(M)$ is uniquely defined. From (4-7.37) there follows

$$\boldsymbol{A}_3 = \operatorname{grad} \theta .$$

If we substitute $\boldsymbol{A}_3$ into (4-7.38), in the interior of G we obtain

$$\Delta\theta = 0 , \tag{4-7.40}$$

which yields

$$\left.\frac{\partial\theta}{\partial n}\right|_S = f^*(M) , \tag{4.7.41}$$

i.e., for the determination of θ we have to solve the second boundary-value problem. $\boldsymbol{A}$ is therefore uniquely determined.

The problem therefore possesses exactly one solution,

$$\boldsymbol{A} = \boldsymbol{A}_1 + \boldsymbol{A}_2 + \boldsymbol{A}_3 .$$

5. Conformal mapping in electrostatics

1. For the solution of two-dimensional electrostatic problems the theory of functions is often used. We shall consider the following problem as an example:

Determine the electric field of several charged conductors whose potentials are equal to $u_1, u_2, \cdots$.

This problem, as is known, leads to the equation

$$\Delta u = 0 \tag{4-7.42}$$

with the boundary conditions

$$u|_{S_i} = u_i , \tag{4-7.43}$$

where S_i designates the surface of the ith conductor. If the field can be regarded as a planar field which does not change along the z axis, then Eq. (4-7.42) and the boundary conditions assume the form

$$\frac{\partial^2 u}{\partial x^2} + \frac{\partial^2 u}{\partial y^2} = 0 \tag{4-7.44}$$

$$u|_{C_i} = u_i \tag{4-7.45}$$

where C_i is the contour of the bounded region S_i.

We write the potential u as the imaginary part of an analytic function

$$f(z) = v(x, y) + iu(x, y)\,, \qquad z = x + iy\,. \tag{4-7.46}$$

Therefore the Cauchy-Riemann differential equations must follow:

$$v_x = u_y\,, \qquad v_y = -u_x \tag{4-7.47}$$

and

$$v_x v_y + u_x u_y = 0\,. \tag{4-7.48}$$

From the boundary condition (4-7.45) it follows that the imaginary part of $f(z)$ on the contour C_i is constant.

From the conditions (4-7.47) we know that

$$v(x, y) = \text{const.} \tag{4-7.49}$$

represents the equation of the lines of force,[119] and the lines of equipotential can be described by the equation

$$u(x, y) = \text{const.} \tag{4-7.50}$$

because of (4-7.48).

To solve the problem under consideration it is sufficient, therefore, to find the conformal mapping of the z plane ($z = x + iy$) on the w plane ($w = u + iv$) for which the boundaries of the conductor are mapped into the straight lines

$$u = \text{const.}$$

or

$$\text{Im}\, w = \text{const.}$$

If such a mapping function $w = f(z)$ is known, then the sought potential is determined from

$$u = u(x, y) = \text{Im}\, f(z)\,.$$

The knowledge of these potentials permits the calculation of the electrical field strength

$$E_x = -\frac{\partial u}{\partial x}\,, \qquad E_y = -\frac{\partial u}{\partial y} \tag{4-7.51}$$

and the calculation of the density of the surface charges along the z axis:

$$\sigma = \frac{1}{4\pi}\sqrt{E_x^2 + E_y^2} = \frac{1}{4\pi}\sqrt{\left(\frac{\partial u}{\partial x}\right)^2 + \left(\frac{\partial u}{\partial y}\right)^2}\,.$$

[119] The equation of the lines of force results from $dx/u_x = dy/u_y$. If one replaces u_x and u_y according to (4-7.47) by $-v_y$ and v_x, respectively, then we obtain $v_x dx + v_y dy = dv = 0$, or $v(x, y) = \text{const.}$

Also, on the basis of the Cauchy-Riemann differential equations we obtain

$$\sigma = \frac{1}{4\pi} | f'(z) | . \tag{4-7.52}$$

2. We shall now determine the field of a one-sided bounded plate condenser, using as an example a condenser which is formed from two infinitely thin metal plates $y = -d/2$ and $y = d/2$. The plates lie in the regions $x < 0$. We avoid the construction of the conformal mapping function which maps the region represented in Figure 71 onto the region $|\operatorname{Im} w| \leqq \pi$, and, instead, apply this mapping directly for the solution of the problem.[120]

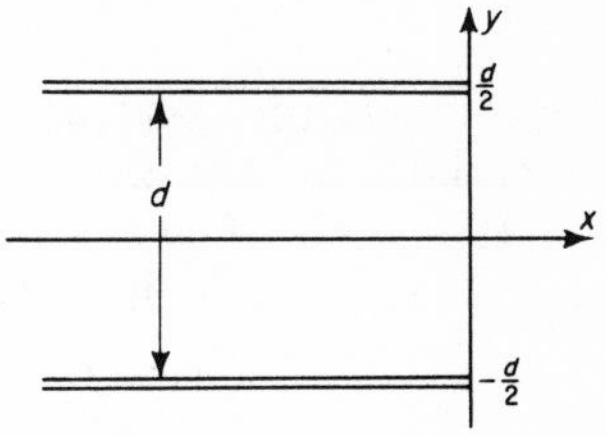

FIG. 71.

The mapping defined by

$$z = \frac{d}{2\pi}(w + e^w) , \qquad w = \varphi + i\psi \tag{4-7.53}$$

carries the lines $z = \pm d/2$, $x < 0$, which cuts the z plane ($z = x + iy$) into the region $|\psi| \leqq \pi$ of the w plane ($w = \varphi + i\psi$) (Figure 72). For the complex potential we choose the function

$$\frac{u_0}{2\pi} w , \tag{4-7.54}$$

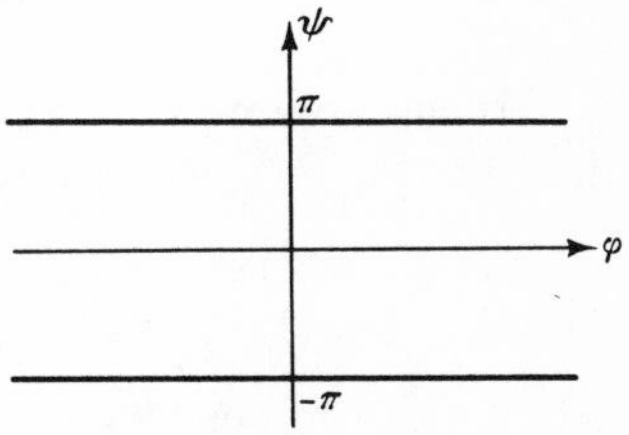

FIG. 72.

where u_0 is the potential difference between the condenser plates. The potential of the electric field is then represented by the function

$$u(x, y) = \frac{u_0}{2\pi}\psi . \tag{4-7.55}$$

Here ψ is connected with x and y by the relations

$$\begin{aligned} x &= \frac{d}{2\pi}(\varphi + e^\varphi \cos \psi) \\ y &= \frac{d}{2\pi}(\psi + e^\varphi \sin \psi) . \end{aligned} \tag{4-7.56}$$

Figure 73 shows the equipotential and the lines of force of a one-sided bounded plate condenser. We now investigate the field in the neighborhood of the boundary of the condenser.

We see from formula (4-7.56) that as $\varphi \to -\infty$

$$x \approx \frac{d}{2\pi}\varphi , \qquad y \approx \frac{d}{2\pi}\psi , \tag{4-7.57}$$

[120] See Ph. Frank and R. v. Mises, Ch. XV, § 5, *op. cit.* fn. 113.

i.e., inside the condenser at large distances from the boundary the field is planar; but as $\varphi \to \infty$

$$\rho = \sqrt{x^2 + y^2} \approx \frac{d}{2\pi} e^{\varphi}, \qquad \theta = \operatorname{arc\,tg} \frac{y}{x} \approx \psi, \tag{4-7.58}$$

i.e., outside the condenser, at large distances from the boundary, the equipotential lines are circles.

If instead of w the complex potential $f = (u_0/2\pi)w$ is introduced so that $w = (2\pi/u_0)f$, then the relationship between z and $f(z)$ is given by

$$z = d\left(\frac{f}{u_0} + \frac{1}{2\pi} e^{2\pi f/u_0}\right).$$

From this it follows that

$$\frac{dz}{df} = \frac{d}{u_0}\left(1 + e^{2\pi f/u_0}\right);$$

on the other hand, for $f = (u_0/2\pi)(\varphi \pm \pi i)$ we obtain

$$\frac{dz}{df} = \frac{d}{u_0}(1 - e^{\varphi}) \quad \text{or} \quad f'(z) = \frac{u_0}{d(1 - e^{\varphi})}.$$

If we assume $u_0 = 1$, then for the density of the charge σ, according to formula (4-7.52), we obtain the value

$$\sigma = \frac{|f'(z)|}{4\pi} = \frac{1}{4\pi d\,|1 - e^{\varphi}|}. \tag{4.7.59}$$

From this we see that as $\varphi \to -\infty$

$$\sigma \approx \frac{1}{4\pi d},$$

and as $\varphi \to \infty$

$$\sigma \approx \frac{1}{4\pi d e^{\varphi}},$$

i.e., in this case, the density of the charge on the outside of the plate decreases as $1/\rho$.

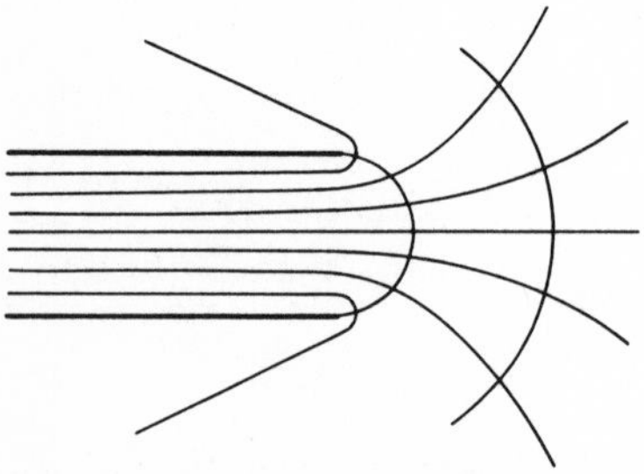

FIG. 73.

Formula (4-7.59) shows that for $\varphi = 0$ (on the boundary of the condenser) $\sigma = \infty$. The boundary of a plane plate possesses an infinite curvature; therefore, in order to charge the plate to a definite potential, an infinitely large amount of charge must be placed on it.

A wide range of problems can be solved with the help of conformal mapping. With this method, for example, the question regarding the influence of the boundary of thick-walled plates of a plane condenser can be answered successfully, as well as a series of questions which are related to the influence of deformation in condensers. The method of conformal mapping can also be used for the treatment of dynamic problems. Its disadvantage is that it can only be used in plane problems which lead to the two-dimensional Laplace differential equation $\Delta_2 u = 0$.

6. Conformal mapping in hydrodynamics

1. For the solution of problems of the motion of a solid body in a liquid, the boundary conditions on the surface of the body play an important role.

In the case of an ideal fluid, the boundary condition is that the normal component of the fluid velocity

$$v_n(x, y, z) = v_x(x, y, z) \cos(n, x) + v_y(x, y, z) \cos(n, y) + v_z(x, y, z) \cos(n, z)$$

for all points on the surface of the body must be equal to the normal component of the velocity of motion of the body. If the body does not move, then the boundary condition on the surface of the body assumes the simplest form

$$v_n = 0\,.$$

If the motion under consideration possesses a potential, i.e., a function φ exists such that

$$\boldsymbol{v} = \operatorname{grad} \varphi\,,$$

then the boundary conditions read

$$\left.\frac{\partial \varphi}{\partial n}\right|_S = 0 \qquad \text{in case the body does not move;}$$

$$\left.\frac{\partial \varphi}{\partial n}\right|_S = u_n \qquad \text{in case the body moves with the velocity } \boldsymbol{u}.$$

From hydrodynamics it is known that the velocity potential for an incompressible fluid satisfies the equation

$$\Delta \varphi = 0\,.$$

Therefore the determination of the potential for the streaming about a solid body in an incompressible ideal fluid is reduced to the solution of the Laplace differential equation

$$\Delta \varphi = 0\,,$$

where on the boundary of the streaming body the boundary condition

$$\left.\frac{\partial \varphi}{\partial n}\right|_S = u_n$$

must hold, i.e., the second boundary-value problem for the Laplace differential equation must be solved.

If the motion is planar, then the solution of the problem can be obtained by using function theory.

For planar motion of an incompressible fluid the continuity equation is:

$$\frac{\partial v_x}{\partial x} = \frac{\partial(-v_y)}{\partial y}\,. \tag{4-7.60}$$

We describe the equation of the stream lines

$$\frac{dx}{v_x} = \frac{dy}{v_y}$$

in the form

$$v_x dy - v_y dx = 0 \tag{4-7.61}$$

an introduce a new function ψ by the relations

$$v_x = \frac{\partial \psi}{\partial y}, \qquad v_y = -\frac{\partial \psi}{\partial x}.$$

From Eq. (4-7.60) it then follows that the left side of expression (4-7.61) is the total differential of the function ψ:

$$v_x dy - v_y dx = d\psi.$$

The one-parameter family of curves

$$\psi(x, y) = C$$

therefore represents the stream lines of the incompressible fluid motion.

If a velocity potential exists, then the equation $\operatorname{rot} \boldsymbol{v} = 0$ is equivalent to

$$\Delta\psi = 0.$$

From the relations for v_x and v_y it then follows that

$$\frac{\partial \varphi}{\partial x} = \frac{\partial \psi}{\partial y}, \qquad \frac{\partial \varphi}{\partial y} = -\frac{\partial \psi}{\partial x},$$

i.e., the functions φ and ψ satisfy the Cauchy-Riemann differential equations. Consequently, the complex function

$$w(z) = \varphi(x, y) + i\psi(x, y)$$

is an analytic function.

Therefore, every irrotational ($\operatorname{rot} \boldsymbol{v} = 0$) planar motion of a fluid has a corresponding definite complex analytic function, and conversely every analytic function corresponds to a definite form of fluid motion, i.e., two motions correspond to an analytic function, since the roles of the functions φ and ψ can be interchanged.

2. In conclusion, we shall treat a concrete example of the application of the theory of functions to the solution of problems for the streaming of a body—here, a circular cylinder—in a planar fluid.

On a circular cylinder at rest of radius $r = a$, let a planar fluid stream impinge which at infinity has the constant velocity u. In the case of a static fluid, we would consider the motion of the cylinder moving with the constant velocity u with respect to the stationary fluid.

As a reference system, we choose a rectangular coordinate system (x, y, z) attached to the cylinder in which the x axis is chosen parallel to the direction of the velocity of the cylinder.

On the surface of this moving body, the boundary condition

$$\frac{\partial\psi}{\partial s} = u\frac{\partial y}{\partial s}$$

must be satisfied, where ∂s is the element of arc on the boundary of the body.

In the case of a motion propagating with the velocity u this condition can be integrated over the surface of the body. We then obtain on the surface of the body

$$\psi = uy + C .$$

Therefore, our problem amounts to the solution of the equation

$$\Delta\psi = 0$$

with the following boundary conditions:

on the surface of the cylinder $\quad \psi = uy + C$

at infinity $\dfrac{\partial\psi}{\partial x}$ and $\dfrac{\partial\psi}{\partial y}$ approach zero.

The last condition means that

$$\frac{dw}{dz} = \frac{\partial\psi}{\partial y} + i\frac{\partial\psi}{\partial x} = v_x - iv_y$$

exterior to the circle C is a single-valued analytic function, which vanishes at infinity. The function w can therefore be represented in the form

$$w = C_1 \ln z - \frac{C_2}{z} - \frac{C_3}{z^2} + \cdots$$

Now we set

$$C_k = A_k + iB_k$$

and determine the constants A_k and B_k from the boundary condition

$$\psi = ua \sin\theta + C ,$$

which are transformed to polar coordinates by $z = ae^{i\theta}$.

For the constants then we obtain

$$A_1 = 0 , \qquad A_2 = ua^2 , \qquad B_2 = 0 , \qquad A_3 = B_3 = 0 , \qquad B_1 = -\frac{\Gamma}{2\pi} .$$

From this there results

$$w = \frac{\Gamma}{2\pi i} \ln z - u\frac{a^2}{z}$$

$$\varphi = \frac{\Gamma}{2\pi}\theta - u\cos\theta\frac{a^2}{r}$$

$$\psi = -\frac{\Gamma}{2\pi} \ln r + u\sin\theta\,\frac{a^2}{r} .$$

The first term in the expression for w denotes the circulation around the cylinder with the intensity Γ. Where there is no circulation, we obtain

$$w = -u\frac{a^2}{z}\,.$$

For the flow about a static cylinder, which at infinity has the velocity u, the complex potential has the form

$$w = uz + \frac{ua^2}{z} + \frac{\Gamma}{2\pi i}\ln z\,.$$

3. With the results for a streaming about a circular cylinder we can solve the problem of the streaming about an arbitrary contour by using the method of conformal mapping. We consider its application to the problem of the flow about a rectangular plate.

On the x axis let us place an infinitely long plate of width $2a$ (Figure 74).

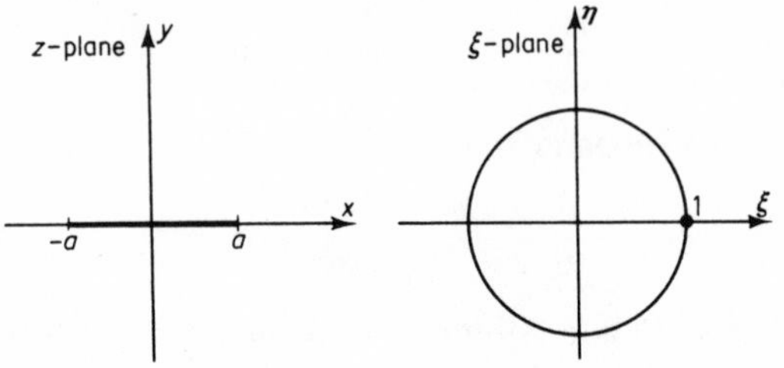

FIG. 74.

On the plate a constant planar flow occurs which at infinity has a velocity c with components u and v. By means of the analytic function

$$z = \frac{a}{2}\left(\zeta + \frac{1}{\zeta}\right) = f(\zeta)$$

we obtain a reversible single-valued mapping of the region exterior to the plate in the z plane onto the region exterior to the unit circle in the ζ plane. Here the point $z = \infty$ corresponds to the point $\zeta = \infty$, and

$$\frac{dz}{d\zeta} = \frac{a}{2} > 0 \qquad \text{for} \qquad \zeta = \infty\,.$$

We shall now investigate the nature of the mapping of the condition at infinity. For the complex potential

$$w(z) = \varphi + i\psi$$

we have

$$\left(\frac{dw}{dz}\right)_{z=\infty} = u - iv = \bar{v}_\infty\,,$$

i.e., the conjugate value of the complex velocity.

We determine now the value of the complex velocity of the fictitious flow in the ζ plane:

$$w(\zeta) = w[f(z)] , \qquad \frac{dw}{d\zeta} = \frac{dw}{dz} \cdot \frac{dz}{d\zeta} .$$

From this we obtain

$$\left(\frac{dw}{d\zeta}\right)_{\zeta=\infty} = k\bar{v}_\infty , \qquad k = \frac{a}{2} .$$

The fictitious flow therefore represents the flow about a cylinder of unit radius and at infinity has the complex velocity kv_∞. For such a motion, the complex potential has the form

$$w(\zeta) = k\bar{v}_\infty \zeta + \frac{kv_\infty}{\zeta} + \frac{\Gamma}{2\pi i} \ln \zeta .$$

From $z = f(\zeta)$ there now follows:

$$\zeta = \frac{z + \sqrt{z^2 - a^2}}{a} , \qquad \frac{1}{\zeta} = \frac{z - \sqrt{z^2 - a^2}}{a} .$$

By use of this expression, we obtain, for the complex potential of a fluid streaming about a plate, the expression

$$w(z) = uz - iv\sqrt{z^2 - a^2} + \frac{\Gamma}{2\pi i} \ln\left(\frac{z + \sqrt{z^2 - a^2}}{a}\right) .$$

If no circulation occurs, we have instead the following relation

$$w(z) = uz - iv\sqrt{z^2 - a^2} .$$

From these relations it is seen that the velocity at the ends of the plate becomes infinitely large. Under real conditions, of course, this is not the case. Our conclusions can be explained on the basis that we have assumed an ideal fluid. With the use of the Bernoulli equation an expression can be found for the forces which the fluid exerts on the streaming body.

The investigation of those forces with which air acts on a wing of an airplane constitutes the subject of aerodynamics. Toward the development of this theory Russian scholars have made outstanding contributions, foremost of which were Joukowski and S. A. Tschaplygin. A paradox arises in the simplest case of a circulation-free flow about a cylinder by a planar fluid in that the flow exerts no force on a cylinder. If, for the propagating flow, a circulation of the velocity about the cylinder exists, then a force appears which acts on the cylinder perpendicular to the fluid velocity at infinity.

The theory of functions can be applied only to planar motions. In the three-dimensional case we must turn to other methods in order to treat the problem of streaming about a solid body by a fluid. The solution of this problem in complete generality is very difficult. Let us consider, for example, the motion of a sphere in a static fluid. Let velocity of the sphere be constant. The problem then consists of solving the equation

$$\Delta\varphi = 0$$

with the boundary conditions

$$\left.\frac{\partial\varphi}{\partial n}\right|_{r=a} = u\cos\theta$$

on the surface of the sphere and

$$\frac{\partial\varphi}{\partial x} = \frac{\partial\varphi}{\partial y} = \frac{\partial\varphi}{\partial z} = 0$$

at infinity. The solution has the form

$$\varphi = Au\,\mathrm{grad}\frac{1}{r}\,.$$

By using the boundary condition, we obtain

$$\varphi = -\frac{a^3 ur}{2r^3}$$

as a solution of the problem.

An ideal fluid was assumed in all the cases considered. For viscous fluids the boundary conditions take another form, and on the surface of the body the so-called adhering condition must be satisfied. This condition states that directly on the surface of the body the velocity of the fluid must coincide in both magnitude and direction with the velocity of the corresponding boundary points of the body.

The problem of flow about a body by a viscous fluid leads to great mathematical difficulties. In the development of this part of hydrodynamics, boundary-layer theory plays a significant role.

7. Biharmonic equation

In Section 2-6 § 1 we found

$$\frac{\partial^2 u}{\partial t^2} + a^2\frac{\partial^4 u}{\partial x^4} = 0 \tag{4-7.62}$$

as the equation of a transverse vibrating rod. The vibrations of an unloaded thin plate whose boundaries are fixed can be described by the analogous equation[121]

$$\frac{\partial^2 u}{\partial t^2} + a^2\left(\frac{\partial^4 u}{\partial x^4} + \frac{\partial^4 u}{\partial y^4} + 2\frac{\partial^4 u}{\partial x^2\partial y^2}\right) = 0 \quad \text{or} \quad \frac{\partial^2 u}{\partial t^2} + a^2\Delta\Delta u = 0. \tag{4-7.63}$$

Here the boundary conditions

$$u = 0 \quad \text{and} \quad \frac{\partial u}{\partial n} = 0 \tag{4-7.64}$$

must be satisfied.

Moreover, the function u must satisfy the initial conditions

$$u(x, y, 0) = \varphi(x, y)\,, \qquad \frac{\partial u}{\partial t}(x, y, 0) = \psi(x, y)\,. \tag{4-7.65}$$

121 V. I. Smirnov, Part III_2, *op. cit.* fn. 15.

If external forces act on the plate which are distributed with the density $f(x, y)$, then the deformation of a plate whose boundaries are fixed can be described by the equation

$$\Delta\Delta u = f, \tag{4-7.66}$$

with the boundary conditions

$$u = 0 \quad \text{and} \quad \frac{\partial u}{\partial n} = 0. \tag{4-7.64}$$

The equation

$$\Delta\Delta u = 0 \tag{4-7.66'}$$

is called the biharmonic equation and its solutions biharmonic functions. These functions must possess continuous derivatives up to and including the fourth order.

The fundamental boundary-value problem for the biharmonic equation reads:

Determine a function $u(x, y)$, which including its first derivatives in the closed region $S + C$ is continuous, in S possesses continuous derivatives up to the fourth order, in S satisfies Eq. (4-7.66) or (4-7.66′), and on the boundary C satisfies the boundary conditions

$$u\,|_C = g(s), \qquad \left.\frac{\partial u}{\partial n}\right|_C = h(s), \tag{4-7.67}$$

where $g(s)$ and $h(s)$ are continuous functions of the arc length s on C.

For the solution of the above-formulated initial value problem (4-7.63)—(4-7.65) by means of separation of variables, we usually set

$$u(x, y, t) = v(x, y)T(t). \tag{4-7.68}$$

If we introduce this expression into (4-7.63) and separate the variables, then for the determination of the eigenvalues we arrive at the equation

$$\Delta\Delta v - \lambda v = 0 \tag{4-7.69}$$

with the boundary conditions

$$v = 0, \quad \frac{\partial v}{\partial n} = 0 \quad \text{on} \quad C. \tag{4-7.70}$$

1. *Uniqueness of the Solution.* We shall prove that the biharmonic equation

$$\Delta\Delta u = 0$$

with the boundary conditions

$$u\,|_C = g(s), \qquad \left.\frac{\partial u}{\partial n}\right|_C = h(s) \tag{4-7.64'}$$

has at most one solution.

Let us assume that two distinct solutions u_1 and u_2 exist. We consider their difference

$$v = u_1 - u_2 \,,$$

which obviously also satisfies the biharmonic Eq. (4-7.66) and the homogeneous boundary conditions

$$v\,|_C = 0 \qquad \frac{\partial v}{\partial n}\bigg|_C = 0\,.$$

By application of Green's formula

$$\int_G (\psi \Delta\varphi - \varphi\Delta\psi) dS = \int_C \left(\psi \frac{\partial \varphi}{\partial n} - \varphi \frac{\partial \psi}{\partial n}\right) ds$$

to the functions $\varphi = v$ and $\psi = \Delta v$, we obtain

$$\int_G (\Delta v)^2 dS = 0$$

and hence

$$\Delta v = 0\,.$$

Now, however, $v\,|_C = 0$. Consequently,

$$v \equiv 0 \qquad \text{and} \qquad u_1 \equiv u_2 \,,$$

i.e., the biharmonic functions are uniquely determined by the boundary conditions (4-7.64).

2. *Representation of a Biharmonic Function by Harmonic Functions.* We first prove the theorem:

Theorem. If u_1 and u_2 are two harmonic functions in a region G, then $u = xu_1 + u_2$ is a biharmonic function in G.

For the proof we use the identity

$$\Delta(\varphi\psi) = \varphi\Delta\psi + \psi\Delta\varphi + 2\left(\frac{\partial \varphi}{\partial x}\frac{\partial \psi}{\partial x} + \frac{\partial \varphi}{\partial y}\frac{\partial \psi}{\partial y}\right). \tag{4-7.71}$$

With

$$\varphi = x \,, \qquad \psi = u_1$$

it follows that

$$\Delta(xu_1) = 2\frac{\partial u_1}{\partial x}\,. \tag{4-7.72}$$

By repeated application of the Δ-operators and by consideration of $\Delta\Delta u_2 = 0$, we obtain

$$\Delta\Delta(xu_1 + u_2) = 0\,.$$

If the region G is so chosen that each straight line parallel to the x axis cuts the boundary of G at two points at most, then the converse of the above-proven theorem also is valid.

For every biharmonic function u in the region G, two harmonic functions u_1 and u_2 can be found such that

$$u = xu_1 + u_2 .$$

For the proof of this statement it is sufficient obviously to consider a function u_1 which satisfies the two conditions

$$\Delta u_1 = 0 \tag{4-7.73}$$

and

$$\Delta(u - xu_1) = 0 . \tag{4-7.74}$$

From condition (4-7.74) and formula (4-7.72) we find

$$\Delta u = \Delta(xu_1) = 2\frac{\partial u_1}{\partial x} . \tag{4-7.75}$$

Eq. (4-7.75) is satisfied by the function

$$\bar{u}_1(x, y) = \int_{x_0}^{x} \frac{1}{2}\Delta u(\xi, y)d\xi .$$

Since

$$\frac{\partial}{\partial x}\Delta\bar{u}_1 = \Delta\frac{\partial}{\partial x}\bar{u}_1 = \frac{1}{2}\Delta\Delta u = 0 ,$$

$\Delta\bar{u}_1$ depends only on y:

$$\Delta\bar{u}_1 = v(y) .$$

We now define a function $\bar{\bar{u}}_1(y)$ so that

$$\Delta\bar{\bar{u}}_1 = \frac{\partial^2\bar{\bar{u}}_1}{\partial y^2} = -v(y)$$

holds, and set

$$u_1 = \bar{u}_1 + \bar{\bar{u}}_1 .$$

This function then obviously satisfies the conditions (4-7.73) and (4-7.74), which was to be proved.

We shall now give another representation of a biharmonic function. Thus we assume that the origin of coordinates lies inside of the region G and each line from the origin touches the boundary of G at only one point. Under these assumptions the following is valid: Every biharmonic function u in G can be represented by two harmonic functions u_1 and u_2 in the form

$$u = (r^2 - r_0^2)u_1 + u_2 . \tag{4-7.76}$$

Here $r^2 = x^2 + y^2$, and r_0 is a given constant.

The proof here proceeds analogously to the preceding one by means of the identity (4-7.71) and the relations

$$\Delta r^2 = 4 , \qquad \frac{\partial u_1}{\partial r} = \frac{\partial u_1}{\partial x}\frac{\partial x}{\partial r} + \frac{\partial u_1}{\partial y}\frac{\partial y}{\partial r} .$$

3. *Solution of the Biharmonic Equation for the Circle.* Given a circle of radius r_0 about the origin of coordinates, we seek a biharmonic function which

satisfies the boundary conditions (4-7.67) for $r = r_0$. As was shown above, the sought function can be written in the form

$$u = (r^2 - r_0^2)u_1 + u_2 , \tag{4-7.76}$$

where u_1 and u_2 are harmonic functions. From the boundary conditions we find

$$u_2 |_{r=r_0} = g . \tag{4-7.77}$$

From this we recognize that u_2 is a solution of the first boundary problem for the Laplace differential equation. Therefore, u_2 can be represented by the Poisson integral

$$u_2 = \frac{1}{2\pi}\int_0^{2\pi} \frac{(r_0^2 - r^2)\, g d\alpha}{r^2 + r_0^2 - 2rr_0 \cos(\alpha - \theta)} . \tag{4-7.78}$$

From the second boundary condition we obtain

$$2r_0 u_1 + \left.\frac{\partial u_2}{\partial r}\right|_{r=r_0} = h . \tag{4-7.79}$$

By differentiation we find that the function

$$2r_0 u_1 + \frac{r}{r_0}\frac{\partial u_2}{\partial r} \tag{4-7.80}$$

also satisfies the Laplace differential equation and therefore can be expressed by the Poisson integral

$$2r_0 u_1 + \frac{r}{r_0}\frac{\partial u_2}{\partial r} = \frac{1}{2\pi}\int_0^{2\pi} \frac{(r_0^2 - r^2)\, h d\alpha}{r^2 + r_0^2 - 2rr_0 \cos(\alpha - \theta)} . \tag{4-7.81}$$

If we differentiate (4-7.78) with respect to r and substitute the value obtained for $\partial u_2/\partial r$ in (4.7.81), then we obtain u_1. Finally, if we substitute in (4-7.76) the expression found for u_1 and u_2, then we obtain the sought function:

$$u = \frac{1}{2\pi r_0}(r^2 - r_0^2)^2\left[\frac{1}{2}\int_0^{2\pi} \frac{-h d\alpha}{r^2 + r_0^2 - 2rr_0\cos(\alpha - \theta)} + \int_0^{2\pi} \frac{g[r_0 - r\cos(\alpha - \theta)] d\alpha}{[r^2 + r_0^2 - 2rr_0 \cos(\alpha - \theta)]^2}\right] .$$

APPENDIX

TABLES OF ERROR INTEGRALS AND SOME CYLINDRICAL FUNCTIONS

In the following pages we list tables of some special functions used for the solution of boundary-value problems of mathematical physics. These tables consist of a compilation of the simple properties of the functions considered.

The error integral

The error integral is defined by

$$\Phi(z) = \frac{2}{\sqrt{\pi}} \int_0^z e^{-\alpha^2} d\alpha .$$

For small values of z, it has the series development

$$\Phi(z) = \frac{2}{\sqrt{\pi}} \left(z - \frac{z^3}{1!3} + \frac{z^5}{2!5} - \cdots \right).$$

An asymptotic representation for large values of z

If we introduce a new variable β in the integral

$$1 - \Phi(z) = \frac{2}{\sqrt{\pi}} \int_z^\infty e^{-\alpha^2} d\alpha$$

by means of $\alpha = z + (\beta/2z)$, then we obtain

$$1 - \Phi(z) = \frac{1}{\sqrt{\pi}} \frac{e^{-z^2}}{z} \int_0^\infty e^{-\beta-(\beta^2/4z^2)} d\beta .$$

Consequently

$$\lim_{z\to\infty} \frac{1-\Phi(z)}{\frac{1}{\sqrt{\pi}}\frac{e^{-z^2}}{z}} = 1 ;$$

i.e.,

$$1 - \Phi(z) \sim \frac{1}{\sqrt{\pi}} \frac{e^{-z^2}}{z} .$$

If we develop $e^{-\beta^2/4z^2}$ in the series

$$e^{-\beta^2/4z^2} = \sum_{n=0}^{\infty} \frac{(-1)^n}{(2z)^{2n}} \frac{\beta^{2n}}{n!} ,$$

multiply this series with $e^{-\beta}$ and integrate from zero to infinity, then we obtain the divergent series

$$\sum_{n=0}^{\infty} \frac{(-1)^n}{(2z)^{2n}} \frac{(2n)!}{n!} = \sum_{n=0}^{\infty} \frac{(-1)^n (n+1)(n+2)\cdots 2n}{(2z)^{2n}} .$$

This divergent series represents the asymptotic development of the function $1 - \Phi(z)$:

$$1 - \Phi(z) \approx \frac{1}{\sqrt{\pi}} \frac{e^{-z^2}}{z} \left(1 - \frac{1}{2z^2} + \frac{3 \cdot 4}{(2z)^4} - \frac{4 \cdot 5 \cdot 6}{(2z)^6} + \cdots \right).$$

CYLINDRICAL FUNCTIONS

Series	Asymptotic representation
1. Bessel functions	
$J_0(x) = 1 - \frac{(x/2)^2}{1!} + \frac{(x/2)^4}{(2!)^2} - \cdots$	$J_0(x) = \sqrt{\frac{2}{\pi x}} \cos\left(x - \frac{\pi}{4}\right) + \cdots$
$J_1(x) = \frac{x}{2}\left[1 - \frac{(x/2)^2}{1 \cdot 2} + \frac{(x/2)^4}{1 \cdot 2 \cdot 2 \cdot 3} - \cdots\right]$	$J_1(x) = \sqrt{\frac{2}{\pi x}} \sin\left(x - \frac{\pi}{4}\right) + \cdots$
$J_\nu(x) = \left(\frac{x}{2}\right)^\nu \frac{1}{\Gamma(\nu + 1)} - \cdots$	$J_\nu(x) = \sqrt{\frac{2}{\pi x}} \cos\left(x - \frac{\pi}{2}\nu - \frac{\pi}{4}\right) + \cdots$
2. Neumann functions	
$N_0(x) = \frac{2}{\pi} J_0(x)\left(\ln \frac{x}{2} + C\right) + \frac{2}{\pi}\left(\frac{x}{2}\right)^2 + \cdots$	$N_0(x) = \sqrt{\frac{2}{\pi x}} \sin\left(x - \frac{\pi}{4}\right) + \cdots$
$N_1(x) = -\frac{2}{\pi x} + \frac{2}{\pi} J_1(x)\left(\ln \frac{x}{2} + C\right) + \cdots$	$N_1(x) = -\sqrt{\frac{2}{\pi x}} \cos\left(x - \frac{\pi}{4}\right) + \cdots$
$N_n(x) = -\frac{1}{\pi}\left(\frac{2}{x}\right)^n (n - 1)! + \cdots$ $(n > 1)$	$N_n(x) = \sqrt{\frac{2}{\pi x}} \sin\left(x - n\frac{\pi}{2} - \frac{\pi}{4}\right) + \cdots$

($C = 0.577215...$ is the Euler constant.)

Series	Asymptotic representation
3. Hankel functions	
$H_\nu^{(1)}(x) = J_\nu(x) + iN_\nu(x)$	$H_\nu^{(1)}(x) = \sqrt{\frac{2}{\pi x}} e^{i\left(x - \frac{\pi}{2}\nu - \frac{\pi}{4}\right)} + \cdots$
$H_\nu^{(2)}(x) = J_\nu(x) - iN_\nu(x)$	$H_\nu^{(2)}(x) = \sqrt{\frac{2}{\pi x}} e^{-i\left(x - \frac{\pi}{2}\nu - \frac{\pi}{4}\right)} + \cdots$

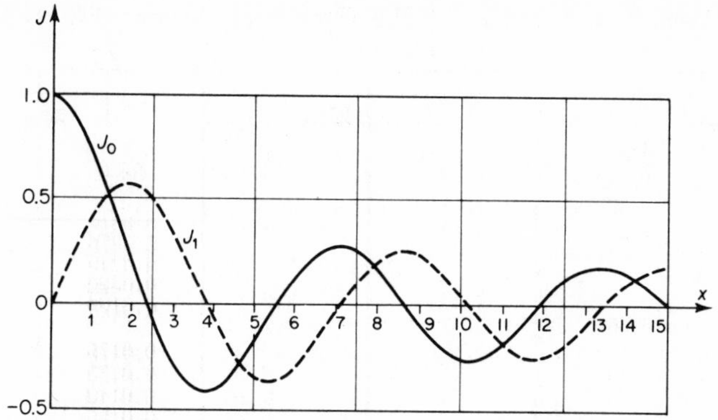

FIG. 75. Graphical Representation of the Bessel Functions or Cylindrical Functions of the First Type $J_0(x)$ and $J_1(x)$.

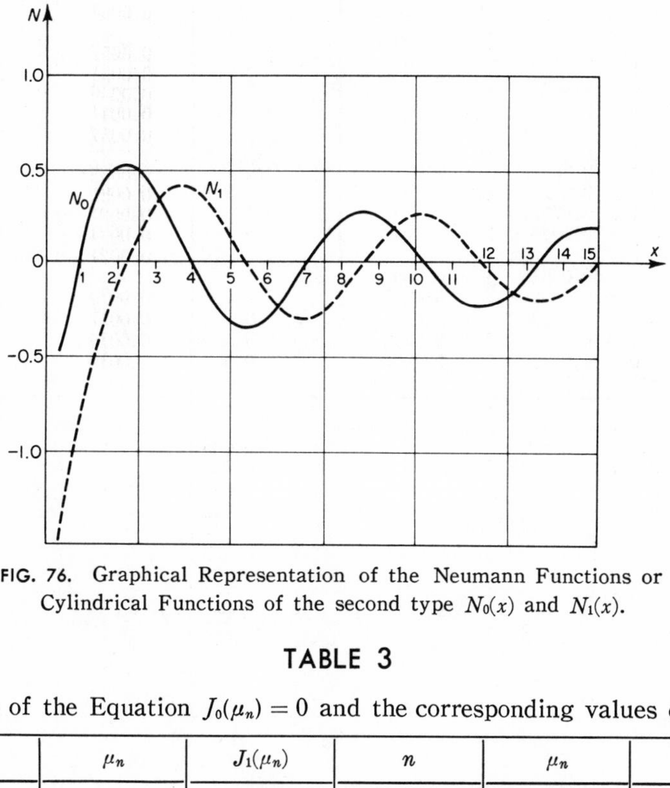

FIG. 76. Graphical Representation of the Neumann Functions or Cylindrical Functions of the second type $N_0(x)$ and $N_1(x)$.

TABLE 3

Roots of the Equation $J_0(\mu_n) = 0$ and the corresponding values of $|J_1(\mu_n)|$

n	μ_n	$J_1(\mu_n)$	n	μ_n	$J_1(\mu_n)$
1	2.4048	0.5191	6	18.0711	0.1877
2	5.5201	0.3403	7	21.2116	0.1733
3	8.6537	0.2715	8	24.3525	0.1617
4	11.7915	0.2325	9	27.4935	0.1522
5	14.9309	0.2065	10	30.6346	0.1442

TABLE 4. Values of the Functions $K_0(x)$ and $K_1(x)$

x	$K_0(x)$	$K_1(x)$	x	$K_0(x)$	$K_1(x)$
0.1	2.4271	9.8538	3.1	0.0310	0.0356
0.2	1.7527	4.7760	3.2	0.0276	0.0316
0.3	1.3725	3.0560	3.3	0.0246	0.0281
0.4	1.1145	2.1844	3.4	0.0220	0.0250
0.5	0.9244	1.6564	3.5	0.0196	0.0222
0.6	0.7775	1.3028	3.6	0.0175	0.0198
0.7	0.6605	1.0503	3.7	0.0156	0.0176
0.8	0.5653	0.8618	3.8	0.0140	0.0157
0.9	0.4867	0.7165	3.9	0.0125	0.0140
1.0	0.4210	0.6019	4.0	0.0112	0.0125
1.1	0.3656	0.5098	4.1	0.0098	0.0111
1.2	0.3185	0.4346	4.2	0.0089	0.0099
1.3	0.2782	0.3725	4.3	0.0080	0.0089
1.4	0.2437	0.3208	4.4	0.0071	0.0079
1.5	0.2138	0.2774	4.5	0.0064	0.0071
1.6	0.1880	0.2406	4.6	0.0057	0.0063
1.7	0.1655	0.2094	4.7	0.0051	0.0056
1.8	0.1459	0.1826	4.8	0.0046	0.0051
1.9	0.1288	0.1597	4.9	0.0041	0.0045
2.0	0.1139	0.1399	5.0	0.0037	0.0040
2.1	0.1008	0.1227	5.1	0.0033	0.0036
2.2	0.0893	0.1079	5.2	0.0030	0.0032
2.3	0.0791	0.0950	5.3	0.0027	0.0029
2.4	0.0702	0.0837	5.4	0.0024	0.0026
2.5	0.0623	0.0739	5.5	0.0021	0.0023
2.6	0.0554	0.0653	5.6	0.0019	0.0021
2.7	0.0492	0.0577	5.7	0.0017	0.0019
2.8	0.0438	0.0511	5.8	0.0015	0.0017
2.9	0.0390	0.0453	5.9	0.0014	0.0015
3.0	0.0347	0.0402	6.0	0.0012	0.0013

LITERATURE REFERENCES OF THE EDITOR

In the following, there is no claim of completeness. Textbooks, monographs, and collected reports, but no journal articles, are given. Special works from journals are given in part in the footnotes of this book. As a rule, only literature after 1900 has been used.

LITERATURE ON THE THEORY OF PARTIAL DIFFERENTIAL EQUATIONS OF HIGHER ORDER

Albrecht, R., and Hochmuth, H. *Exercises in Higher Mathematics*. Part III. R. Oldenbourg: Munich, 1956.

Bateman, H. *Partial Differential Equations of Mathematical Physics*. Dover Publications: New York, 1944.

Baule, B. "Mathematics for Scientists and Engineers," in *Partial Differential Equations*. Volume VI, 5th edition. S. Hirzel: Leipzig, 1955.

Bergmann, S., and Schiffer, M. *Kernel Functions and Differential Equations in Mathematical Physics*. Academic Press, Inc.: New York, 1953.

Bernstein, D. L. *Existence Theorems in Partial Differential Equations*. 2nd printing. Princeton University Press: Princeton, 1951.

Bieberbach. L. *Introduction to the Theory of Differential Equations in the Real Domain*. Springer Verlag: Berlin, 1956.

———. *Theory of Differential Equations*. 3rd printing. Springer Verlag: Berlin, 1930.

Borgnis, F. E. and Papas, C. H. *Boundary-value Problems in Microwave Physics*. Springer Verlag: Berlin, 1955.

Budak, B. M., Samarskii, A. A., and Tychonoff, A. N. *A Collection of Problems for Mathematical Physics*. Gostechisdat: Moscow, 1956.

Collatz, L. *Numerical Treatment of Differential Equations*. 2nd printing. Springer Verlag: Berlin, 1955.

———. *Eigenvalue Problems with Technical Applications*. Academic Verlagsgesellschaft: Leipzig, 1949.

———. "Numerical and Graphical Methods," in *Handbook of Physics*. Volume II, Mathematical Methods, Part II. Springer Verlag: Berlin, 1955.

First Conference on Equations with Partial Derivatives. Louvain, 1953 (CBRM). George Thone: Liège, 1954.

Second Conference on Equations with Partial Derivatives. Bruxelles, 1954 (CBRM). George Thone: Liège, 1955.

Contributions to the Theory of Partial Differential Equations. Princeton University Press: Princeton, 1954.

International Conference on Linear Equations with Partial Derivatives. Trieste, 1954; Edizioni Cremonese, Rome, 1955.

Courant, R., and Hilbert, D. *Methods of Mathematical Physics*. Volume I, 2nd printing; Volume II, 1st printing. Springer, Verlag: Berlin, 1931 and 1937, respectively.

Courant, R., and Schiffer, M. *Dirichlet's Principle: Conformal Mapping and Minimal Surfaces*. Interscience Publishers, Inc.: New York, 1950.

Duff, G. F. D. *Partial Differential Equations*. University of Toronto Press: Toronto, 1956.

Duschek, A. *Lectures on Higher Mathematics*. Volume III. Springer Verlag: Vienna, 1953.

Frank, Ph., and R. v. Mises. *Differential and Integral Equations of Mechanics and Physics.* Part I, 2nd printing; Part II, 2nd printing. F. Vieweg: Braunschweig, 1930 and 1935, respectively.

Ford, L. R. *Differential Equations.* 2nd edition. McGraw-Hill Book Co., Inc.: New York, 1955.

Forsyth, A. R., and Jacobsthal, W. *Textbook of Differential Equations.* (Translated from the English.) 2nd edition. F. Vieweg: Braunschweig, 1912.

Freda, H. *The Method of Characteristics for the Integration of Linear Hyperbolic Partial Differential Equations.* Mem. sci. math., fasc 84. Gauthier-Villars: Paris, 1937.

Friedman, B. *Principles and Techniques of Applied Mathematics.* John Wiley & Sons, Inc.: New York, 1956.

Geronimus, J. L., and Steklov, V. A. *Integration of the Differential Equations of Mathematical Physics.* (Translated from the Russian.) Verlag Technik: Berlin, 1954.

Godeaux, L. *Mathematical Analysis.* Volume III. Sciences and Letters: Liège, 1947.

Gosse, R. *The Method of Darboux for the Equation* $s = f(x, y, z, p, q)$. Mem. sci. math., fasc 12. Gauthier-Villars: Paris, 1926.

Goursat, Ed. *Lessons on the Integration of Equations with Partial Derivatives of the Second Order in Two Independent Variables.* 2 vols. A. Hermann: Paris, 1896 and 1898, respectively.

Guldberg, A. "Partial and Total Differential Equations," in *E. Pascal, Repertory of Higher Mathematics.* Volume I, Part II, 2nd printing. B. G. Teubner: Leipzig, 1927.

Gunter, N. M., and Kusmin, R. O. *Collection of problems in Higher Mathematics.* Volume II. (Translated from the Russian.) VEB Deutscher Verlag der Wissenschaften: Berlin, 1957.

Hadamard, J. *Lectures on Cauchy's Problem in Linear Partial Differential Equations.* Reprinting of the 1st edition of 1923. Dover Publications: New York, 1952.

———. *Cauchy's Problem and Linear Hyperbolic Partial Differential Equations.* (Revised translation of the preceding title.) Hermann et Cie: Paris, 1932.

Hahn, H., Lichtenstein, L., and Lense, J. "The theory of Integral Equations and Functions of Infinitely Many Variables and Their Application to Boundary-value Problems for Ordinary and Partial Differential Equations," in *E. Pascal, Repertory of Higher Mathematics.* Volume I, Part III, 2nd edition. B. G. Teubner: Leipzig, 1929.

Heilbronn, G. *Integration of Equations with Partial Derivatives of the Second Order by the Method of Drach.* Mem. sci. math., fasc. 129. Gauthier-Villars: Paris, 1955.

Hildebrand, F. B. *Methods of Applied Mathematics.* Prentice-Hall, Inc.: New York, 1952.

Hoheisel, G. *Collection of Problems in Ordinary and Partial Differential Equations.* 2nd edition. W. de Gruyter: Berlin, 1952.

———. *Partial Differential Equations.* 3rd edition. W. de Gruyter: Berlin, 1953.

Horn, J. *Partial Differential Equations.* 4th edition. W. de Gruyter: Berlin, 1949.

Hort, W., and Thoma, A. *Differential Equations of Technology and Physics.* 6th edition. J. A. Barth: Leipzig, 1954.

Janet, M. *Lessons on Systems of Equations with Partial Derivatives.* Gauthier-Villars: Paris, 1929.

———. *Systems of Equations with Partial Derivatives.* Mem. sci. math., fasc. 21. Gauthier-Villars: Paris, 1927.

John, F. *Plane Waves and Spherical Means Applied to Partial Differential Equations.* Interscience Publishers: New York, 1955.

Julia, G. *Exercises in Analysis.* Volume IV. Gauthier-Villars: Paris, 1935.

Kamke, E. *Differential Equations of Real Functions.* 3rd edition. Akademische Verlagsgesellschaft: Leipzig, 1956.

Kantorowitsch, L. W., and Krylov, W. I. *Approximate Methods of Higher Analysis.* (Translated from the Russian.) VEB Deutscher Verlag der Wissenschaften: Berlin, 1956.

Krylov, A. N. *On Certain Differential Equations of Mathematical Physics.* 5th edition. Gostechisdat: Moscow, 1950.

Kupradse, W. D. *Boundary-value Problems of Vibration Theory and Integral Equations.* (Translated from the Russian.) VEB Deutscher Verlag der Wissenschaften: Berlin, 1956.

Ladyzhenskaya, O. A. *Mixed Problems of the Theory of Hyperbolic Partial Differential Equations.* Gostechisdat: Moscow, 1953.

Lense, J. "Partial Differential Equations," in *Handbook of Physics.* Volume I, Mathematical Methods, Part I. Springer Verlag: Berlin, 1956.

Leray, J. *Hyperbolic Differential Equations.* Institute for Advanced Study: Princeton, 1955.

Lewin, W. I., and Grosberg, J. I. *Differential Equations of Mathematical Physics.* (Translated from the Russian.) Verlag Technik: Berlin, 1952.

Lichtenstein, L. "New Developments in the Theory of Partial Differential Equations of the Second Order of the Elliptic Type," in *Encyclopedia of Mathematical Sciences.* Volume II, Part III, Second half. B. G. Teubner: Leipzig, 1924.

Love, A. E. H. *Textbook of Elasticity.* (Translated from the English.) B. G. Teubner: Leipzig, 1907.

Madelung, E. *Mathematical Aids for Physicists.* 6th edition. Springer Verlag: Berlin, 1954.

Malkin, I. G. *The Methods of Liapunov and Poincare in the Theory of Non-Linear Vibrations.* Gostechisdat: Moscow, 1949.

Margenau, H., and Murphy, G. M. *The Mathematics of Physics and Chemistry.* 2nd edition. D. van Nostrand Co., Inc.: New York, 1956.

Miller, F. H. *Partial Differential Equations.* 6th reprint. John Wiley & Sons, Inc.: New York, 1953.

Miller, K. S. *Partial Differential Equations in Engineering Problems.* Prentice-Hall, Inc.: New York, 1953.

Miller, N. *A First Course of Differential Equations.* University Press: Oxford, 1935.

Milne, W. E. *Numerical Solutions of Differential Equations.* John Wiley & Sons, Inc.: New York, 1953.

Miranda, C. *Equations with Partial Derivatives of the Elliptic Type.* Springer Verlag: Berlin, 1955.

Morse, P. M., and Feshbach, H. *Methods of Theoretical Physics.* 2 vols. McGraw-Hill Book Co., Inc.: New York, 1953.

Muskhelishvili, N. I. *Some Fundamental Problems of the Theory of Elasticity.* 4th edition. Akademie-Verlag: Moscow, 1954. (This work contains a complete list of references which primarily give an insight into the Soviet literature in this field.)

Page, C. H. *Physical Mathematics.* D. van Nostrand Co., Inc.: New York, 1955.

Panov D. J. *A Collection of Formulas for the Numerical Treatment of Partial Differential Equations by Difference Methods.* (Translated from the Russian.) Akademie-Verlag: Berlin, 1955.

Pertowski, I. G. *Lectures on Partial Differential Equations.* (Translated from the Russian.) B. G. Teubner: Leipzig, 1955.

Picard, E. *Lessons on Certain Types of Simple Equations with Partial Derivatives with Some Application to Mathematical Physics.* Nouveau tirage. Gauthier-Villars: Paris, 1950.

Proceedings of the Conference on Differential Equations (Dedicated to A. Weinstein.) University of Maryland Book Store: College Park, Md., 1956.

Purday, H. F. P. *Linear Equations in Applied Mechanics.* Interscience Publishers, Inc.: New York, 1954.

Rashevski, P. K. *Geometrical Theory of Partial Differential Equations.* Gostechisdat: Moscow, 1947.

Reed, M. B., and Reed, G. B. *Mathematical Methods in Electrical Engineering.* Harper & Bros.: New York, 1951.

Riquier, C. *The Method of Majorant Functions and Systems of Equations with Partial Derivatives.* Mem. sci. math., fasc. 32. Gauthier-Villars: Paris, 1928.

———. *Systems of Equations with Partial Derivatives.* Gauthier-Villars, Paris, 1910.

Rothe, R. *Higher Mathematics.* Part III, 8th edition; Part IV, No. 5/6, 7th edition. B. G. Teubner: Leipzig, 1954 and 1955, respectively. Part VI, I. Szabo and B. G. Teubner: Stuttgart, 1953.

Runge, C. and Willers, F. A. *Numerical and Graphical Quadrature and the Integration of Ordinary and Partial Differential Equations.* B. G. Teubner: Leipzig, 1915.

Sauer, R. *Initial Value Problems of Partial Differential Equations.* Springer Verlag: Berlin, 1952.

Sauter, F. *Differential Equations of Physics.* 2nd edition. W. de Gruyter: Berlin, 1950.

Schlogl, F. "Boundary-value Problems," in *Handbook of Physics.* Volume I, Mathematical Methods, Part I. Springer Verlag: Berlin, 1956.

Schwank, F. *Boundary-value Problems.* B. G. Teubner: Leipzig, 1951.

Smirnov, M. M. *Problems in the Partial Differential Equations of Mathematical Physics.* (Translated from the Russian.) VEB Deutscher Verlag der Wissenschaften: Berlin, 1955.

Smirnov, V. I. *Textbook of Higher Mathematics.* (Translated from the Russian.) Part II (Chapter VII), 2nd edition; Part IV (This book is included in the text (Chapter III) in the valuable references from the original work.) 1st edition. VEB Deutscher Verlag der Wissenschaften: Berlin, 1958.

Sneddon, I. N. *Elements of Partial Differential Equations.* McGraw-Hill Book Co., Inc.: New York, 1957.

Sobolev, S. L. *Equations of Mathematical Physics.* 3rd edition. Gostechisdat: Moscow, 1954.

Sommerfeld, A. "Boundary-value Problems in the Theory of Partial Differential Equations," in *Encyclopedia of Mathematical Sciences.* Volume II, Part I, first half. B. G. Teubner: Leipzig, 1900.

———. "Partial Differential Equations of Physics," in *Lectures on Theoretical Physics.* Volume VI, 4th edition. Akademische Verlagsgesellschaft: Leipzig, 1957.

Stepanov, V. V. *Textbook of Differential Equations.* (Translated from the Russian.) VEB Deutscher Verlag der Wissenschaften: Berlin, 1956.

Sternberg, W. "The Theory of Boundary-value Problems in the Domain of Partial Differential Equations," in *E. Pascal, Repertory of Higher Mathematics.* Volume I, Part III, 2nd edition. B. G. Teubner: Leipzig, 1929.

Transactions of the Symposium on Partial Differential Equations. University of Cali-

fornia, Berkeley, 1955. Interscience Publishers, Inc.: New York, 1955.
Tricomi, F. G. *Lessons on Equations with Partial Derivatives.* Gherardi: Torino, 1954.
Vekua, I. N. *New Methods for the Solution of Elliptic Differential Equations.* Gostechisdat: Moscow, 1948.
Weber, E. von "Partial Differential Equations," in *Encyclopedia of Mathematical Sciences.* Volume II, Part I, first Half. B. G. Teubner: Leipzig, 1900.
Webster, A. G. and Szego, G., *Partial Differential Equations of Mathematical Physics.* (Translated from the English.) B. G. Teubner: Leipzig, 1930.

LITERATURE FOR THE POTENTIAL THEORY (CHAPTER 4, § 5 OF THIS BOOK)

In addition to the books already enumerated, the theory is explained in the following works.

Burkhardt, H., and Meyer, F., "Potential Theory," in *Encyclopedia of Mathematical Sciences.* Volume II, Part I, first Half. B. G. Teubner: Leipzig, 1900.
Gunter, N. M. *Potential Theory and its Application to the Basic Problems of Mathematical Physics.* (Translated from the Russian.) B. G. Teubner: Leipzig, 1957.
Kellogg, O. D. *Foundations of Potential Theory.* Springer, Verlag: Berlin, 1929.
Korn, A. *Five Treatises on the Potential Theory.* F. Dummler: Berlin, 1902.
Liapunov, A. M. *Studies in Potential Theory.* Gostechisdat: Moscow, 1949.
Lichtenstein, L. "New Developments in Potential Theory," in *Encyclopedia of Mathematical Sciences.* Volume II, Part III, first Half. B. G. Teubner: Leipzig, 1909.
Neumann, E. R. *Studies of the Methods of C. Neumann and G. Robin for the Solution of the Two Boundary-value Problems of Potential Theory.* B. G. Teubner: Leipzig, 1905.
Plemelj, I. *Potential Theoretic Investigations.* B. G. Teubner: Leipzig, 1911.
Rothe, R. *Higher Mathematics.* Part VII by W. Schmeidler (also treats potential theory.) B. G. Teubner: Stuttgart, 1956.
Sternberg, W. *Potential Theory.* 2 vols. W. de Gruyter & Co.: Berlin, 1926.
Sternberg, W., and Smith, Turner L. *The Theory of Potential and Spherical Harmonics.* 3rd edition. University of Toronto Press: Toronto, 1952.

LITERATURE ON THE THEORY OF SPECIAL FUNCTIONS (APPENDIX OF THIS BOOK)

Besides the references given above, special functions are also discussed in the following works. Tables and Tabular work will not be included in the reference list. We have used L. M. Ryshik, and I. S. Gradstein: *Tables* (Translated from the Russian), VEB Deutscher Verlag der Wissenschaften, Berlin, 1957, as a reference for special values of these functions. This book contains a list of references which gives further references to tables.

Angelesco, A. *On Some Polynomials Generalizing the Polynomials of Legendre and Hermite and the Approximate Calculation of Multiple Integrals.* Gauthier-Villars: Paris, 1916.
Appell, P., and de Feriet, J. Kampe. *Hypergeometric and Hyperspherical Functions: Hermite Polynomials.* Gauthier-Villars: Paris, 1926.
Bateman, H. *Higher Transcendental Functions.* 2 vols. McGraw-Hill Book Co., Inc.: New York, 1953 and 1955.

Bowman, F. *Introduction to Bessel Functions.* Longmans, Green and Co.: New York, 1938.

Goudet, G. *Bessel Functions and Their Application in Physics.* 2nd edition. Masson et Cie.: Paris, 1954.

Graf, J. H., and Gubler, H. *Introduction to the Theory of Bessel Functions.* 2 Parts, 2nd edition. K. J. Wyss: Bern, 1900.

Gray, A., Mathews, G. B., and MacRobert, T. M. *A Treatise on Bessel Functions and Their Applications to Physics.* 2nd edition. Macmillan: London, 1922.

Hilb, E. "Spherical Functions, Bessel and Related Functions," in *E. Pascal, Repertory of Higher Mathematics.* Volume III, Part III, 2nd edition. B. G. Teubner: Leipzig, 1929.

Lagrange, R. *Polynomials and Legendre Functions.* Mem. sci. math., fasc. 97. Gauthier-Villars: Paris, 1939.

Lebedev, N. N. *Special Functions and Their Applications.* Gostechisdat: Moscow, 1953.

Lense, J. *Spherical Functions.* Akademische Verlagsgesellschaft: Leipzig, 1950.

Magnus, W., and Oberhettinger, F. *Formulas and Theorems for the Special Functions of Mathematical Physics.* 2nd edition. Springer Verlag: Berlin, 1948.

McLachlan, N. W. *Bessel Functions for Engineers.* 2nd edition. Clarendon Press: Oxford, 1955.

Meixner, J. "Special Functions of Mathematical Physics," in *Handbook of Physics.* Volume I, Mathematical Methods, Part I. Springer Verlag: Berlin, 1956.

Nielsen, N. *Handbook of the Theory of Cylindrical Functions.* B. G. Teubner: Leipzig, 1904.

Petiau, G. *The Theory of Bessel Functions.* CNRS, Masson et Cie: Paris, 1955.

Prasad, G. *A Treatise on Spherical Harmonics and the Functions of Bessel and Lamè.* 2 vols. Mahamandal Press: Benares, 1930 and 1932.

Relton. F. E. *Applied Bessel Functions.* Blackie & Son, Ltd.: London, 1946.

Schafheitlin, P. *The Theory of Bessel Functions.* B. G. Teubner, Leipzig, 1908.

Smirnov, V. I. *Textbook of Higher Mathematics* (Translated from the Russian.) Part III, Section 2, Chapter VI. VEB Deutscher Verlag der Wissenschaften: Berlin, 1955.

Sonin, N. J. *Investigations of Cylindrical Functions and Special Polynomials.* Gostechisdat: Moscow, 1954.

Wangerin, A. "Theory of Spherical Functions and Related Functions, in Particular the Lamè and Bessel Functions," in *Encyclopedia of Mathematical Sciences.* Volume II, Part I, Second Half. B. G. Teubner: Leipzig, 1904.

Watson, G. N. *A Treatise on the Theory of Bessel Functions.* University Press: Cambridge, 1922. (This book contains an enlarged literature list in which all publications on the Bessel functions prior to 1922 are given.)

Weyrich, R. *Cylindrical Functions and Their Applications.* B. G. Teubner: Leipzig, 1937.

Whittaker, E. T. and Watson, G. N. *A Course of Modern Analysis.* 4th edition. University Press: Cambridge, 1952.

INDEX